MATHEMATICS

IN THEORY AND PRACTICE

DESCARTES
EUCLID
LAPLACE
NEWTON
EINSTEIN
(x+y)²=x²+2xy+y²
22/7
π
√-1
Leslie S. Haywood
LEIBNIZ
NAPIER
KEPLER

MATHEMATICS

IN THEORY AND PRACTICE

A NOVEL AND SIMPLIFIED APPROACH
IN WHICH MATHEMATICAL PROCESSES
ARE RELATED TO EVERYDAY AFFAIRS

Edited by W. W. SAWYER, B.A.

CONTRIBUTORS

F. E. Bowman, M.A.
C. L. Johnson, B.Sc.
W. W. Sawyer, B.A.
R. Wesley, B.Sc.

ODHAMS PRESS LIMITED · LONG ACRE · LONDON

FOREWORD

BY PROFESSOR H. LEVY, M.A., D.Sc., F.R.S.E.

IT IS sometimes maintained that mathematics comes easily only to those who have a special gift or flair for it, and that those who are born without this ability in a scientific age are necessarily handicapped from the cradle to the grave.

Nothing could be further from the truth. Of course, some people are colour blind or tone deaf, and these defects will naturally limit their powers as painters or musicians. They will miss experiences that others more fortunately built will enjoy. But nowhere is there any evidence of a mathematical sense in which some people may be deficient at birth. Like any other language, of course, the language of mathematics has to be learnt so that the person may be able to speak intelligently and express his thoughts clearly.

Within the first five years of life most children have already learnt how to construct sentences and where the various kinds of words have to come in a sentence. The child feels its way to these rules unconsciously, as a kind of habit, and having acquired them can express its thoughts, can argue and think.

So it is with mathematics, and anyone who can learn to speak and to express his thoughts through marks on a piece of paper can equally learn to do mathematics. There is no special ability here.

One of the first problems that a good teacher has to face is involved in the idea that mathematics is divorced from ordinary life. This is not so with the teacher of French or German. There the student extends his or her vocabulary and sentence structure to cover objects and ideas already familiar. With mathematics he has not only to extend his vocabulary outside the range of what he usually hears at home, but to ideas and to objects that he has been led to believe belong to a totally unfamiliar world.

We can appreciate, therefore, how extremely valuable is any attempt to bring back the subject of mathematics into the scheme of everyday life from which it has been artificially divorced.

Because the authors of this book realize this difficulty to the full, and because they therefore set out deliberately to remove the mystery from mathematics by bringing the subject within the circle of ideas of the ordinary person, I find their work so valuable. The book is not only a mine of information, hitherto unsuspected, in ordinary topics; it is a revelation to the teacher himself of what can be done when we realize the difficulties of a personal or of a social nature with which the normal individual is surrounded when he attempts to master something that should have become part of his make-up.

CONTENTS

$\angle ADB = 62\tfrac{1}{2}°$ $\angle BDC = 6°$

Height of spire $= AB + BC$

$AB = 55 \tan 62\tfrac{1}{2}°$

$= 55 \times 1\cdot9210$

$= 105\cdot655$

$BC = 55 \tan 6°$

$= 55 \times \cdot1051$

$= 5\cdot7805$

\therefore *Height of spire*

$(AB+BC) = 111\cdot435$ ft.

$6°$ $62\tfrac{1}{2}°$ D

B

C \longleftarrow 55' \longrightarrow

MEASURING THE HEIGHT OF A CHURCH SPIRE

A theodolite is being used to determine the height of the church spire. Inset are the calculations. The only known distance is from the base of the spire to the base of the stand. All the other dimensions can be calculated by trigonometry.

CHAPTER I

ON BEING YOUR OWN TEACHER

THERE is probably nothing so dreary and dull in the whole world as an ordinary arithmetic school-book.

Even the writers of text-books seem to feel this, for they have begun to write books with titles which suggest that the contents make arithmetic such fun! But when you look inside you find—with a few notable exceptions—that it is much the same old stuff again.

Obviously, it is very difficult to get away from the old arithmetic methods. In this volume the utmost has been done to produce a book on mathematics which is not quite so dull as the usual text-book. That is all that is claimed for the moment.

This book is written for home study. That means that you, the reader, are trying to be at the same time the teacher and the pupil. There are certain disadvantages in studying at home, but there are also certain important advantages.

To begin with, you are learning of your own free will. In the average school class, three-quarters of the class do not want to learn at all and would be glad to escape.

Again, in class teaching, the teacher tries to find something that will interest all the pupils of that class. But if there are thirty students, there will be thirty different sets of interests. You have to seek out things to interest only one person, and that is yourself, and you know what you are interested in.

It will probably help you to teach yourself if a beginning is made by explaining the difficulties of teaching mathematics, and why it is that class teaching is so often a failure that it makes children dislike the subject.

If you are able to understand these difficulties you will then know what to avoid in teaching yourself, and, if you have previously been taught badly, you may be able to correct the harm that has been done.

TRADITIONAL MISTAKES

LACK OF PURPOSE

Perhaps the most serious defect in old schools (and in some of the schools today) is *lack of purpose.*

The lessons strike the children as being futile, as leading nowhere. Boys and girls are always asking, "Why do we have to do this?" "What does it lead to?"

These are very reasonable questions. You have only one life to live, and you do not want to waste it on futile and unnecessary things. You have every right to ask such questions. These questions have often been asked, but is there a satisfactory answer?

The fact is that nobody knows why mathematics is taught in schools. Teaching mathematics is a custom, like shaking hands. We have got used to it. People cannot imagine schools without an arithmetic lesson.

If you look through the examples in an average arithmetic book, you will find the great majority of them to be artificial and quite pointless. There are problems about cows eating grass, and water running out of baths—things that no farmer or bather ever dreams of calculating.

FINDING THE PURPOSE

Our minds are so constructed that above everything else they demand a purpose. You cannot really concentrate on something that you feel to be pointless.

It is quite different when you have a definite purpose in mind. Take an example, not of just working out money sums or questions about stones, pounds and ounces, but of something that many people are confronted with during the holiday season. Some years ago a man undertook to organize a camping holiday at an all-in cost of £1 a week. This had to cover the hiring of ground and tents, as well as food. It all had to be worked out very carefully. If there had been too little food, the campers would have rioted. If there had been too much the man would have been bankrupt.

He found this quite exciting. But he would not have found it in the least exciting if it had only been a question in an arithmetic book, if it had been an imaginary camp with imaginary food and imaginary prices, and if there had been no thought in his head that one day he might be running a camp in reality.

There must be many people who feel like that, and the solution for them is obvious—let your mathematical problems come up naturally in things that interest you—in working out whether you can afford to do something you want to, in measuring or designing something you want to make, in scoring at games, in working out the odds in football pools or dog-racing, in settling a political argument; or in any of the other things that may interest you.

If you find that mathematics never comes into any of the things you are doing, or that you hope to do, the moral is clear: there is no need for you to learn mathematics at all, except possibly as a recreation, or to broaden your mind. Now you will see a difficulty there has been in writing this book: we do not know who you are, neither do we know in what you are interested.

You may be an engineering apprentice struggling with National Certificate, or a doctor studying the statistics in favour of some new cure for a disease; you may be a surveyor, or an electrician, or a chemist, or a grocer's assistant; you may be a millionaire trying to show how poor the rich are, or a revolutionary trying to show how much could be saved by abolishing rents; you may be interested in model aircraft or in botany, in dress designing or atomic bombs. In each case, you will be using some kind of mathematics. In each case, whole books could be written to deal with your special needs. Obviously, this book cannot satisfy the special interests of everyone.

We have tried to use illustrations in this book that will satisfy some people, and will show others that mathematics can be used for quite interesting purposes. There may be too many illustrations connected with engineering, woodwork, or model aeroplanes, and too few dealing with other interests. But, in any case, this book is not intended to be taken as something finished and complete. We hope rather that it will stimulate you to collect for yourself examples that you find interesting, that it will lead you, in fact, to write your own book on mathematics, and the applications of mathematics that you consider important.

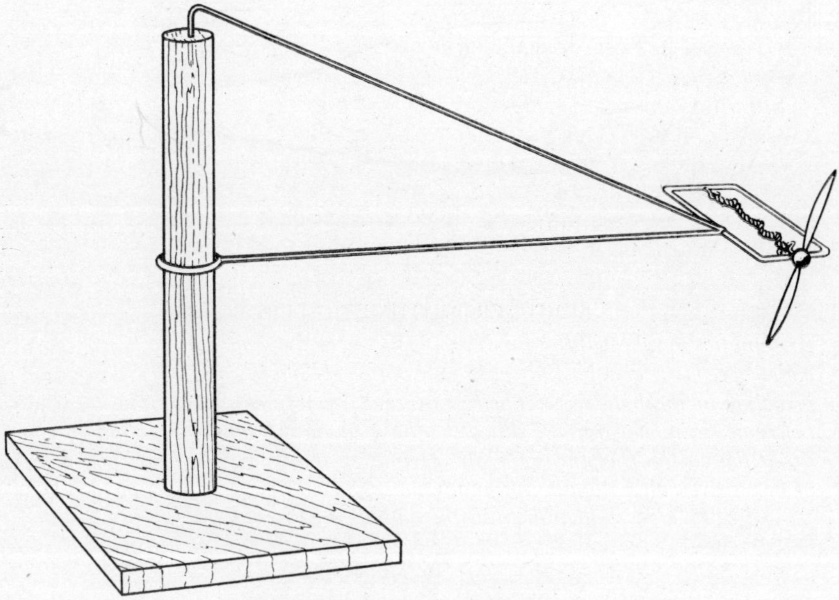

BRIGHTER MENSURATION.

Here is a simple and easily made model which will show you what mensuration is for. A model aeroplane propeller, with rubber to drive it, is mounted on the stiff-wire frame. The rubber is given about a hundred turns, and the aeroplane is then released. The number of times that the aeroplane flies round the pole is counted. The distance that it has travelled is then worked out. The effect of putting more or fewer turns on the rubber can be studied. The real object of this model is to brighten up the classroom, so that a class coming to do mathematics will feel that it may be quite interesting. This model was suggested by a Leicester student, J. Spencer. The way schoolchildren feel about mathematics could be revolutionized, if mathematics were more closely linked with science, handwork and hobbies. The mathematics of mensuration is discussed more fully in Chapter VI.

You will find in any good library, or technical reference room, plenty of books on the particular things upon which you are keen. We hope that this book will give you a sufficiently good understanding of the *foundations of mathematics* (there is insufficient space to attempt anything more) to enable you to appreciate and follow the mathematics in such books.

LACK OF REAL THINGS

Another serious defect in the traditional classroom was the absence of things to see and touch and handle. Children were expected to reason accurately about the acreage of fields, without ever seeing a field or knowing what an acre looked like. They were expected to understand tons and

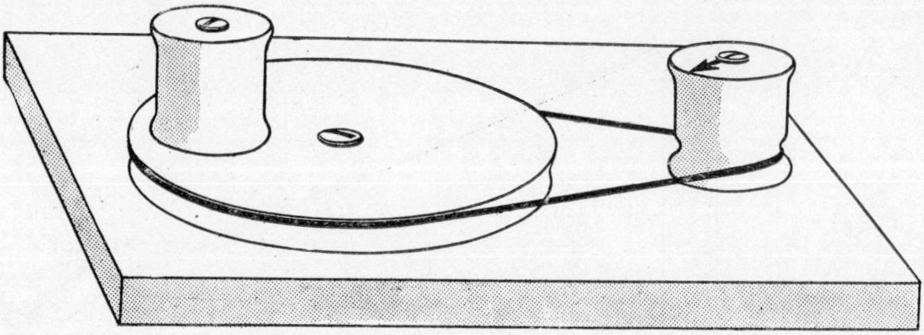

BRIGHTER ARITHMETIC LESSONS.

Arithmetic should lead somewhere. The piece of apparatus shown above is constructed of cheap materials—cotton reels and wood. It illustrates the principle of the belt drive. The cotton reel is one inch across. The large wheel is five or six inches across. When you have made this apparatus, find how many times the cotton reel turns for one revolution of the large wheel. The principle of belt drive can be applied in many pieces of home-made machinery, a few of which are illustrated below as examples.

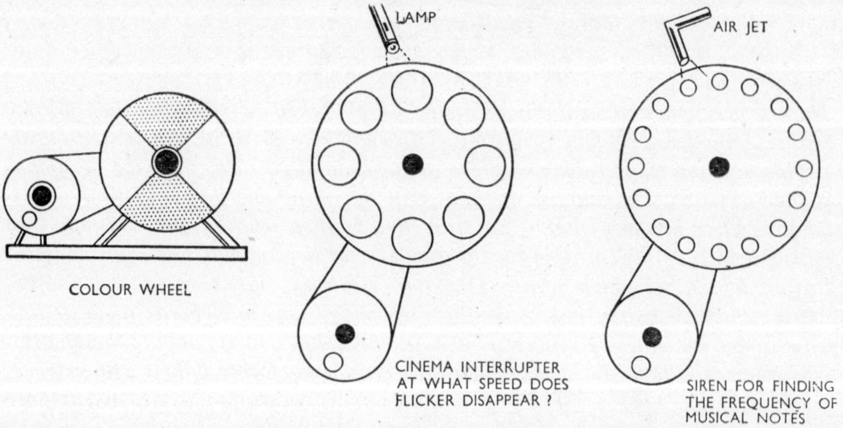

hundredweights without ever seeing a weighing machine; to convert gallons into litres without ever having held in their hands a gallon measure or a litre wine bottle. This worked quite well with perhaps one-quarter of the class. The other three-quarters, however, were unable to imagine things without actually experiencing them.

In this book we have talked as much as possible about things, actual objects. If you can follow what we say just by using your imagination, that is all right. But if you find difficulty in imagining what we are describing, *make the actual thing for yourself.* Often you will find that this overcomes the difficulty straight away. Or you may find that after two or three weeks of handling an object you come to understand it.

SILLY RESTRICTIONS

Many mistakes in mathematics teaching have been due to the fact that the teacher had no idea what mathematics was, or (as we have already noted) why it was taught. Some teachers, for instance, had the idea that the arithmetic lesson was a good opportunity for teaching neatness. They frowned on rough working in pencil, or blots, or work crossed out. The result of this was that pupils worked at a snail's pace, or even became so paralysed that they would not write anything at all, for fear it might be wrong and need to be crossed out.

Mathematicians do not usually work like this. If a problem is brought to a mathematician, he may easily see that there are four or five different ways of tackling it. He does not know which way is going to lead most easily to the result. So he tries them all in turn, scribbling furiously away with a pencil. Some mathematicians are careful to write in exercise books, so that they do not lose their work. Others simply use the backs of old envelopes. But in either case, they think nothing of crossing out whole pages of working: they may make mistakes of method, or slips in arithmetic; and it is only after several times checking the work and correcting any mistakes, that they think of writing out the finished solution at all neatly. And nobody cares. So long as the enquirer receives the true answer at the end, it does not matter how many waste-paper baskets the mathematician has filled with old envelopes or exercise books. That is the mathematician's private affair.

Another foolish custom is to put a ban on short methods. Mathematicians, in real life, are always trying to find the quickest, shortest and easiest method of solving a problem. They have invented all kinds of devices to lessen labour. There are calculating machines of various types. There are special instruments, such as slide-rules, that are widely used in industry though rarely mentioned in school. There are paper charts, such as nomograms. There are books of standard results, ready-reckoners. There are special methods, such as logarithms.

All of these are of great value to the practical man, who has an urgent problem that he wants to solve in the shortest possible time.

But some teachers still seem to think that mathematics is really meant to be a kind of torture, or penance for sins; they frown on anything that makes

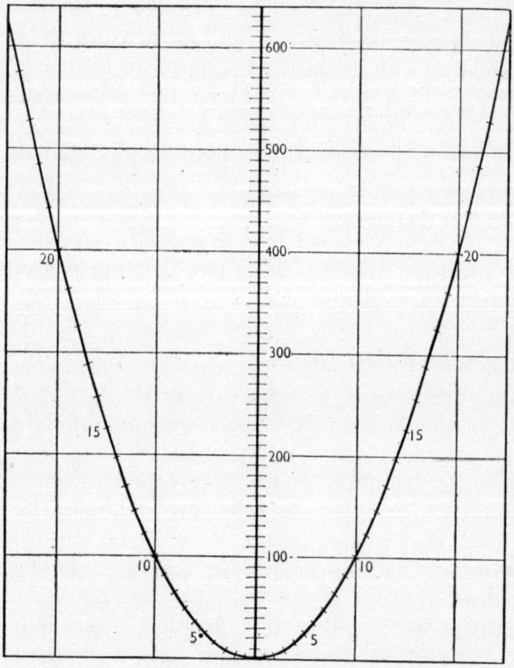

LABOUR SAVING DEVICES. *Much boredom may be saved by using suitable aids to calculations. Some devices give exact answers; others, rough answers which are often sufficient for practical purposes or as a check on a long piece of exact calculation. This Nomogram appeared in a magazine published at Magdalen College School, Brackley. (See also Chapter X.) In order to multiply two numbers, put a ruler or pencil through these numbers on the curves: where the ruler intersects the central line, its scale gives the required product. For division use the reverse procedure.*

(Designed by M. Landau).

the work shorter, and insist on the longest possible methods, the most out-of-date procedure, being used. There are still some examinations in which the regulations say: "Tables of logarithms must not be used."

The most sensible examination would be one in which the student was allowed to work in the same way as a practical man works in real life—that is to say, in the midst of all the reference books and charts that he needs—and given problems just as they occur in practice. This would be a real test of ability in natural conditions. There are many people who pass examinations and are completely incapable of applying their knowledge to any useful purpose afterwards.

SHOULD LEARNING BE PAINFUL ?

Some people will say, "You are making things too easy for them. It is good for students to struggle with difficulties."

Of course it is good for students to overcome difficulties, but the difficulties should be real difficulties, not difficulties artificially created. There is no virtue in shovelling with a teaspoon when a shovel could be used.

In any case, there is so much mathematics to be known, and so much need for mathematics in new technical developments, that new devices do not imply less effort from the student. They mean that with the same effort the student can learn very much more.

In this book every opportunity will be taken of using modern methods for reducing drudgery, and thus setting free time and energy for intelligent understanding.

The common-sense attitude to the question "Should learning be made difficult?" may best be seen by considering an illustration. Suppose a boy wishes to make a table as a present for his parents. It would certainly be unsatisfactory if the boy gave way to a feeling of weariness, and left the table in a half-finished condition. That would show lack of persistence in a freely chosen task.

But, although the table was being made for a useful purpose, there would be nothing wrong in the boy enjoying the actual work of making it. In fact, the more he enjoyed the work, the more care one would expect him to devote to it.

There would certainly be no gain in forcing him to use blunt tools, or timber of inferior quality. There might perhaps be some special reason for using a very hard wood, like mahogany, if that would produce a superior result in the end.

Very much the same considerations apply to work in mathematics, or any other subject. The work should be undertaken for some object: the student should be persistent enough to undertake all labour that is unavoidably necessary: but when two methods of approaching a problem lead equally well to the same result, there is no virtue in choosing the harder way. In fact, it is downright foolishness.

MATHEMATICS SHOULD NOT BE TAKEN NEAT

There is nothing to be ashamed of, then, in finding the most pleasant way of learning mathematics.

Very often mathematics is best learnt by doing something else. In this respect, mathematics is like any other implement. You do not learn how to use a spade by examining spades, or a hammer by studying hammers. You learn about spades by using a spade to dig, and you learn about hammers incidentally in the course of driving in nails.

Arithmetic comes into many games—counting for table quoits, adding for wall quoits and darts, adding as far as twenty-one for pontoon, and so on. Practically every game has some kind of arithmetic in it. There is no reason why children should not, in the first place, form a desire to understand arithmetic in order to join in games that older children play.

Scoring at games has this important feature—it helps you to feel the meaning of numbers. Suppose two boys are trying to hit a target, each in turn taking three throws, and the game finishing when one has scored ten direct hits. If one boy has scored nine, and it is the turn of the other, who has scored seven, to throw, this boy knows that he must score with all three shots, or the first boy will have a very good chance of finishing the game at the next turn. In the course of playing games, emotions come to be connected with numbers, and that is the all-important thing in learning—what you feel.

You are much more likely to feel something if mathematics comes incidentally into some real activity, than if you sit down and say, "Now I am going to do some mathematics."

Of course, the mathematics of games will not take you very far. Games are mostly useful for making fairly young children familiar with the meaning of numbers.

A little more advanced work comes into any activity involving measurement.

There are a large number of applications of mathematics to scientific questions. It is not possible to mention all of these in this book because often a lot of space would be necessary to explain scientific matters that some readers could not be expected to know. If you are familiar with any branch of science you will know of many examples in which mathematics is used.

Science, of course, can be dull. Some scientific experiments, in which you merely verify a law that you already know, are not very exciting.

Some scientific experiments produce very interesting results, and you feel you would like to demonstrate these to people you know. The question then arises as to whether the apparatus you have will be sufficiently sensitive, or sufficiently powerful, for the effect to be clearly seen. It is here that a mixture of experiment and calculation becomes necessary.

For example, there is a device that is (or was) used on the railways, to show when the lamp in a signal had gone out. It depended on the fact that when the lamp went out, it became cooler, and a piece of metal placed above the lamp shrank. But the change of the length of a piece of metal due to heating or cooling is very small—only a few millionths of its length for each degree of temperature. The question is, how to arrange things so that this minute change will produce visible effects. It is particularly interesting to solve this problem with the extra condition that only home-made apparatus is to be used.

Generally, very interesting calculations come into the design of scientific experiments, and something is lost if you simply copy the experiments described in books.

The more inventive you are by temperament, the more opportunities you should have to use mathematics in working out new ideas, and the more help mathematics can be to you.

If you are content to be told what to do by somebody else, or just to do what was done last time, mathematics will not be of much interest to you.

For those who are not of scientific bent, some indications are given of the use of mathematics in social and historical questions (Chapter II).

Mathematics has also some applications of interest to artistic people, and these are mentioned in various places in this book.

HOW TO ATTACK PROBLEMS

Many people have the following idea of mathematics. The teacher tells you how to solve certain problems. Part of what you are told you forget: part you remember. If you are given a problem to solve that the teacher has explained to you and you have remembered, you are all right, and you get on with the job. If the method has never been explained to you, or if you have heard about it and forgotten, you sit looking at the paper: you are stumped.

Mathematics is not in the least like this. The main object of mathematics is to teach you to think things out for yourself, to accustom you to invent your own methods. It is this *habit* of relying on yourself, of thinking for yourself, that you must acquire. It is more important that you should acquire this habit than that you should actually succeed in solving a problem.

Now, of course, if you are hazy about what a quadratic equation is, it is no use sitting down and thinking about quadratic equations. You cannot get useful results by thinking about something, if you are not clear what the thing is.

You should begin by taking some subject with which you are thoroughly familiar and thinking about that for yourself. You may find puzzles in newspapers suitable for this purpose. Newspaper puzzles are usually about things with which everybody is familiar, but they need thinking out.

As you get used to thinking for yourself, you can gradually go on to more complicated things.

It is never any use thinking about a problem, unless you are quite sure what the problem *is*. If you are puzzled by some mathematical symbol that seems to you to have no meaning, you should try to find out (either from friends or from books) what it is *for*, what kind of problem it is meant to solve. That may give you some way of seeing what it means.

To begin with, you are not concerned with finding a method for answering a question. Your first job is to get quite clear about the meaning of the question; to get a picture of what is happening. It is rather like being sent to take charge of some undertaking in a foreign land. Before you start making changes you will (if you are wise) go round and get to know everything about the place where you are and the people in it. You want a complete picture of everything that goes on. It is just the same with the mathematical problem. This is rarely explained to students. Far too often the impression is given that one should just sit down and start to answer the question straight away.

Here is an example of the correct procedure. Suppose you have the following question to answer. (This question is probably of no practical value. It is mentioned mainly because it is very suitable for experimenting with.)

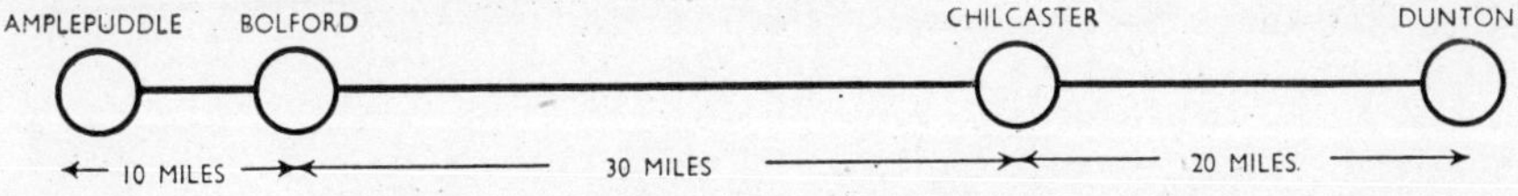

Amplepuddle, Bolford, Chilcaster and Dunton are four towns on a straight road, placed as shown above:

A certain firm intends to build a factory somewhere on the road between

Amplepuddle and Dunton. It is reckoned that each week the firm will deliver two articles to Amplepuddle, ten to Bolford, six to Chilcaster, and seven to Dunton. The cost of transport of each article is £1 a mile. Where should the factory be placed so as to make the cost of transport as low as possible (all other considerations being ignored for the purposes of the problem)?

This is not a stock question. There is no rule giving the answer; no teacher (one imagines) includes this type of problem in the syllabus.

If you had to investigate such a problem, you could begin by simplifying it. Instead of having four towns, you could try with only two towns, say, like this:

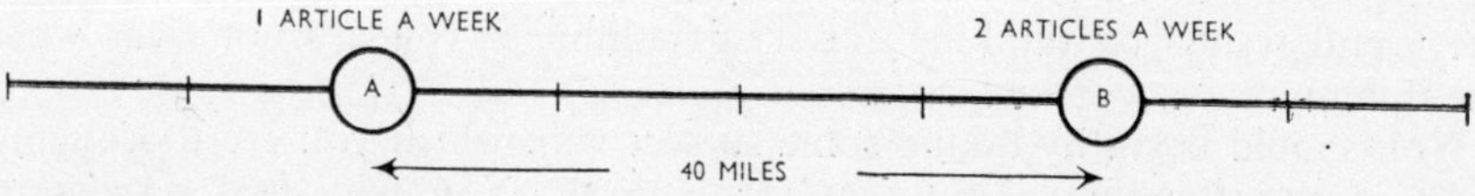

Then you would experiment, taking the factory first at *A*, then ten miles from *A*, then 20 miles from *A*, and so on. Work out the cost of transport in each case, and enter the results in on the map, like this:

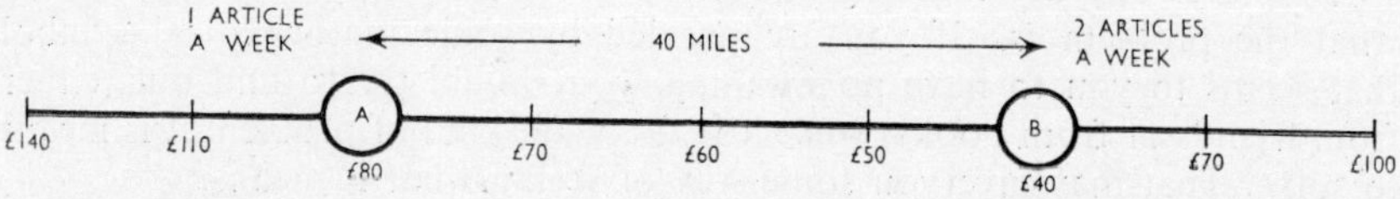

You will notice that we have tried the effect of putting the factory in all sorts of positions—not only between *A* and *B*. This is to make the picture as complete as possible.

You may also notice how the cost changes by steady steps. As we approach *A* from the left, the cost of transport falls by £30 a week every time the factory site is brought ten miles nearer to *A*. Between *A* and *B*, each step of ten miles towards *B* brings the cost down by £10. After we pass *B*, the cost again begins to rise, going up by £30 for every extra ten miles away from *B*.

In this case the cheapest thing will be to build the factory in the town *B*.

Now we can vary the demand in the two towns, and do the same working. The following results will be found for the various cases:

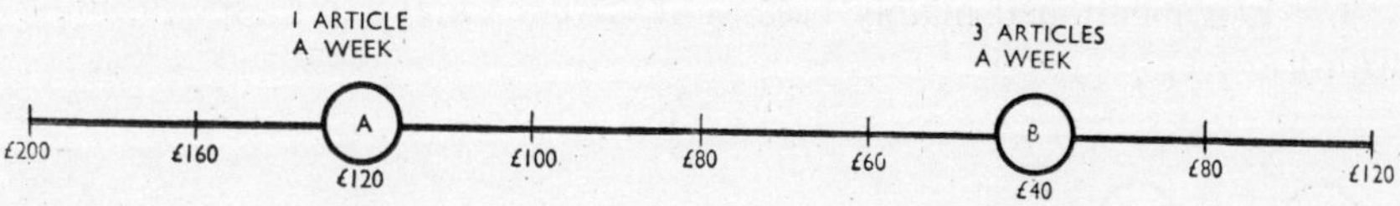

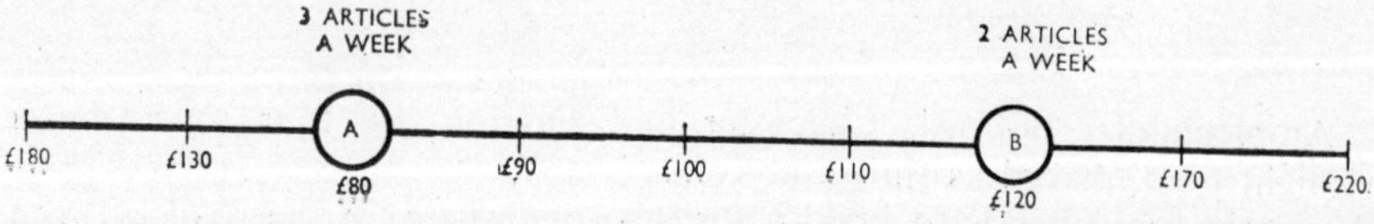

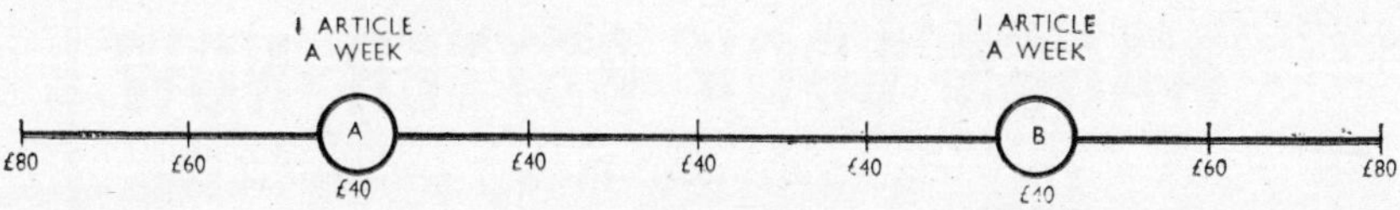

Looking at these diagrams we notice something. Except in the case where the demand in the two towns A and B is equal, it is always cheapest to have the factory *in one of the two towns.* It never pays to have it on the road between two towns. (The case when the demand in the towns is equal is exceptional: then it does not matter where the factory is sited, so long as it is between A and B, or in either of the towns.)

It is probable that few people would guess this result—that *the factory should be in one of the towns*—straight away. So soon as you start experimenting with possible positions for the factory it becomes clear. (It would appear very clearly indeed if you happened to be familiar with the method of graphs, described in Chapter VIII of this book, and you made a graph of the cost of transport for various positions of the factory.)

Now we have a clue to the problem. We start to consider the case of three towns, with the idea in our mind, "It *may* be that the best position will be in one of the towns."

We test this idea for three towns, trying various positions for the towns (though always along a straight road), and various demands for the articles in the towns. We find that the idea does work for three towns as well.

By now we are prepared to bet that it holds for four, or five, or six, or any number of towns. There should be just a grain of reserve in our minds—because we have only guessed this, we have not proved it—but it seems good enough as an idea to work on. Assuming for the moment that it is so, we have as good as solved the original problem about the four towns. The factory is to be in one of the four towns. We work out the cost of transport for the four possible sites—Amplepuddle, Bolford, Chilcaster, and Dunton. Whichever of these four results is the smallest amount tells us the town to choose.

Admittedly it has taken us some time and no small amount of work to get to the answer—but it would have taken us far longer if we had just sat and chewed a pencil and hoped for an inspiration.

The method that has been used here—taking the problem, simplifying it, experimenting with possible answers, spotting something, guessing a general law, getting back to the original problem and applying this law to it—is one that can be applied to almost any problem. It is the method by which mathematicians work when they are making a new discovery—and all mathematics had to be discovered once, by somebody.

You will find that if you accustom yourself to work in this way, you will gradually become quicker at spotting answers: you will acquire the habit of spotting small clues: you will get more and more ideas for possible ways of tackling problems, as your experience grows. It may be slow at first, but it will lead you somewhere, and you will be a real mathematician. The

WAGES LOOK BETTER NOW

MARRIED, TWO CHILDREN

Income	Old Tax			New Tax		
265	—			—		
270		19	6	—		
300	9	15	0	—		
350	24	7	6	3	18	9
400	39	0	0	13	10	0
500	76	2	6	44	12	6
600	121	2	6	84	0	0
700	166	2	6	123	7	6
800	211	2	6	162	15	0
900	256	2	6	202	2	6
1,000	301	2	6	241	10	0
1,250	413	12	6	342	15	0
1,500	526	2	6	455	5	0
2,000	776	2	6	680	5	0

MARRIED COUPLES, THREE CHILDREN

Income	Old Tax			New Tax		
320	—			—		
325		16	3	—		
350	8	2	6	—		
400	22	15	0	3	0	0
500	52	0	0	24	15	0
600	96	2	6	61	10	0
700	141	2	6	100	17	6
800	186	2	6	140	5	0
900	231	2	6	179	12	6
1,000	276	2	6	219	0	0
1,250	388	12	6	320	5	0
1,500	501	2	6	432	15	0
2,000	751	2	6	657	15	0

PARROTS 'INHERIT' £6,000

So that the grey parrots may have larger cages, with tree trunks and swings, the London Zoo receives over £6,000 in the will of a London woman.

5 Flavour Variations for your Stew

(1) With beef, try 1-2 cloves.
(2) With pork, add some sage.
(3) With mutton, some mace and mint.
(4) With any meat, one bay-leaf.
(5) Some of your bottled tomatoes.

ARMY RELEASES
Groups 19 to 23

Owns £2,200 home, must live in a fowlhouse

POOL 1 10 Results 624/-
CERTIFIE
POOL 2
for 2d ·2·0
22 Pts.
£53·14·9 £11·9·6
POOL 4 4 Aways
12 RESULTS POOL
£2460 for 2d ·5·0
11 Correct £52·0·6 10 Correct £3·1·6
EASY SIX 492/-
All Pools to Units of 1/- except 2d Points Pool & 12 Results Pool

MORE BASIC PETROL
25 per Cent Increase

£164,660,000
Compensation for the Coalowners

329,454 UNEMPLOYED IN JANUARY

NUMBERS IN THE NEWS

The numbers shown here are out of date now. When this book was being written these numbers were quite topical. You can form some idea of how widely numbers enter into everyday life by keeping a scrapbook of newspaper cuttings such as are shown in the above illustration. It is often the case that the whole point of a headline lies in numbers—"Boy falls 200 *feet," "Man of* 80 *marries ninth wife,"* "7,000 *troops patrol town."*

other way, mugging things up like a parrot, will never lead you to be, or do, anything worth while.

THE IMPORTANCE OF SMALL CLUES

One of the main differences between successful mathematicians and unsuccessful students is this—the mathematicians like pottering about with numbers, and think about numbers in their spare time. The unsuccessful students do not like mathematics: they try to rush through their work as quickly as possible, and then forget all about it.

You can see much the same kind of difference at a railway exhibition—the difference between the boy whose main interest in life is railways, who thinks, talks and dreams about railways, and the aunt who may bring him there, and is interested only in a railway as something to convey her from one place to another. Needless to say, the boy will see the meaning of fine points in the exhibition that mean nothing to his aunt. He has the background to appreciate them; she has not.

The main reason why an enthusiasm for railways is regarded as natural, and an enthusiasm for mathematics as unnatural, is that mathematics is a compulsory subject in schools. Railway operation is not.

In the subjects themselves there is no great difference. So if you want to do well at mathematics, you must try to imagine that you live in a country where mathematics is not a school subject, and try to approach it as if it were a hobby. You must try to like it, and to let your mind wander in mathematical channels in odd moments.

It is not meant that you should sit down with an algebra book, grit your teeth, and say, "I am going to like this." That certainly will not work. You should start at the other end. Try to find something mathematical in which you really are interested. With most people there is something—perhaps some trick or puzzle, or some odd fact about numbers—that they find really interesting. Start from *this* and let your mind embroider around it. See if you can make up some similar trick or puzzle. Notice any curious fact that turns up in the course of working something out. Keep a notebook of things you have noticed and discovered for yourself. At first, they may be only unimportant little trifles—even so, it is pleasant to have discovered something, however small. And the habit of discovery will grow on you.

Odd scraps of information can be very useful. For instance, if you look at the numbers in the nine-times table:

9
18
27
36
45
54
63
72
81
90

you will notice that the numbers in each line add up to nine.

$$9 = 9$$
$$1 + 8 = 9$$
$$2 + 7 = 9$$
$$3 + 6 = 9 \quad \text{etc.}$$

If you think of this from time to time, until you get so used to it that it does not need any effort to remember it, it can be of practical use. For instance, very many people find it hard to remember 6×9 and 7×8. They may know that the results are 54 and 56, but they cannot remember which is 6×9 and which is 7×8. But you would immediately say to yourself, the numbers 5 and 4 in 54 add up to 9; the numbers 5 and 6 do not. So 54 must be the one that is in the nine-times table.

The more you think about numbers, the more you will come to feel that each number has its own character, that 54 is quite a different sort of number from 56.

And all the time you are thinking about numbers, try to *see* and *feel* the meaning of the numbers, that this one is a very large one, that that is a very small one, that this number is mid-way between those two numbers, and so on. We shall return to this theme in Chapter II.

HOW TO OVERCOME DIFFICULTIES

From time to time in reading any book on mathematics, you will come to something that puzzles you. In this book we have tried to be as clear as possible; even so, some difficulties probably remain.

One reason for this is lack of space. This book deals with arithmetic, algebra, geometry and trigonometry. About each of these, several books could be written; so, obviously, we cannot deal in full detail with every possible point.

It may help you to understand this book if you know how we have tried to overcome this difficulty—shortage of space. We believe that in each part of mathematics there is a *guiding idea*, and that once you have grasped this guiding idea you can work out the details for yourself.

Most people go right through school without grasping the guiding ideas of mathematics and, as a result, they have to learn rules by heart. Once you have formed the habit of learning by rule without understanding, you have made it very difficult for yourself to become a mathematician. Being a mathematician is not so much a question of knowing something, as of having the *habit* of thinking things out for yourself.

In most chapters of this book, we have begun by explaining the *object* of the work, what it is for. Geometry, for instance, is concerned with making things the right shape, with finding the shapes most suitable for certain purposes.

Once you have understood the object, the aim of the inquiry, you should put the book down, and think to yourself, "How would I go about that?" When you begin the geometry chapter, for instance, you should think what objects in ordinary life have to be made to a particular shape, and how you would go about making these. After you have stirred up your mind in this way, you can read the rest of the chapter. Very likely you will find in it several things that you have already thought of for yourself. You will be able to say to yourself, "I know everything on this page already. I need not bother learning it by heart."

The more you think about things for yourself, the more you will see that mathematical methods are natural and obvious. This should be your aim;

to keep thinking about the methods of mathematics until you feel you could have discovered them for yourself, until you see them as reasonable and natural. The more you can learn to do this, the less strain there will be on your memory. You will come to see that there are certain places where you can go off the rails, and these you must remember: but in between it is just a matter of going along doing the obvious thing.

Accordingly, if you find that you cannot follow some step in an argument, you should first ask yourself, "Can I see what the writer is trying to do?" If you do not understand the aim, you certainly will not be able to understand the method.

When you understand what the aim is, you may be able to work the answer out for yourself, and compare it with the conclusion reached in the book. If they are the same, you can at any rate say, "I do not know how *he* finds that out, but I know how *I* would." You can then read on, but keep the question in mind. Look at it from time to time over a period of months: you may well find that what is being done will suddenly flash on you.

It may be that the method used to solve some problem is one that has been mentioned earlier in the book. You may not have noticed it, or you may have noticed it and forgotten it. You should, therefore, ask yourself, "Is this work like anything that has been done earlier?" You can then search through the book, and you may come to some section that throws light on the difficulty.

Sometimes you will find that the best thing to do is simply to read on, and the difficulty will be cleared up by some later remark. It is very difficult to explain an idea, so to speak, all at once. Very often it takes several pages with particular examples to make clear what is being done. This should be borne in mind,

It pays to read a book through, without at first bothering too much whether every point is understood. This helps you to see the book as a whole. For instance, the arithmetic chapters of this book have to cover all the types of calculation that are going to be used anywhere in the book. You may wonder why square roots have to be worked out: you will find the answer only when you come to the algebra and geometry chapters. You may wonder why such things as 10^{-3} were invented. You will find the answer only when you come to the chapter on Labour-Saving Devices.

You will find that most of the algebra and geometry chapters use only very simple arithmetic. This, of course, has been done on purpose, so that it will be possible for you to read about algebra and geometry before you have fully mastered the more difficult parts of arithmetic.

You are strongly advised not to try to read the chapters exactly in the order in which they are written. Read right through first of all, if you like, skimming over the harder parts; but when you get down to mastering the work in earnest, do not try to have a complete knowledge of Chapter V before you look at Chapter VI, or a complete knowledge of Chapter IX before you look at Chapter XI. Read the parts that you find you can learn easily, and gradually isolate the sections that you are going to find really hard.

The most difficult parts may make you need to seek other advice. (Though

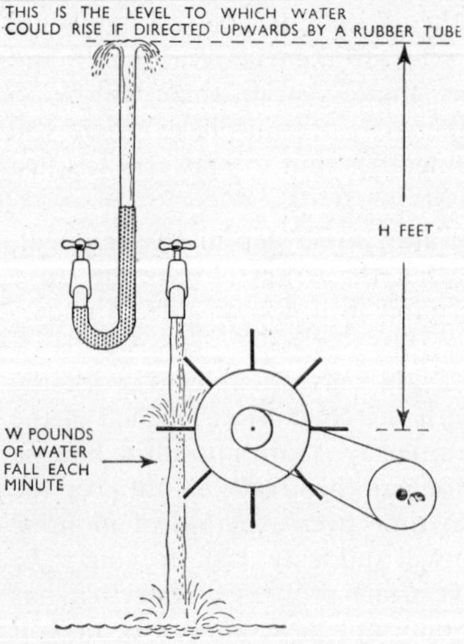

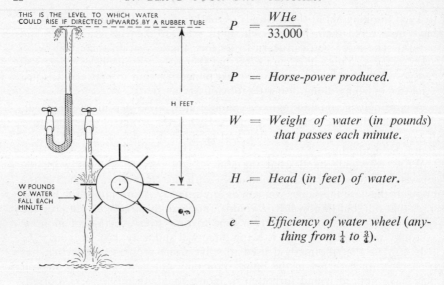

$$P = \frac{WHe}{33{,}000}$$

P = *Horse-power produced.*

W = *Weight of water (in pounds) that passes each minute.*

H = *Head (in feet) of water.*

e = *Efficiency of water wheel (anything from $\frac{1}{4}$ to $\frac{3}{4}$).*

HORSE-POWER OF WATER WHEELS.

An engineer often has to ask himself "Will this design be found powerful enough for the work that it will have to accomplish?" The formula shown above might equally well be used by a model engineer who may be working by a kitchen sink, or by the designer of the power station at Niagara Falls.

good advice is difficult to get. So many people have learned mathematics without really understanding it; they are the blind leading the blind.) You may find some book in a local library that uses quite a different method, and so sheds some light on the difficulty.

There is no one perfect way of teaching mathematics. Each person requires a different type of approach. It is up to you to look into books of all kinds, and pick out those that particularly suit your own style of thinking. Even with these, you must always be turning the results into your own language. "The writer pictures this result to himself in *that* way. He finds that the simplest way of seeing it. But what is the simplest way for *me* to see it?" The only book that will really meet your needs is the book you write yourself —and you should always be on the job of writing it. Keep notebooks, and jot down in them any way of explaining mathematical results that seems particularly good to you. A very good way of learning mathematics is to teach somebody else. In seeking ways of making the subject clear to the person you are coaching, you are forced to make it clear to yourself.

One or two things you will find have been explained twice, in different parts of this book. This arose first of all through different chapters being written by different writers. It seemed best to leave the two explanations in, as this helps to bind the different chapters together. Also, there is the possibility that if one explanation is not understood, the other may be.

In the earlier chapters of this book we have tried very hard to keep the work simple and clear. In some of the later chapters, on the other hand, we have let ourselves go a bit, so as to cater, to some extent, for the more advanced reader, or for the student who wants to see what can be done with mathematics. A reader who finds that some points in these later chapters are not clear should not be discouraged. As was said earlier, a whole book could easily be devoted to matters that we have had to discuss in a single chapter. These chapters are bound to be a little like encyclopedia articles.

Exercises

1. In the design of a cinema projector, the following problem arises.

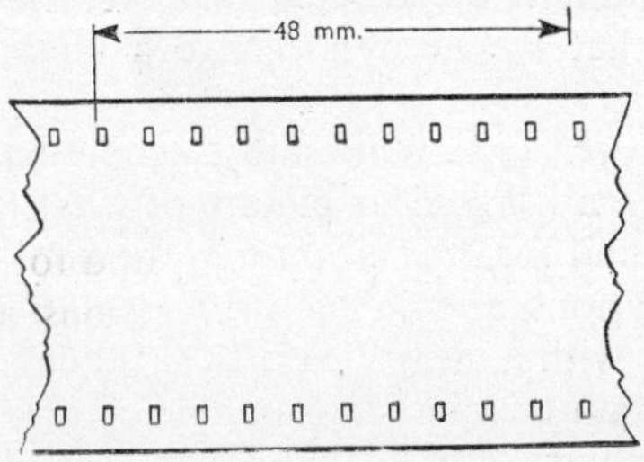

Above is part of a strip of film. It is to be pulled through a projector by means of a cog as illustrated below. It will be seen that this cog has 32 teeth.

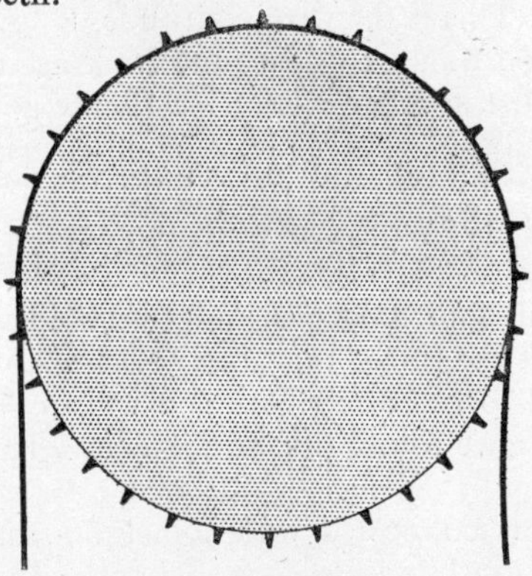

If a cog of this design were used, what would be its circumference and radius? In the design of any machine, a host of small problems of this type will arise. They do not call for any very advanced mathematics, but to deal with them you need a good understanding of elementary mathematics, such as is dealt with in this book.

2. We saw on page 19 that the figures of numbers in the 9 times table always add up to 9.

What do they add up to in the 3 times table?

3. Is it true that if you multiply any number by itself and then divide by 4, there may be a remainder of 1 or 0?

What remainders can occur if, instead of dividing by 4, you divide by 5? Or by 6? Or by 7?

4. How many different telegraph signals can be made from dots and dashes

(*a*) containing two signs only (e.g., · —),

(*b*) containing three signs only (e.g., — · —),

(*c*) containing four signs only (e.g., · · · ·)?

Is there any simple rule to give the answers?

5. When playing pontoon to have what is called a natural, you have to have an ace together with a king, queen, jack or ten. Thus, A♠, J♦ is a natural.

How many different naturals are you able to find?

6. Every domino is marked with two numbers (counting blank as 0). If the numbers go up to 6, how many dominoes are there in a set? How many would there be if the numbers went up to 9?

CHAPTER II

THE MEANING OF NUMBERS

EVERYONE who knows how to read knows how to count. Counting comes very much into our daily lives. Every time you give change for sixpence, or watch a game of football, or set cups and plates for a meal, you are forced to count.

You might think, then, that we could take it for granted that everybody understood what numbers meant, and that we need not have a chapter devoted to the meaning of numbers.

This chapter has been included for two reasons. While most people have a general idea of what numbers mean, and a fairly clear picture of what the simplest numbers, such as two or three, stand for, it is clear from the kind of mistakes that are made both in examinations and in factory calculations that many people cannot handle numbers with a clear idea of what they are doing. One should be able to *feel* whether an answer is reasonable or not.

Another reason for going over this elementary work is that it is the foundation on which everything else is built.

FEELINGS OF ANXIETY

Again, there are very many people who know how to do calculations, but try to avoid them if they possibly can. This is the wrong attitude. Knowledge is a weapon for use in life, and one ought to go round looking for something to apply one's knowledge to, just as a boy with a new knife goes round looking for something to cut. But, often, schools leave children with just the opposite attitude. They teach them to get sums right, but the whole subject is surrounded with feelings of anxiety and dread which paralyse the mind.

If you suffer from this feeling, you will find it helpful to go right back to the beginning, and take another look at the things that used to scare you. Often you will find that they have ceased to be so terrible. You will say to yourself, "Is that all it was? I wonder why we found that so difficult?" This chapter gives you the chance to do that.

The fear of numbers is worst when it is connected with something that reminds you of school. If you see a question like this:

Find the H.C.F. and L.C.M. of 510, 357 and 1,785

you may well feel that this is a mystery. You never see anything like that out of a text-book.

But suppose numbers turn up in some other connection, like this, for instance:

You do not feel that there is anything frightening or mysterious about these numbers.

If you are a cricketer you can see that England has made a good beginning at Old Trafford, being nearly up to Australia and having five wickets in hand.

If the exciting story occurs in a magazine of about 80 pages, you know that you will have to look for page 69 somewhere near the back cover, with 11 pages left in which the writer can explain what stirred in the shadows, or in which other stories can be finished.

If you fancy yourself at writing short stories, you imagine what you could

The wedding group is easily counted.

The concert audience would take longer to count—it may run into hundreds.

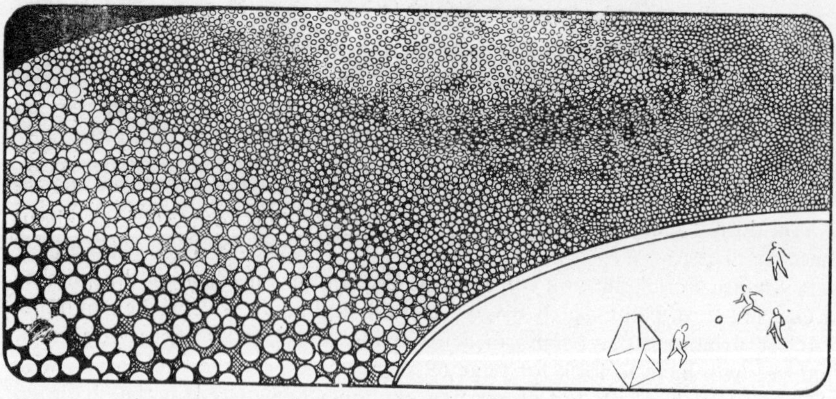

To count a football crowd would be very exhausting. It runs into many thousands.

do with the £15,000 prize—throw up your job, perhaps, and go round the world, or take your family to live in the country, or whatever it is you have always wanted to do and have been unable to afford.

In the same way, everyone knows how much, or how little, can be done with 24 clothing coupons, and what the significance is of the numbers on the dartboard.

Numbers, as they turn up in real life, are not mysterious. Numbers become mysterious only when they are separated from the real things of life.

In all the examples given above, you were able to *feel* something about the numbers. The Australian cricketers could feel that England was nearly up to their score; the reader had a feeling where to look for page 69; the storywriter had a feeling that £15,000 was a lot of money, and so on.

To do arithmetic easily, and to enjoy it, one needs to develop this *feeling* about numbers; to feel that one number is very close to another, or very much bigger than another, or half-way between two other numbers, and so on.

The meaning of small numbers is easily grasped—as, for instance, the numbers of dots on the face of dice.

You can recognize the value of cards up to 10 even if the numbers are not printed on the cards.

But we cannot see the meaning of large numbers at a glance. It is very difficult to guess the number of people at a concert, or in a cinema, or in a football crowd as illustrated on page 26.

In these illustrations, one can see that the wedding group could be counted in a short time: the concert audience one could also count, but it would be rather tiring to do so: to count the football crowd would be an almost endless task. This gives one some rough idea of how these numbers compare with each other.

When large numbers are involved, as in stocktaking, it is helpful if the objects are arranged in regular groups. A grocer or wine merchant may keep his bottles in boxes that hold a dozen each. In this way, as the illustration on page 30 shows, he can save himself much trouble.

In banks, pound notes are kept in bundles of twenty, so that a cheque for £100 can be met simply by counting out five bundles.

In an army, about 60 men form a platoon, 4 platoons a company, 4 companies a battalion. By having these larger units, one is able to avoid the use of large numbers. You can see that 2 battalions fighting against 7 battalions are at the same disadvantage as 2 men fighting 7 men.

But these methods of grouping are not very systematic. All sorts of different numbers come in—12 bottles to a case, 20 pounds to a bundle, 60 men to a platoon, 4 platoons to a company. For general calculations, we do not want to have to remember a whole lot of disconnected numbers like this (though, unfortunately, we still have to do it for money sums, and for weights and measures). The rule used for counting is much simpler; grouping is always by tens.

Thus, if we had to count the small cubes of metal shown here

we should begin by arranging these in groups of ten, with as few odd ones left over as possible.

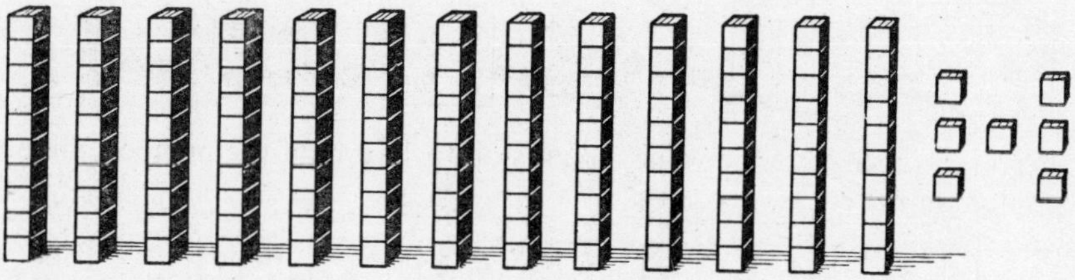

There are still too many tall piles to recognize at a glance, so we group these, so far as possible, in sets of ten again, like this:

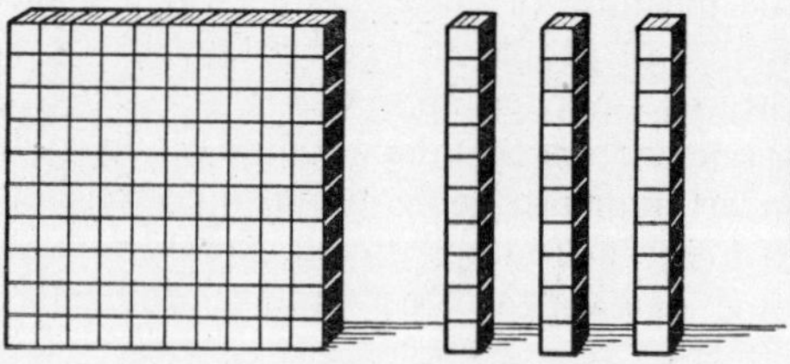

We can now describe our number as

ONE like this

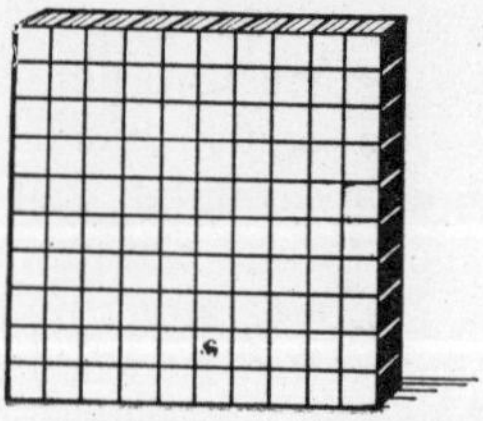

THREE like this 

SEVEN like this 

Names have been given to these groups.

A single object is called a UNIT. A group like this  is called TEN.

A group like this 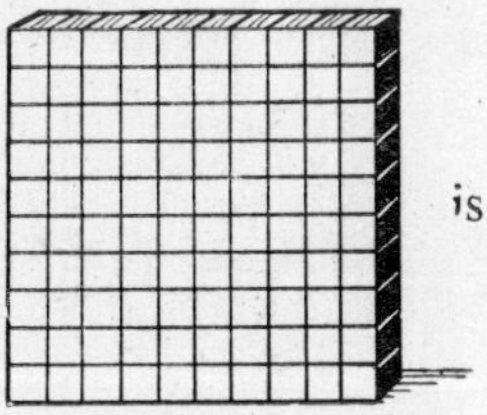 is called a HUNDRED.

The collection of cubes that we counted above is, therefore,

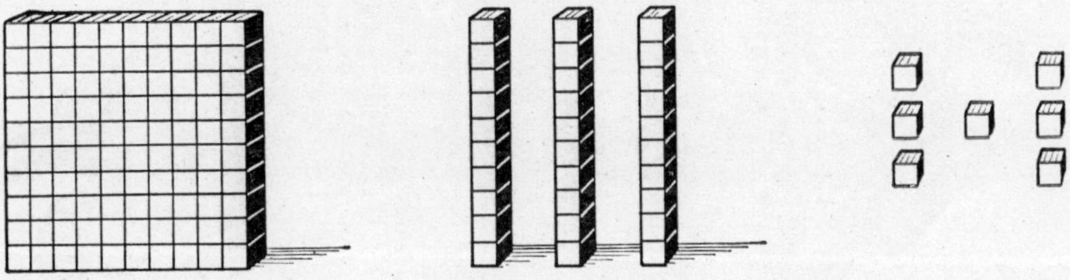

1 HUNDRED 3 TENS 7 UNITS.

This number is usually written simply as 137.

Still larger groups may be formed. Ten hundreds grouped together are called a thousand.

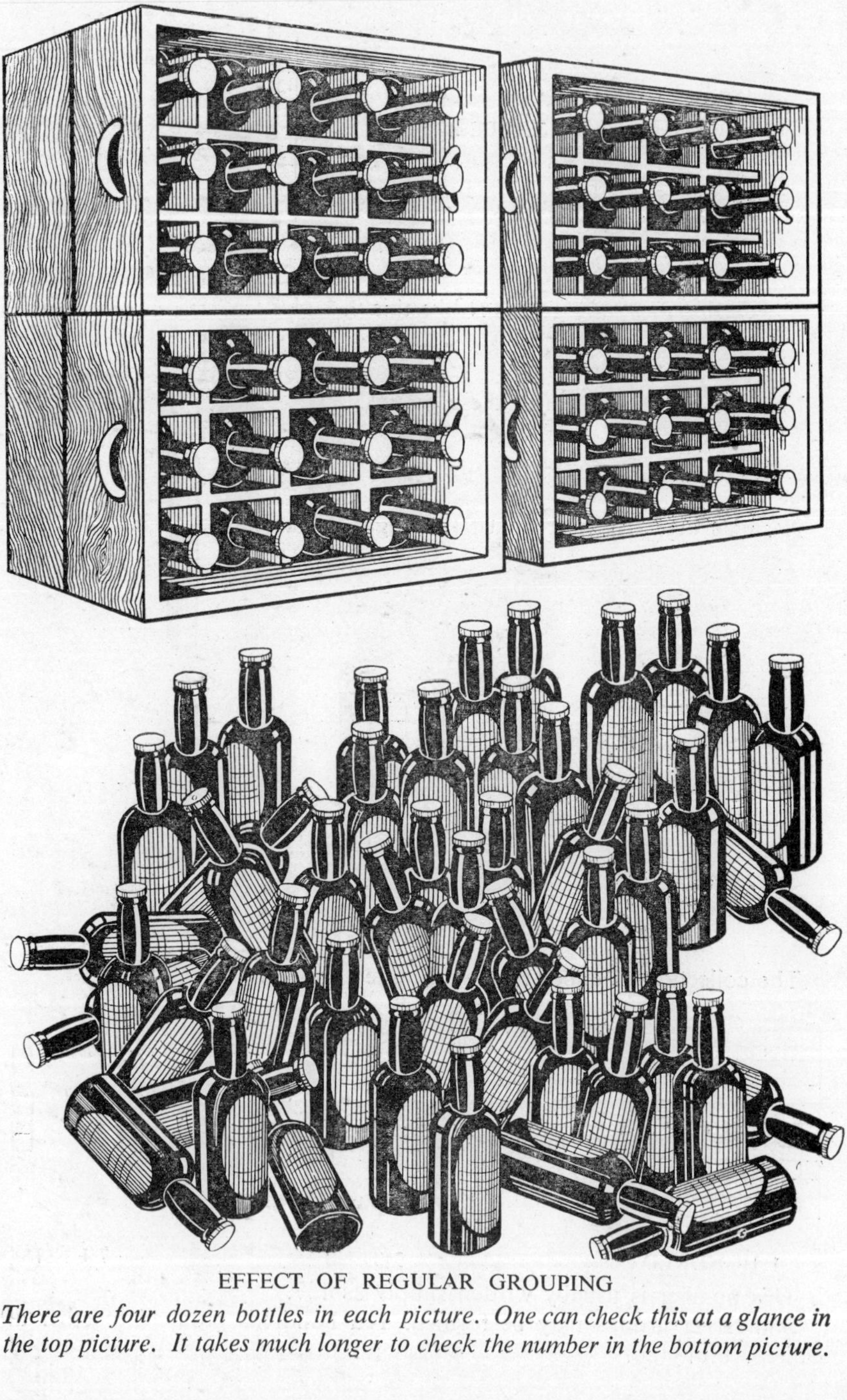

EFFECT OF REGULAR GROUPING

There are four dozen bottles in each picture. One can check this at a glance in the top picture. It takes much longer to check the number in the bottom picture.

WOMEN'S SHOES

MEN'S SHOES

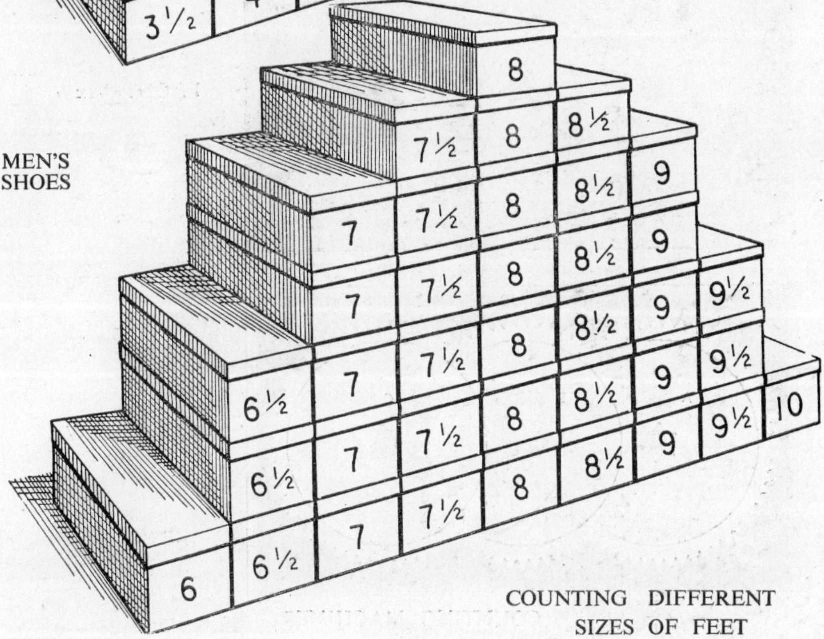

COUNTING DIFFERENT SIZES OF FEET

Small shops cannot afford huge stocks of shoes. If a shopkeeper can afford a stock of only 37 pairs of men's shoes and 37 pairs of women's, how many of each size would he order? Careful count has been made of the number of each size sold. Diagrams show how the order should be made so as to have the best chance of meeting requirements with a stock of 74 pairs of shoes.

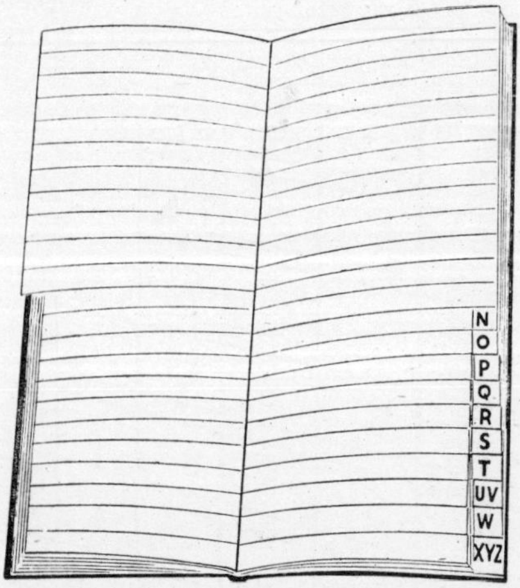

MAKING AN ADDRESS BOOK FROM A NOTEBOOK

Counting comes into this simple piece of work. One has to count the lines on each page, to see if there are twenty-six lines or more. If there are, each letter of the alphabet can go on a separate line. Then the pages of the book have to be counted, to see how many pages can be given to each letter. As printed address books are usually more expensive than notebooks or exercise books, it pays to do this job yourself.

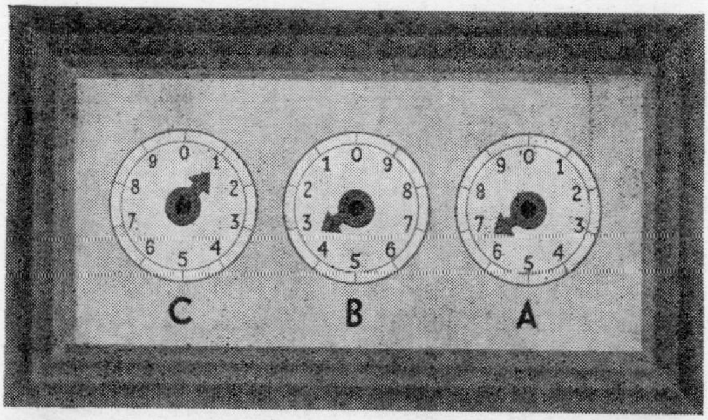

FRONT VIEW

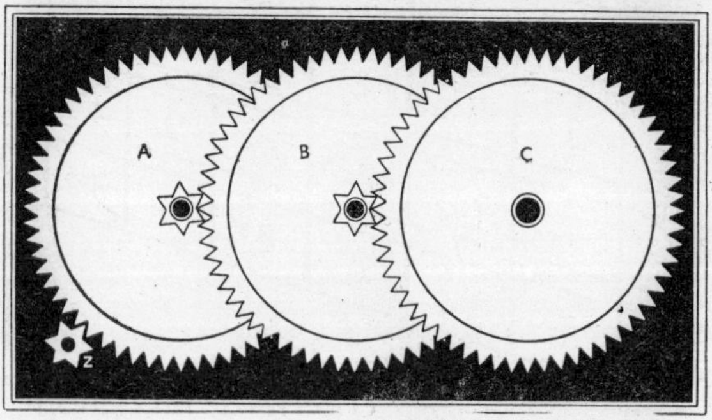

BACK VIEW

COUNTING MACHINES

Gas meters are counting machines. Gearwheels A *and* B *are made so that* A *has to go round ten times for* B *to go round once.* B *has to go round ten times for* C *to go round once. At one turn of* Z, *the pointer on* A *moves one division. These machines help you to see the meaning of numbers like "a hundred" or "a thousand". If you turn the little wheel* Z *you can see how very slowly the hundreds pointer,* C, *moves.*

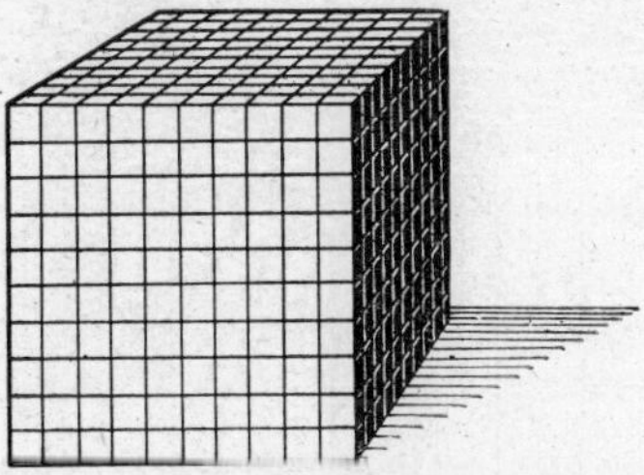

A THOUSAND SMALL CUBES

We may again form a group consisting of ten thousands.

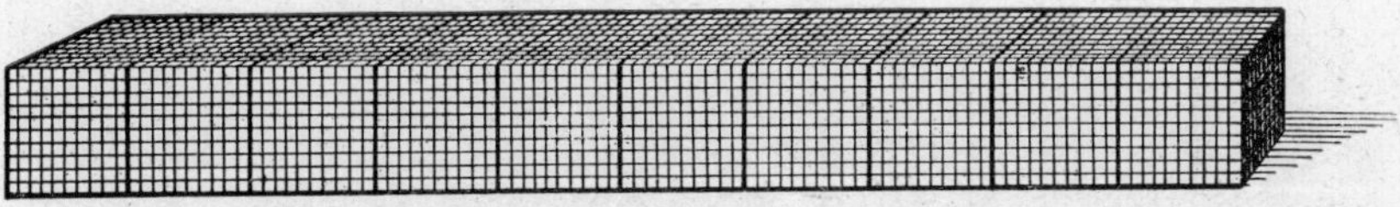

TEN THOUSAND SMALL CUBES

The next group is again ten times as big, and is called a HUNDRED THOUSAND. In shape, it might appear like this:

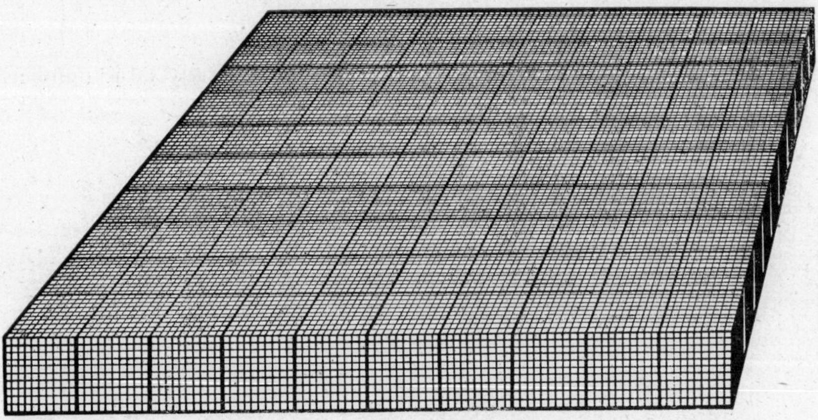

A HUNDRED THOUSAND SMALL CUBES

Ten of these would form a group of A MILLION.

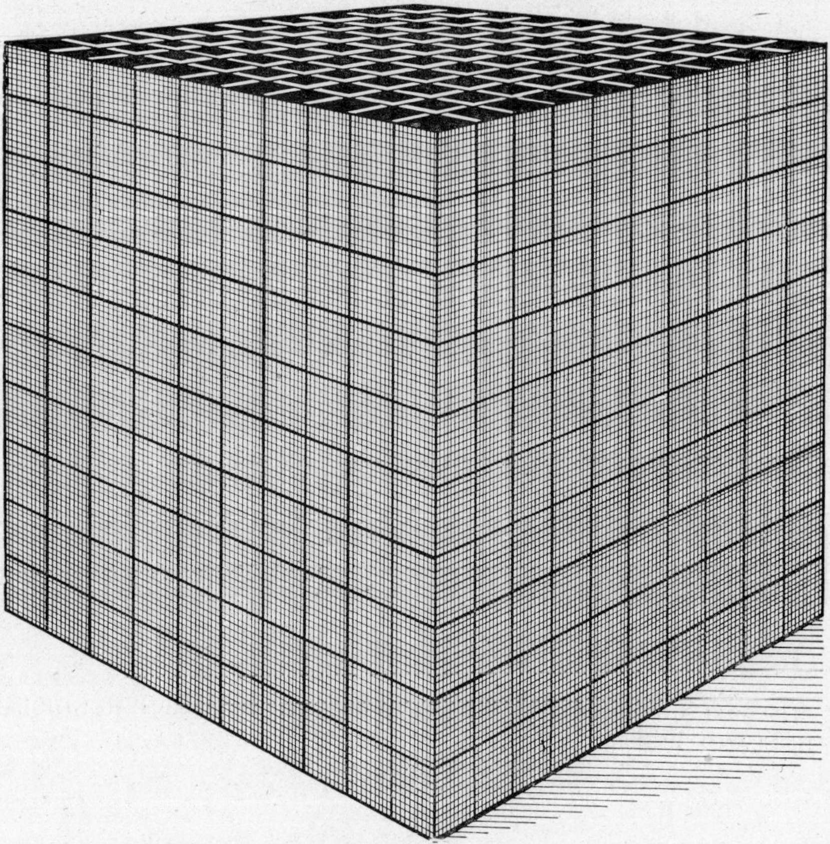

A MILLION SMALL CUBES

We may use these blocks to picture the meaning of any large number. Thus 1,132,137 we could picture as:

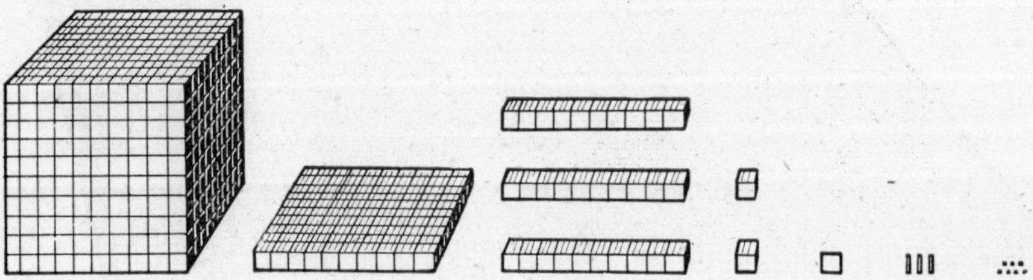

You will see that it has been difficult to draw this figure. In order to make the block for a million small enough to go on a sheet of paper, we have had to make the tens and units so small that you can hardly see them. There is something to be learnt from this. Ones, tens and even hundreds and thousands are very small compared to a million. If you are trying to get an idea of how large a number like 1,132,137 is, you need not bother much about the figures at the end.

You will notice this in official statistics. For instance, it was announced that British exports in January 1946 amounted to £57,000,000. The exact figure may have been something like £57,143,921 15s. 6d. You would not really be any wiser if you knew the exact figure. It is far easier to understand how exports are doing if you just have the round figures—33 millions a month at the beginning of 1945, 39 millions at the end of 1945, 57 millions in January 1946 and 60 millions in February 1946.

A diagram can be made quite easily to illustrate these figures,

BRITISH EXPORTS

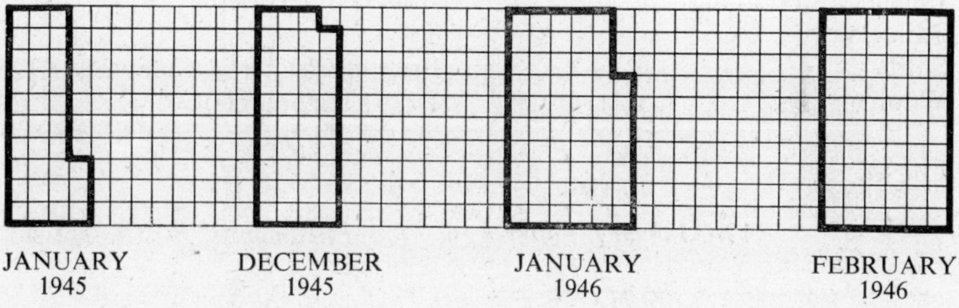

but you cannot show the odd £143,921 15s. 6d. on these diagrams.

In dealing with very large numbers, it is necessary to keep a sense of proportion. A junior clerk was once told to estimate the cost of making certain alterations in a factory. He worked it out with great care and reported that the cost would be £146 17s. 3½d. All this exact working was wasted labour. If he had said, "The cost will be about £150, boss," that would have been quite as useful.

Of course, the meaning of a number can be illustrated in many different ways.

We have had one way already, using cubes and blocks made up from cubes. Blocks like this can actually be made without much trouble, and can be useful for teaching young children in school.

In the diagram to illustrate British Exports, squared paper was used. Each little square represented £1,000,000. That is another way of representing numbers.

Again one may think of numbers in connection with the pages of a book. This book, for instance, contains 384 pages. Shut it, look at the side of it, and try to open it straight away at page 186. Shut it again and try to open it at page 45, and then at page 230, and so on. This is an exercise that will enable you to test for yourself how good you are at feeling where a number comes among the other numbers.

One may also think of numbers spread out along a straight line, like the numbers on a ruler or a thermometer.

You may be able to think out other ways of seeing what numbers mean.

22nd January. From our Special Correspondent.

WAGE INCREASES IN SOME INDUSTRIES (OCTOBER, 1945) SINCE AUGUST, 1939

Agriculture	101	Local Authorities	43
Coal	93	Bricklaying (Labourers)	42
Cotton	72	Engineering (Fitters)	41
Confectionery	69	Trams	39
Shipbuilding	56	Boots	37
Railways	54	Lorry-driving	35
Engineering (Labourers)	54	Bricklaying (Bricklayers)	33
Tailoring	53	Tobacco	31
Shirts	53	Printing (Printers & Compositors)	25
Wool	46	Docks (Labourers)	23

19th January. Letter from "Rural Economist".

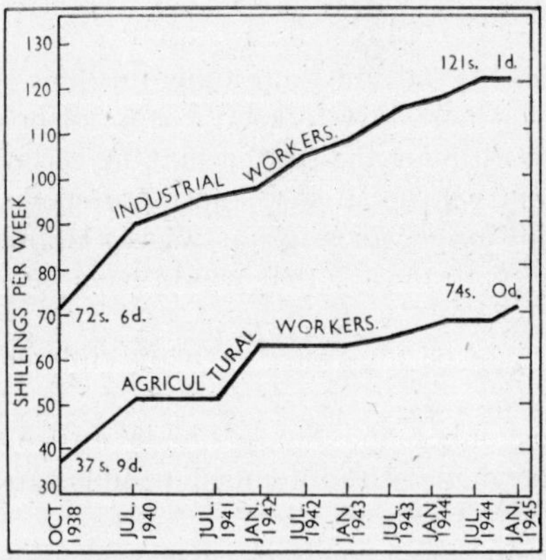

This graph shows how the average earnings of adult male industrial and agricultural workers have changed. The letter goes on to say that agricultural workers are now 12s. a week farther off from equality with industrial workers than they were before the war.

TWO SIDES OF A QUESTION

How differently the same facts may appear to different people is shown by the extracts above. Both are from the Manchester Guardian *in January,* 1946. *The figures in the table make it appear that the agricultural workers received more increase in wages than industrial workers between* 1938 *and* 1945. *The graph has the effect of giving the reverse impression.*

Do not let yourself be tied to any one method. Use whichever method you find most convenient for the particular purpose you have in hand.

But always, when you are dealing with numbers, think all the time of the meaning of the number you are using. Think whether it is a very large or a very small number. Think which figures used in writing it are important and which are only details. Think how it compares with other numbers in the sum. Think what numbers are its neighbours. In this way you can often save yourself from making ridiculous mistakes.

THE CARRYING PRINCIPLE

In arithmetic, as in many other things, it is important to distinguish between principles and questions of detail.

In dealing with large numbers, we saw that it was convenient to collect things together in groups. These groups might be called dozens, bundles, battalions, hundreds or whatever you like. The exact way in which one group is formed out of others—4 platoons make one company and so on—

THE CHANGING FORTUNES OF NATIONS — AND CLASSES

TONNAGE OF MERCHANT NAVIES BEFORE AND AFTER THE WAR

	1939	1945
U.S.A.	12,100,000	56,800,000
British Empire	23,300,000	19,600,000
Norway	6,400,000	3,950,000
Netherlands	3,300,000	2,090,000
Greece	2,700,000	1,700,000
France	2,900,000	1,300,000
U.S.S.R.	1,500,000	1,200,000

HOW THE NATIONAL INCOME IS DIVIDED

Millions of Pounds

	1938	1943	1944	1945
Rent	380	384	384	385
Interest and Profits ..	1,317	2,460	2,487	2,445
Salaries	1,100	1,430	1,473	1,585
Wages	1,735	2,845	2,890	2,840
Forces Pay	78	999	1,167	1,228
National Income ..	4,610	8,118	8,401	8,483

It should be borne in mind, (i) that these figures are before tax has been paid, (ii) that the cost of living rose rapidly between 1939 *and* 1945.

are matters of *detail*. An army might at any time decide to change the number of platoons in a company. It is much less likely that an army would decide to do without having names for large groups such as battalions and regiments.

The idea of grouping is the *principle;* the exact way in which groups are made up of smaller groups is a matter of *detail*. Provided you are clear on the principle, you can always refresh your memory of the details by consulting a reference book.

Systems of weights and measures in particular are full of absurd and irritating details, which it is a pure waste of time to commit to memory, except for jobs that you have to do very often.

Both for systems of weights and measures and for ordinary numbers, a principle holds that we may call the *principle of carrying*.

This principle is much the same as the idea of getting change for money. If you have twelve pennies you can always change them for one shilling. Or, the other way round, if you have one shilling you can always change it for twelve pennies.

In ordinary numbers, this means that, whenever you find it convenient to do so, ten units can be grouped together to form a single ten; or the other way round, a single ten can be broken up into ten loose units, thus:

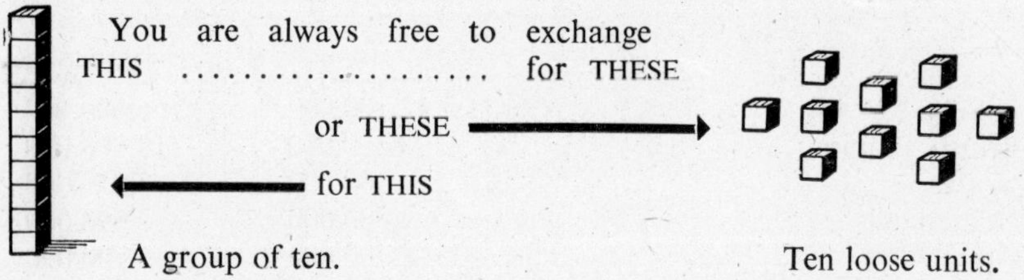

You are always free to exchange
THIS .... for THESE
or THESE
for THIS

A group of ten. Ten loose units.

In the same way, ten tens may always be grouped into one block of a hundred; or one block of a hundred may be broken up into ten blocks of ten.

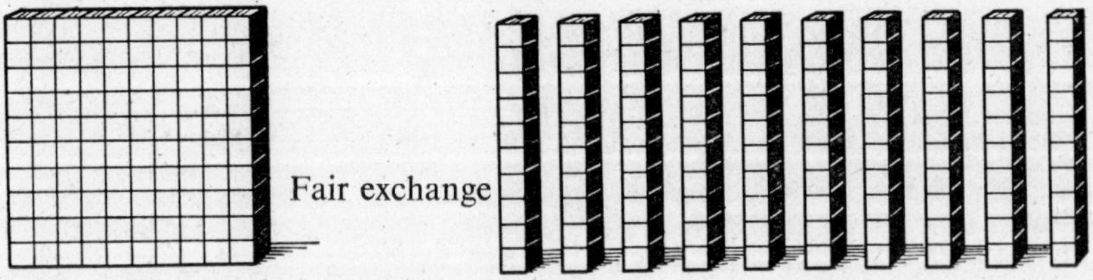

THIS for THESE

One way of getting practice in carrying is to play games using counters—ten white counters for one blue counter, ten blue counters for one red one, and so on.

It will often happen that you have, for example, one red counter, two blue ones and three white ones, and you lose 5 points to one of the other players, so that he wants five of your counters. You have not 5 loose white counters, so you are compelled to change one of your blue counters for ten of another player's white ones. Then you can pay your debt.

1 red = 10 blue 1 blue = 10 white

Red  Blue 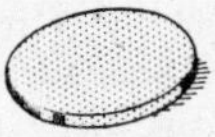 White 

You have these:

To pay a debt of 5 white counters, you must first change one of your blue counters for 10 white ones.

Then you can pay your debt.

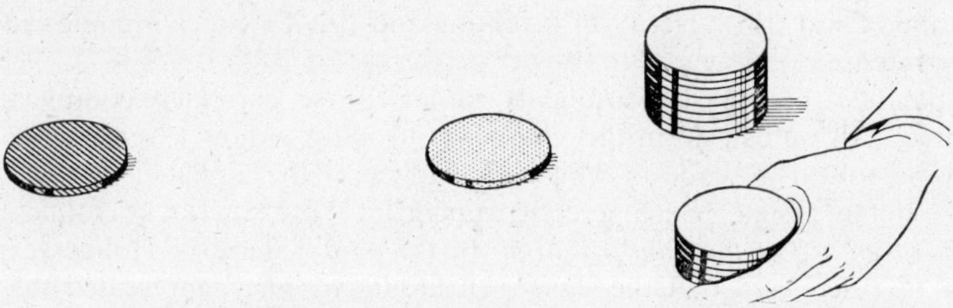

Of course, all kinds of extra complications may creep in. You may have one red only and have to pay out two whites. In that case, you must first change one red for ten blues, and then one of these blues for ten whites.

CARRYING SEEN ON A COUNTING MACHINE

If you set a counting machine at 1,000,000 *and turn it* back *one unit, you see the figures change all along the row. If you want to see why this happens, the best way is to make counters to represent tens, hundreds, thousands, tens of thousands, hundreds of thousands and millions. Starting with one counter for a million, pay out one unit.*

But if you play cards enough you will find out all these particular cases for yourself.

In the language of arithmetic, of course, a blue is a ten, a red is a hundred, and so on.

If any piece of working in an arithmetic question puzzles you, it is nearly always possible for you to see what it means by coming back to blue and red counters.

Of course, it takes rather a long time if you have to think every sum out in terms of counters. That is why one has to practise doing sums by the usual methods, to save time. But if ever you are in a difficulty, if ever you want to see *why* something is done, you can work the sum out in counters.

In essence, all there is to be known about adding, subtracting, multiplying and dividing is contained in this idea of carrying; exchanging one red for ten blues. If you understand it properly, you can think the rest out for yourself.

CODES AND CIPHERS

An interesting type of problem that requires only the use of counting and a good deal of common sense and intelligent guesswork, is the deciphering of codes.

Every country uses special codes for telegraphing important secret messages, and in every country experts study the code messages sent by the others in the hope of discovering the code, and finding out what is really going on. In time of war, this activity of inventing and solving codes becomes particularly intense.

The codes used by Governments are, of course, extremely complicated to unravel. All we can do in this chapter is to indicate how a very simple code may be solved—a code in which each letter of the alphabet is represented by a definite sign. Such a code comes into the Sherlock Holmes story *The Adventure of the Dancing Men.* In this story Sherlock Holmes explains how he discovered that the signs of five dancing men represented the word NEVER. Another famous detective story in which it is shown how to solve a simple code is Edgar Allan Poe's *The Gold Bug*.

The method depends on the fact that the letters of the alphabet are not all used to the same extent. Very few words contain *x*, *z*, *j*, or *q*. Very many contain *e*, *t*, *i*, *a*, *o*, *n*, *s*.

The table shows roughly how many times each letter is likely to occur in a message containing 1,000 letters.

A 76	E 118	I 78	M 24	Q 5	U 36	Y 20
B 16	F 45	J 4	N 66	R 56	V 12	Z 2
C 32	G 16	K 6	O 67	S 65	W 20	
D 40	H 48	L 42	P 19	T 83	X 4	

Of course, you cannot expect the letters to turn up always exactly in this proportion. You will soon find this out for yourself if you take paragraphs from a book or newspaper, and count the letters.

Nearly always *e* is the most frequent letter. There are exceptions even to this rule. There is, for instance, the well-known verse from the Rubaiyat of Omar Khayyam,

The moving finger writes and having writ
Moves on, nor all thy piety nor wit
  Shall lure it back to cancel half a line
Nor all thy tears wash out a word of it.

In this verse *a* and *t* occur 12 times, *i*, *l*, *n*, *o* ten times each, and *e* only nine times. Another example, is Humbert Wolfe's verse:

Thank God! you cannot bribe or twist
The honest British journalist
But seeing what the man will do
Unbribed, there's no occasion to.

This contains *t* 13 times, *o* 11 times, *n* 10 times, *e* 9 times. In poetry, one is more likely to find unusual results for the number of letters, as a poet may use one particular sound again and again to produce some special effect.

The shorter a message is, the more likely is it that the letters will occur

STUDY OF GAMES OF CHANCE

In many games two dice are thrown together. All the 36 *throws shown above are equally likely. The least likely scores are* 2 *and* 12. 2 *only occurs once, in the top left corner. The chance of throwing* 2 *is thus* 1 *in* 36. *It is* 35 *to* 1 *against* 2 *being thrown. The same applies to the score of* 12. *What are the chances of the other scores? What is the most likely score? You can test the answers by actually throwing dice a large number of times.*

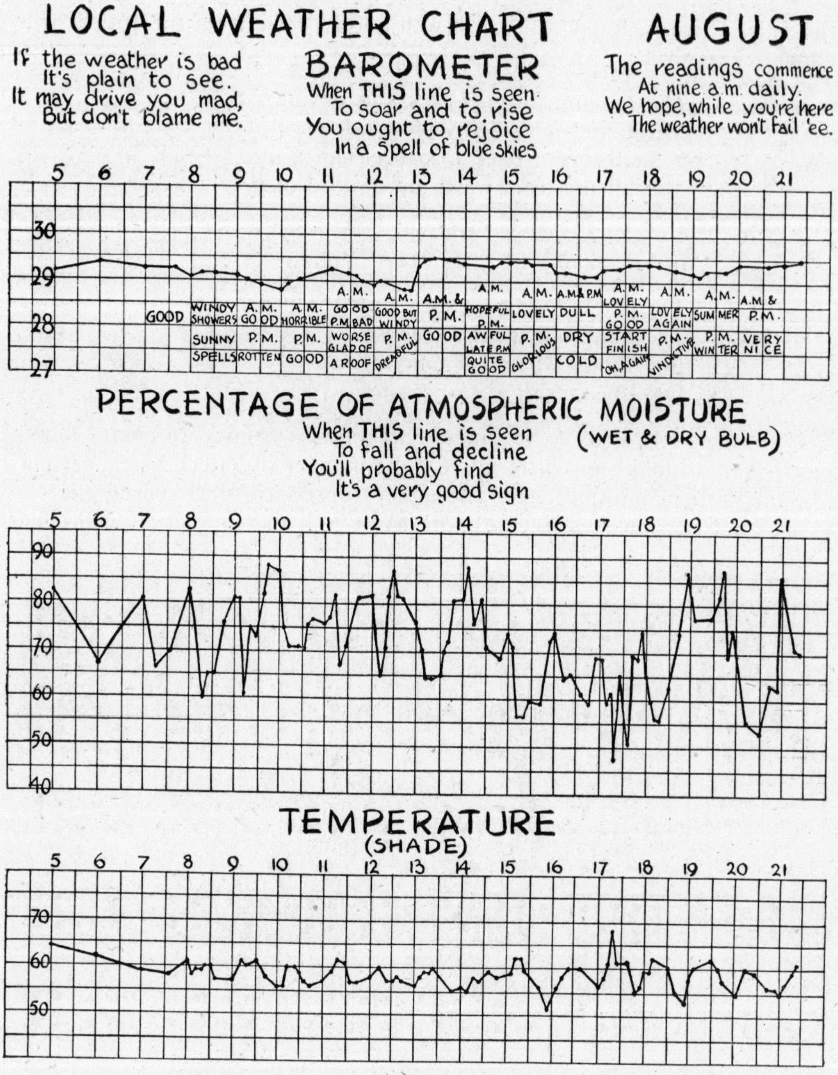

WHAT IS THE WEATHER GOING TO BE?

This weather chart was made by a gentleman living in Lynton, North Devon. As no official facilities were available, he obtained a barometer and a wet and dry bulb thermometer, and exhibited the chart outside his house. Rhymes were added when it was found that the public were unable to interpret the charts without explanation. The chart was a centre of interest and visitors clustered round it and several composed rhymes, polite ones thanking the unknown meteorologist for his efforts, ruder ones about the behaviour of the weather, and stuck these rhymes around the chart. How far does the weather agree with what would be expected from the above charts?

out of their usual frequencies. It is much easier to decode a long message than a short one.

Counting will usually show which sign is *e*. Then there is a whole bunch of common letters, *t*, *i*, *a*, *o*, *n*, *s*. One usually has to find which letter is *t* by looking for some common word, such as *the*. If you can spot a set of three letters, . . *e*, that occurs very often, it is possible that the first letter is *t*, and the middle one *h*.

Solving codes is a good exercise, simply because there are no rules of thumb. One has to guess and try, and if it does not work, guess again.

Printers' sets of type are also based on the fact that the letters do not occur equally often. In a fount of type you will find many *e*s and few *z*s. The proportions for a printers' fount are generally based on the figures given in the table that appears on page 45.

TWO VERSES IN CODE

E is the most common letter. The word THE occurs several times. A word of one letter must be A or I. The last word of the second line is a girl's name.

```
-6?¾ 6!½?7- 5:- 7: 7:)?)
-6? 2!33?7 ):7) :2 ?½?
?½?7 -6? )9?33 :2 (:)?)
;) 7:- ¼6!- -6?¾ )488:)?)
.4- 9:(? -6!7 9;71 1;),3:)?)
!71 9:(? -6!7 9?7 .?3;?½?

-6? .(;33;!7- )9?33 :2 ¼!-?(
-6? .(!½? )9?33 :2 ! )-:7?
-6? )9?33 :2 1?¼ !71 -6471?(
-6? :31 .:7?) .4(;?1 471?(
!(? -6;75) ;7 ¼6;,6 -6?¾ .3471?(
!71 ?(( ;2 3?2- !3:7?
```

AN HISTORIC DOCUMENT IN CODE

Every sign in this code represents a letter of the alphabet. Signs of punctuation are not represented. The sign ″ stands for a single letter.

Clues for solving. The letter that occurs most often is, as usual, E. The letter that occurs next most often is T. Putting in all the T's and E's you will soon find which word is THE. From the shorter words you should soon spot one or two more letters, particularly A and O. Make use of words like ″55. This is a three-letter word, with the last two letters the same. There are not very many words like this. You should guess to a certain extent. For instance, if you find a word A.E this may be ACE or APE or ALE, but it is far more likely to be ARE. You should try the most likely possibility, and see if it works, before trying the least likely words.

You can make up further examples of this kind, by asking your friends to put messages into code. Books on codes and ciphers can be found in most public libraries.

```
*& =85£ ,=&?& ,-.,=? ,8 /& ?&5( &%2£&7,
,=", "55 6&7 "-& @-&",&£ &O."5
,=", ,=&+ "-& &7£8*&£ /+ ,=&2- @-&",8-
        *2,= @&-,"27 .7"52&7"/5& -2)=,?
,=", "687) ,=&?& "-& 52(& 52/&-,+
        "7£ ,=& 9.-?.2, 8( ="9927&??
,=", ,8 ?&@.-& ,=&?& -2)=,? )8%&-76&7,? "-&
27?,2,.,&£ "687) 6&7 £&-2%27) ,=&2- 3.?, 98*&-? (-86
,=& @87?&7, 8( ,=& )8%&-7&£
,=", *=&7&%&- "7+ (8-6 8( )8%&-76&7, /&@86&? £&?,-.@,2%&
8( ,=&?& &7£? 2, 2? ,=& -2)=, 8( ,=& 9&895& ,8 "5,&-
8- "/852?= 2, "7£ ,8 27?,2,.,& 7&* )8%&-76&7, 5"+27)
2,? (8.7£",287 87 ?.@= 9-27@295&? "7£ 8-)"72?27) 2,?
98*&-? 27 ?.@= (8-6 "? ,8 ,=&6 ?="55 ?&&6 68?,
524&5+ ,8 &((&@, ,=&2- ?"(&,+ "7£ ="9927&??
```

TESTING BELIEFS

One of the most important applications of counting is the testing of beliefs, by means of statistics.

It is very necessary to find some way of checking beliefs, because a belief is often based on very scanty evidence. This is particularly likely to be so when strong emotions are aroused.

During the blackout a man often used to step outside his house without using a torch. On the pavement opposite his house was a lamp-post. One

GEAR WHEELS

Gear wheels are used in most machines. Many simple experiments in counting can be done with gear wheels. How many teeth are there on the two wheels here? How many times must the small wheel turn for the large wheel to turn once? If these were connected by a chain, as on a bicycle, how many times would the small wheel turn for each turn of the big one? Would it be the same number as before or not? Large models of gear wheels can be made by cutting out of thick cardboard, or with a fretsaw from thin sheets of wood. One can also study how the hour hand of a clock is geared to the minute hand; how the gear of a bicycle works; how the camshaft of a motor-car is geared to the crankshaft; how a lathe is set for screw-cutting; how the dials of a gas-meter work; and of course there are many other examples.

night he crossed the road in the dark, and as he stepped up the pavement opposite he knocked his head violently against the lamp-post. He found himself saying, "Why is it that, with all this pavement to walk on, I *always* bump into the lamp-post?"

A little later, when the pain had subsided, he wondered how many times he had actually bumped into that lamp-post. He could definitely remember doing it once before, but that was all. That was enough, at the moment of the shock, to make him think he always bumped into it.

Actually, the proportion of times he had hit the lamp-post corresponded quite reasonably with the proportion of pavement that it occupied.

It seems to come very easily to the human mind to produce quite unfounded generalizations.

You will quite often hear people say, "It always rains on my half-day off." There may be times when there is some justification for such a statement, because weather statistics are quite unlike any other statistics. They do peculiar things.

For instance, one would expect all the days of the week to have an equal chance of being fine or wet. In the long run, this must be so, unless there is some seven-day cycle in the weather. But in the short run, one has to be careful. For instance, in 52 weeks in the year 1900, there were 24 fine Mondays, 24 fine Tuesdays, 24 fine Wednesdays, 25 fine Thursdays, 28 fine Fridays, 39 fine Saturdays, and 31 fine Sundays in London: Saturday seems to have a remarkable advantage over the other days—*in this particular year.*

The figures for rainfall are available for other years. Some readers may like to hunt out these figures and from them try to settle the question of whether there is a finest day of the week. It is possible that the results for other years will cancel out the advantage Saturday had in 1900. But this may be wrong.

We can be sure that a deep depression taking off from Iceland does not bother in the least whether it is our half-holiday or not. We are not as

Lower Case	a	b	c	d	e	f	g	h	i	j	k	l	m	n	o	p	q	r	s	t	u	v	w	x	y	z
	74	18	34	42	118	24	18	50	74	6	8	42	26	66	66	20	6	58	66	84	38	12	20	6	20	4

Capitals	A	B	C	D	E	F	G	H	I	J	K	L	M	N	O	P	Q	R	S	T	U	V	W	X	Y	Z
	8	8	6	6	12	6	8	10	10	6	4	8	18	8	8	8	4	8	12	12	6	4	8	4	6	4

Small Capitals	A	B	C	D	E	F	G	H	I	J	K	L	M	N	O	P	Q	R	S	T	U	V	W	X	Y	Z
	8	3	4	5	13	3	3	6	8	2	2	5	6	8	8	3	2	7	8	10	4	2	3	2	3	2

Figures, etc. ..	1	2	3	4	5	6	7	8	9	0	.	,	;	:	-	'	!	?
	10	6	6	4	4	4	4	4	8	12	40	50	8	6	10	10	2	3

AVERAGE RECURRENCE OF EACH LETTER

This table shows how often each character occurs. These proportions are based upon the statistics of the average recurrence of the various letters in English literature. This table, which is more comprehensive than the one on page 40, is reproduced by permission of the Monotype Corporation.

important as all that—to anyone except ourselves. Nature is indifferent to us.

It is not a matter of great importance what people believe about the weather, except so far as weather beliefs may express a generally crazy attitude to life. It is a matter of great importance what people think about each other, and here the same tendency to generalization may be dangerous.

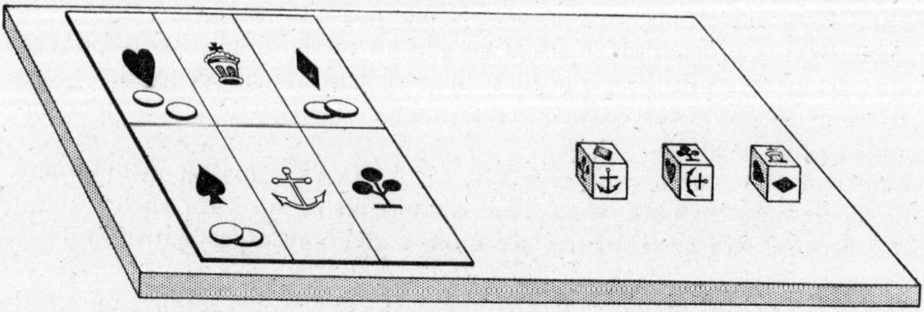

CROWN AND ANCHOR

This is a mug's game, except for the banker. Three dice are thrown. The banker pays those who have backed the signs that are thrown—diamond, club and crown in the case shown above—and takes the money of the others. If two diamonds are thrown, the banker pays double to the players who backed diamonds. If three diamonds are thrown, the banker pays threefold to the backers of diamonds. The same rules apply to the other signs. The game looks fair. It appears that the banker will pay three and take money from three. Actually it works like this:

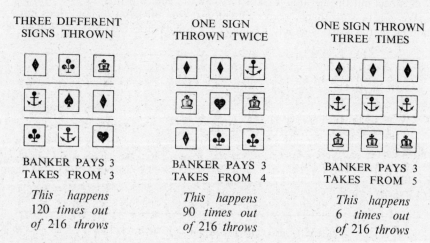

THREE DIFFERENT SIGNS THROWN

BANKER PAYS 3
TAKES FROM 3

This happens 120 times out of 216 throws

ONE SIGN THROWN TWICE

BANKER PAYS 3
TAKES FROM 4

This happens 90 times out of 216 throws

ONE SIGN THROWN THREE TIMES

BANKER PAYS 3
TAKES FROM 5

This happens 6 times out of 216 throws

If you have the patience to write out the 216 possible throws, you can check the numbers given above. You will find that in the long run the banker wins. This game, although it is very popular, is forbidden by the army authorities.

If you are swindled by an Irishman, or a Jew, or a member of some odd religious sect, or a man with one blue and one brown eye, your anger is likely to take the form of a general theory about *all* Irishmen, or *all* Jews, or *all* sectarians, or *all* men with odd eyes. This is likely to lead you to be unfair to a large number of excellent individuals, and in turn to make them bitter against you, so that both sides will be losers.

You can guard against this danger by making a habit of checking your beliefs. Often you will be amazed to find how little evidence there is for something you have firmly believed.

People have a tendency to forget one side of the evidence. Suppose we take the idea that some folk have, that red-haired people are likely to be hot-tempered. If you wanted to establish the truth of this belief, it is not enough to say, "Why, look at Bill Smith's wife. She has bright red hair, and I never knew anyone with a worse temper."

To prove that red-haired people were hot-tempered, you would have to show that a larger percentage of red-haired men and women were fiery in temperament than was the case for the population as a whole. You would have to determine carefully the number of people with red hair who were placid, and people without red hair who were violent.

The most systematic way of going about it would be to consider a large number of people, taken at random, and make up a table something like this (the numbers are fictitious):

Red-haired and hot-tempered. 27	Red-haired and normal temper. 51
Hot temper, but not red hair. 102	Normal temper, not red hair. 193

On the basis of a table like this (if the numbers were genuine, and not just made up, as they are here) you could form a reasoned judgment of the question. It is recommended that inquiries of this kind should be made as a recreation. There are plenty of possible subjects for inquiry—all kinds of beliefs about people, such as that high cheek bones indicate strength of will, or that fat people are good-humoured—are rhymes like:

Red sky at night, shepherd's delight,
Red sky at morning, shepherd's warning

reliable? The Meteorological Department claims that its forecasts are true nine times out of ten; is this true? Various people, from political correspondents to racing tipsters, claim to have inside knowledge: are their forecasts more or less reliable than the guesses of ordinary people?

The importance of having all the facts may be illustrated from a medical question; how are we to decide whether a new cure is good or not? Let us suppose that some disease is raging, and suppose that, of every 1,000,000 people who are not specially treated, 100,000 die in an epidemic. Let us suppose that 1,000,000 people are given an injection, and of these 5,000 die. We could put the results in a table like this:

Outcome for 1,000,000 people

	Live	*Die*
No treatment	900,000	100,000
Injected	995,000	5,000

It is clear that the injections give one a better chance of surviving. The treatment reduces deaths from 1 in 10 to 1 in 200.

Now you might easily hear someone say, "I don't believe in these injections. My cousin works at the cemetery, and he says they've brought five thousand of them in there—all had the treatment." In fact, some time ago a campaign against diphtheria immunization was waged, very much on these lines.

The fact that 5,000 have died, although injected, by itself means nothing. One needs to know 5,000 *out of how many*? Again, some of the 5,000 might have been very old or very weak people, who were due to die soon, anyway: or they might have come to be injected far too late, when they were practically at death's door. Some of them, of course, might have been genuine failures of the treatment—people with some physical peculiarity, which made the injection unsuitable for them. By investigating this possibility, it might be possible to improve the efficiency of treatment still further.

On the figures given above, there is no doubt that the treatment has improved the situation.

WAS THE BLACK-OUT RESPONSIBLE?

CHILD PEDESTRIANS KILLED.

Twelve Months	*Sep.*	*Oct.*	*Nov.*	*Dec.*	*Jan.*	*Feb.*	*Mar.*	*Apr.*	*May*	*June*	*July*	*Aug.*	*Total*
					DAYLIGHT								
1939/40	76*	64	56	56	25	29	65	68	85	63	86	100	773
1940/41	89	107	100	85	56	73	112	114	130	110	113	99	1,188
1941/42	108	107	77	75	65	58	102	90	111	96	86	85	1,060
1942/43	92	103	94	78	58	85	96	92	67	104	81	80	1,030
1943/44	83	83	67	63	61	95	92	119	111	93	106	91	1,064
1944/45	106	81	73	53	43	94	94	74	97	93	93	84	985
					DARK								
1939/40	7*	3	14	18	7	4	4	—	6	—	3	7	73
1940/41	6	3	13	17	7	2	4	5	7	—	2	4	70
1941/42	5	5	5	11	5	2	4	2	—	3	1	2	45
1942/43	2	5	9	17	5	3	4	1	—	1	—	1	48
1943/44	—	6	8	5	11	5	2	—	—	—	—	—	37
1944/45	2	7	13	13	6	5	3	—	1	—	—	—	50
					TOTAL								
1937/38	73	52	54	56	61	80	96	77	65	70	78	67	829
1938/39	64	71	71	64	50	79	72	70	81	59	75	70	826
1939/40	83	67	70	74	32	33	69	68	91	63	89	107	846
1940/41	95	110	113	102	63	75	116	119	137	110	115	103	1,258
1941/42	113	112	82	86	70	60	106	92	111	99	87	87	1,105
1942/43	94	108	103	95	63	88	100	93	67	105	81	81	1,078
1943/44	83	89	75	68	72	100	94	119	111	93	106	91	1,101
1944/45	108	88	86	66	49	99	97	74	98	93	93	84	1,035

* Calculated.

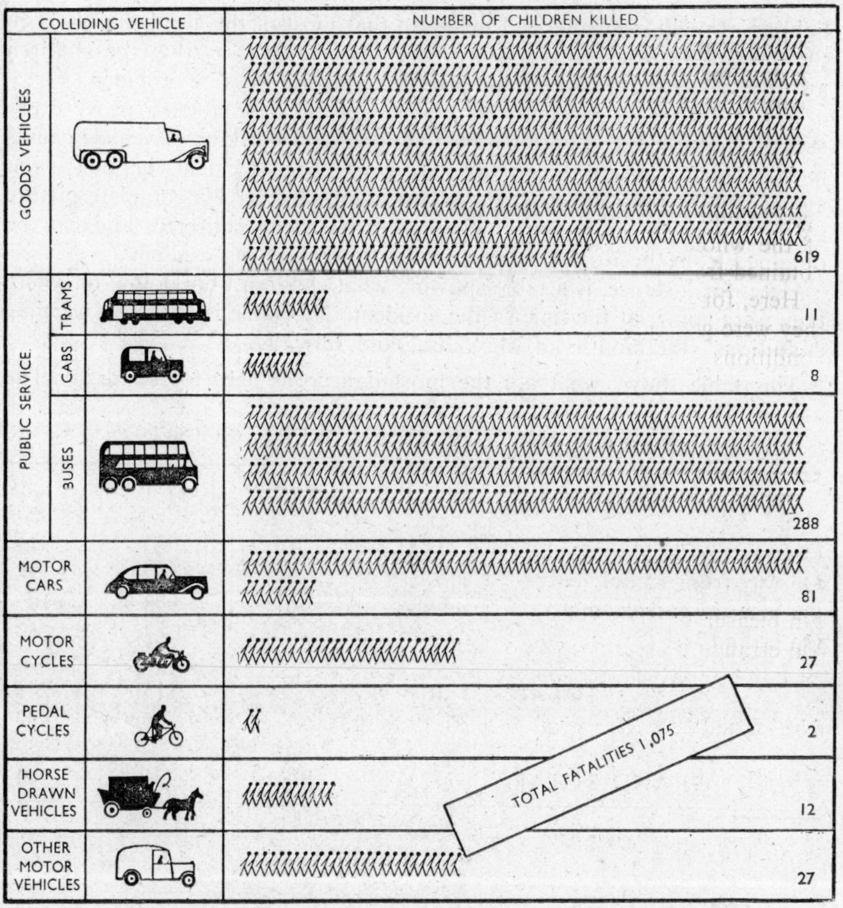

CHILD PEDESTRIANS KILLED BY ROAD VEHICLES

Figures are often of interest to historians. One can show, for instance, how the deaths from fevers fell off after the "age of drains" began in the eighteen-seventies.

Figures may also be useful when you want to get something done. Suppose, for instance, you were a Town Councillor and that you had become concerned about road accidents to children—perhaps as the result of actually seeing an accident, or knowing parents who had lost a child. You decide something should be done about it.

As soon as you mention the matter, you will find that people express all sorts of contradictory views. Some will say that the death rate is so high among children because they have nowhere except the roads in which to play: others will say that it is because children have to walk to and from school, and run errands. If you propose building a by-pass, people will say that most of the accidents are due to local traffic. If you propose better lighting at night, someone will maintain that most of the accidents occur in the daytime. If you propose more parks, people will say that the children are little devils and would not go into the parks if more were provided.

If you are to cut through this tangle, you must be able to prove every statement you make. You must be able to show what type of vehicle causes most accidents; where the children are going when accidents happen; what age of child is most affected, and so on—you must have a complete picture of the whole situation. Such information has been collected, and can be obtained from the Royal Society for the Prevention of Accidents.

Here, for instance, is a table showing what children were doing, or where they were going, at the time of the accident. This table is based on wartime conditions—the months of May, June and July 1942.

This table shows what are the most dangerous ages for children. The

WHERE THE CHILDREN WERE GOING

	Ages 0–4	*Ages* 5–9	*Ages* 10–14	*Total*
On way to school	2	10	3	15
On way from school ..	2	22	2	26
On pleasure, or playing ..	98	91	8	197
On errand	1	7	2	10
TOTAL	103	130	15	248
Not stated	19	18	6	43
GRAND TOTAL	122	148	21	291

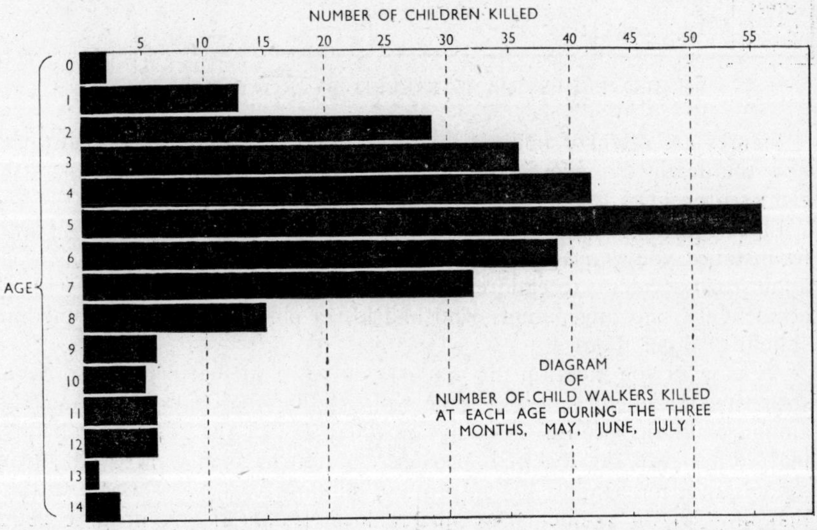

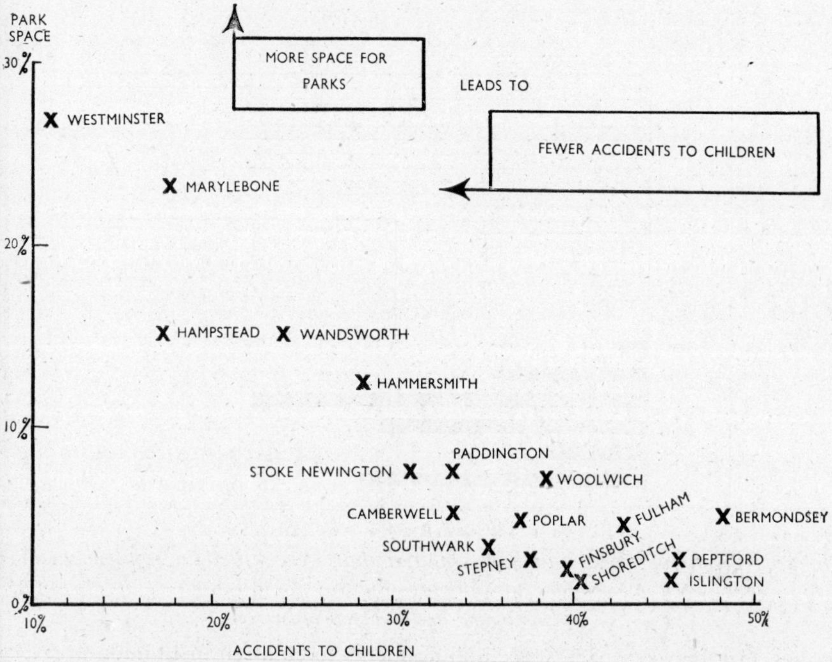

DOES MORE PARK SPACE TEND TO REDUCE ACCIDENTS?

Here is a graph showing the proportion of accidents to children to the amount of park space available. It will be seen that generally, the statement "More space for parks leads to fewer accidents to children" is true.

illustration on page 49 shows what types of vehicle were involved in collisions with children.

It would be possible to meet the objection that, even if parks were open, the children would not go there. Some very striking figures show the

	Proportion of open spaces	*Proportion of accidents to children, as a percentage of all accidents*		*Proportion of open spaces*	*Proportion of accidents to children, as a percentage of all accidents*
Bermondsey	5·0%	46·3%	Southwark ..	3·1%	35·3%
Deptford ..	2·2%	43·4%	Camberwell ..	5·2%	33·6%
Islington ..	1·5%	42·9%	Paddington ..	7·2%	33·6%
Fulham ..	4·2%	42·2%	Stoke Newington	6·5%	30·8%
Shoreditch	1·4%	40·0%	Hammersmith	12·2%	28·3%
Finsbury ..	2·0%	38·8%	Wandsworth ..	14·6%	23·8%
Woolwich ..	7·0%	38·2%	Marylebone ..	23·6%	17·8%
Stepney ..	2·5%	37·4%	Hampstead ..	14·8%	17·1%
Poplar ..	4·5%	37·0%	Westminster .	27·5%	10·8%

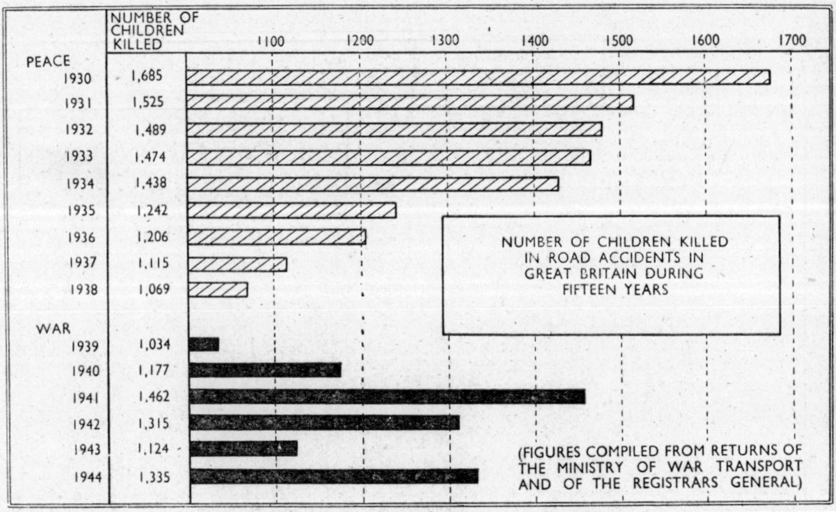

EFFECT OF WAR ON ACCIDENTS

Figures given for 1930-7 *include children that were killed in road accidents while they were passengers in vehicles. Figures for* 1938-44 *relate to child pedestrians and cyclists only.*

connection between park space and accidents to children in London areas.*

Of course, the meaning of these figures might be challenged. An opponent might maintain that park-space was not the real cause of few accidents, but that there were more open spaces in the districts where the richer people lived, where wives did not need to go to factories, where nurse-maids could take charge of the children, where people had smaller families—and so on. To prove your case up to the hilt, you would need to meet these arguments.

Of course, there are other, less spectacular ways of killing children besides road accidents. One of the most significant of all statistics is Infant Mortality, the death rate for babies less than one year old, per thousand births. This not only tells us what happens to babies: it reflects the general state of wealth or poverty in a district, the health of the parents, and housing conditions.

The figures below relating to some few years ago, give some idea of what Infant Mortality reveals.

Type of District	*Infant Mortality* (*Deaths before age of* 12 *months, for every* 1,000 *born*)	*Typical Examples*
Comfortable, residential – –	20–40	Hastings – – 35 Dundee, Ward 10 19
Low-paid workers –	80–110	Stoke-on-Trent – 85 Dundee, Ward 6 113

*We are indebted to Mr. Lowndes, Head of the School of Commerce, Leicester College of Technology, for calling attention to these figures.

It is possible that still higher figures were recorded in distressed areas, such as Jarrow, during a depression, and it has been said that in a Ceylon tea-plantation infant mortality rises to as much as 300. The documents in question may be referred to and it is left to readers to investigate whether these impressions are accurate or not.

SOLUTIONS TO CODES

On pages 43 and 44, in the subject of codes and ciphers, there are two verses and an historic document in code. Here are the solutions.

The two verses are from G. K. Chesterton's *The Song of Quoodle*, a poem giving a dog's opinion of men.

A !	E ?	I ;	O :	T -	Y $\frac{3}{4}$
B .	F 2	L 3	P 8	U 4	
C ,	G 5	M 9	R (	V $\frac{1}{2}$	
D 1	H 6	N 7	S)	W $\frac{1}{4}$	

The historic document is from the *Declaration of Independence*. "We hold these truths to be self-evident, that all men are created equal, that they are endowed by their creator with certain unalienable rights, that among these are life, liberty and the pursuit of happiness, that to secure these rights governments are instituted among men, deriving their just powers from the consent of the governed; that whenever any form of government becomes destructive of these ends, it is the right of the people to alter or abolish it, and to institute new government, laying its foundation on such principles, and organising its powers in such form as to them shall seem most likely to effect their safety and happiness."

Exercises

1. Here is a problem in counting. Below you will see an illustration of sailors sending messages by Semaphore signalling. The sailor in the boat is receiving a message from the sailor on the top of the cliff, and retransmitting

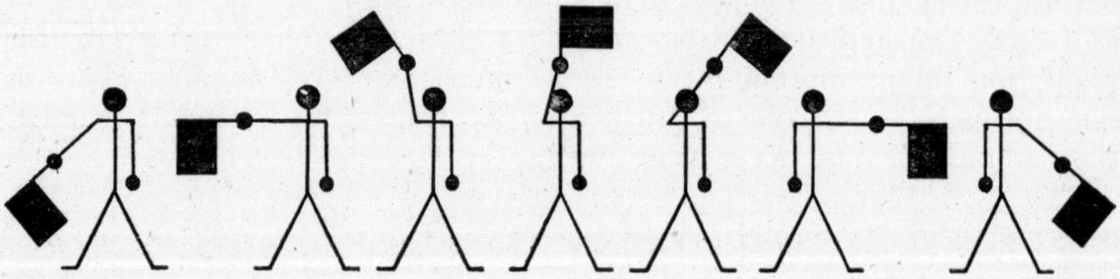

the same message to the third sailor at the foot of the cliff. You will see that there are seven different possible positions for each flag. How many different signals can a man send with two flags?

2. There are 40 letters in this problem. Guess first, and then check by counting, what numbers correspond to the capital letters.

(For example, A is number 3.)

zzAzzzzzzBzzzzzzzzzCzzzzzzzzDzzzzzzzzzEz

3. In this problem A is the forty-ninth letter and C is the sixty-first. What is your guess for B and D?

zzzzzzzzzzzzzzzzzzzzzzzzzzzzzzzzzzzzzzzzzzzzzzzzAzzzzzBzzzzzCzzzzzDzzz

4. How the blind read—Braille type. Books for the blind are made by raising knobs on sheets of paper. In the figures below, the large dots represent knobs. There may be as many as six knobs in a single sign, or some of the six spaces may be left empty (small dots represent empty spaces). These signs may represent letters, or punctuation marks, or words that are often used.

How many different signs can be made with this system ?

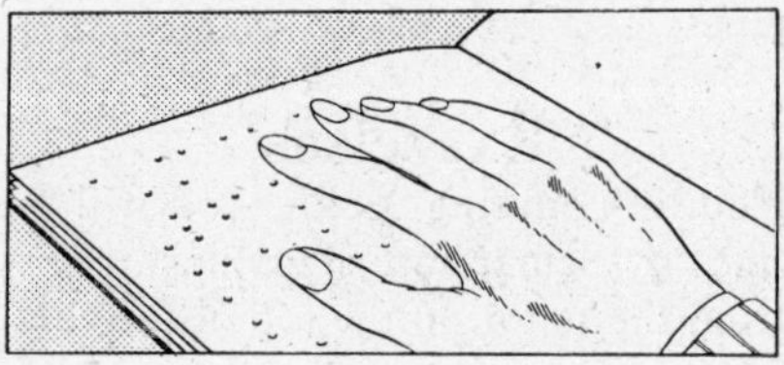

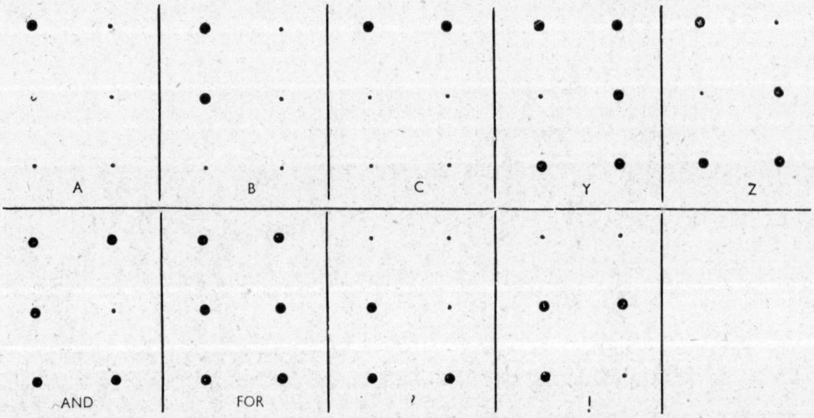

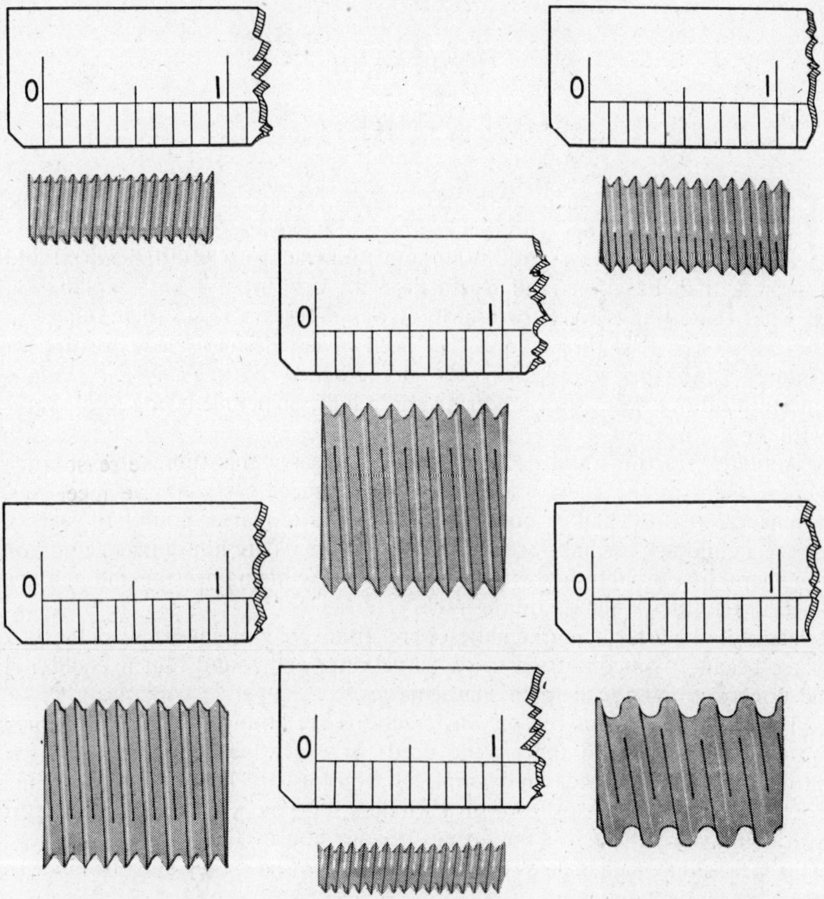

5. Different sizes of screw can be recognized by counting the number of threads to the inch. What is the number of threads for each of the screws shown in the illustration above?

6. In 1939 there were 22,962,000 men and boys in Great Britain, and 24,799,000 women and girls. Draw a diagram to illustrate these numbers.

7. Find out how many people a bus will carry in the town where you live. Count the numbers in the queues, and draw a diagram showing how the number in a queue compares with the number a bus will hold.

8. Draw a diagram showing the incomes of people in various trades and professions.

9. The Chancellor of the Exchequer estimated revenue for 1945-6 at £3,265,000,000. This guess proved to be £19,000,000 out. Would you regard this error as being (i) very large, (ii) reasonable, (iii) very small? Draw diagrams to show the estimated income, and the size of the mistake made.

CHAPTER III

MEASURING

IN VERY old-fashioned arithmetic books, children used to have one subject after another thrown at them. First there would be Numbers and Counting, then Addition and Subtraction, Multiplication and Division, then Fractions and Decimals, with very little, if any, explanation of what these things were for or why it was necessary to do them. One had the impression that these things had been invented simply as a torture for children, and this impression was strengthened by the most ridiculous questions about the cost of a herring and a half, or people trying to fill baths with holes in them.

Actually, fractions and decimals are quite reasonable things if you come across them in the right way. Fractions we meet every day of our lives, whenever we buy half a pound of coffee or a quarter-pound of sweets, or see a child ask for half-fare on the bus. Decimals are not quite so common in general life, though they are a matter of course in engineering and in a few special activities, such as timing races.

Nearly all parts of mathematics were discovered or invented in the first place because someone tried to do something, and found that it could not be done without the help of mathematics.

There is one obvious reason why fractions are bound to come very much into modern life, and that is the need for exact measurements. Electric fittings in houses provide an example. If you buy an electric bulb, or a plug for an electric fire, or an iron, or a wireless set, you want to be sure that it will be the correct size for the fittings in your house. Otherwise it is useless. This means that such articles must be of standard sizes; they must be made to exact measurements.

It would be possible to have everything made one inch across, or two inches, or three inches, but this would be inconvenient. Sometimes it would be quite impossible; for instance, we often want to use screws much less than one inch thick, and it is essential that screws shall be accurately made.

We are forced to find some way of measuring things that are less than one inch long, or more than one inch but less than two inches, and so on.

This means that instead of having a ruler marked at every inch, like this:

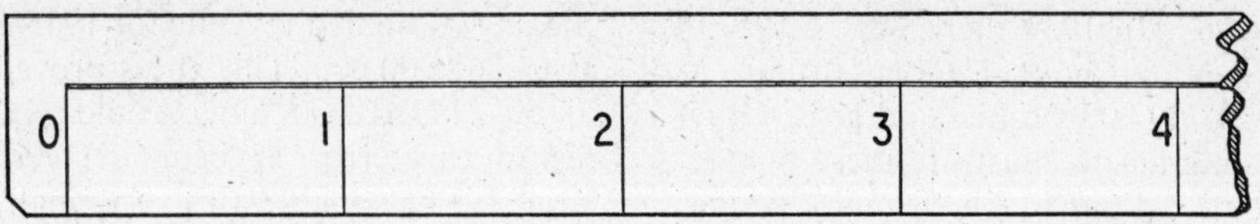

we have to design a ruler with marks in between those shown above.

Nearly every ruler does, in fact, have such marks on it, as you know. These marks measure fractions of an inch. (*Fraction* is the same word as *fractured*, a word used to describe *broken* bones. A fraction of an inch is a piece that you get when an inch is *broken up*.)

In some schools, fractions seem to be left alone so that children of ten or eleven do not know what a fraction is. The idea may be that you can have very hard questions about fractions, such as "What is $\frac{7}{8}$ of $\frac{3}{4}$ of $2\frac{1}{2}$ divided by $4\frac{1}{4}$?", and that children should not be asked to do such difficult work until they have done many examples of very dull sums about addition and multiplication.

Now it is true that questions like that *can* be asked about fractions, though in real life they very rarely appear. The sort of question that occurs in real life is often something rather more like the following.

PANELS OF WOOD

These panels may be used on 101 *different occasions by the handyman, for making and repairing many things in the home. Panels are supplied only in the sizes shown at the side. Send now for the latest prices of these panels.*

No.	Size	No.	Size
G2.	9 x 4 x $\frac{1}{8}$ in.	J2.	15 x $10\frac{1}{2}$ x $\frac{1}{8}$ in.
G3.	9 x 4 x $\frac{3}{16}$ in.	J3.	15 x $10\frac{1}{2}$ x $\frac{3}{16}$ in.
G4.	9 x 4 x $\frac{1}{4}$ in.	J4.	15 x $10\frac{1}{2}$ x $\frac{1}{4}$ in.
H2.	14 x 7 x $\frac{1}{8}$ in.	K2.	20 x 8 x $\frac{1}{8}$ in.
H3.	14 x 7 x $\frac{3}{16}$ in.	K3.	20 x 8 x $\frac{3}{16}$ in.
H4.	14 x 7 x $\frac{1}{4}$ in.	K4.	20 x 8 x $\frac{1}{4}$ in.

Here is an advertisement for panels of wood. You will notice that the thickness of the wood is in each case a fraction. If you are buying wood, you want to know which thickness to order. The thicker wood is more expensive, and it is also more tiring to saw. On the other hand, if you make something out of very thin wood, it is liable to break. When you are ordering your wood you want to be able to judge how thick the wood should be, so that it will be strong enough for the job in view, but not too exhausting to cut, and not more expensive than is absolutely necessary.

Now you do not need higher mathematics to answer this question. All you need is to take a rule, and look at it, and see where $\frac{1}{8}$ inch is marked, where $\frac{3}{16}$ inch is marked, and where $\frac{1}{4}$ inch is marked.

That is quite simple to do: it is a thing that every boy or girl with carpentry as a hobby can do when seven or eight years old. But it definitely is learning about fractions. Children who work at hobbies in their homes have a very great advantage in lessons at school. Some schools have recognized the value of letting a child *use* fractions in carpentry or other handwork for a year or two before sitting down to learn fractions from a blackboard or text-book. In this way, the child gets to know what a fraction means, what it is. Fractions become familiar things.

That is all we are trying to do in this chapter—to see what a fraction is; to learn to picture a fraction, so that when a fraction is mentioned in later chapters we shall be able to imagine it clearly.

Suppose, then, we have a ruler and we are trying to find suitable names for the marks that occur between the whole inches.

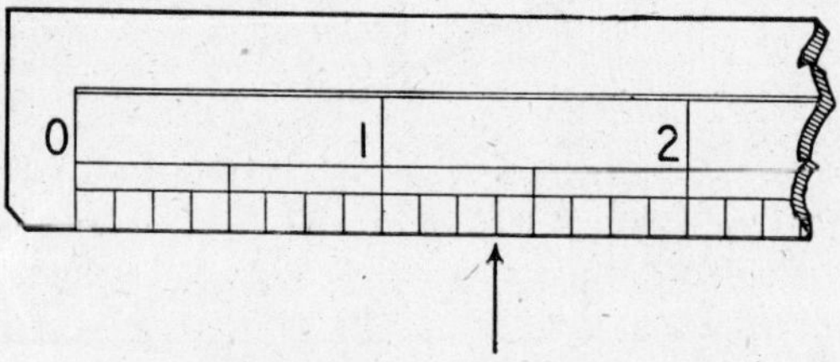

In this diagram we want to find a suitable name for the mark opposite the arrow.

We should get to this mark if we went one inch along the ruler, beginning from the end, and then went along three of the little divisions. We might say to ourselves, "It's one inch and then three of the little blighters."

We should know, of course, that "three of the little blighters" meant this:

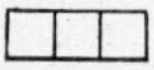

But other people might not understand. After all, there are all kinds of ways of dividing up an inch.

You might do it like this

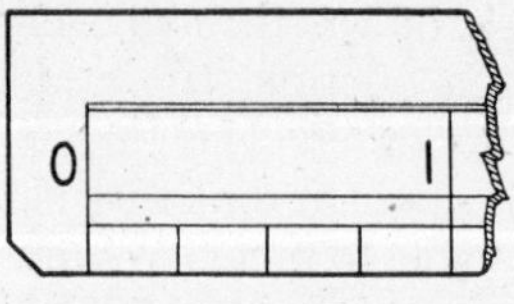

or like this

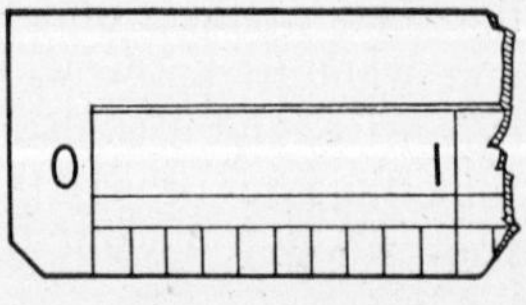

or like this

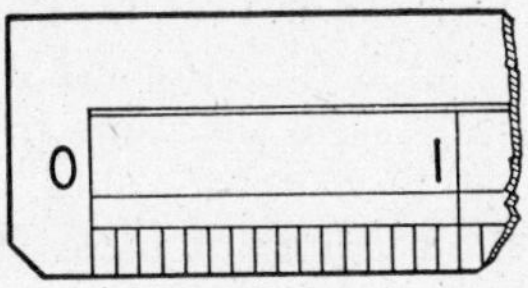

So that when we said "three of the little blighters" people would not know whether we meant

a

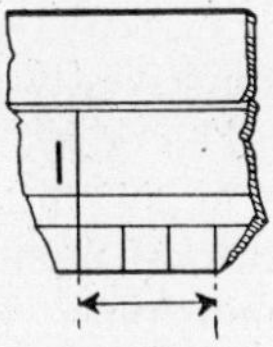

(which we do mean)

or b

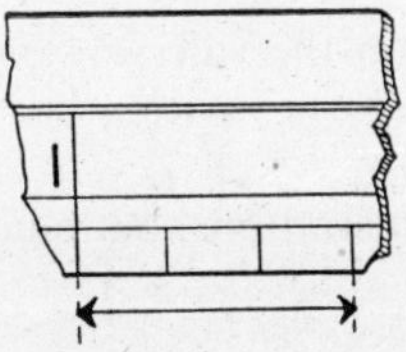

or c

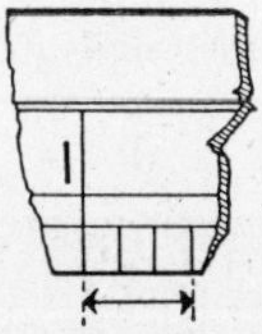

or d

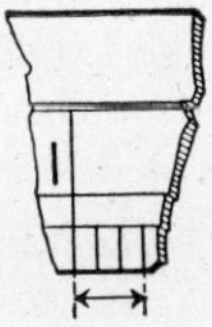

It is, therefore, necessary to find names for the small divisions, so that people know which "little blighter" we mean, and how little it is.

A way of doing this has been invented, and it is really quite a simple one.

If an inch is divided into 4 equal pieces, each piece is called a 4th of an inch.

If an inch is divided into 8 equal parts, each piece is called an 8th.

If an inch is divided into 10 equal pieces, each is called a 10th.

If an inch is divided into 16 equal pieces, each is called a 16th.

In the diagram of the ruler with the arrow underneath on Page 58, each inch is divided into 8 equal parts, so each part is an 8th.

Instead of "three little blighters" we may say, in more scientific language, "three 8ths".

There are many different ways of writing this. We may put it all in words —"three eighths", or all in numbers—"3 8ths". This last way of writing it is not very clear. If the 3 and the 8 became too close it might look as if 38 (thirty-eight) had something to do with it, which it has not. So to keep the 3 and the 8 apart, a sloping line can be put in, like this—3/8ths. Sometimes

A SIMPLE GAUGE

Thickness of wood, leather or metal sheets can be measured with this gauge. Such a gauge as this is cheap and simple to construct.

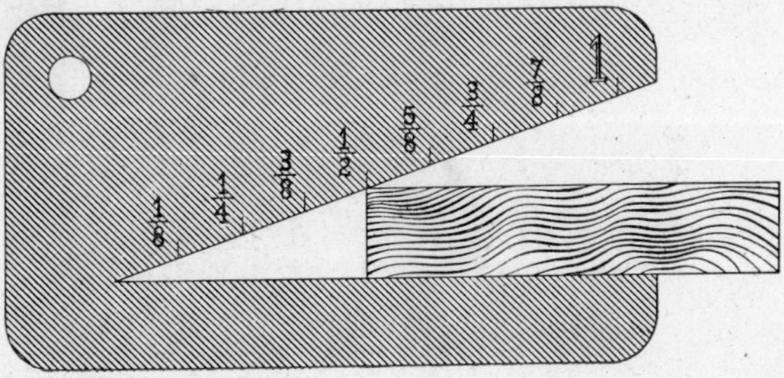

people do not bother to put in the "ths" and just write 3/8. Sometimes the 3 is put over the 8—this is the most usual arrangement—$\frac{3}{8}$.

Whichever of these is used, the same thing is meant. Something (in our example, an inch) has been divided into 8 equal pieces, each of which is, therefore, called an 8th. Three of these 8ths have been taken.

On Page 59, at (a) we have 3/8 inch
at (b) we have 3/4 inch
at (c) we have 3/10 inch
at (d) we have 3/16 inch.

In deciding what to call a fraction we have to ask ourselves two questions. First, how many "little blighters" are there in it? This gives us the first (or top) number of the fraction. Second, we ask, how many "little blighters" make up an inch? This gives us the second (or bottom) number.

(The learned name for the top number is the numerator, and for the bottom number the denominator.)

The length we were originally trying to name on the rule was one whole inch and then three-eighths of an inch. This would be written in figures—$1\frac{3}{8}$ inches.

Some examples on measuring are given in the illustrations, but much better

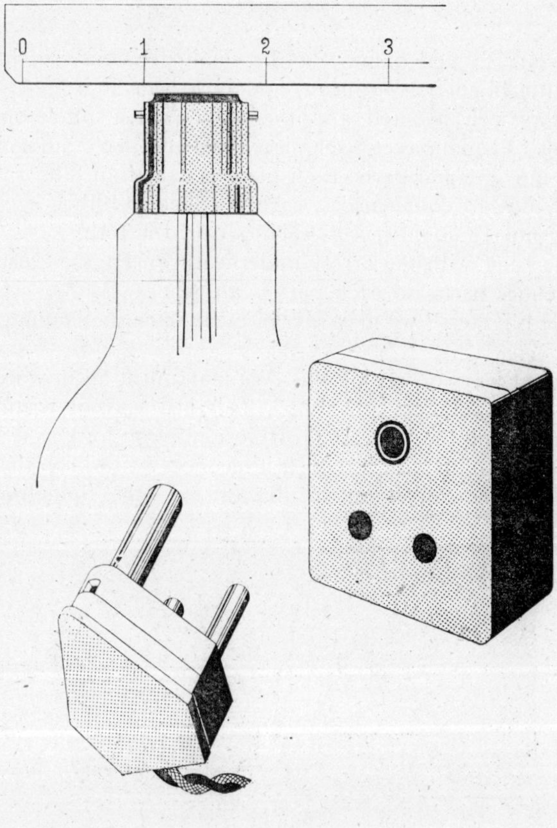

THE NEED FOR FRACTIONS

It is essential that electric fittings shall be made to standard sizes. But many of the parts are less than an inch in size. The base of the electric light bulb is less than an inch across. The same is true of the pins in the plug. But these must be made accurately to size, so that it is necessary to have measurements smaller than an inch. Fractions and decimals are intended to meet this need.

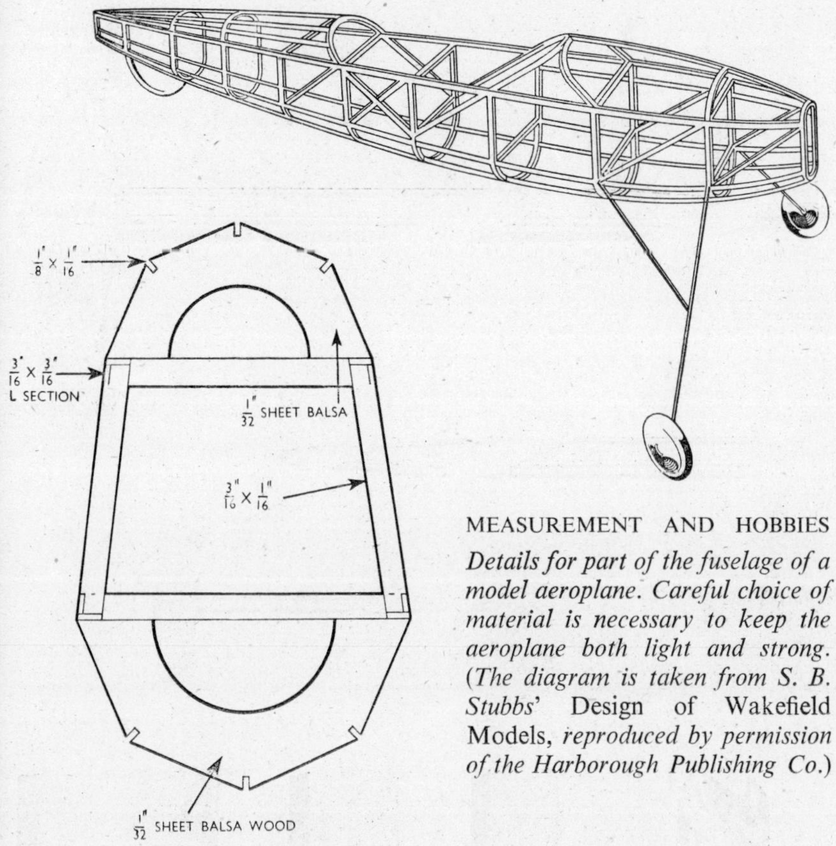

MEASUREMENT AND HOBBIES

Details for part of the fuselage of a model aeroplane. Careful choice of material is necessary to keep the aeroplane both light and strong. (The diagram is taken from S. B. Stubbs' Design of Wakefield Models, *reproduced by permission of the Harborough Publishing Co.)*

than any example in a book is the measuring that you do on some real thing that you are making or repairing.

If you keep measuring things, you will become so well acquainted with fractions that, when you see a fraction written down, you will immediately be able to imagine what it means and roughly how big it is. If you have learnt what a fraction means, *this is all you need to learn.* Of course, there are rules about fractions that some people try to learn by heart, but if you really understand what a fraction is, you will see that these rules are quite natural. It is just the same with other things. If you know what a bucket of molten lead *is*, you do not need to learn by heart, "It is unwise to sit down on a bucket of molten lead."

By looking at the illustrations and measuring exercises in this chapter, you will be able to test your understanding of fractions. If you find that you are not clear on any point, you can try reading the early part of this chapter again, or you can take a ruler and examine it carefully and see if that clears up your difficulty. Or you can ask a carpenter or engineer to explain to you what a particular fraction means. But, whatever you do,

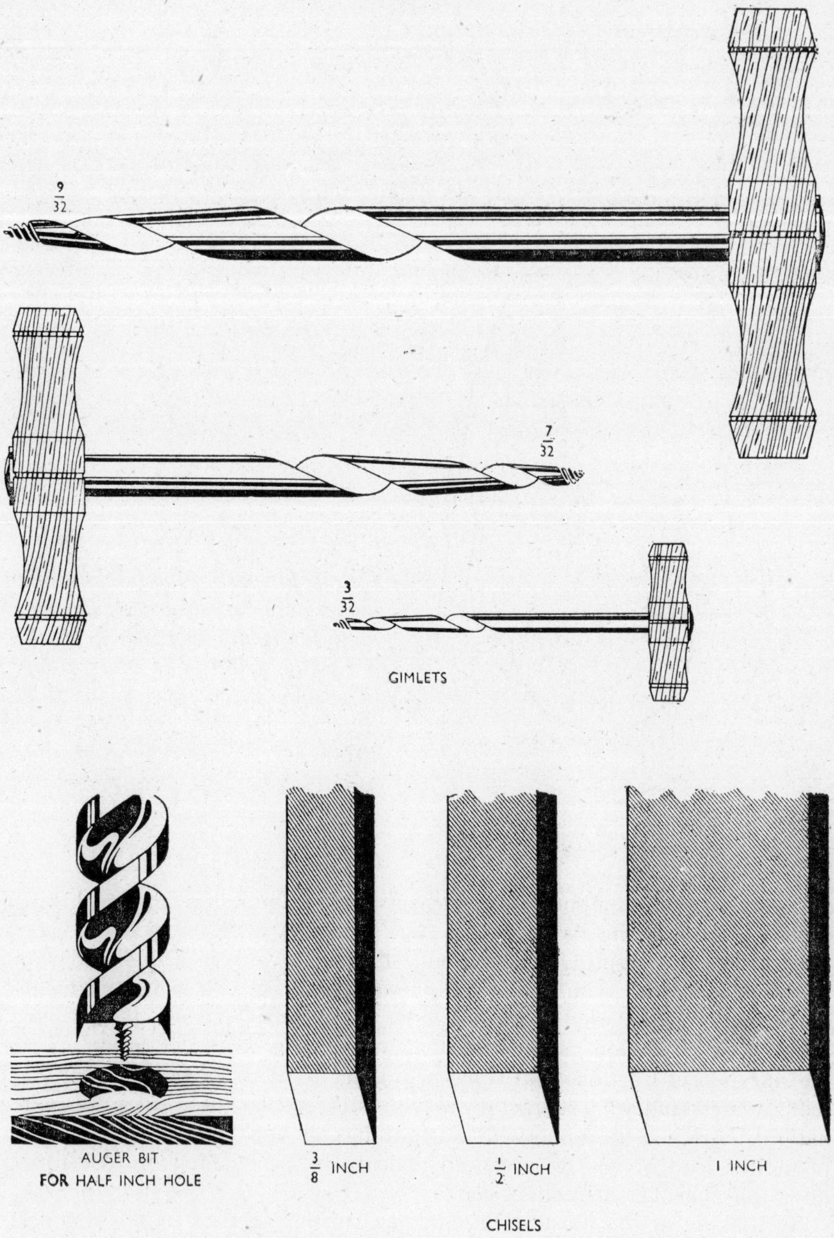

CARPENTER'S TOOLS AND THEIR SIZES

This illustration shows examples of three kinds of tools used by a carpenter. You will notice that fractions are in daily use for specifying the size of tools.

No. 2685. Set of 3 Punches

3/- per set. 1 of each.

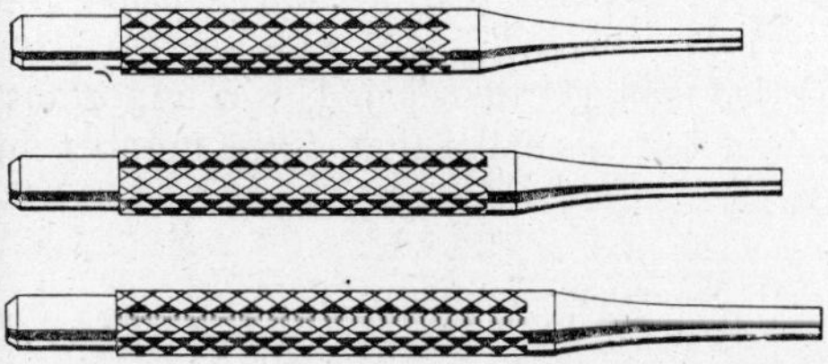

	Length	Diam. at point	Main Diam.
A	$2\frac{1}{4}''$	$\frac{1}{16}''$	$\frac{3}{16}''$
B	$2\frac{3}{8}''$	$\frac{5}{64}''$	$\frac{3}{16}''$
C	$2\frac{1}{2}''$	$\frac{3}{32}''$	$\frac{3}{16}''$

FRACTIONS AND ENGINEERING

This illustration is based on advertisements in engineering manufacturers' catalogues. You will note that in each of the dimensions quoted there are fractions.

do not go on reading from here without having a clear understanding of what fractions mean. The essential thing that you need to know about fractions is contained between the beginning of this chapter and here.

Once you know what fractions are, the next thing to do is to start experimenting with them. There are very many things that can be discovered quite easily.

Suppose, for instance, we start out to make illustrations of the fractions. We begin with the simplest ones: 1/2, 1/3, 2/3, 1/4, 2/4, 3/4, 1/5, 2/5, 3/5, 4/5 and so on, and we get illustrations that look like this:

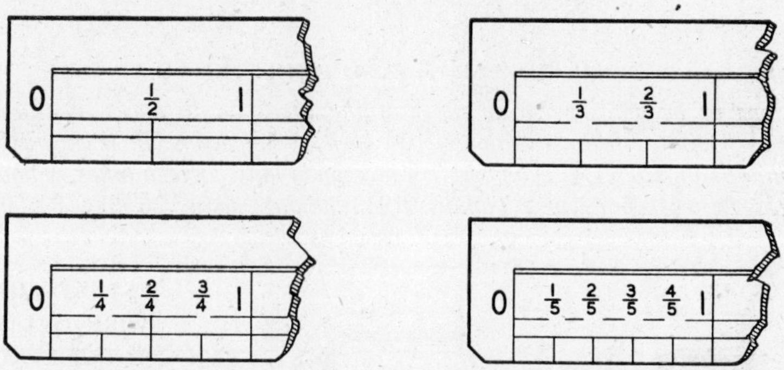

You will notice that 2/4 comes in the same place as 1/2. So it is possible for two fractions that are differently written to mean the same thing. Can you find other examples of this? On the ordinary school ruler, which has inches divided into 4ths, 8ths, 10ths, 12ths and 16ths, you can find many examples.

Later on in this book (Chapter IV) there will be explanations on simplifying fractions, cancelling, and so on. Cancelling is just another name for what has just been discovered about 2/4 being the same as 1/2.

If you can discover something about cancelling *for yourself*, by playing about with fractions and rulers, you will find this part of Chapter IV very easy to read, for you will have a good idea of what it is about before you come to it, and you will recognize your own ideas there.

Another thing that it is good to do is to take two fractions—say 1/2 and 1/4 —and ask yourself, "Which of these is the bigger?" Of course, as you can see from the illustration on Page 63, 1/2 is bigger than 1/4. This is important because 2, the number in the bottom of 1/2, is smaller than 4, the number in

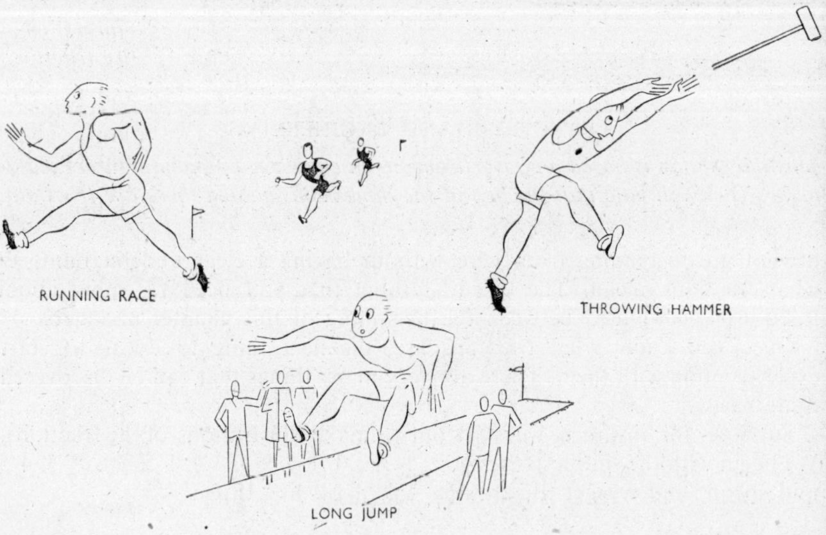

MEASUREMENT AND ATHLETICS

Fractions or decimals occur in most of the times or distances measured in athletics. Here are a few examples: 100 *yards*, 9·4 *seconds* (*F. Wykoff*, 1930). *One mile*, 4 *minutes* 1·6 *seconds* (*A. Anderson*, 1944). *Fifteen miles*, 1 *hour* 19 *minutes* 48·6 *seconds* (*E. Tamila*, 1937). *Long jump*, 26 *feet* 8¼ *inches* (*J. C. Owens*, 1935).

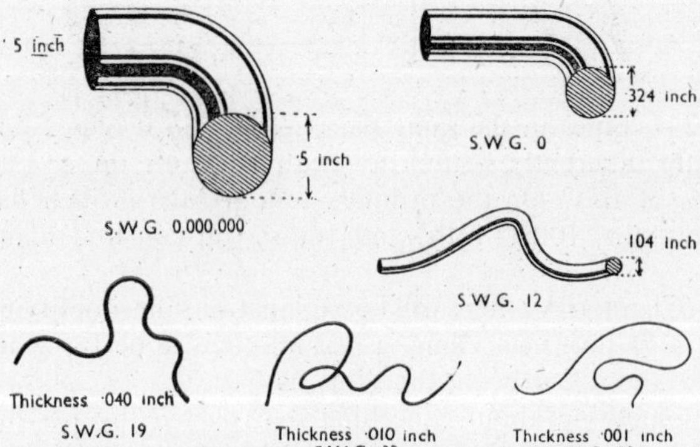

STANDARD WIRE GAUGE

In advertisements you will often see wire specified as S.W.G.18, or some other number. In this illustration are a few examples of the meaning of wire-gauge numbers. A complete list of wire-gauge sizes may be found in any engineer's reference book.

CHILDREN'S SHOES

Size	Length in inches	Size	Length in inches
0	4	7	$6\frac{1}{3}$
1	$4\frac{1}{3}$	8	$6\frac{2}{3}$
2	$4\frac{2}{3}$	9	7
3	5	10	$7\frac{1}{3}$
4	$5\frac{1}{3}$	11	$7\frac{2}{3}$
5	$5\frac{2}{3}$	12	8
6	6	13	$8\frac{1}{3}$

ADULTS' SHOES

Size	Length in inches	Size	Length in inches
1	$8\frac{2}{3}$	8	11
2	9	9	$11\frac{1}{3}$
3	$9\frac{1}{3}$	10	$11\frac{2}{3}$
4	$9\frac{2}{3}$	11	12
5	10	12	$12\frac{1}{3}$
6	$10\frac{1}{3}$	13	$12\frac{2}{3}$
7	$10\frac{2}{3}$	14	13

SIZES OF BOOTS AND SHOES

Comfortably fitting boots and shoes cannot be obtained if there is a whole inch between each size and the next. Fractions of an inch, therefore, have to appear in the standard sizes, as illustrated in the table at the top of this page.

the bottom of 1/4. In fact, as the numbers at the bottom get bigger, the fractions get smaller. Looking at the same illustration you will see that 1/2, 1/3, 1/4, 1/5 are so arranged that the biggest fraction comes first, and the smallest last.

Is the same true of 2/3, 2/4, 2/5, 2/6, 2/7?

Sometimes it is not very easy to see which of two fractions is the larger. For instance, which is larger, 2/3 or 3/5? You can find the answer by measuring on the diagram given on page 63.

The object of these experiments is that you should form the habit of seeing in your mind the meaning of what you are writing or saying, so that it becomes impossible for you to write something down without a picture of it appearing in your imagination.

If you can do this, it will save you from making many mistakes. Take for instance the following question which causes much difficulty in schools, and even in colleges.

A piece of plywood 1/2 inch thick is glued to another piece 1/3 inch thick. How thick is the piece of plywood thus made?

People make all kinds of shots at this. They realize that the thicknesses of the pieces of wood have to be *added*, and they think, "Well, there's a 2 in 1/2 and a 3 in 1/3, perhaps if we add the 2 and the 3 together, that will give us the number at the bottom for the answer." So they add 2 and 3 together, making 5, and say 1/5 inch is the answer.

Now think what this means. Here are three pieces of plywood, 1/2 inch, 1/3 inch and 1/5 inch thick.

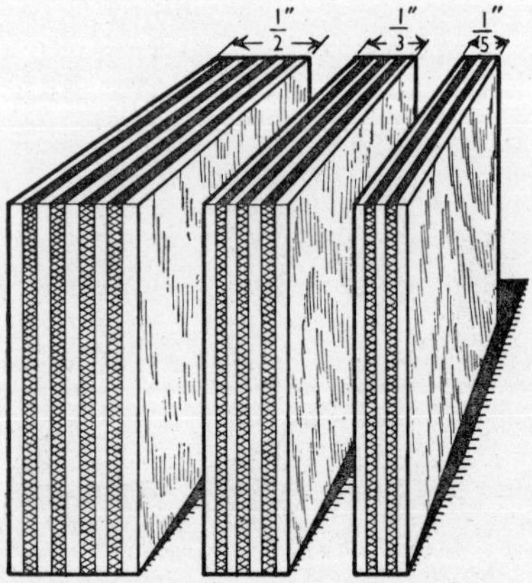

According to the answer given above, the two pieces on the left *joined together* are the same thickness as the piece on the right. But the piece on the right is thinner than either of the pieces on the left, and is far thinner that the two of them put together. So this answer is completely ridiculous.

Sometimes people add together the 1's on top of 1/2 and 1/3, as well as adding the 2 and 3 at the bottom. They then get the answer 2/5 inch for the thickness of the double sheet. If you illustrate this answer, you will see that it also is hopelessly wrong.

In short, guessing does not pay. Both mistaken answers could have been avoided by someone who had learnt to *see* what he was doing.

The picture of the plywood shows quite clearly that the answer 1/5 inch is wrong, but it does not give much of an indication as to what is the right answer.

The main advantage of this way of going about things is that it stops you giving the wrong answer and using the wrong method. If you are always

> It is queer how particular people are about letters being in line.

THOUSANDTHS OF AN INCH CAN BE IMPORTANT

In the sentence above some letters are a few thousandths of an inch too high, others are a few thousandths of an inch too low. The bad effect can be clearly seen.

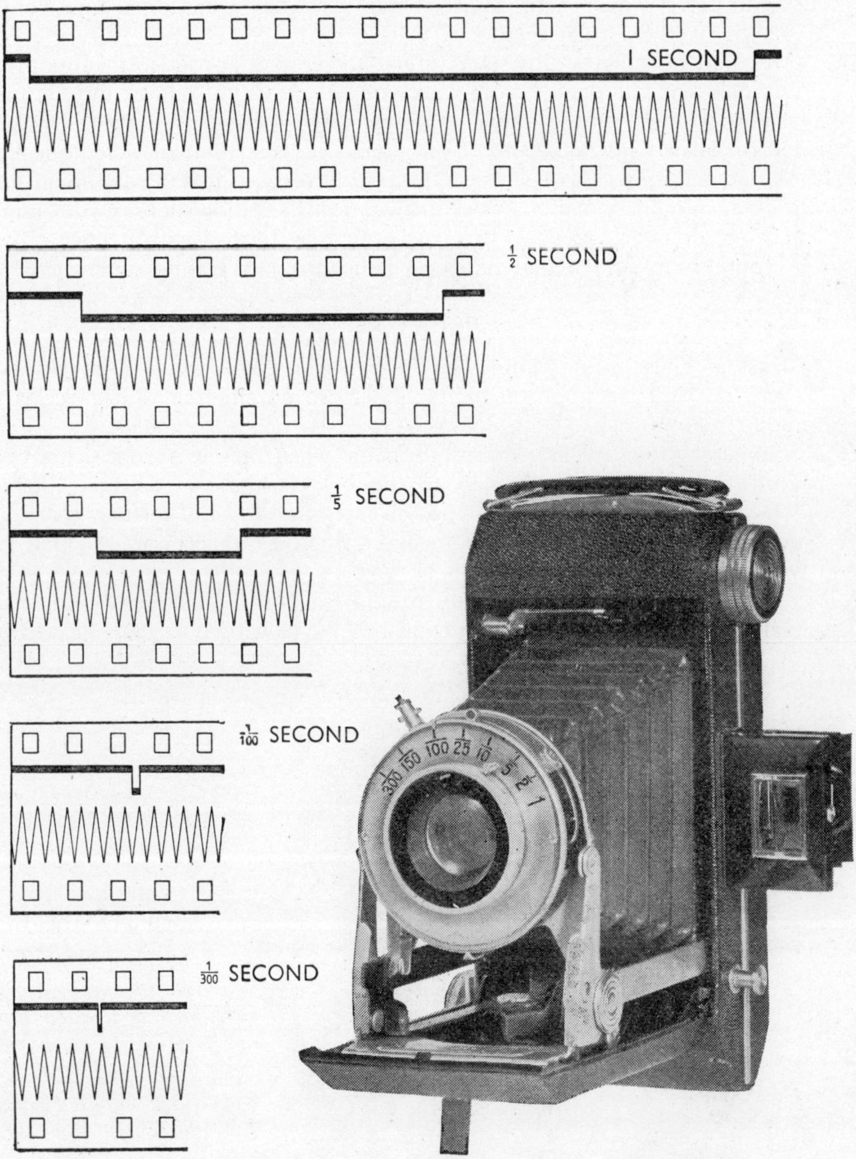

TIMING A CAMERA SHUTTER

The action of the shutter is recorded on a moving film. The heavy line shows when the shutter opens and closes. The wavy line keeps a record of the time; it goes up and down fifty times each second, and it is produced by an oscillograph connected to the electric mains supply. Camera shutters are very carefully designed so that the time of exposure is accurate.

able to detect which methods are wrong, it is only a matter of time before you discover the right method.

It is not intended at this stage to give the correct answer to this question. You may know it already from what you have learnt at school. Or you may be able to discover the answer by means of experiments. If not, you will find the answer in Chapter IV. Until then, you have an unanswered question in your mind, and this is a good thing to have, as it irritates the mind into thinking. You may find in a week or two, if this question sticks in your mind, that one or two ideas of your own about how to deal with it have grown in your brain—and if that happens, you are really getting somewhere.

DECIMALS

Just as children at school who have learnt about whole numbers ask, "Why do we have to go on to fractions?" so do children who have learnt about fractions ask, "Why do we have to go on to decimals?"

Some children are in an absolute panic when they leave one school for another, because someone says to them, "Ah, they do decimals there."

Decimals, like fractions, were not invented as a form of torture. Decimals were, in fact, invented in order to make fractions unnecessary, so that the work could be done more easily.

We have seen that it is difficult to add fractions. We have just come up against the problem of adding 1/2 and 1/3. We have tried to guess the answer

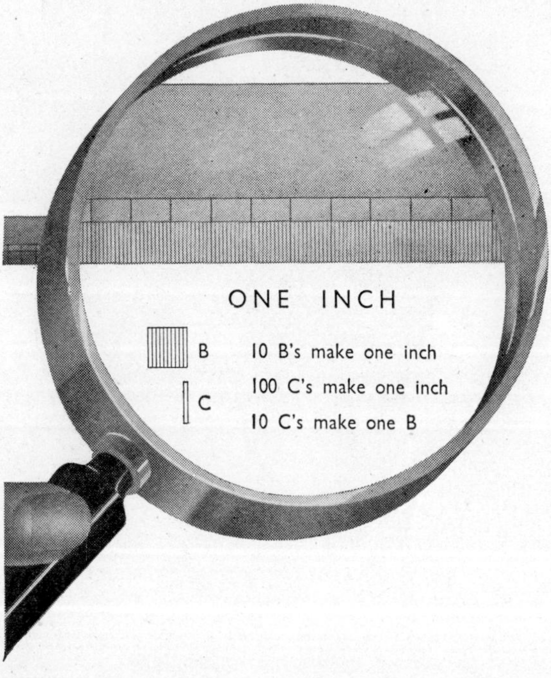

DECIMALS OF AN INCH

Here is a magnification of one inch. An inch is divided into ten equal parts, B. Each part B is divided into ten equal parts C. One inch contains 100 *Cs. Each C is therefore* 1/100 *part of an inch or* ·01 *inch, and each B is* 1/10 *part of an inch, or* ·1 *inch.*

ARITHMETIC FOR ARTISTS

This illustration shows an artist who has been asked to design a coat-of-arms for a Society that has recently been formed. He makes his original design on a small piece of card. When this has been approved he draws a network of squares over the design. He then lightly draws a similar network of squares, on a much larger scale, over the large shield, so as to ensure that the correct proportions are kept. In doing this there is a certain amount of calculation to be made. You can use the same idea for painting stage scenery, and for other work that requires an increase, or perhaps a decrease, of scale.

to this, and have found two incorrect answers. We still do not know what the correct answer is.

This type of difficulty does not exist at all in decimals. Decimals are just as easy to add as ordinary numbers.

The idea of a decimal is really very similar to the idea used in counting with ordinary numbers.

In counting we group things together always by tens. We group ten units together to make ten, ten tens together to make a hundred, ten hundreds

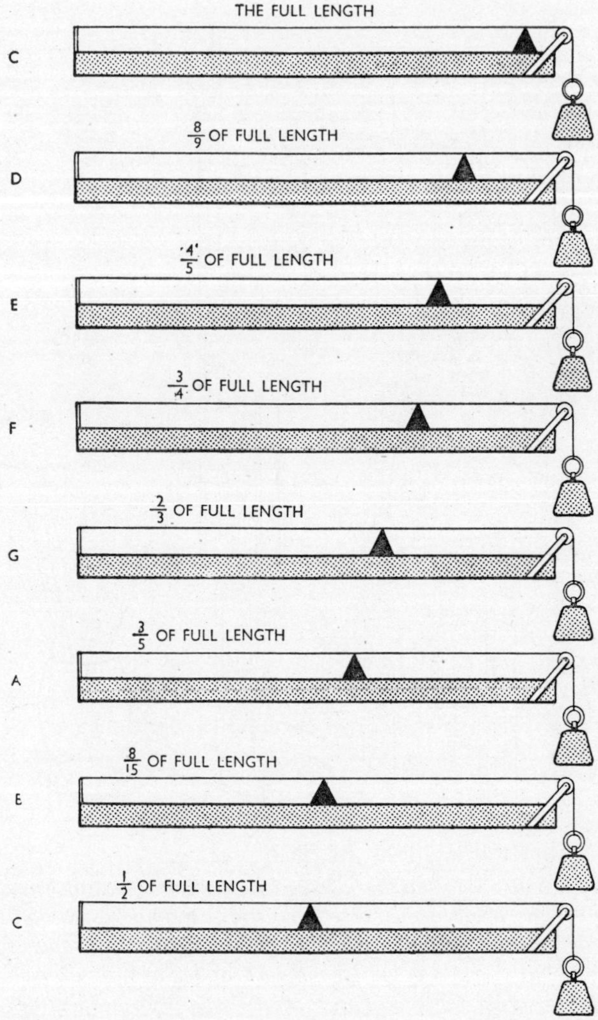

THE SIMPLEST MUSICAL INSTRUMENT

This consists of a wire passing over a pulley and kept taut by a weight. A wedge can be moved up and down the base of the instrument. The diagrams here show the positions of the wedge for the notes of an octave. The wire is plucked to the left of the wedge. By halving the length of the wire to the left of the wedge, the note emitted is made to rise by an octave. For people interested in music, a pleasant way of learning arithmetic is by studying the theory of how a musical note is produced. The pitch of a note, the overtones or harmonics, the quality of sound from a gramophone or wireless set are all connected with simple arithmetical relationships.

together to make a thousand. When we write 2,496 we mean 2 groups of a thousand, 4 groups of a hundred, 9 groups of ten, and 6 units.

We might measure a line and find it to be 2,496 inches long. By counting inches, we can obtain a way of measuring things very much larger than an inch.

But decimals are designed for the opposite purpose—for measuring things smaller than an inch; the thickness of a screw, the thickness of a cotton thread, the thickness of a piece of paper.

To measure such things we do not need to group inches together. We need to do the opposite—to take an inch and break it up into smaller pieces.

We do this by the same rule as for counting—we always go by tens. First of all we take an inch and break it up into ten equal pieces.

WALTZING MATILDA

COMIN THROUGH THE RYE

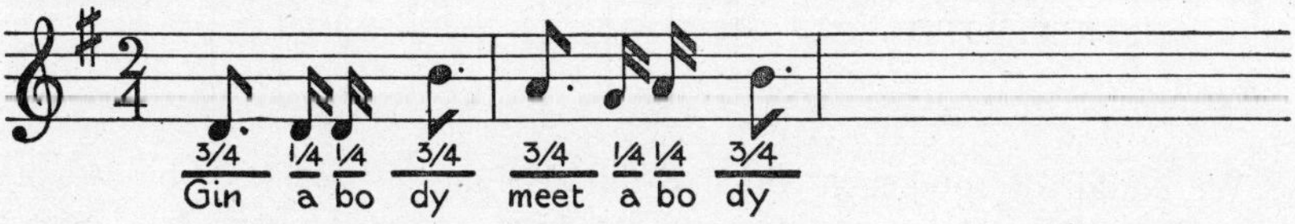

MADEMOISELLE FROM ARMENTIERES

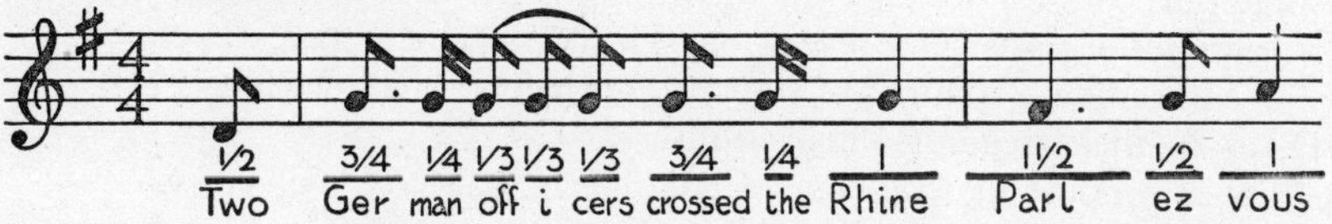

RHYTHM AND FRACTIONS

The rhythm of a song depends on how long each note is sounded. Different musical signs denote different fractions of a crochet. The more lively the rhythm, the more complicated fractions are likely to be used. This is very noticeable in Scotch songs, such as "Comin' through the Rye", above. "The Road to the Isles" would be a still better example. Little quarter-notes come into nearly all Scotch songs with a dancing rhythm. "Mademoiselle from Armentieres", has thirds as well as quarters. This complication is more due to the words "officers" than to the rhythm of the tune itself. Notice how the longest note in the tune, of $1\frac{1}{2}$ *beats, gives the slowing-down effect for "Parlez vous".*

ONE INCH

IS

BROKEN INTO TEN PIECES

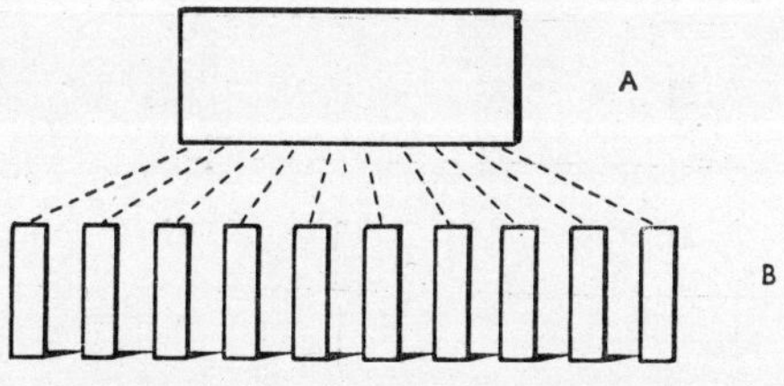

Then we take one of the pieces B and break it up again into ten equal pieces.

ONE PIECE

IS AGAIN

BROKEN INTO TEN

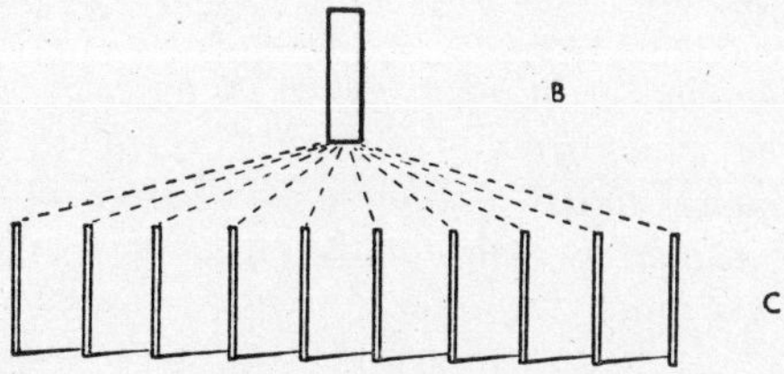

Then we take one of the pieces C and again break it into ten still smaller pieces.

AND THE PROCESS
IS
REPEATED

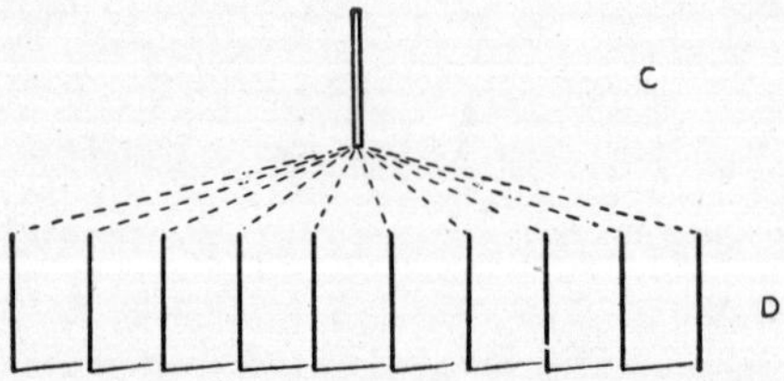

We could, of course, go on like this as long as we liked, but we have already gone as far as is necessary for most practical purposes. There are some purposes for which even smaller units are necessary, but the principle is always the same. One keeps on splitting into ten pieces.

We have now a number of standard measures, which we label A, B, C, and D, as in the foregoing illustrations.

Let us suppose that we have actual objects that have been chosen as having the correct thicknesses. We might find a piece of wood just the same

	Points	Height in inches	
	24	$\frac{1}{3}$	William Shakespeare
	12	$\frac{1}{6}$	If I may reply to a point (Interruption)
	9	$\frac{1}{8}$	A considerable volume of public opinion
	8	$\frac{1}{9}$	Refined young man seeks post with short hours and good pay.—Reply Box 321.
	$4\frac{3}{4}$	$\frac{19}{288}$	Change at Crewe.

TYPE SIZES

In order to avoid the use of fractions, printers use a unit that is much smaller than an inch—a point. Seventy-two points are equivalent to one inch. Even with this small unit it is sometimes necessary for fractions to be used; for example, $4\frac{3}{4}$ points as shown above. The squares on the left of the table show the number of points taken up by each particular line. You may wonder why the actual depth of the type face shown on the right is less than that of the square: this is to allow a small space at the top and bottom of the letters so that there is room for the top (known as ascender) of letters such as "h", and for the tail (known as descender) of letters such as "p" and "q". It also allows a small space to appear between one line and the next.

thickness as B. It should be possible to find cardboard the same thickness as C, and some very thin paper the right thickness for D. These are our standards, and with them we can build up a great variety of lengths.

Suppose we take 4 pieces such as B, 7 pieces of cardboard as thick as C, and 3 pieces of paper as thick as D

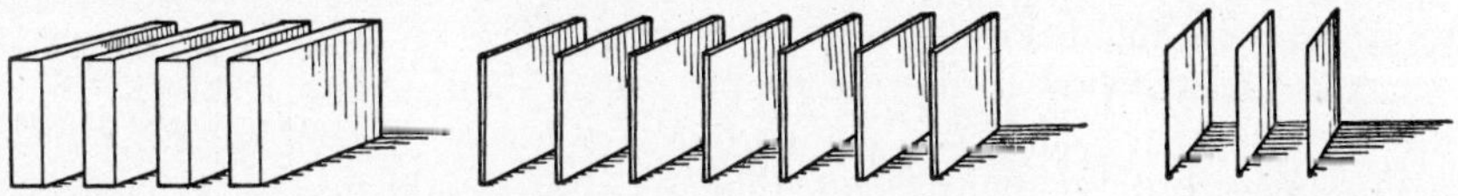

and place them in close contact with each other;

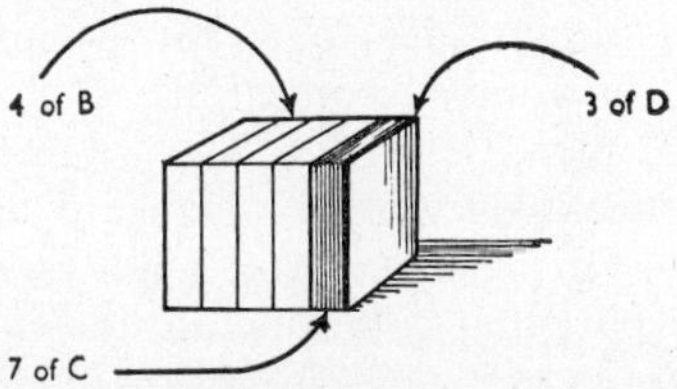

you can hardly hope to see the separate sheets of thin paper now, but we know they are there, and we know that this length is made up of 4 of B, 7 of C, 3 of D.

We might decide to write this length like this:

B	C	D
4	7	3

Usually it is not written like that, but instead is written ·473, with the understanding that the first figure after the dot tells us how many B pieces are used, the one after that how many C, the one after that how many D.

Thus ·218 would be a thickness built up from 2 of B, 1 of C, and 8 of D.

Sometimes it happens that not all the standard blocks are used. For instance, we might make up a thickness using 3 of B, none of C and 2 of D. This would be written ·302.

Or we might make up a thickness using 1 of C and 2 of D. As there are no Bs used, we must write 0 in the position showing how many Bs are used. Accordingly, this would be written ·012.

If we had to represent the thickness of a single D piece, this would be written ·001. The first two noughts show that no B and no C blocks are being used.

The length made up by one C piece alone would be written ·010. If you like to leave off the last nought you may do so, since ·01 means no B and one C, which is what we want. As D is not mentioned at all, we know that no D piece has to be put in. If any D pieces had been wanted there would have been a third number to show how many. As there is no third number, we know this is not the case.

In the same way, the length of one B piece alone may be written ·100 or ·10 or ·1; all mean the same thing.

In factories blocks known as Johannsen blocks are used to build up required lengths. These blocks are often referred to as "Joeys" for short. The principle of Joeys is the same as the principle of the blocks B, C and D that we have used to build up different lengths. The only difference is due to the fact that our C and D pieces are very thin and easily injured. Johannsen blocks are so arranged in standard sizes that one can get any required length without using very thin blocks. It is not necessary for us to go into the details of this now. For the purpose of understanding what decimals are it is best to use the simple system of B, C and D blocks that have been described above.

For practice it is not necessary that the sizes should be exactly correct. If you look for some wood 1/10 of an inch thick, some cardboard one-tenth as thick as the wood, and some very thin paper that will be accurate enough to give you a rough idea of what decimals mean—with this material you can build for yourself collections of blocks to illustrate such lengths as ·425 inch, ·002 inch, ·7 inch, ·83 inch, ·022 inch, and so on.

Often when you see decimals written, there are figures in front of the stop as well as after it. For instance, you might see that something was 43·125 inches long. The part that comes before the stop means the number of complete inches. Thus, 43·125 inches means that there are 43 whole inches, together with 1 piece B, 2 pieces C and 5 pieces D. For lengths less than 1 inch, a nought is often put before the stop; thus, 0·5 has the same meaning as ·5.

The stop is called the *decimal point.*

It is not very convenient to keep on talking about "Piece B", "Piece C", "Piece D" and so on. Let us find more usual names for these pieces.

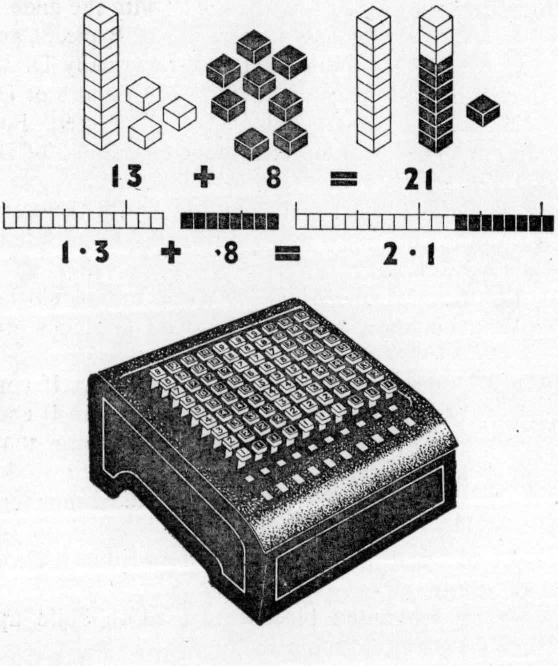

DECIMALS AND CALCULATING MACHINES

It is not necessary to have special calculating machines to do decimal sums. As the example at the top of the illustration shows, the rules for adding decimals are just the same as those for ordinary numbers. For monetary calculations the same machines are used, although the money system does not work in tens. The machine operators, if working in pounds, change all moneys to pounds and decimals.

We began with one inch, which we called A. Then we divided A into ten pieces of type B. Each B must, therefore, be one-tenth (1/10) of an inch.

B in turn was divided into ten pieces of type C. As ten Cs make one B, and ten Bs make one A, it is clear that A contains a hundred Cs.

So C must be one-hundredth part of A, that is to say 1/100 inch.

In the same way, you can see that one inch contains a thousand parts D, so that each D is one-thousandth of an inch (1/1000 inch), sometimes shortened to "a thou."

Instead of talking about B, C, and D, we may now say that 43·125 inches means 43 inches, together with

1 tenth of an inch,
2 hundredths of an inch,
and 5 thousandths of an inch.

So far we have been talking about measuring lengths, because that is something you can actually do and see before your eyes. You can make things one-tenth of an inch and one-hundredth of an inch long and take a good look at them.

But there is no reason why decimals should be used only for measuring lengths. Decimals can be used for anything that can be divided into ten equal parts. You can speak, if you want to, of 2·1 pints, or 3·45 seconds, or 8·72 pounds weight.

So, in our explanation above of 43·125 inches, we may leave out the reference to inches and say simply that

43·125 means 43 whole units, together with
1 tenth,
2 hundredths,
and 5 thousandths.

DECIMALS AND CALCULATING MACHINES

As we mention elsewhere, many calculations are today performed by calculating machines.

Decimals are particularly suitable for calculating machines because decimals are based on grouping by tens, just like ordinary numbers. Slipping back for a moment into speaking of A, B, C and D, we have ten Ds make one C, ten Cs make one B, and ten Bs make one A. This is just the same system as ten units making a ten, ten tens a hundred, and ten hundreds a thousand.

As a result of the two systems being based on the same idea, it is possible to use an ordinary calculating machine to do sums with decimals.

But you cannot use a calculating machine to do sums with ounces, pounds, stones, quarters, hundredweights and tons, because in this system of weights the carrying is based on all kinds of different numbers—16 ounces making one pound, 14 pounds one stone, 2 stones one quarter, and so on up to 20 hundredweights one ton. To do such work a special calculating machine would have to be built.

In most modern offices, calculating machines are used. Of course, the present money system is not at all suitable for a calculating machine, with

DECIMAL PARTS OF £1

¼d.	·00104	10d.	·04166	10/-	·500
½d.	·00208	11d.	·04583	11/-	·550
1d.	·00416	1/-	·050	12/-	·600
2d.	·00833	2/-	·100	13/-	·650
3d.	·0125	3/-	·150	14/-	·700
4d.	·01666	4/-	·200	15/-	·750
5d.	·02083	5/-	·250	16/-	·800
6d.	·025	6/-	·300	17/-	·850
7d.	·02916	7/-	·350	18/-	·900
8d.	·03333	8/-	·400	19/-	·950
9d.	·0375	9/-	·450	20/-	1·000

12 pence to the shilling and 20 shillings to the pound. In order to get round this, girls who work calculating machines have to learn what is really a new money system—every amount of money is expressed in pounds and *decimals of a pound.*

At the beginning each girl is given a printed table, such as is shown above, from which she can read off any sum of money as a decimal of £1. Thus 10/- is ·5 of £1, 2/- is ·1 of £1. 7/5¾ is ·37395 of £1.

Thus, if a girl had to find the cost of 1,760 articles at £2/7/5¾ each, she would set the machine for multiplying 1,760 by 2·37395. After the machine had worked out the answer to this question, the tables would again be used to turn the result back into pounds, shillings and pence.

With some practice, the girls get to know by heart the value of each sum of money as a decimal.

For such work it is not necessary for a girl to do long calculations in ordinary arithmetic, since the machine does these. It is an advantage to know the general idea of what a decimal is.

This point seems worth mentioning, as it is not widely realized that money sums are now done by decimals rather than by the method used in the older text-books.

AREAS

We have seen that *lengths* can be measured with feet and inches and fractions or decimals of inches. A different kind of measure is needed to answer such questions as, "How much land does this farm contain?" or "How much linoleum is necessary to cover this floor?"

Both of these questions are questions about *areas*. We can see the meaning of *area* by thinking about what can be done with a piece of linoleum.

Suppose you buy a piece of linoleum two yards wide and ten yards long.

A

Probably you will use it to cover a room which is something like 4 yards wide and 5 yards long. This you can do by cutting it in the middle

B

and then putting the two pieces side by side.

C

But it might happen that in some large mansion or institution a long corridor might require a strip of linoleum along the middle. In that case, the piece of linoleum shown at A might be cut lengthwise

D

and the pieces joined end to end

E

giving a strip one yard wide and 20 yards long.

There are, of course, many other shapes which could be covered with the same piece of linoleum—rooms with fireplaces sticking out in the middle and with extra space in corners to make up for it—and all kinds of jigsaw shapes that one could make up. But all these shapes contain the same amount of linoleum.

A mathematician expresses this by saying that *the areas of the figures are equal.* (*Figure* here means *shape*—as for a woman's figure—not *number*.) You can always test for yourself whether two figures are equal in area by asking yourself, "Could I make this shape by cutting that one into pieces, and then fitting the pieces together again?" If it is possible to do this, the areas are equal.

If the floor of a large room could be covered with linoleum by taking three pieces like A (chopping them up if necessary), we should say the area of the floor was three times the area of A.

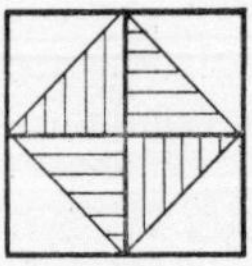

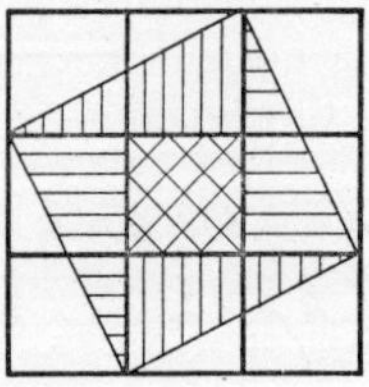

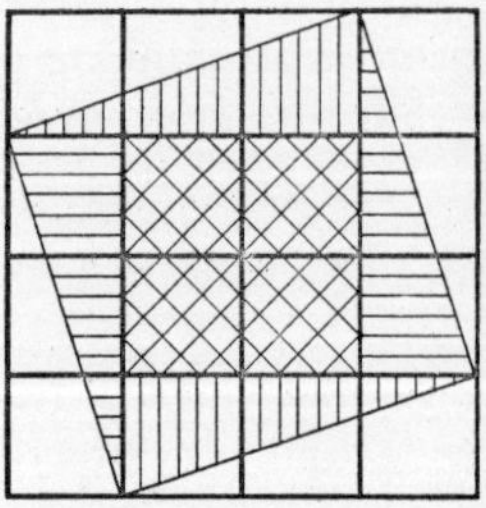

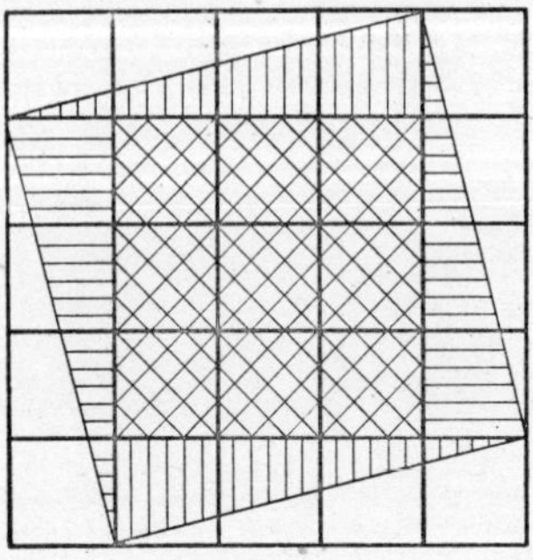

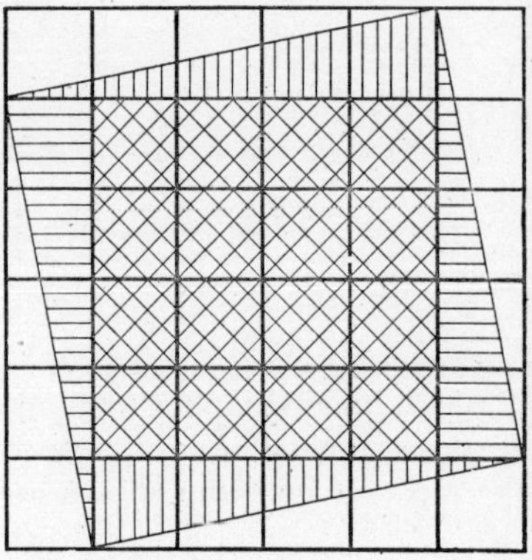

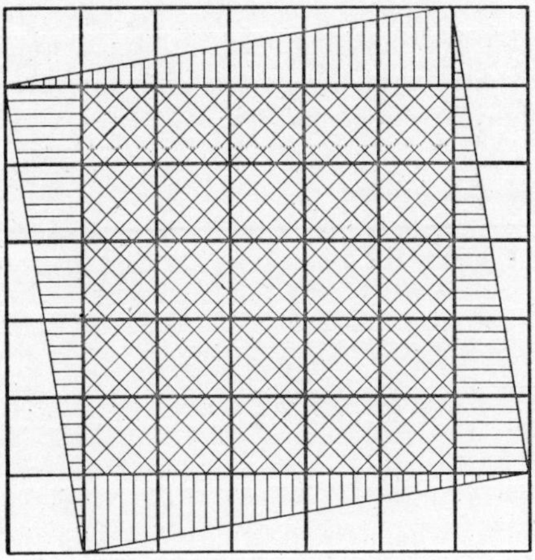

AN IMPORTANT JIG-SAW PUZZLE

The shaded part of these figures can, in each case, be covered by cutting up an exact number of the little squares, S. Thus, two squares S, properly cut up, will exactly cover the shaded patch in the first figure. How many squares are necessary for each of the other figures? Do you notice any connection between the answers to this and the square numbers of the figure that appears on page 79?

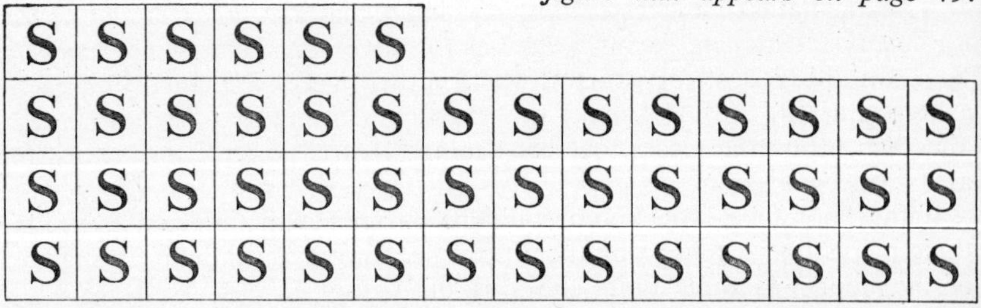

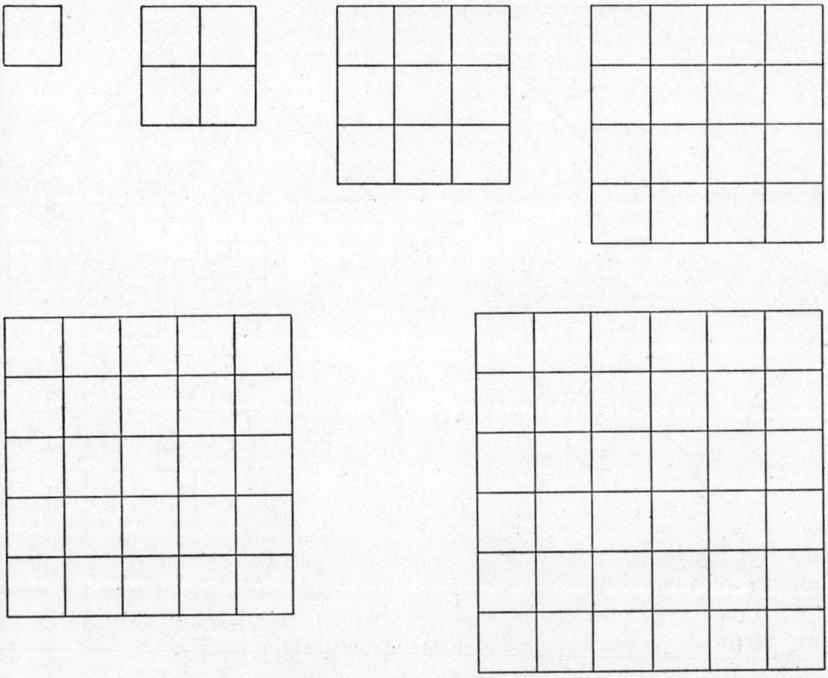

THE SQUARE NUMBERS

Count the number of squares in each of these six figures. Write down the numbers that you find. They are called the square numbers. It will be a help to you if you are able to recognize them. Is there any relation between these and the figures on page 78?

From this it is easy to see how areas are measured. We start with a standard piece. Here is a square, one inch wide and one inch high.

F

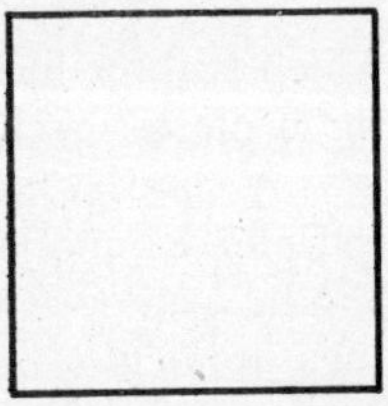

Any shape that can be made by cutting this square up and fitting the bits together again is said to have an area of *one square inch*. All the shapes on the top of page 80 are made from the square shown at F; each has, therefore, an area of one square inch.

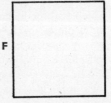

In figures G, H and I, shown on page 80, the dotted lines show where you would have to cut these shapes, in order to get pieces from which you could make the original square F.

The question of finding the area in square inches of a given shape simply means, then, "How many pieces of material, each exactly like F, should we need to cover this shape?"

Now, of course, there are rules in the arithmetic books for finding the areas of shapes, but for the moment do not bother about these. Experiment for yourself. Make pieces of paper just like F and see how many are needed

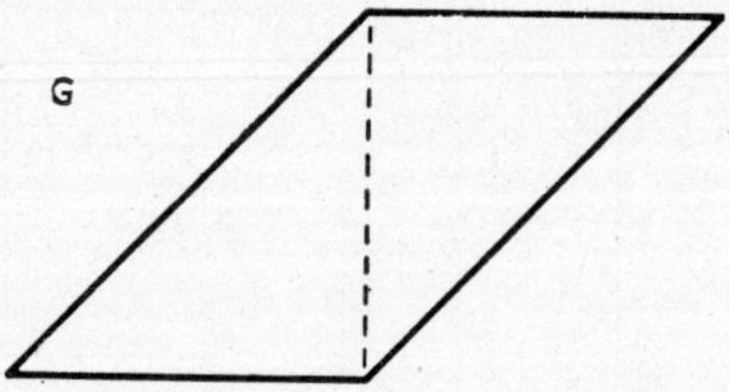

G

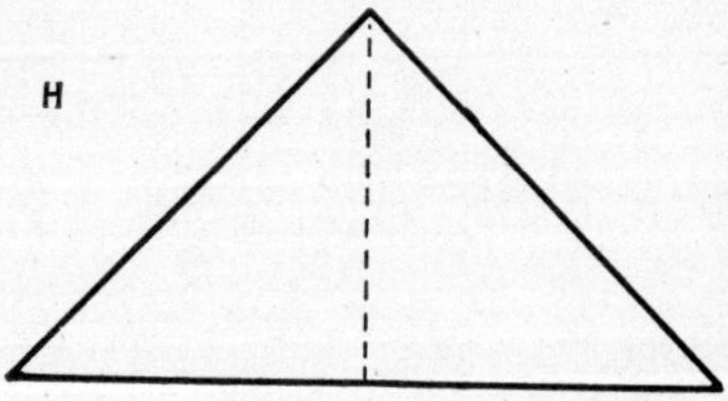

H

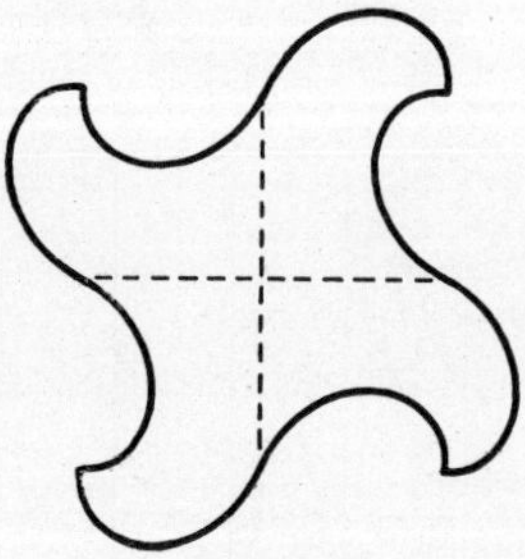

I

J

to cover the shape. Sometimes, you will find you can fill the space with a number of squares like F. At other times, you will find that odd pieces are left over which are smaller than F—that is to say, fractions will come in, just as they did when we were measuring straight lines.

For instance, this shape,

K

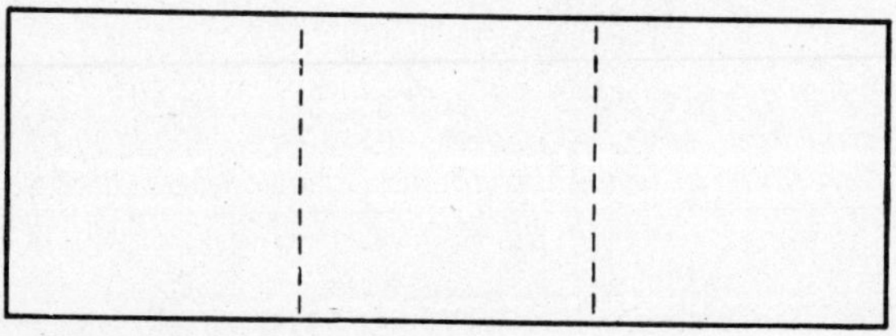

which is three inches long and one inch high, can obviously be split up into three pieces, each like F. So its area is 3 *square inches*.

Any shape which could be made from K, by chopping it up and moving the bits around, would also have an area of 3 square inches.

You can try for yourself sketching shapes like K, but with different measurements—say four inches long and two inches high, for example—and counting how many squares F would be needed to cover each.

An example of a shape which brings fractions in is shown at L.

L

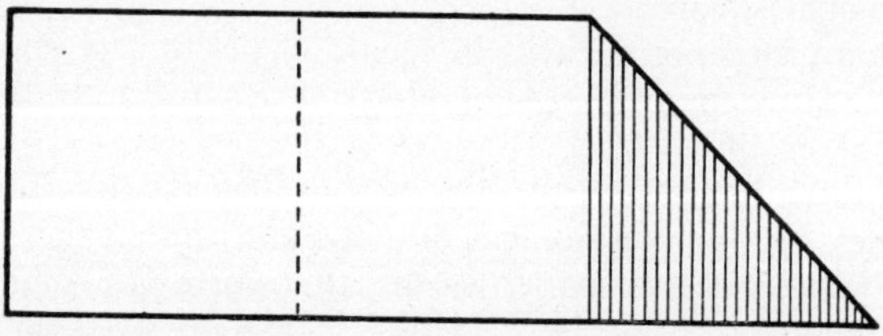

Here we can put two squares F in, but there still remains the shaded part. How are we to find the area of the shaded part?

We notice that two pieces, each exactly like the shaded part of L, can be fitted together to make a single square F, thus:

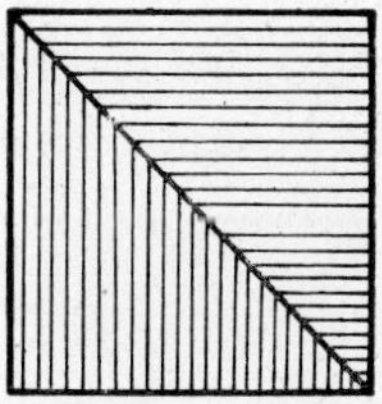

Each must, therefore, be one-half of F. So the shaded part of L is $\frac{1}{2}$ of F. The whole of L is, therefore, $2\frac{1}{2}$ times F; that is to say, $2\frac{1}{2}$ square inches in area.

In the same way, we can illustrate other fractions of a square inch. For instance, here is a square inch divided up into four little squares. Since there are four equal parts making up the whole, each part must be a quarter ($\frac{1}{4}$) of the whole. 3 squares are shaded, so the shaded part is three quarters ($\frac{3}{4}$) of the whole. So the shaded part is $\frac{3}{4}$ of a square inch in area; the unshaded part, $\frac{1}{4}$ square inch.

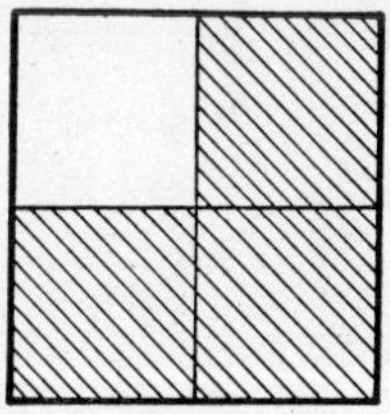

SQUARE FEET AND FEET SQUARE

One little difficulty should be mentioned. People sometimes get confused by the difference between "two square inches" and "two inches square". These are not the same thing.

"Two square inches" we have already met. It means this—

TWO
SQUARE INCHES.

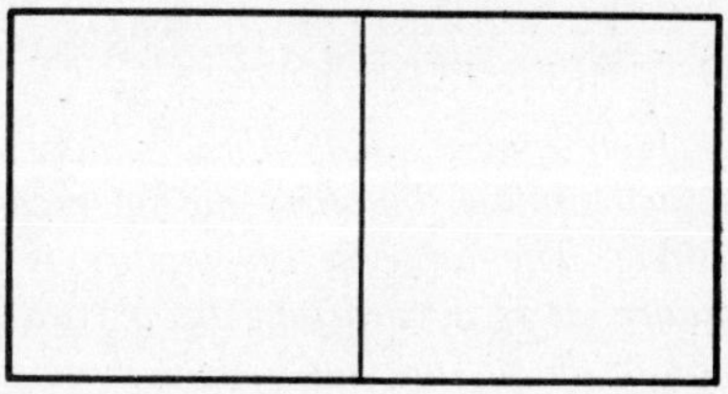

"Two inches square" means that we have a square, each side of which is two inches long.

THREE SQUARE FEET AND
THREE FEET SQUARE

"Three feet square" and "three square feet" sound very similar, but they do not mean the same thing. The table in the picture is three feet square. It is a yard long by a yard wide. The man in the picture has bought three square feet of veneer with the intention of covering the table top with it. As you can see, this quantity is far from being sufficient for the job.

The best way to learn how many square feet go to one square yard is not to learn it parrotwise, but every time you meet this question draw a little sketch of a square yard, and count the number of square feet in it.

As you can see, the square below contains 4 square inches. So "two inches square" is "four square inches".

The words of this sentence may sound confusing to you, but words do not always give the correct impression. If you look at the actual things, the diagrams, the difference between them is plain enough.

In the same way, one yard is three feet, but one square yard is *not* three square feet. Look at the illustration on the top of page 84.

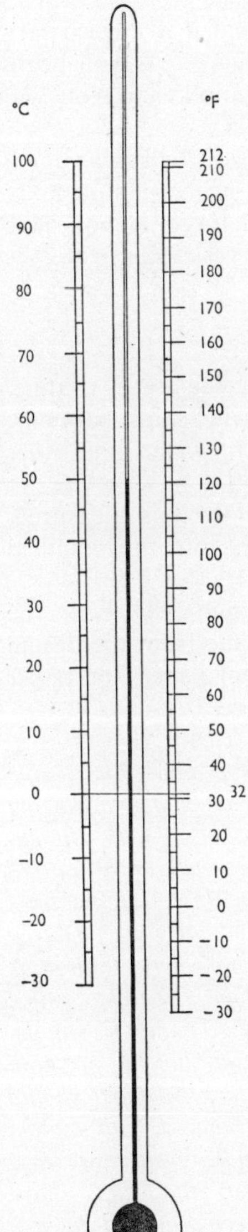

TWO INCHES SQUARE

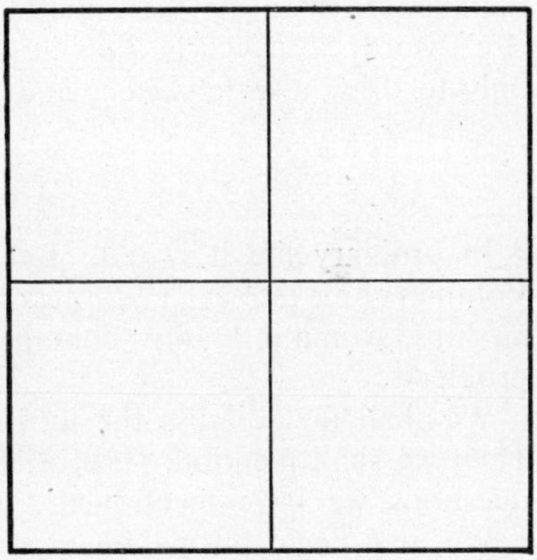

MEASURING TEMPERATURE

On the Centigrade scale water freezes at 0°. As it is possible to have temperatures much colder than this, it is necessary to use numbers with a minus sign to indicate temperatures below zero. Water boils at 100° Centigrade. On the Fahrenheit scale, for some peculiar reason, water freezes at 32° and boils at 212°. Like some other picturesque institutions, the Fahrenheit scale survives more because we have got used to it than because it serves any useful purpose. Degrees Centigrade are found from degrees Fahrenheit by the formula $C=\frac{5(F-32)}{9}$. *Minus numbers are very important in algebra. The thermometer scale helps you to see what a minus number means. When you begin to read about algebra, you will find it a useful exercise to work out —22° Fahrenheit in degrees Centigrade, and other similar examples.*

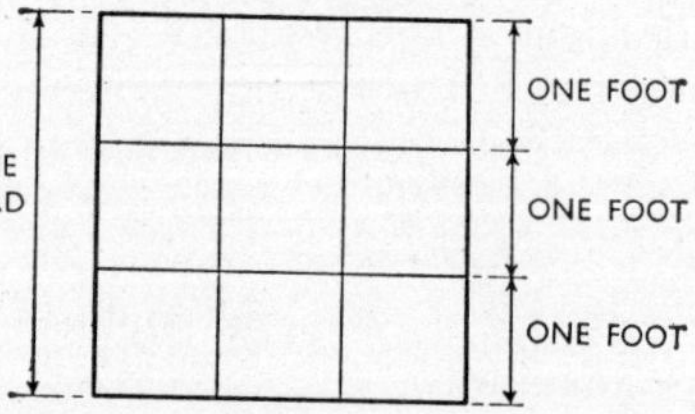

When you have done this a few times you will find that it is unnecessary to draw the actual picture as shown on the top of this page. As you begin to draw it, the complete picture will flash into your mind, and you will know the correct answer.

But more important than just *knowing* the answer, you will *understand* the answer. It will not be something you have learnt by heart on somebody else's word. So it will lie easy in your mind. If you ever forget it, you have only to draw a little sketch, and it will come back to you again.

VOLUMES

In ordinary life it is not often that one needs to calculate a volume. Volumes come into calculations for the design of boats, rafts, ships, balloons, airships, swimming tanks, containers for storing petrol or water, and other problems.

We shall first discuss the meaning of volume and how it is measured. Then we shall mention, very briefly, how volume comes into the practical questions we have mentioned.

We may begin by making a standard measure for volume. A box, one inch high, one inch long and one inch broad, can be made from the design shown. It should be made watertight. (If it is made from paper, the paper

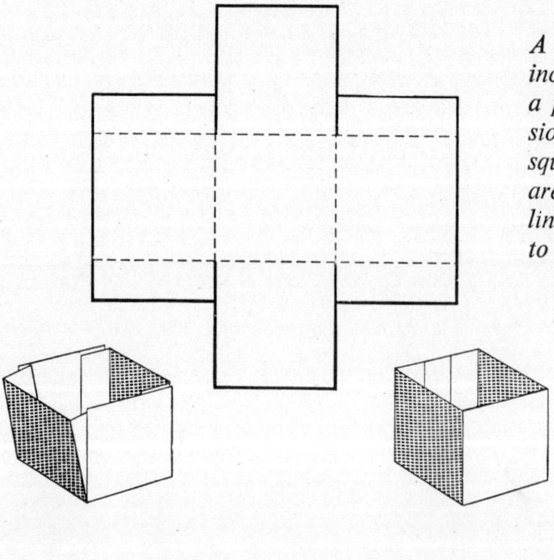

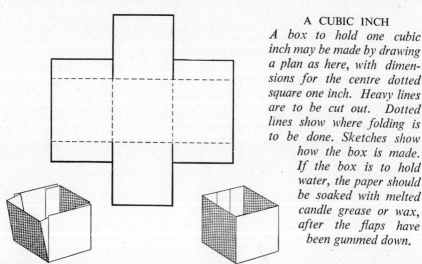

A CUBIC INCH

A box to hold one cubic inch may be made by drawing a plan as here, with dimensions for the centre dotted square one inch. Heavy lines are to be cut out. Dotted lines show where folding is to be done. Sketches show how the box is made. If the box is to hold water, the paper should be soaked with melted candle grease or wax, after the flaps have been gummed down.

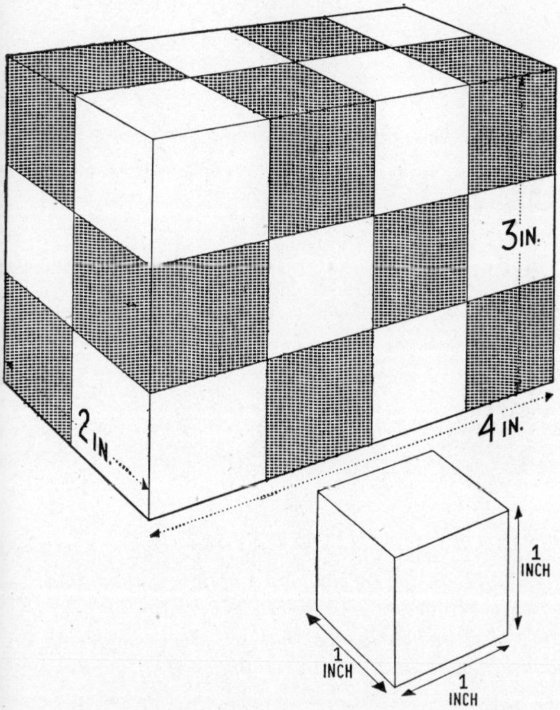

FINDING VOLUMES BY COUNTING

It is very often possible to find the volume of a body simply by counting cubes. You may have a question such as this. If a block of iron measures 4 inches long, 3 inches high and 2 inches wide, find the volume of this block. If the block were to be cut up into cubes having one-inch sides, you would find that it would contain 24 cubes, as shown in this illustration. The volume of this block is, therefore, 24 cubic inches.

should be soaked with melted candle-wax.) The amount of water this box will hold is called "one cubic inch".

Measuring the volume in any other container is now simple. We simply see how many boxes full of water are necessary to fill it. For instance, if a cocoa tin requires exactly 35 boxes full of water to fill it, we say that the cocoa tin holds a volume of 35 cubic inches. If the tin is filled by 35 boxes full of water and then a box half full, the tin holds $35\frac{1}{2}$ cubic inches of water.

In this way we can measure the volume held by any vessel. Sometimes we want to measure the volume of something that is solid, as, for instance, a block of iron. We might do this by pressing the iron into a mould, and then seeing how many boxes full of water were necessary to fill the hole in the mould. Or we might put the iron into a saucepan that had previously been filled to the brim, and measure how many boxes full of water overflowed.

Sometimes you can see the answer without doing any experiment. For instance, if you have a block of iron four inches long, three inches high and two inches thick, you can see that it could be cut up exactly into 24 inch cubes, so that its volume is 24 cubic inches. (See the diagram above.)

Volumes can be measured in terms of cubic feet or cubic yards, instead of in cubic inches.

To measure volumes in cubic feet one would make a box one foot in length, breadth and height.

To measure volumes in cubic yards the box would have to be one yard

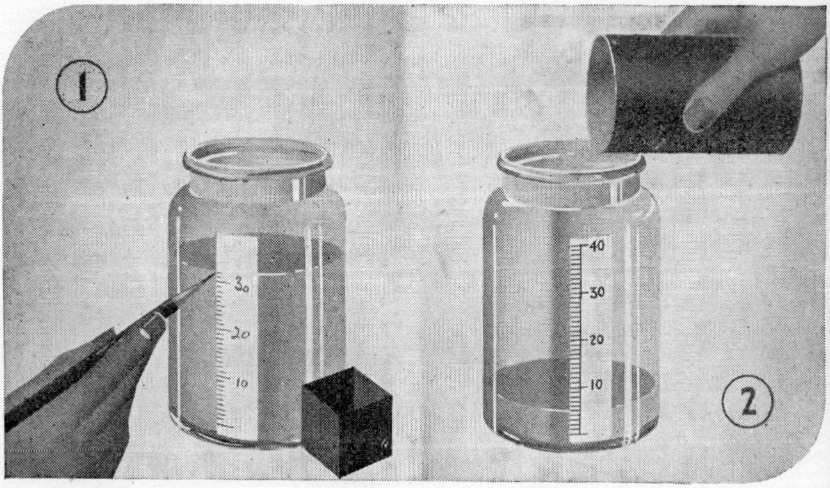

EXPERIMENTS ON THINGS THAT FLOAT

Here are some experiments that may be carried out on things that float:—
(1) *Making a measuring jar. Water is poured into an ordinary jam jar, a cubic inch at a time (the cubic inch measure that has been suggested on page* 84 *may be used) and the height of the water is marked at each stage.*

(2) *This home-made measuring jar is then used to measure the volume of water held by a tin.*

(3) *Weights are then put into the tin until the tin will just float without any water finding its way into the tin.*

By such experiments as these, one can discover the principles used to design ships, rafts, and floating objects of every kind.

in length, breadth and height. Sand is usually sold by the cubic yard. Lorries used for selling sand have the volume of sand that they can hold marked on them, in cubic yards.

Volume can also be measured in pints and gallons. A gallon contains slightly more than 277 cubic inches. Try designing a petrol tank for a motor car, and see how many gallons you can make it hold without it being absurdly large. Then compare it with the sizes of petrol tanks that you see on lorries and motor cars. The space required for storing petrol is an important question in the design of an aeroplane.

One of the most interesting applications of calculations about volume is the design of floating objects—swimming tanks, rafts, and ships.

You can test for yourself the principle involved. All you need is a kitchen sink, a few empty tins, and a set of weights. First of all, measure the volumes of the tins you have (see page 86). Then run some water into the kitchen sink, sufficient for the tins to float in. Put weights into the tins, and find what weight can be put into each tin so as to bring it to the verge of sinking. You will find that the weight that just sinks the tin depends on the volume of the tin. For each cubic inch the tin contains, you can put in a weight of slightly more than half an ounce. (The figure is something like 0·58 ounce.)

This rule holds however large the vessel may be. A vessel of one cubic foot will carry rather more than 60 pounds. A vessel containing 36 cubic feet will support a ton, when on the verge of sinking.

Usually when boys build rafts they do not allow sufficient volume to support the weight they want the raft to carry. The difficulty can be overcome by fixing very large tins at the sides of the raft. (The other difficulty is the tendency of rafts to capsize. The calculations in regard to this question are not very simple. Probably the best thing to do is to test the stability of any design by making a small model to scale, and seeing how it floats.)

One of the striking inventions of the Second World War was the swimming tank—the arrangement of a canvas screen round a tank so that the tank would float. When the inventor, Nicholas Straussler, first thought of this idea he must have asked himself, "Is it possible to carry a tank on a reasonable size of float?" The answer would have been worked out by the rule mentioned above—36 cubic feet for every ton, and then a margin for safety. (The 36 cubic feet for each ton rule applies when the top of the float is right down to the water-line. The slightest splash of water into the float will then cause the whole thing to sink.)

The calculation depended, therefore, on the volume inside the canvas screen. You can, if you are interested, design canvas screens suitable for carrying different types of tanks.

THE MATHEMATICAL MUSEUM

One of the biggest mistakes made in teaching arithmetic in the old days was that children were expected to learn everything simply by sitting down at desks and reading and writing. They were expected to understand inches

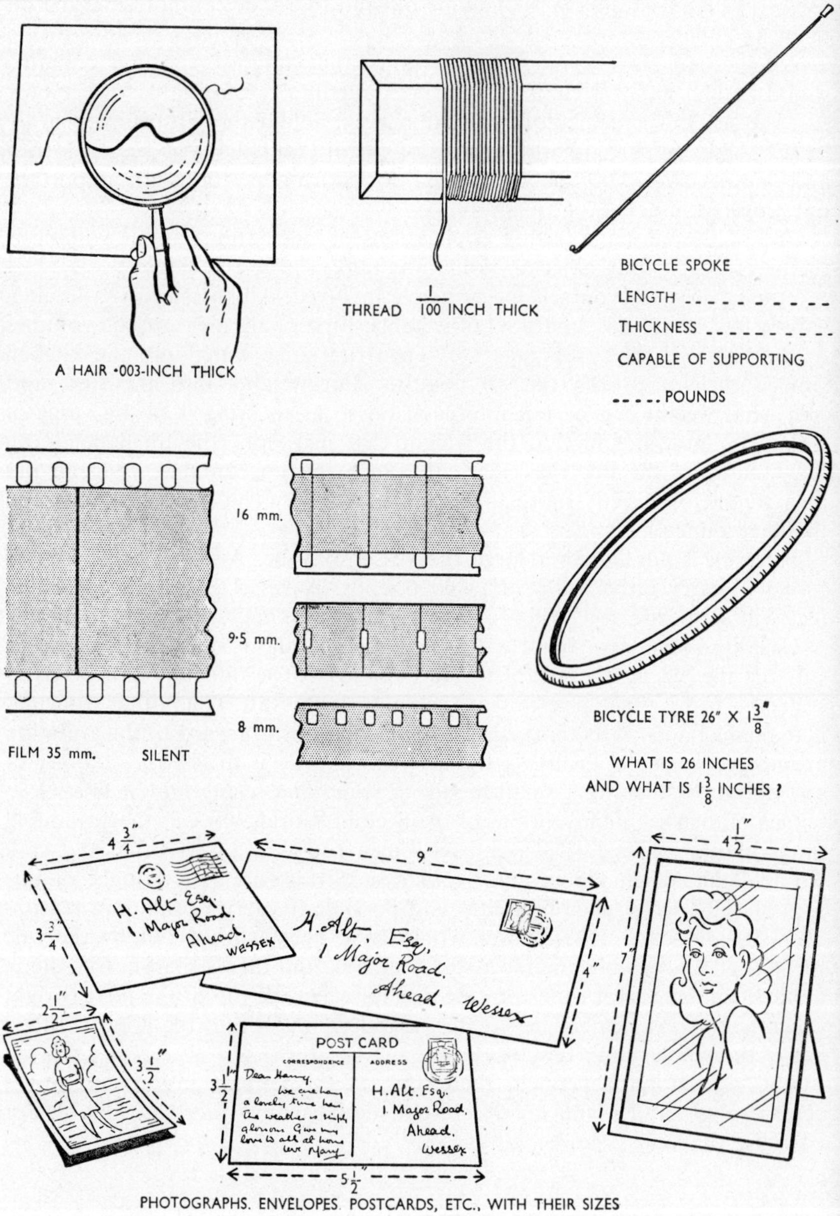

SUGGESTIONS FOR THE MATHEMATICAL MUSEUM (1)

A few common objects arranged to show the meaning of fractions and decimals of inches, and measurements in millimetres.

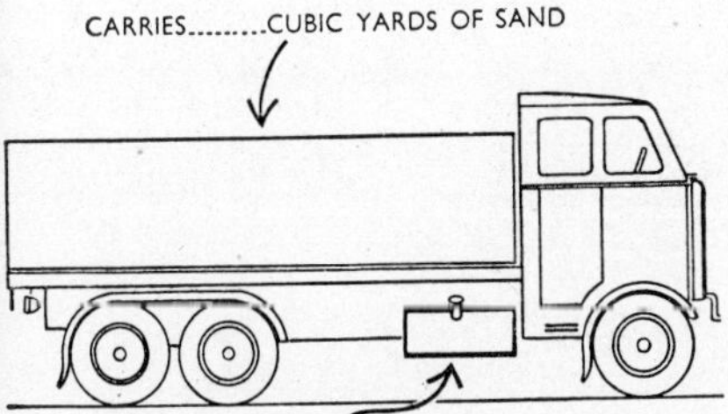

PETROL TANK OF LORRY
MEASUREMENTS.........X.........X ....
HOLDS.........GALLONS
SUFFICIENT FOR.........MILES

PLATE FROM END OF PASSENGER COACH

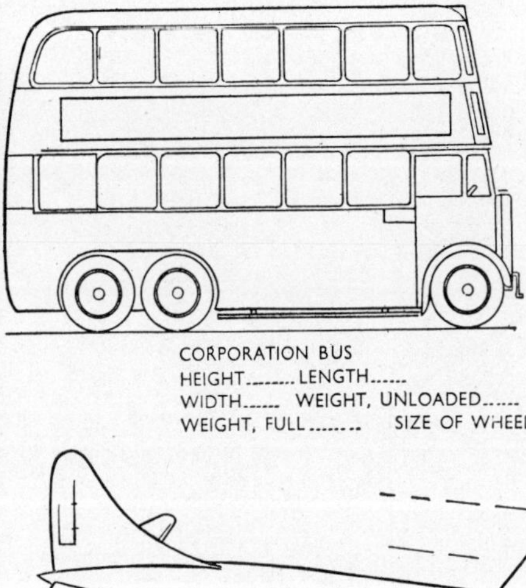

CORPORATION BUS
HEIGHT.........LENGTH......
WIDTH...... WEIGHT, UNLOADED......
WEIGHT, FULL......... SIZE OF WHEELS.........

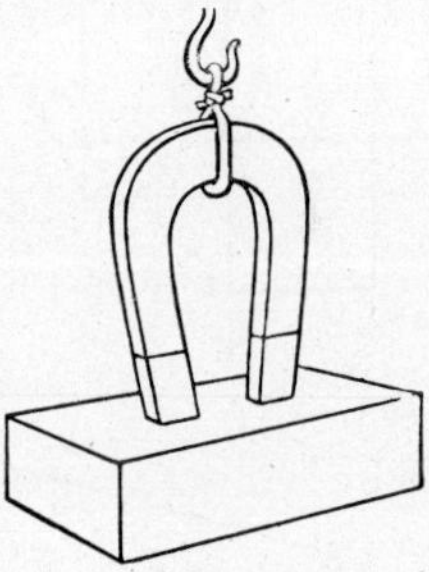

MAGNET HOLDING.........
POUNDS OF IRON

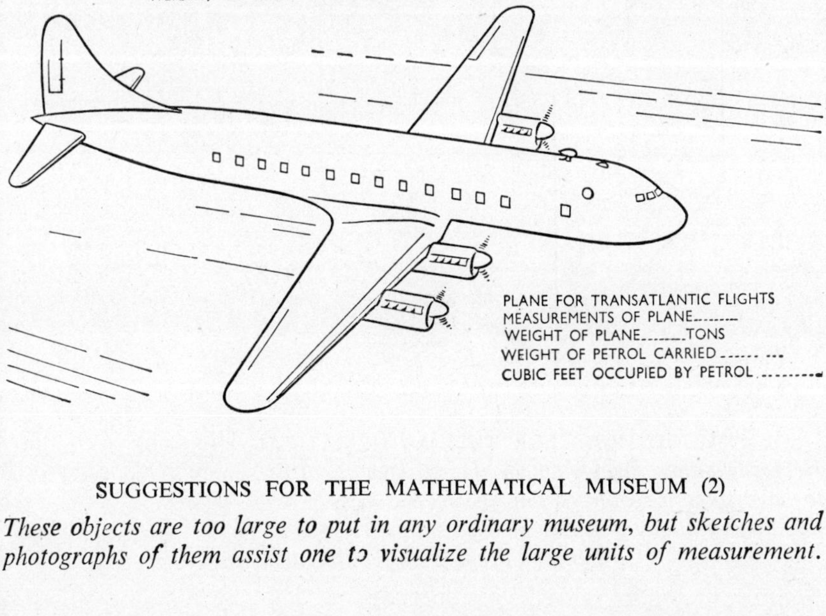

PLANE FOR TRANSATLANTIC FLIGHTS
MEASUREMENTS OF PLANE.........
WEIGHT OF PLANE.........TONS
WEIGHT OF PETROL CARRIED.........
CUBIC FEET OCCUPIED BY PETROL.........

SUGGESTIONS FOR THE MATHEMATICAL MUSEUM (2)

These objects are too large to put in any ordinary museum, but sketches and photographs of them assist one to visualize the large units of measurement.

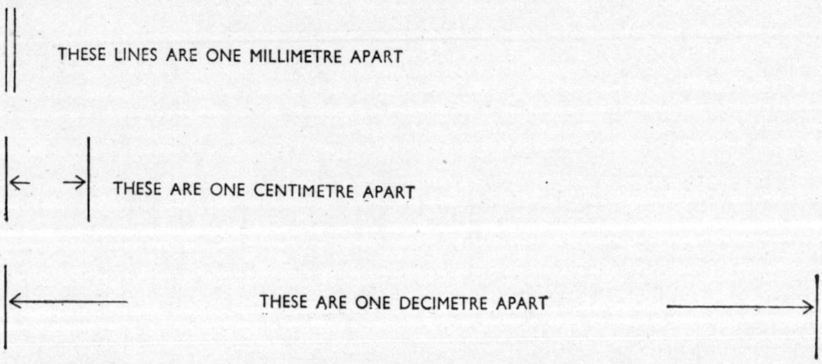
THESE LINES ARE ONE MILLIMETRE APART
THESE ARE ONE CENTIMETRE APART
THESE ARE ONE DECIMETRE APART

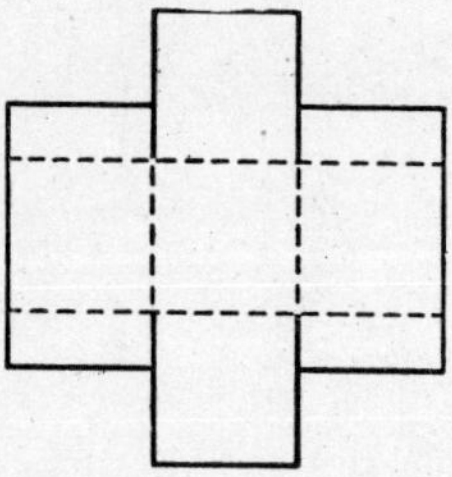

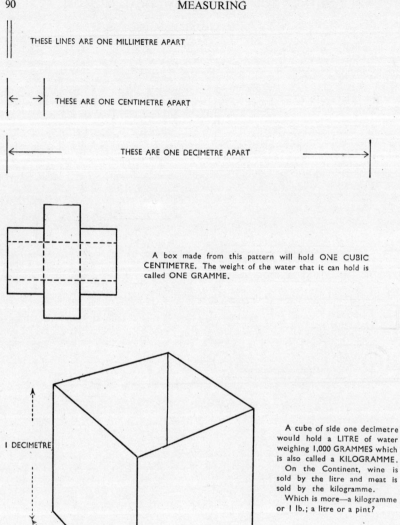

A box made from this pattern will hold ONE CUBIC CENTIMETRE. The weight of the water that it can hold is called ONE GRAMME.

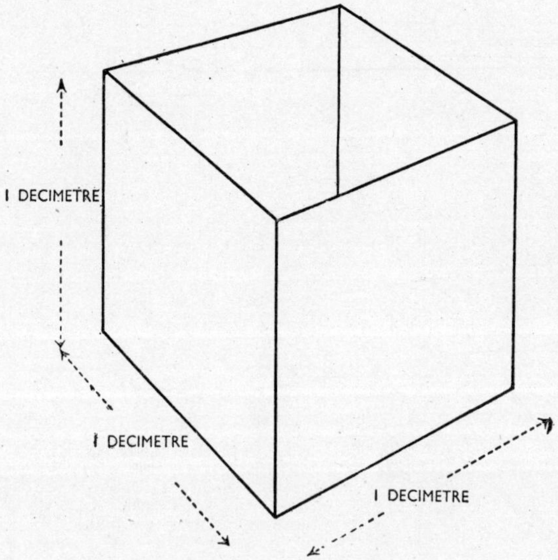
I DECIMETRE
I DECIMETRE
I DECIMETRE

A cube of side one decimetre would hold a LITRE of water weighing 1,000 GRAMMES which is also called a KILOGRAMME.

On the Continent, wine is sold by the litre and meat is sold by the kilogramme.

Which is more—a kilogramme or 1 lb.; a litre or a pint?

SUGGESTIONS FOR THE MATHEMATICAL MUSEUM (3)

Here is another suggestion for the Mathematical Museum. It is a good plan to have something illustrating the metric system. You might have a piece of wood one millimetre square or one centimetre square. You could have anything so that you are able to feel the dimension.

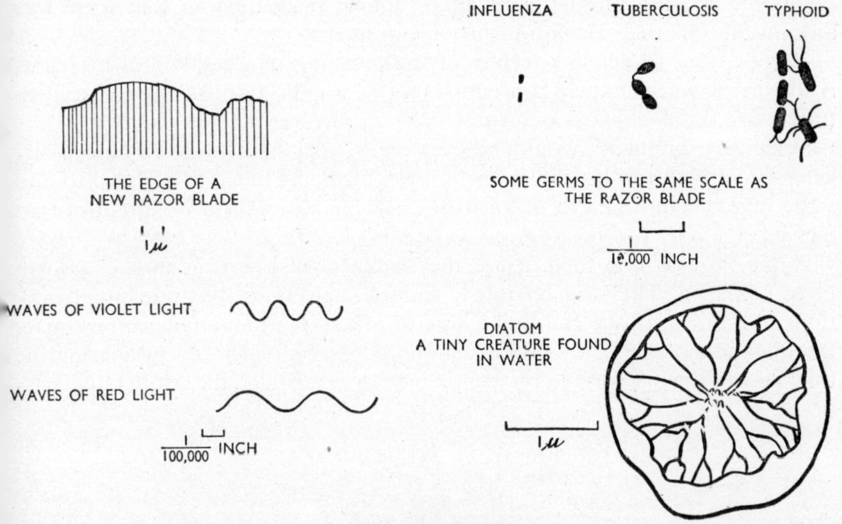

SMALL THINGS

These things are small, but even smaller things exist. An atom is about $\frac{1}{100,000,000}$ *inch in size, and it is made up of parts that are much smaller; perhaps a thousand times smaller. X-rays are a thousand times shorter than light rays. Even shorter waves come from the stars and from atomic bombs.*

1μ *stands for* $\frac{1}{1,000}$ *of a millimetre, which is about* $\frac{1}{25,000}$ *inch.*

and centimetres and kilogrammes and litres and gallons and rods, poles and perches, without ever having seen any of these things.

Some people are able to learn in this way. Some boys and girls are clumsy with their hands but are able to form very clear pictures in their minds. They usually prefer to learn by reading books, rather than by working with their hands and, of course, they should be allowed to learn in the way that suits them.

But for most people it is hard to think about things which one has never seen or had a chance to handle. For them it should be a rule always to get hold of an actual example of the thing being studied. If you are going to study pounds and ounces, have some pound and ounce weights in front of you.

It is a very great help to have a feeling of how large and how heavy things are. It will often save you mistakes. Everybody makes slips. The great thing is to be able to notice when you have gone wrong. For instance, suppose you have to work out the weight of some part of a machine, which is about six inches in size. Suppose you get the answer to be 10 tons. You know you have made a slip somewhere. The answer is far too large.

You can only check your working in this way if you have some idea of what an inch and a ton mean. To a foreigner, accustomed to working in kilogrammes and centimetres, it might not be at all obvious that there was any mistake in the calculation just mentioned.

A good way to get this feeling of the meaning of weights and measures is to start a mathematical museum—that is, a collection of objects to illustrate every kind of measurement.

Some measurements would be quite easy to illustrate—one could easily get a 6-inch nail to illustrate 6 inches, for instance. But one has also to find some object a thousandth of an inch thick, and another a hundredth of an inch thick.

Again, how is one to measure the thickness of a cotton thread or of a piece of paper? They are obviously suitable objects to illustrate small fractions of an inch, if one can find a way of measuring them. One can estimate the thickness of paper by taking a hundred sheets or so and measuring the thickness of the pile formed by them. One can get a rough idea of the thickness

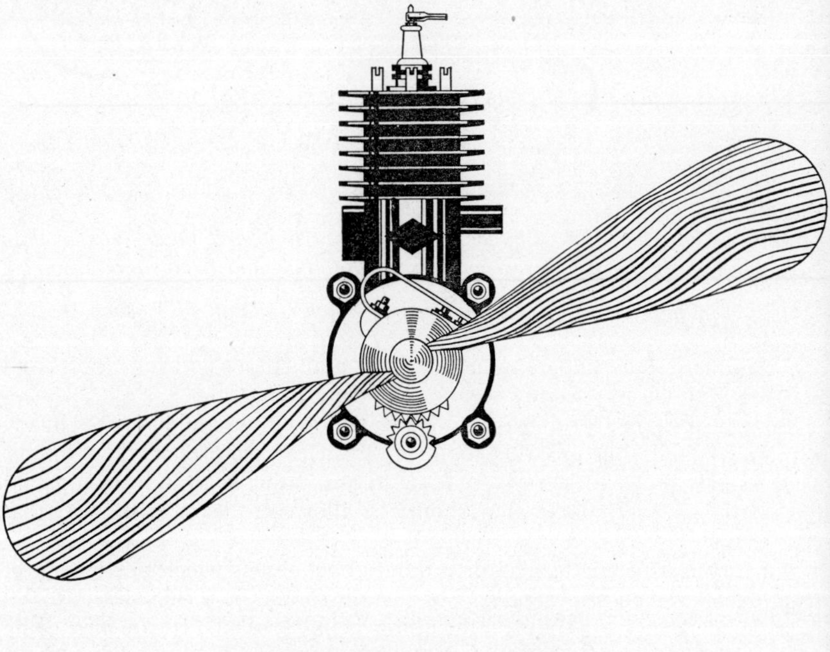

MEASUREMENT AND HOBBIES

Measurement is often required for hobbies. The specification of an Apex petrol engine for model aircraft includes the following:

Type - - - -	*Two cycle, three port rotary valve,* 6 *c.c.*
Bore - - - -	·780 *in. diameter.*
Stroke - - -	13/16 *in.*
Horse-power - -	1/5 *H.P. at* 6,000 *revolutions per minute.*
Minimum Revolutions	700 *per minute.*
Maximum Revolutions	8,000 *per minute with* 11 *in. diameter propeller.*

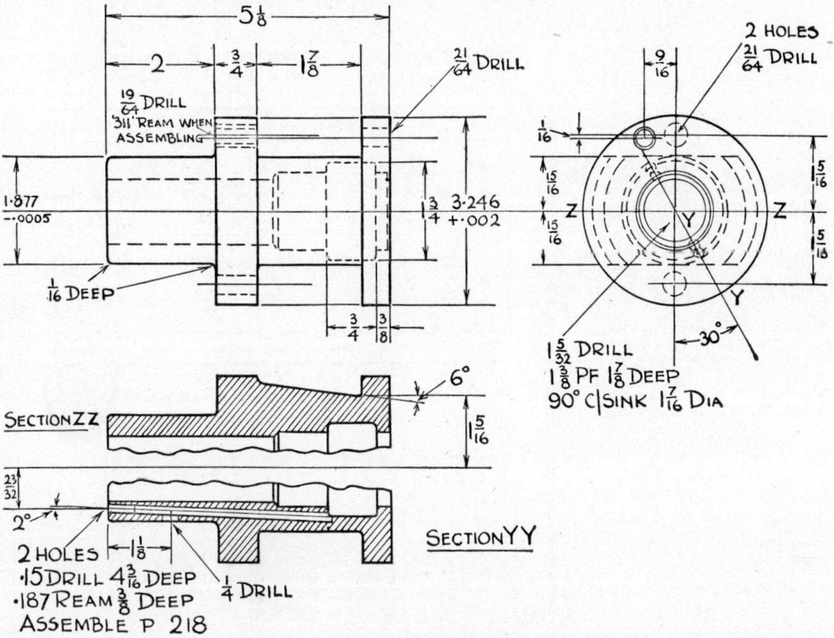

FROM AN ENGINEER'S BLUEPRINT

Fractions, decimals, and geometry as the engineering designer meets them. It is necessary for the designer and draughtsman to calculate the sizes and shapes of things that they have never seen. This is a drawing of part of a machine that never existed. The drawing was made in the course of the design by the research department of a factory. Certain modifications were then thought to be desirable, so this design was scrapped.

of a piece of thread by winding the thread round a ruler, and noticing how many times the thread can be wound to the inch.

Very few people seem to have any clear idea of what an acre is. An acre is rather a large thing to put in a glass case, but there is no reason why the museum should not contain a sketch of some well-known place in your town, with a note of how many acres it covers. It is interesting to ask half a dozen people to guess the size of a field, or a public square, or a block of buildings in acres. One gets the most contradictory answers.

The museum should contain a pint and a gallon measure—preferably home-made. The size of a pint one can get from a milk-bottle. You can also mark the measure in cubic inches. How many cubic inches do you think a pint milk-bottle should contain? Guess first, and then measure it.

Nearly all scientific measurements are made not in inches and feet, but in centimetres or metres. One should, therefore, have a ruler with centimetres, and a standard measure for cubic centimetres. There should be a

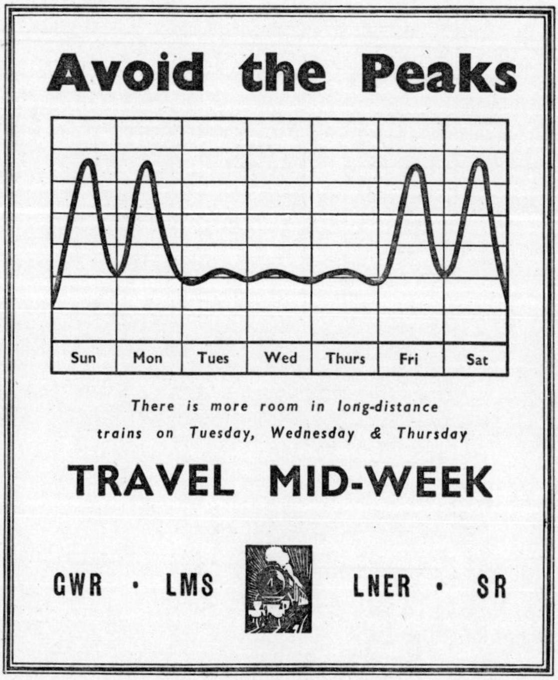

USE OF GRAPHS

Graphs are used when something has to be made very clear. Millions of people read this advertisement and never realized that they were using a mathematical device, the graph.

(*By courtesy of the Railways' Advertising Committee*)

gramme and a kilogramme weight, and a litre measure. How to construct these is shown on page 90.

The meaning of different weights should be illustrated too. They need not be the usual sort of weights that are used with scales, but may be stones, or washers, or odd pieces of scrap iron and brass. You can make a note of the weights of really large objects. Buses have the weight marked on the side —this is required by law; so do railway carriages and railway trucks. Have a look at such things, and make a note of how much each weighs. You can use your own taste in the kind of objects that interest you, but you should try to cover the whole range of weights.

Some suggestions for a mathematical museum are given in the illustrations, but you should not tie yourself down to these. Collect your own illustrations from things that are easily obtainable in your district, or that are of special interest to you.

Exercises

1. What are the measurements of a page of this book?
2. How long are the lines of type on page 80 of this book?
3. *Roughly*, how many square inches does a page occupy?
4. Draw lines $\frac{2}{3}$ foot and $\frac{3}{4}$ foot in length. Which line is the longer? By how much?
5. Draw a line 2·5 inches long and measure its length in inches and fractions of an inch.

6. In the illustration on the right there are three twist drills, a spanner and an engineer's gauge. How thick is each drill? How large are the openings in the two ends of the spanner? What sizes do the slots in the engineer's gauge measure?

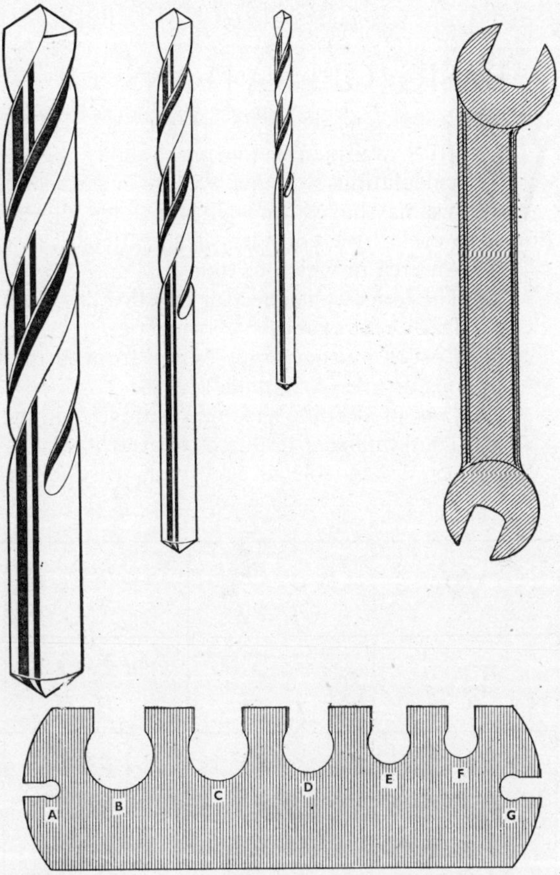

7. How many centimetres are there in an inch?

8. How many times does 1·5 inches go into 6 inches? How many times does it go into 9 inches?

9. Which is the larger, 0·3 inch or 1/5 inch, and by how much?

10. How many times does 0·3 inch go into $2\frac{1}{2}$ inches, and what is left over? Give your answer in decimals and also in fractions.

11. Fifty sheets of cardboard form a wad 3 inches thick. How many hundredths of an inch thick is each sheet? How would this be written as a decimal?

12. If there are two squares, one is three square feet and the other three feet square, which is the larger?

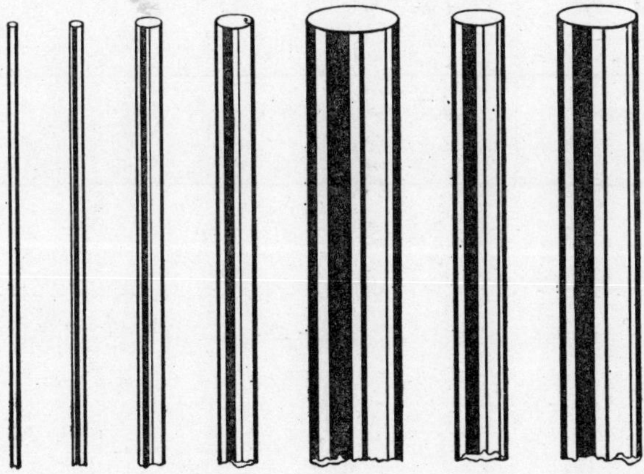

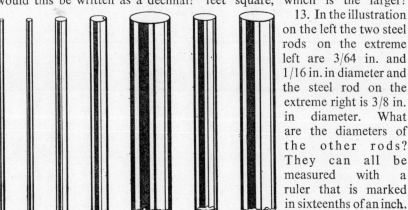

13. In the illustration on the left the two steel rods on the extreme left are 3/64 in. and 1/16 in. in diameter and the steel rod on the extreme right is 3/8 in. in diameter. What are the diameters of the other rods? They can all be measured with a ruler that is marked in sixteenths of an inch.

CHAPTER IV

BASIC OPERATIONS OF ARITHMETIC

WHEN we plan a touring holiday we usually face up to a few calculations whether we are mathematical or not. For example, we may have a fortnight for doing all we want to do, and the intention is to cycle. We consider such matters as:

(1) An area in which to tour.
(2) The longest distance for any one day (Arithmetic).
(3) Daily cost of meals (Arithmetic).
(4) Cost of journey home by rail from furthest point in event of misfortune (Arithmetic).
(5) Cost of sleeping accommodation (Arithmetic).
(6) Total financial resources for the holiday (Arithmetic).

Most people are able to cope with these factors and to succeed in their

DAY	IN	OUT	HOURS WORKED
W	8.0 1.0	12.0 5.0	8
Th	7.5 1.0	12.0 5.5	9
F	8.0 1.0	12.0 5.0	8
S	8.0	12.0	4
M	8.0 1.0	12.0 5.0	8
T	8.0 1.0	12.0 6.0	9

RATE ---------- HOURS WORKED ---------------

WAGES DUE ------------------

planning. Although a good deal of simple arithmetic is involved, it all boils down to adding, subtracting, multiplying, and dividing.

In the same way, indeed, nearly all mathematics consists of these same four kinds of calculation, and a certain amount of skill in knowing when to use which. The drudgery of arithmetical working is cut down today by labour-saving devices, so that the chief problem is to apply common sense to answering the question. "Shall we add or subtract or multiply or divide?" After each operation, the result should be tested to see if it is reasonable.

In the first part of this chapter, we shall consider some problems and decide *how* they should be tackled, without going into the smaller details of how to calculate. This will enable us to learn something of the nature of the mathematical countryside.

Problem A.—A worker is paid by the hour. His time sheet for a certain week is shown on page 96. How many hours will he be paid for?

This requires addition and subtraction.

Problem B.—His rate of pay is 2s. 6d. per hour. What is his wage for the week?

The hours are now transformed into half-crowns, and as there are many we prefer to change them to pounds as far as possible. There are 46 half-crowns: will the number of pounds be more or less than 46?

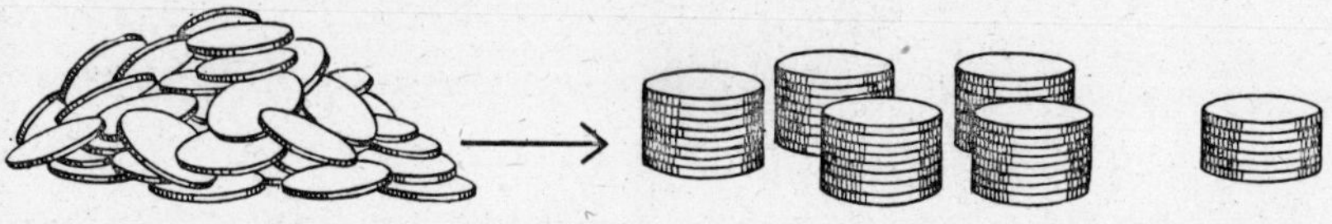

The diagram shows there will be fewer pounds than half-crowns, and it shows that to arrive at the answer we must find how many eights there are in 46, as every eight half-crowns make £1.

This is called division, and is written

$$46 \text{ half-crowns} = £\frac{46}{8} \text{ (or } £46 \div 8)$$

We can answer this quickly if we know that five eights make 40, i.e. if we have learned by heart the multiplication tables of fairly low numbers, or have some tables in writing to which reference can be made.

Division, then, is really multiplication in reverse; a matter of selecting the right item in the multiplication table.

The answer to the problem, obtained by division, is £5 15s. We are satisfied that the answer is reasonable, because we are familiar with this rate of pay giving this kind of weekly wage. The accuracy of the answer can be checked by another method of working which will be seen in the next example.

Problem C.—What are the labour costs to the employer for the week if the worker is assisted by a lad who receives 6d. per hour?

The total labour cost per hour is now 3/-, so we may think of each of our 46 hours as being 3 shillings.

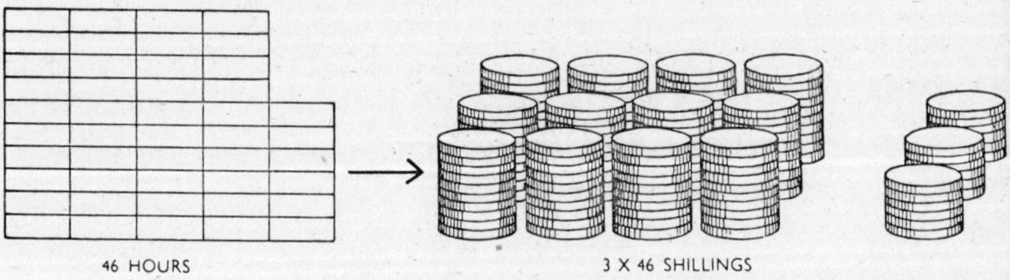

As the number of shillings will be greater than 46, we are clearly doing multiplication.

Again, this money would be more convenient in pounds, and every 20 shillings make £1, so we must find how many twenties there are in the total.

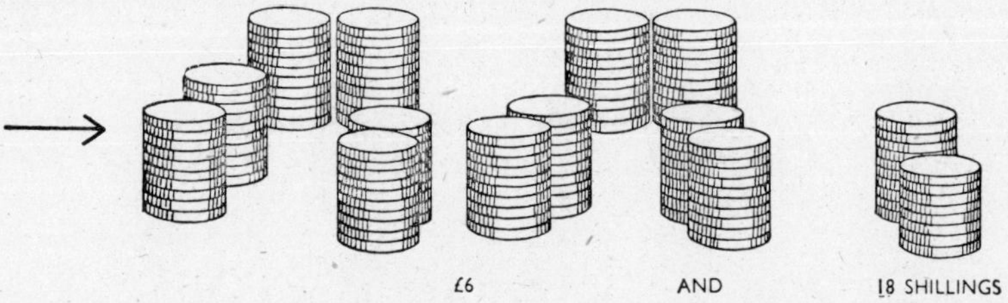

This is division, as in problem B.

The pictures have shown us the way through the arithmetic to the answer. We might very well have used actual counters and coins to find the result by experiment. A great many children would get more fun out of their arithmetic lessons if they were allowed to *do* their sums instead of *work out* their sums.

We have found the answer £6 18s. without much difficulty, although it has involved multiplication and division. Before we have finished this chapter we shall have become wise to a few tricks which by-pass the need for detailed pictures: we shall still keep pictures in our minds but shall not always find it necessary to draw them.

Using the language of arithmetic to interpret the pictures we may write

$$\text{Total labour cost} = 3 \times 46 \text{ shillings}$$
$$= £\frac{3 \times 46}{20}$$

It is quite a good plan to save up the actual working to the end of the task, because it is often easier. In this case, the arithmetic is first multiplication:

$$£\frac{3 \times 46}{20} = £\frac{138}{20}$$

and then division: $£\frac{138}{20} = £6\ 18\text{s.}$

If the answer to B was right, then the answer to C should be $\frac{1}{5}$ as much again, because the 6d. per hour for the lad is $\frac{1}{5}$ of the 2s. 6d. per hour for the man.

$$\frac{1}{5}\times £5\ 15s. = £1\ 3s.$$

This added to £5 15s. gives £6 18s., the answer to C.

Here is a picture of what has been done.

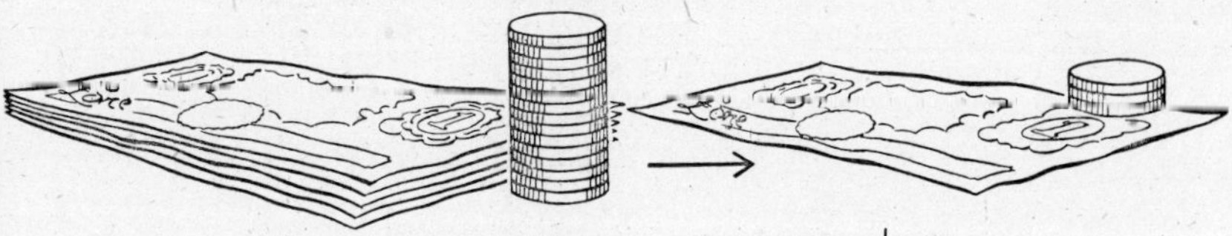

It will be noticed that changing small units to larger units involves division (which makes the resulting number smaller than the original). A good many people get muddled over this becausc they will not condescend even to see the pictures in their mind, let alone draw the kind of sketch that has been used in these examples.

Problem D.—A bus must not be more than 26 ft. long and 7 ft. 6 in. broad, the seats must be at least 2 ft. 2 in. from back to back, and allow 16 in. width for each person. The gangway must be at least 1 ft. wide. Assuming that these regulations give comfort to the passengers, see how many persons can be seated on the top deck of a full-sized double-decker.

The best method is to make a model plan with bits of cut card or paper to represent seats.

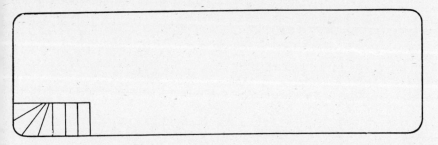

Allow space for a staircase opening 24 in. wide and 5 ft. long.

It is interesting to note how various types of buses fulfil these regulations, and to decide why each designer selects his own solution to the problem.

What is the largest number of seats that can be put along one side?

The arithmetical question is: How many 2 ft. 2 in. lengths are there in 26 ft.? This is an indication of division.

Largest number on one side$=\frac{26 \text{ ft.}}{2 \text{ ft. } 2 \text{ in.}}=\frac{26}{2\frac{1}{6}}$ (using ft.), or $\frac{312}{26}$ (using in.)

$= 12$. (This is neither feet nor inches, but a pure number.)

Problem E.—A car had been standing for some time with the side and tail lamps on. The driver discovered that his lamps gave a very weak glow, showing that the battery was nearly discharged; it proved too weak to provide energy for the petrol pump and the ignition circuits. If only he could start the engine, the dynamo would provide the energy. He went to a nearby electrical shop and bought some dry batteries. How many cells (1·5 volts) did he need to do the work of the car battery (6 volts), and start the engine from the starting handle?

Voltage required = 6 volts
Voltage of dry cell = 1·5 volts

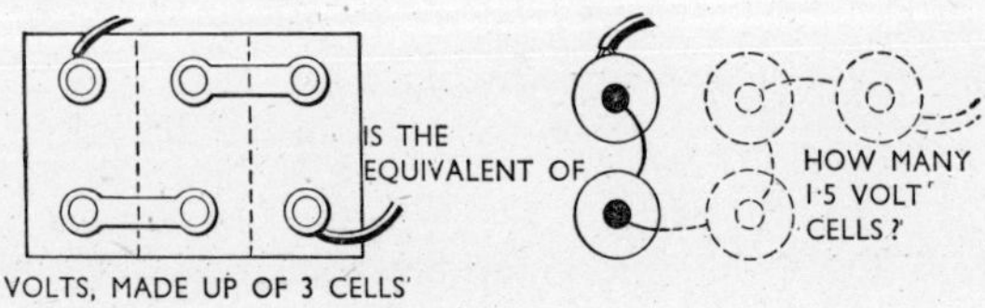

The question simply is: "How many one-and-a-half's are there in 6?" We are so used to dealing with money that we know how many three-halfpences there are in sixpence almost without mental effort: the question requires the same arithmetic.

The process involved is, of course, division.

Number of cells needed = 6 volts ÷ 1·5
= 4

This is extremely simple, but the shop, the elementary science and the arithmetic, together saved an awkward situation for the motorist concerned.

Problem F.—A householder is considering the lighting problem of the kitchen which is lit by two 60-watt lamp bulbs. How would the running costs of a 40-watt fluorescent tube compare with this? (We will suppose that electricity costs 5d. per unit.)

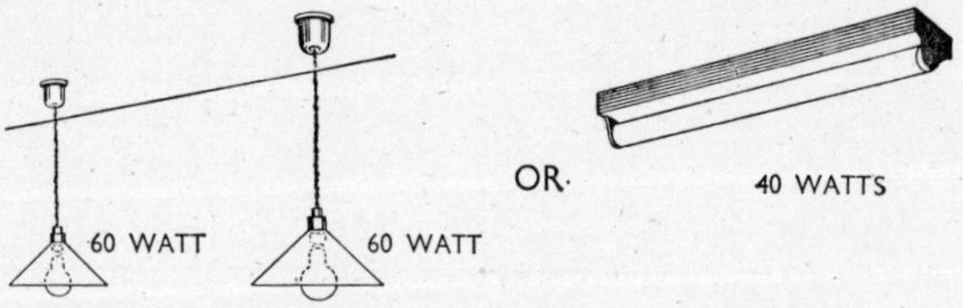

This problem in many a more complex form is one that people really meet. The essence of the question is the comparison of costs for a unit of time, and as electricity is paid for by the kilowatt-hour (or 1,000 watt-hours) one hour is chosen as the unit of time.

1,000 watts used over one hour costs 5d.

Two 60-watt lamps are using 120 watts each hour. As 120 watts are $\frac{120}{1,000}$ of 1,000 watts, the running cost of the two bulbs will be $\frac{120}{1,000}$ of 5d. per hour or $\frac{3}{25}$ of 5d. per hour.

In the same way, 40 watts are $\frac{40}{1,000}$ of 1,000 watts, and the 40-watt tube will cost $\frac{40}{1,000}$ (or $\frac{1}{25}$) of 5d. per hour.

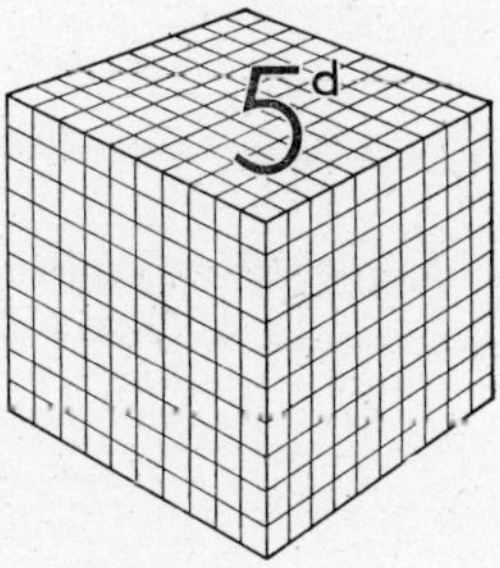

Here is a simple basis for a comparison of costs—the old installation costs $\frac{3}{5}$ penny per hour, while the new would cost $\frac{1}{5}$ penny per hour.

There would be other matters to consider before scrapping the bulb installation, but none more important than this saving of $\frac{2}{5}$ penny per hour, or the reduction of running costs by two-thirds.

Problem G.—Making a roller front to a cupboard.

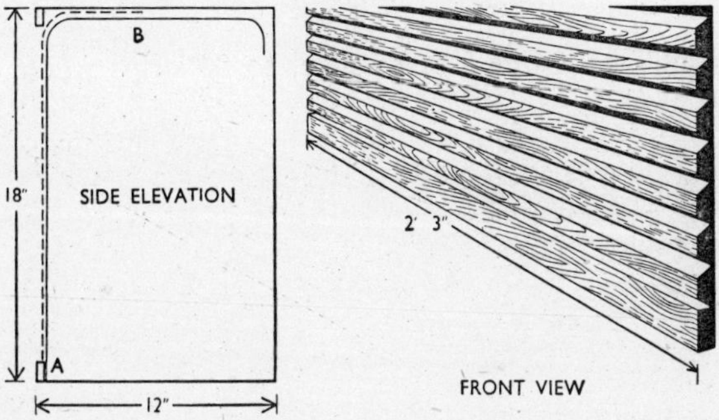

The cupboard front is flexible; it slides upwards and backwards inside the cupboard top, and downwards at the back. It is held in a metal guide at its edges. $\frac{3}{4}$ in. strips of wood are glued to a canvas backing. What length of $\frac{3}{4}$ in. wood is needed for the job?

This is going to involve division, because the question will eventually be asked, how many $\frac{3}{4}$ in. are there in the length A to B?

It will also involve multiplication, because the length of one strip will have to be multiplied by the number of strips.

First stage	Length made up by strips, A—B	= 24 in.
	Width of one strip	= $\frac{3}{4}$ in.
	Number of strips needed	= 24 in. $\div \frac{3}{4}$ in.
Second stage	Length of one strip	= 27 in.
	Total length of strips	= 27 in. $\times$ No. of strips
		= 27 in. $\times \frac{24}{\frac{3}{4}}$
		= 27 in. $\times$ 24 in. $\div \frac{3}{4}$

As timber is usually measured in feet, this will have to be changed to feet, by dividing by 12.

Dividing by $\frac{3}{4}$ is the same as multiplying by $\frac{4}{3}$.

$$\text{Total length required} = 27 \times 24 \times \frac{4}{3} \times \frac{1}{12} = 72 \text{ feet.}$$

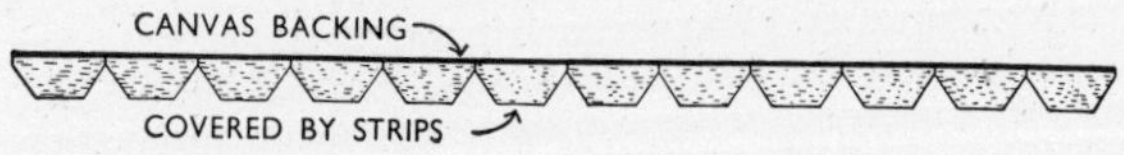

VIEW OF THE SIDE EDGE OF THE ROLLER FRONT

Rough check.—(It is most annoying to buy 72 ft. and to find when commencing work it will only do half the job).

If the strips were 1 in. wide and 2 ft. long,

twelve strips would make one foot of slide, so 24 strips would be needed for the complete slide,

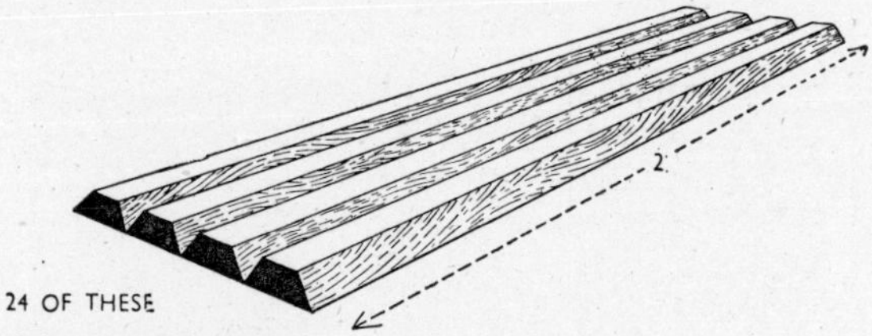

making a total length of 48 ft.

In actual fact they are both longer and narrower. Therefore, well over 48 ft. will be needed.

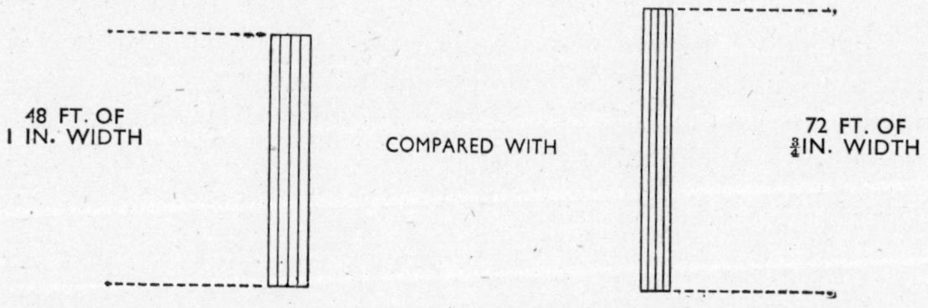

This confirms the answer, 72 ft. as reliable.

As promised, we have concerned ourselves so far only with understanding the nature of the problems and deciding how to set about them. We have met fractions and decimals in some of them and have glossed over the technical matters that arise in dealing with them. The foregoing examples might have been simplified so that fractions and decimals did not appear, but you will probably agree that they represent everyday matters where fractions and decimals insist on appearing more frequently than whole numbers. Before we tackle any details of calculation, we will look at some more everyday mathematical jobs that do not require tricky calculation.

Our aim will be to get the feel of addition, subtraction, multiplication, and division, so that we may *know* when to use which without a lot of bother.

WHEN TO DO WHAT

WHEN TO ADD

We decided to form a chess club, but chess-men were difficult to buy in our village. We had to scrounge the men and make the boards. Now lots of homes have odd chess-men lying about at the bottom of drawers or cupboards. We would collect from our acquaintances what we could and then make up as many sets as possible.

Here is the result of the first few days' efforts.

	Pawns		*Bishops*		*Knights*		*Rooks*		*Kings*		*Queens*	
	W	*B*	*W*	*B*	*W*	*B*	*W*	*B*	*W*	*B*	*W*	*B*
Jones	7	6	2	0	0	1	3	2	1	1	2	1
Smith	8	11	1	2	$\frac{1}{2}$	2	1	2	0	2	1	2
Brown	10	11	3	2	$1\frac{1}{2}$	0	5	1	2	1	1	0
White	14	12	4	4	2	0	2	2	1	0	1	2
Black	13	15	2	4	0	3	3	4	1	2	1	0

The arithmetical process here is addition: we collected together all kinds of pieces (including headless Knights and baseless Knights) and added together the numbers of similar kinds.

WHITE PAWNS

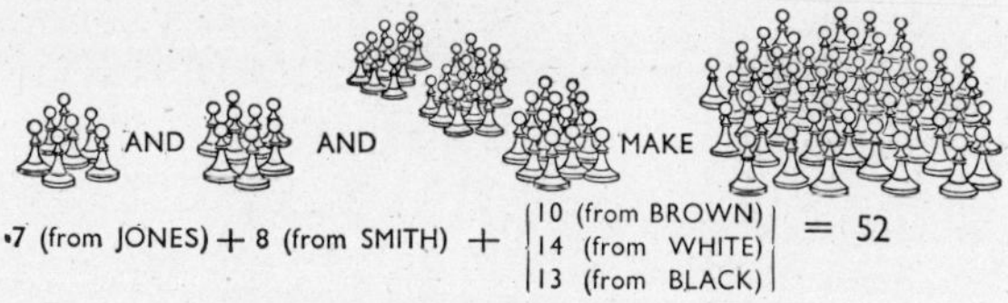
AND
AND
MAKE
7 (from JONES) + 8 (from SMITH) +
10 (from BROWN)
14 (from WHITE)
13 (from BLACK)
= 52

DIVISION BY 8

GIVES 6 SETS AND 4 OVER (or $6\frac{1}{2}$ SETS)

WHEN TO DIVIDE

We then examined the situation to find out what sets we could make up from our collection. Here is a summary of the collection.

		White	*Black*
(8 of each colour)	Pawns	52	55
(2 of each colour)	Rooks	14	11
(2 of each colour)	Knights	4 when repaired	6
(2 of each colour)	Bishops	12	12
(1 of each colour)	Kings	5	6
(1 of each colour)	Queens	6	5

In the brackets, we have put the number required for a complete set. The pawn strength in each colour for a complete set is 8, so every group of 8 contained in the 52 will feed one complete set. How many are there in 52? Here is the arithmetical question which corresponds with the club secretary's action of splitting, sharing or dividing the 52 pawns to make groups of eight.

The question "How many ——s are there in ——?" signifies *division.*

The point to note about division is that it is a splitting up of a particular sort; fair sharing, in fact, where the groups formed are all strictly equal.

WHEN TO SUBTRACT

Smith fancied his skill on the lathe, and undertook to do the turning if the secretary found the timber and told him what men were needed to make up all the scrounged chess-men into sets.

We recast the table appearing at the bottom of page 103 on the lines suggested in the preceding paragraphs and added a column for entering Men needed. This table (shown below) reveals that there are more sets of pawns than any other. If you look into the matter you will find that two complete sets only could be made: the knights were the weak spot.

	Sets in hand		*Sets to be made*	*Men needed*
	White	*Black*		
Pawns ..	$6\frac{1}{2}$	$6\frac{7}{8}$	7	
Rooks ..	7	$5\frac{1}{2}$	7	
Knights ..	2	3	7	
Bishops ..	6	6	7	
Kings ..	5	6	7	
Queens ..	6	5	7	

Now we are finding "what must be added to what we have to obtain what we need?" This is called *subtraction.* The pattern for subtraction is:

Suppose that the target is 8
and that we have 4 already.
We therefore need 8 – 4 more.

See if you can complete the end column *Men needed.*

WHEN TO MULTIPLY

Even then Smith could not start work. We had to buy the wood. We were going to use 1 in. × 1 in. hard wood for the turning, and reckoned on needing an average length of $2\frac{1}{2}$ in. per man. What length would be needed altogether to make up 7 complete sets?

How many men were needed (of all the various ranks)? As each was the equivalent of $2\frac{1}{2}$ in. of wood we needed 36 pieces (Do you agree?) each of $2\frac{1}{2}$ in. length.

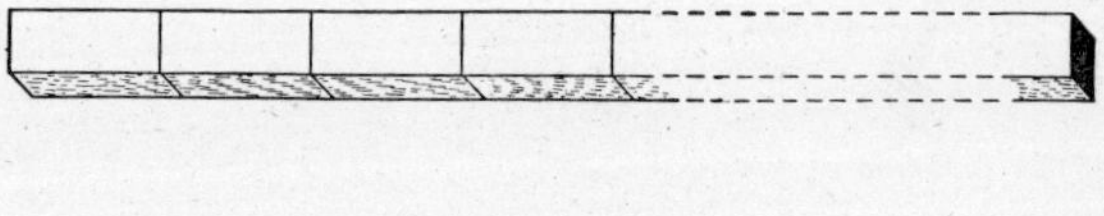

The total length we needed was made up of 36 *equal-sized* bits, and was $36 \times 2\frac{1}{2}$ in.

You can check this process, called multiplication, by doing a scale drawing to show inches.

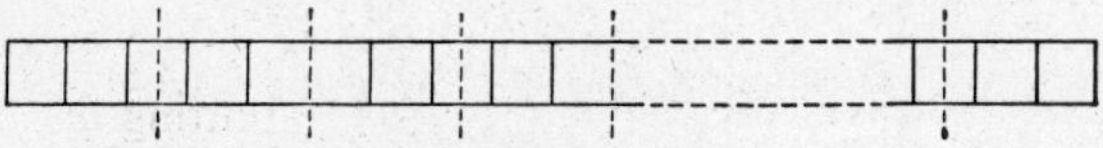

36 lengths of $2\frac{1}{2}$"

There are 36 2-in. strips making	72 in.
and 36 $\frac{1}{2}$-in. strips making	18 in.
=	90 in.

Again, the wood must be paid for at the rate of $1\frac{1}{2}$d. per inch. This again will involve *multiplication*, because we are putting together a lot of equal-sized numbers—three-halfpences in this case.

No doubt the cost will be shared equally (divided) by the members of the chess club, and that will mean a *division* of the cost by the number of members.

EXAMPLES OF ADDITION

Collecting together different quantities into one pool.

(1) Reckoning up the weekly income for the family.

(2) Reckoning up the family's weekly expenditure on necessities.

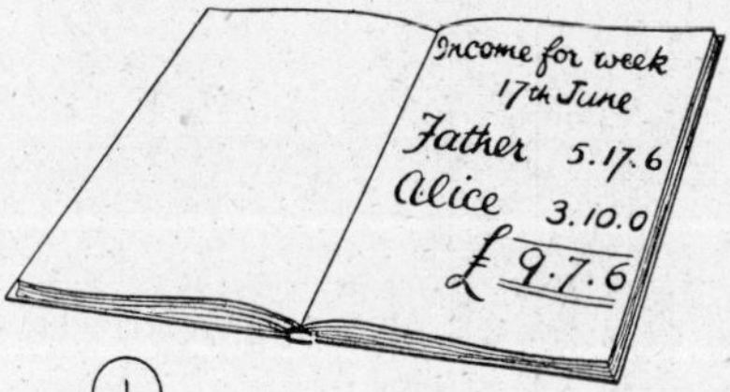

(1)

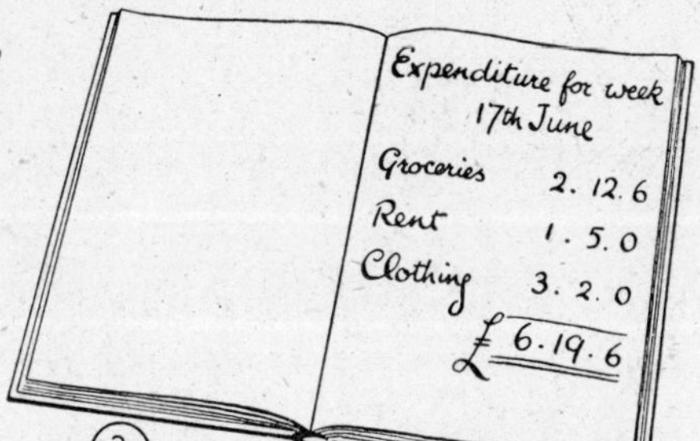

(2)

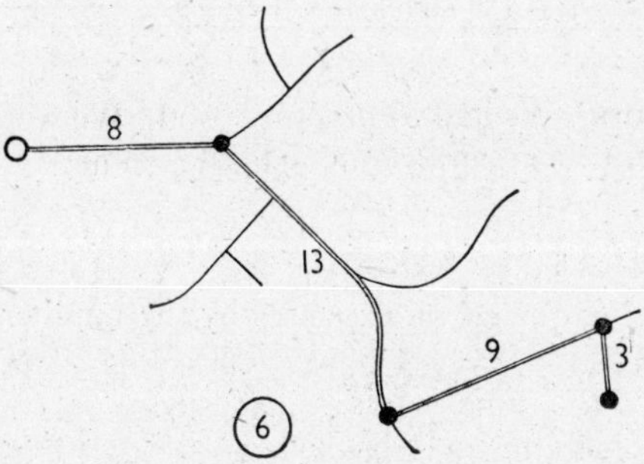

(6)

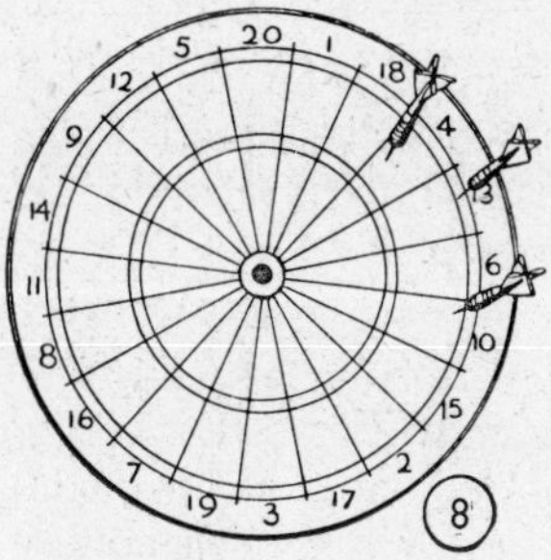

(8)

(3) Finding how much boundary fencing is needed for an awkward-shaped plot.
(4) Finding the total load carried by the mains leads to electrical equipment of various kinds in parallel.
(5) Scoring in bridge, cricket, table-tennis (for change of service).
(6) Estimating from the map the distance involved on a certain journey.
(7) Finding the total resistance in a series circuit of several conductors.
(8) Scoring at darts (the total of the player's three arrows—especially the poor player who is never sure of getting what he aims for).

EXAMPLES OF SUBTRACTION

(1) Estimating change for your silver coin on the bus.
(2) Calculating from the milestone how much further you have to go.
(3) Finding what will be left on the roll when a certain length has been measured and cut off.
(4) Striking the balance on a balance-sheet.

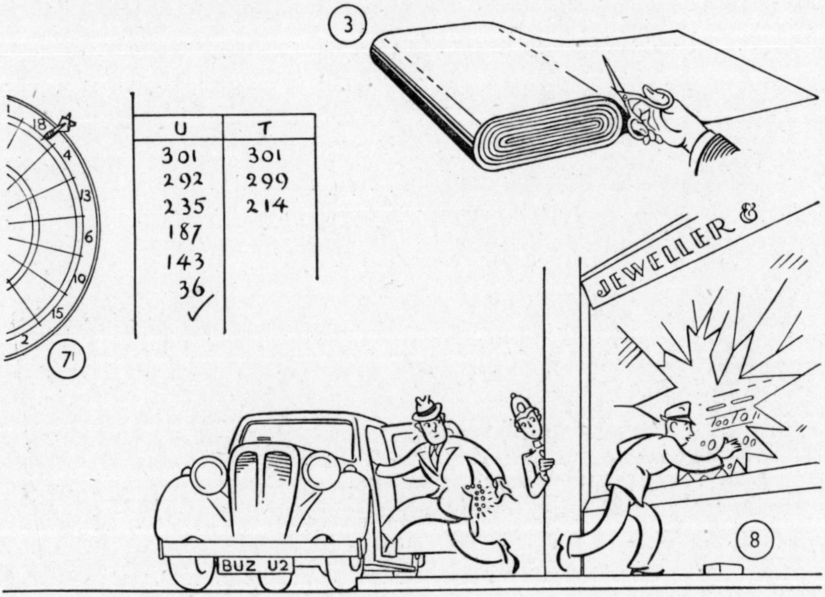

(5) Finding a rise in temperature.
(6) Finding the load carried by a lorry.
(7) Scoring at darts (chalking up the new score after each player).
(8) Robbery.

EXAMPLES OF MULTIPLICATION

(1) Buying for one's friends (multiplying one's own expenses by the number of friends).
(2) Working out costs for quantities of the same goods.
    (a) Weekly expenditure on cigarettes at 4 packets a week, costing 3s. 4d. each.

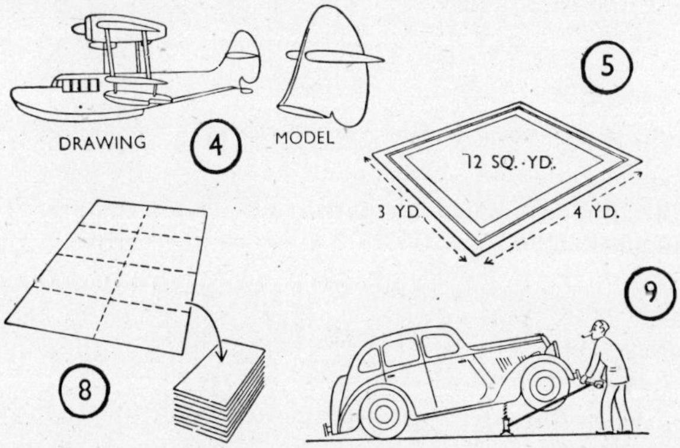

(b) Cost of a number of yards of carpet at 25s. per yard. ? ft. of wood at ? per ft.

(3) Distance covered in a given time at a given speed.

(4) Making the parts of a model from a reduced scale drawing.

(5) Working out areas and volumes from the linear dimensions.

(6) Finding the weight of a body, given its volume and density.

(7) Finding the circumferences of circles, and the perimeters of regular polygons (equilateral triangles, squares, pentagons, etc.).

(8) Breaking down (reducing) larger units into smaller ones (pounds to shillings, hundredweights to pounds, years to days, degrees to minutes).

(9) Machines giving mechanical advantage.

EXAMPLES OF DIVISION

(1) Sharing a bill equally among a number of people.
- (a) Thieves dividing the spoils (equally).
- (b) Mother sharing the chocolates equally among the children.

(2) Finding the rate of cost when given the cost of a certain quantity.

(3) Finding the average speed, given the distance covered in a certain time.

(4) Making a scale drawing on a reduced scale.

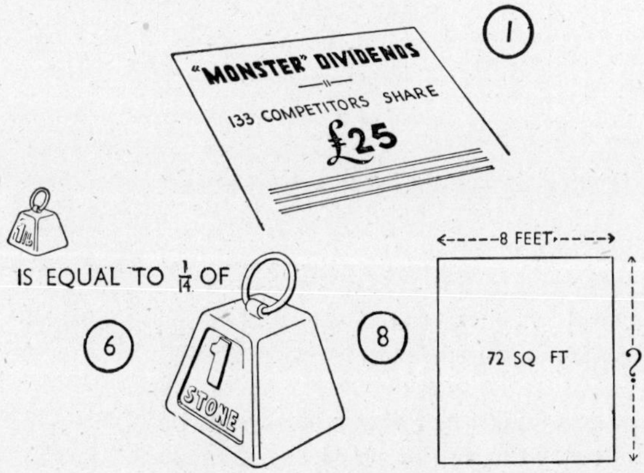

(5) Calculating the size of one object when the size of a given number of these objects is a known amount.
(6) Converting (reducing) a given quantity stated in small units to larger units (pence to shillings, ounces to pounds, etc.).
(7) Finding the length of material of given cross-sectional area to make up a known volume.
(8) Finding the dimensions of a figure from its known area and another known dimension.
(9) Finding how many times one quantity is contained in another of similar kind.

Our examples show that you rarely meet addition or subtraction or multiplication or division alone: one process is nearly always tied to another. We are going to assume that you are able to deal with each of these four processes as they apply to simple numbers. If you are not able to, the best thing for you to do at this stage is to give yourself plenty of practice on sums arising from such matters as those that have just been listed under the four separate headings, and refresh your memory in the ways suggested at the end of this chapter (Pages 139 and 140).

The next thing we shall dwell on is the various ways of relating quantities to one another. These relationships carry us forward towards the more fascinating and the more useful aspects of mathematics.

SAVING AND SPENDING

Weekly wages depend upon the amount of work done (measured by time or piece).

A. There may be a plan to save a certain fixed sum of money each week, say, 10/-.

B. Or it may be decided to save always $\frac{1}{8}$ of the weekly earnings.

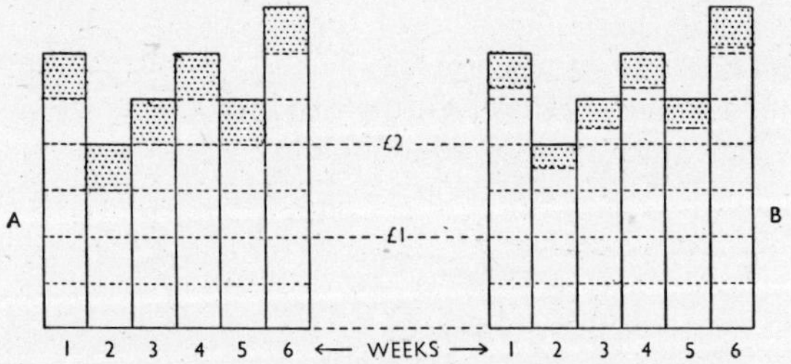

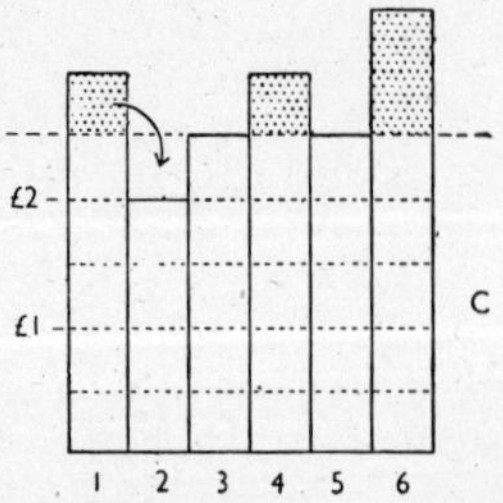

C. Or, again, the decision could be on a fixed weekly expenditure, regardless of income, say, £2 10s.

Which of these should be chosen to be sure of having saved £4 in eight weeks?

Which plan would be best for ensuring that the saving will *always* leave something to meet additional expenses?

Over any period of weeks the total savings would be

A. 10/- multiplied by the number of weeks.

B. The sum of the weekly earning divided by 8.
C. The difference between gross earnings and £2 10s. multiplied by the number of weeks.

In this problem we are free to choose a scheme of relating savings to earnings. In dealing with nature we are often confronted by "laws" relating numbers, leaving no choice.

I. Ohm found out that whatever current of electricity is passing through a conductor, there is a fixed relationship between the pressure (usually known as voltage) and the rate of flow of the current (usually measured in amperes). His experiments showed that:

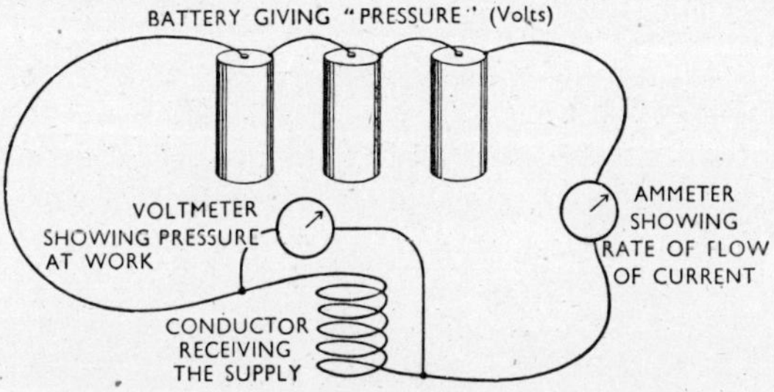

$$\frac{\text{Volts}}{\text{Amps.}} = \text{a constant number for the conductor.}$$

For example, if in one experiment:

E.m.f. (Pressure) = 12 volts
Current = 3 amps.

$$\text{giving } \frac{\text{Volts}}{\text{Amps.}} = \frac{12}{3} = 4,$$

he knew that for a current of 2 amps. he would need to apply a pressure of 8 volts to the conductor

$$\text{because } \frac{\text{Volts}}{2} = 4.$$

This relationship between two numbers is called ratio. Ohm's law, then, states that

the ratio of e.m.f. to current for any conductor is constant.

II. On the other hand, the law relating one age to another states that the difference between the ages is always 3 years.

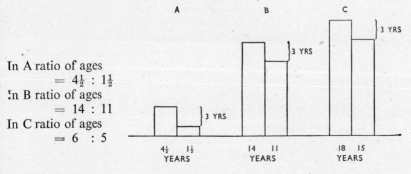

In A ratio of ages
$= 4\frac{1}{2} : 1\frac{1}{2}$
In B ratio of ages
$= 14 : 11$
In C ratio of ages
$= 6 : 5$

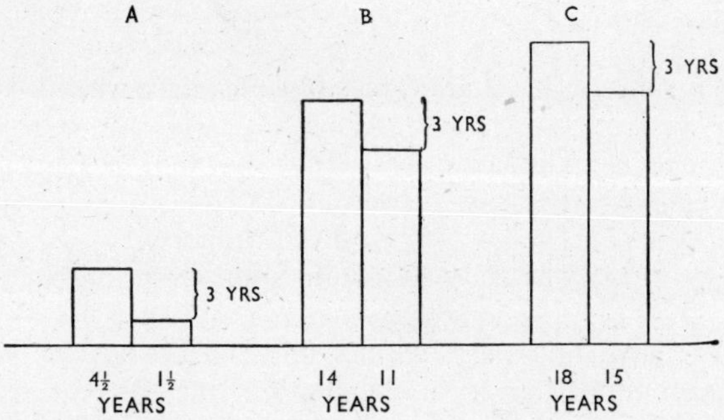

In this case, the relationship of ratio conveys no information because it is not constant.

III. Again, when an amount of gas is kept at the same temperature, its volume and pressure are related by yet a different arithmetical law:

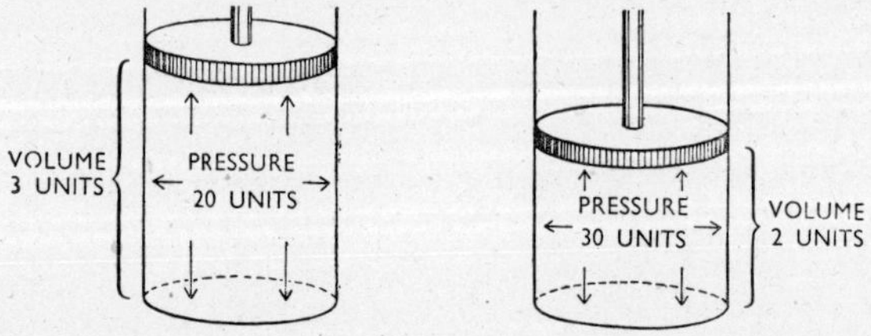

This law may be stated thus:

The product of pressure and volume of a gas is constant while the temperature remains constant.

IV. A fourth way in which quantities may be related is shown by the ellipse.

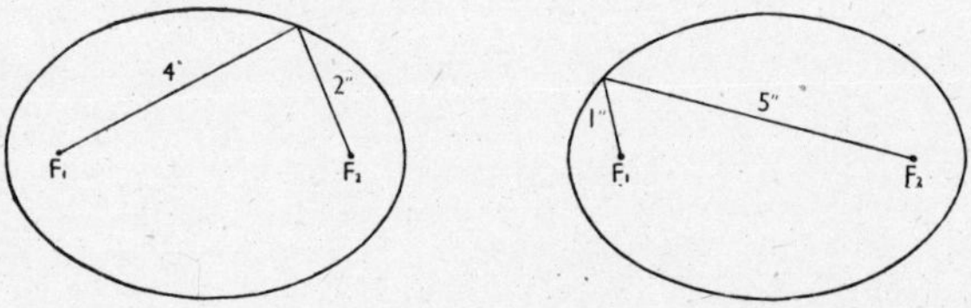

The sum of the distances of any point on the ellipse from the two foci is constant.

This law is used in drawing ellipses—you may try it for yourself by fixing two pins to act as foci and putting a loop of thread over them. The pencil point is then moved round with the thread always held taut.

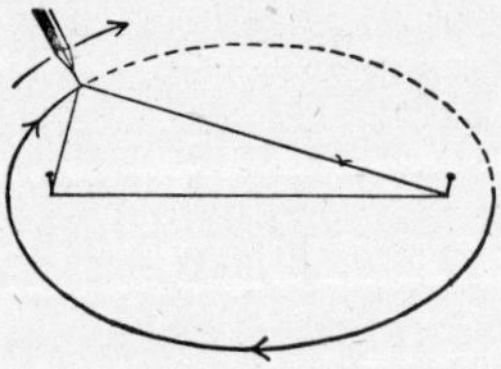

To sum up, there are four simple laws by which numbers may be related.

(1) The law of constant ratio
(2) The law of constant difference
(3) The law of constant product
(4) The law of constant sum

We shall find these relationships occurring over and over again, as we bring our mathematical skill to bear on different problems. There will be other relationships, too, but they will all be built up on the same basic operations known as the four rules.

RATIO : THE ELASTIC MEASURE

A machine requires an effort of 1 lb. to overcome a load of 2 lb. What effort is required for a load of 25 lb.?

We shall expect 4 lb. to overcome 8 lb., and $\frac{1}{2}$ lb. to overcome 1 lb.

In other words effort and load are inseparably related to each other: what happens to one (doubling, halving, etc.) must happen to the other. Mathematically, we say that the load is *directly proportional* to the effort (and vice versa). We can think of them as two parts of the same piece of elastic.

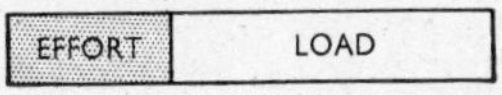

Ratio of effort to load.

We will call the piece of elastic the ratio of effort to load.

Stretching it will not alter the fact that the load end is twice as long as the effort end.

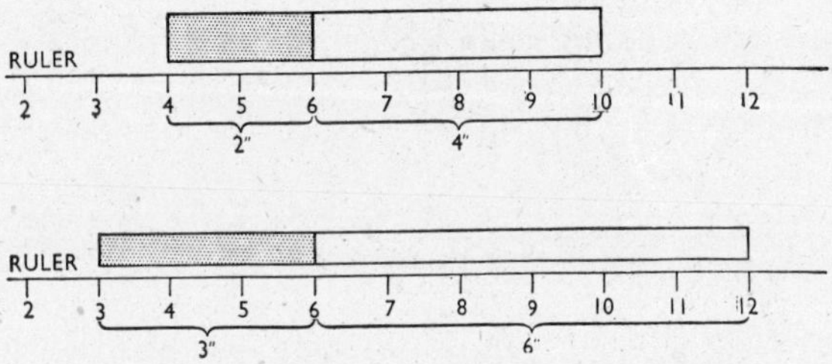

As it always tells the same story, we may use it as a kind of measure for finding what effort is required for a particular load. We were asked what effort would raise a load of 25 lb., so we stretch the elastic measure over a scale until the load end covers 25 divisions. It does not matter in the least what the units on the scale are, provided they are equal units. We may use a ruler marked in eighths of an inch or quarters of an inch, or centimetres, or millimetres, or even a chain measure for that matter.

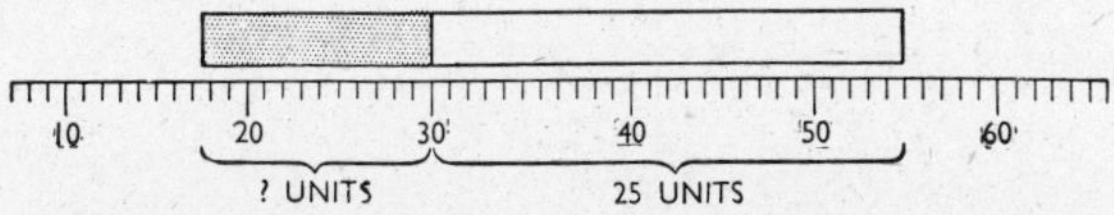

We then read off the effort part of the measure against the scale and get the answer, $12\frac{1}{2}$ lb.

The arithmetic behind this is the use of the ratio 1 : 2, or $\frac{1}{2}$, to state the relationship between effort and load for this machine.

Effort $\propto$ Load ($\propto$ means is proportional to)

This is a general statement applying to *all* machines (neglecting friction) and the ratio tells us *exactly* how the two are related.

Effort $= \frac{1}{2} \times$ Load

The same instrument (the ratio) can be used for finding what *load* any particular effort, say 5 lb., will raise.

$$\text{Load} \propto \text{Effort},$$

or, in the case of our particular machine,

$$\text{Load} = \frac{2}{1}\times\text{Effort}$$

$$\therefore \text{ load raised by 5-lb. effort} = \frac{2}{1}\times 5$$
$$= 10 \text{ lb.}$$

It is true that intelligence is required to determine which way round the ratio should be used, but intelligence is a surer guide than blind mechanical methods. We can be sure of getting the ratio the right way round if we ask ourselves whether we should be making the answer greater or less than the number we are operating on: $\frac{2}{1}$ is an *increasing* operator, while $\frac{1}{2}$ is a *decreasing* operator.

Man has invented an immense number of machines to help him to use his own puny efforts to overcome large forces. You have watched the man lifting a tree-trunk by hauling in an endless chain, you have watched the navvy lifting cobble stones by means of a crow-bar. The idea is quite simple, and you will soon understand it if you do a few simple home-made experiments with a lever. Any strong rod or bar (such as a long poker), will do.

First find its point of balance or fulcrum, and mark it. Then mark off (with chalk) equal intervals of distance from this point towards both ends of the rod (inches, or half-inches, or centimetres will do).

Now find two weights, one exactly twice as heavy as the other (grocery packages usually go by weight) which can be suspended by string from the lever. Put one of them on a chalk mark and adjust the position of the other until the lever is in equilibrium.

Calculate the two distances and write them down.

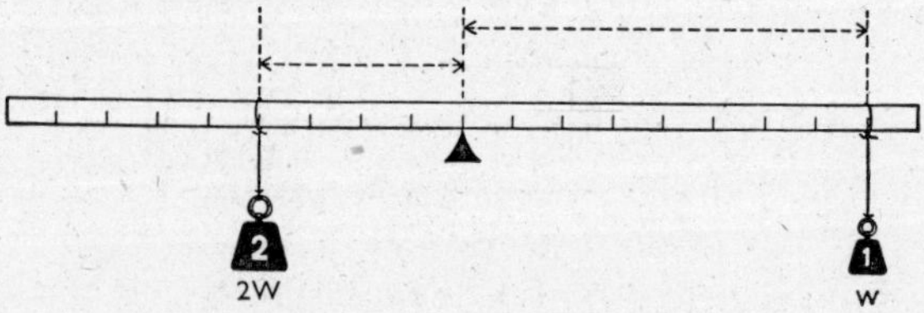

Repeat the experiment for different distances and put your results in the form of a table. You should get a list similar to this.

	1	2	3	4
Distance of W from fulcrum	4 units	10 units	6 units	8 units
Distance of 2W from fulcrum	2 units	5 units	3 units	4 units

You can see the connection between the distances of the weights from the fulcrum. W is always twice as far away as $2W$. We call this relationship between two similar quantities a ratio, and may say that the ratio of the distance of W from the fulcrum to distance of $2W$ from the fulcrum is 2 to 1 $\left(\text{or } 2:1, \text{ or } \frac{2}{1}\right)$.

Suppose you repeat your experiment using two weights of which one is three times as great as the other (ratio of weights = 3 : 1). This time your list of results should show that their distances from the fulcrum are governed by the ratio 1 : 3.

Therefore, when ratio of weights = 3 : 1,
ratio of their distances = 1 : 3.

We are then tempted to generalize thus:

$$\text{Ratio of weights} = \frac{1}{\text{Ratio of distances}}$$

$$\text{i.e.,} \quad \frac{\text{Weight A}}{\text{Weight B}} = \frac{\text{Distance of B}}{\text{Distance of A}}$$

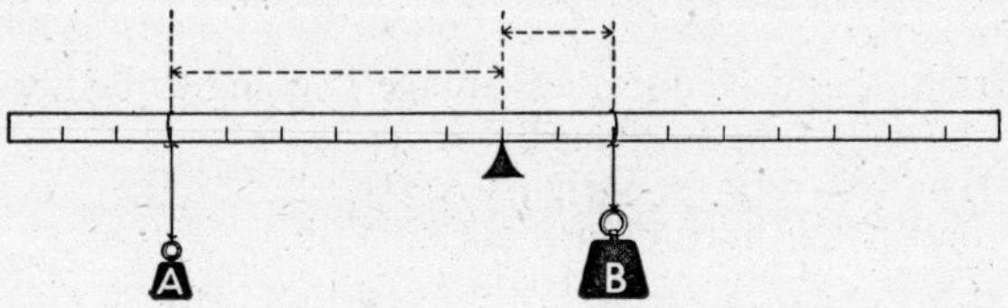

For example, you would expect equilibrium from a 9-lb. weight and a 12-lb. weight (ratio 3 : 4) to be obtained when their distances from the fulcrum are 16 inches and 12 inches respectively (ratio 4 : 3).

If ratio of weights = 3 : 4, then ratio of distances (respectively) = 4 : 3.

Before you leave these experiments, test the validity of this law in as great a variety of ways as you can. You have learnt some science which calls in mathematics to help it express itself. You will discover that the mathematical statement above is the law for all levers in which the weight of the rod itself can be ignored.

The scientist talks of the *mechanical advantage* of his machines and means *the ratio of load to effort* (the two opposing forces). The mechanical advantage of a lever is decided by the distance from the fulcrum of the effort and the load, and the ratio of these two is a factor in the design of any lever machine.

For example, the butcher's steelyard enables him to use tiny weights to counterbalance large ones. You can make a steelyard for weighing up to 7 lb. for yourself.

A long metal rod is pivoted near one end. The weight of the arm on the right is counterbalanced by an iron weight on the left.

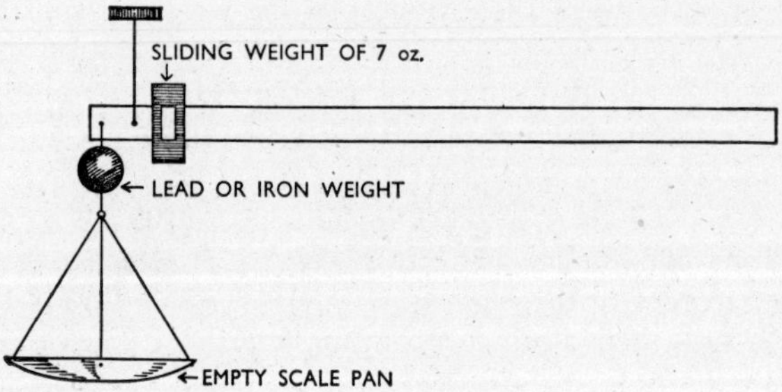

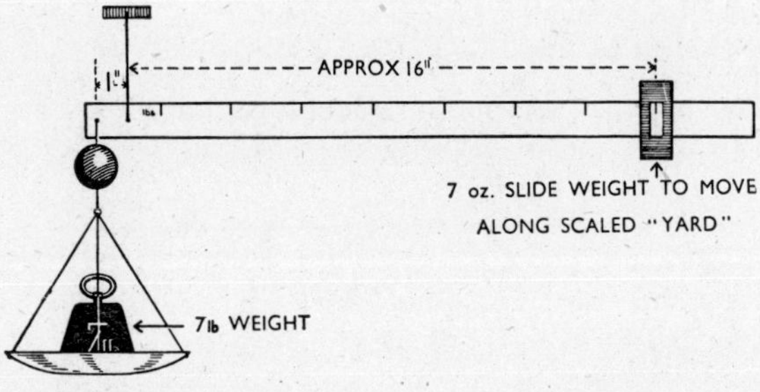

In our diagram, the mechanical advantage is going to be about 16 : 1 for an effort near the end of the steelyard.

That is, ratio of weights = 16 : 1
and if the maximum load is 7 lb.

$$\text{the maximum effort is } \frac{1}{16} \times 7 \text{ lb.} = 7 \text{ oz.}$$

If the slide weighs about 7 oz. and is adjusted to balance the empty pan when it is near the fulcrum, the zero position and the 7 lb. position can be marked. A scale is then marked in 7 equal divisions for pounds and each division into 16 smaller ones for ounces.

Nearly all weighing machines use this idea. The weighbridge for weighing lorries, for example, builds up a big ratio of mechanical advantage by using a train of levers.

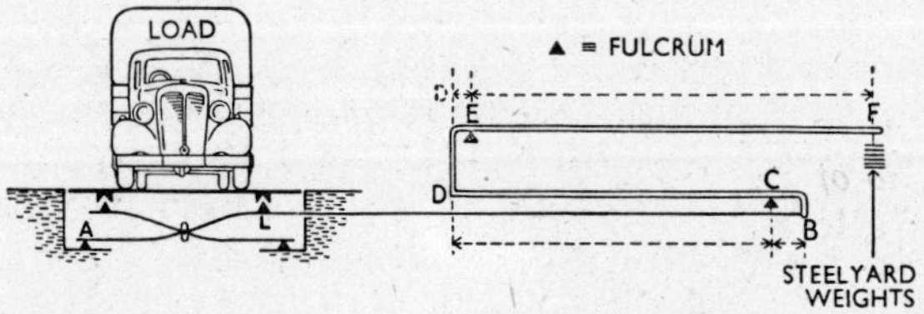

Mechanical advantage of AB = 3 : 1 (because AB is 3 times AL)
Mechanical advantage of BD = 10 : 1 (because DC is 10 times BC)
Mechanical advantage of DF = 20 : 1 (because FE is 20 times DE)

$$\therefore \text{ Mechanical advantage of weighbridge } = 3 \times 10 \times 20 : 1$$
$$= 600 : 1$$

and the steelyard weights are $\frac{1}{600}$ of the load weights, i.e., if the load is one hundredweight there will be $\frac{1}{600}$ cwt., marked 1 cwt., to counter balance it at F.

Ratio plays such a prominent part in mathematics that it will repay us to dwell on the topic for a while.

You wish to add a seconds hand to the dial of your home-made electric clock. What arrangement of cogwheels is needed?

As the second hand should turn clockwise we must have an odd number of wheels carrying transmission from the spindle bearing the minute hand to the new hand. For every revolution of the minute hand, the second hand makes 60 revolutions.

Ratio of speeds of revolution of minute hand to second hand = 1 : 60.

∴ Gear ratio linking them between two points of transmission = 60 : 1.

The large wheel *A* on the minute spindle is in mesh with a small wheel *b*.

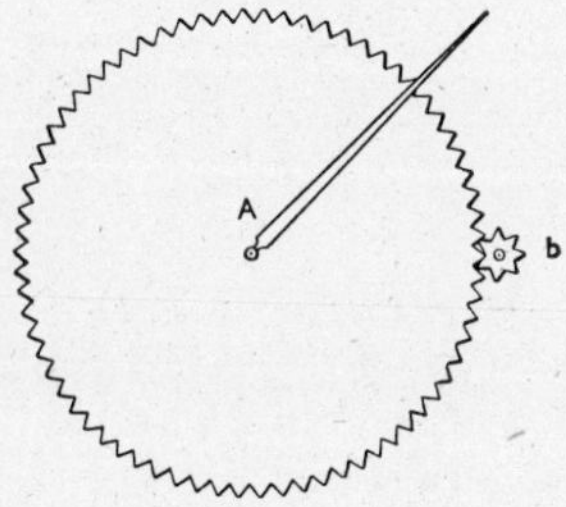

If there are 70 teeth on *A* and 7 on *b*, their gear ratio will be 10 : 1 (i.e., *A* will make one revolution while *b* makes 10).

Now *b* is carried on a spindle which also carries a large wheel *B*.

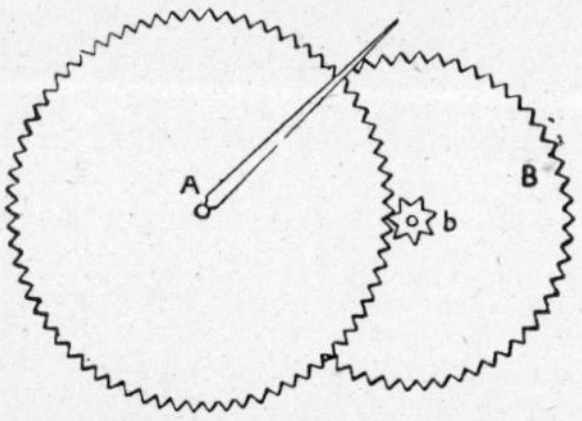

While *b* makes one turn, so will *B*.

B is in mesh with a small wheel *c* on the second-hand spindle.

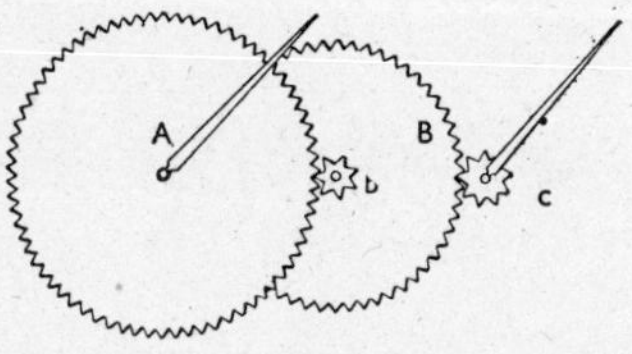

If B carries 54 teeth and c carries 9, their gear ratio is 6 : 1.

While A makes one revolution b will make 10, and while bB makes 10 revolutions c will make 60 revolutions.

What alternative gear ratios $A : b$, $B : c$ can you suggest for the same purpose?

DERAILLEUR GEARS ON A CYCLE

The principle of the gearbox is shown in a simple form on a cycle carrying derailleur gears.

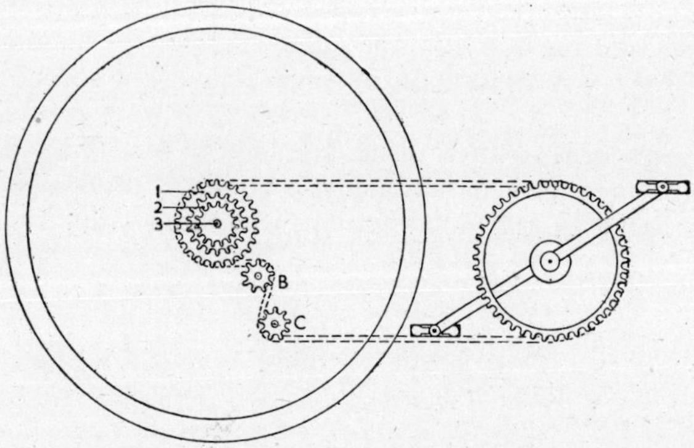

The gear ratio on any gear can be found by counting the revolutions of the rear wheel to one revolution of the crank wheel.

Then, count the number of teeth on each of these two wheels over which the chain runs. B and C may be disregarded as they are only introduced to guide the chain on to the selected gear and take up the slack in the chain. On a cycle that was examined the teeth ratio was 45 : 18, i.e., 5 to 2, for middle gear. On top it was 45 : 15, i.e., 3 : 1, and on bottom it was 45 : 25, i.e., 9 : 5.

The road wheel was marked $26 \times 1\frac{1}{4}$: this means that its diameter was 26 in. The circumference was consequently approximately 81 inches.

MORE FORCE TO OVERCOME
LOW GEAR
LOW SPEED

LITTLE OR NO FORCE TO OVERCOME
HIGH GEAR
GREAT SPEED

MAKING THE BEST USE OF GEARS

∴ Distance travelled for one revolution of pedals on middle gear

$$= 81 \text{ in.} \times \frac{5}{2}$$
$$= \frac{405}{2} \times \frac{1}{12} \text{ ft.}$$
$$= 17 \text{ ft. approximately.}$$

It will be seen from these results that the gear selection causes the cyclist to cover less ground per pedal revolution when he is climbing and has greater forces to overcome.

HANDLING FRACTIONS

We must now look into some of the techniques for arithmetical operations. It has been assumed that you know only how to add, subtract, multiply and divide whole numbers. In playing games like darts, cribbage, bridge, cricket, golf, and table-tennis a large amount of adding and subtracting is being done all the time. Travelling, shopping, give rise to multiplication and division of a fairly simple kind.

(i) Lorries carrying materials like sand, granite and soil are usually loaded and then put on a weighbridge so that buyer and seller can know what amount of material changes hands. A lorry, therefore, must bear a statement of its tare weight, i.e., unloaded.

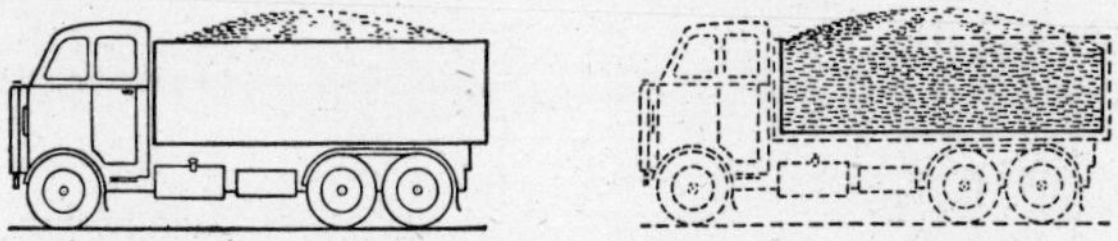

Suppose (1) Weight of lorry and load = 5 tons $13\frac{5}{8}$ cwt.
(2) Tare weight of lorry = 2 tons $5\frac{1}{4}$ cwt.
Therefore weight of load = 5 tons $13\frac{5}{8}$ cwt. – 2 tons $5\frac{1}{4}$ cwt.

We will concern ourselves with the fractional parts of the hundredweight, the "little blighters" we met in Chapter III.

$$\frac{5}{8} - \frac{1}{4}$$

The important point to be borne in mind is that these fractional bits relate to the parent unit, written 1.

They might be pictured like this:

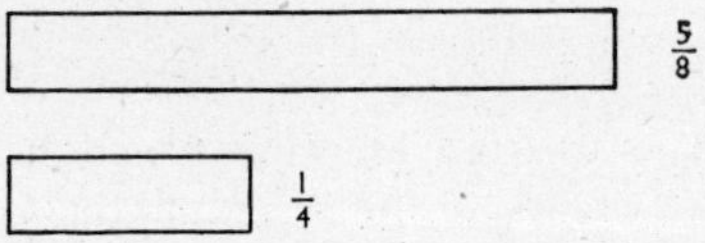

but it is better to look at them in terms of the unit—like this:

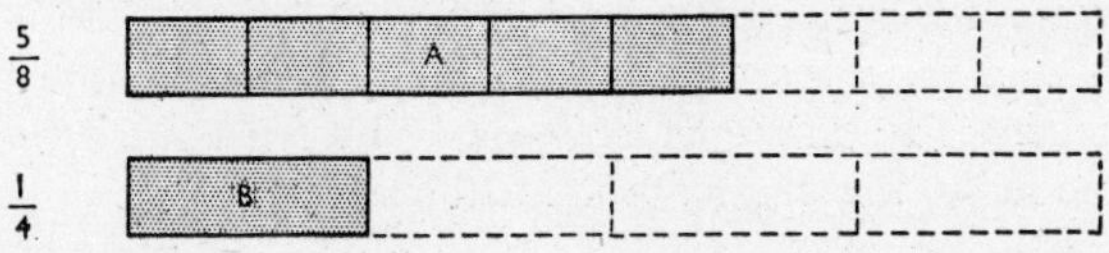

We can then *see* the subtraction. From A take away an amount the size of B.

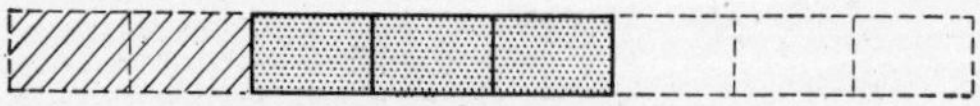

We have three eighths left, for the pictures show

(1) Every $\frac{1}{4}$ contains 2 eighths.

(2) 5 eighths − 2 eighths = 3 eighths.

In the language of arithmetic:—

$\frac{5}{8} - \frac{1}{4} = \frac{5}{8} - \frac{2}{8} = \frac{3}{8}$

The trick is to make the fractions have the same name (denominator) so that we may look at them not as fractions, but as different quantities of the same new unit (the eighth).

(ii) Here is another example. Suppose we had no smaller unit of English money than the shilling. We might then have to deal in fractions of shillings for small purchases, and do sums like this.

From half a shilling take away a third of a shilling.

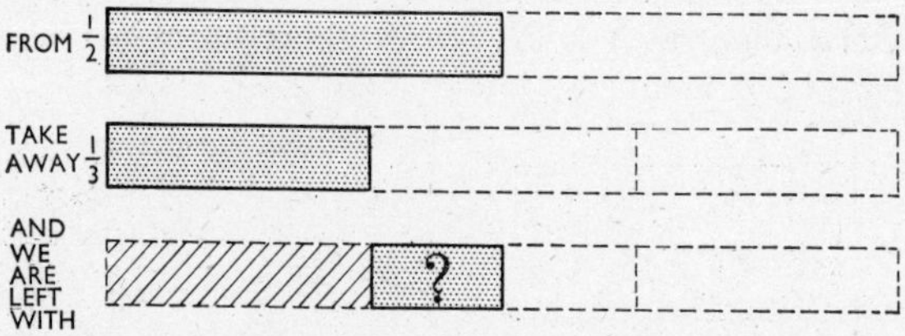

How many of these (?) are there in one shilling? If you cannot tell for certain by thinking about it, do an experiment with a strip of paper following the diagrams, and find out how many bits like the remainder (?) go together to make up the whole.

There are six bits like this in the whole and each bit is named one sixth. It has now been found that:

1 half − 1 third = 1 sixth.

or $\frac{1}{2} - \frac{1}{3} = \frac{1}{6}$

This is obviously true as soon as the given fractions are broken down into numbers of sixths:

$$\tfrac{1}{2} - \tfrac{1}{3} = \frac{3}{6} - \frac{2}{6} = \frac{1}{6}$$

Notice that as soon as this breaking down is done the sixths become in effect mere names like chairs or horses, and the rest of the calculation is done with the *numerators*, the 3 and the 2.

(iii) A third example is this.

Find the difference between $\frac{3}{4}$ and $\frac{2}{3}$.

(In mathematics the word difference has a more definite meaning than in ordinary language. The difference between 3 and 5 is 2, i.e., it is the number that must be added to the smaller to make the larger).

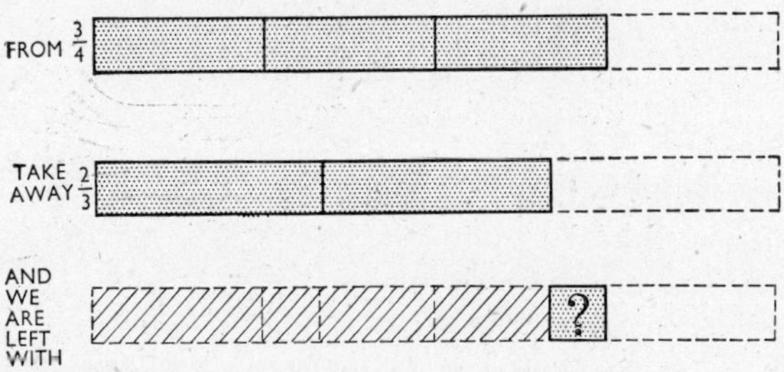

How many bits this size (?) are there in the whole? If you cannot think of the answer and feel certain, try another experiment with paper strips.

The remainder (?) is one-twelfth of the whole. It has been found that:—

$$\tfrac{3}{4} - \tfrac{2}{3} = \tfrac{1}{12}$$

We could have calculated the remainder using our experience in the previous example, thus, break down the fractions into numbers of portions of the same size—in this case twelfths.

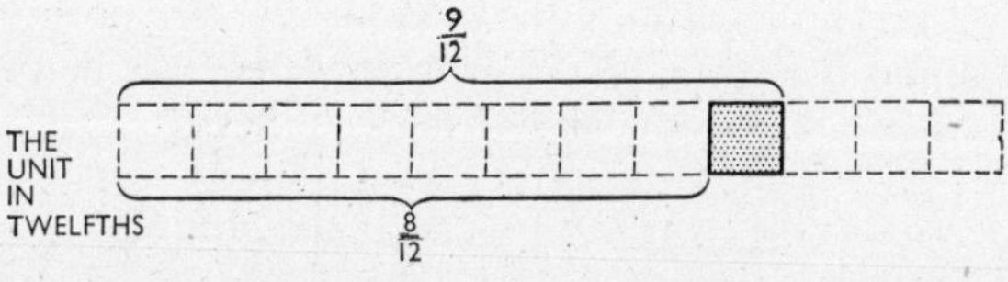

Halfs, thirds and fourths are such natural fractions arising from everyday sharings that it is not surprising to find them in our coinage. Adding and subtracting such fractions leads so often to twelfths and sixths that it is convenient to find a coin, the penny, worth one twelfth of a shilling. Every time we do sums involving pence we work among fractions in disguise. If we are happy among pence we should have no qualms about using *any* fractions.

Summary.—Addition and subtraction of fractions is done by converting all given fractions to a common denominator so that they can be gathered together in terms of this denominator.

Add together $\frac{1}{4}$, $\frac{2}{3}$, $\frac{1}{2}$ and $\frac{3}{5}$

The common denominator we seek must be a *multiple* of 4, of 3, of 2, and of 5, i.e., it must be wholly divisible by each. As five is the largest we must find a suitable multiple of 5.

You will find that 60 is the number we want.

$$\tfrac{3}{4} + \tfrac{2}{3} + \tfrac{1}{2} + \tfrac{3}{5} = \frac{45 + 40 + 30 + 36}{60} = \frac{151}{60}$$

The fraction line is arithmetical language meaning that the numerator 151 is to be divided by the denominator 60. Hence the sign $\div$ for division.

$$\tfrac{151}{60} = 2\tfrac{31}{60}$$

This rather artificial exercise was chosen to sum up the procedure for the addition and subtraction of fractions. You will find later portions of the book calling for familiarity with these operations, so exercises at the end of the chapter should be attempted to make sure you have grasped them.

(iv) A current of electricity of $\frac{1}{5}$ ampere feeds four equal components arranged in parallel. What is the strength of the current in each of them?

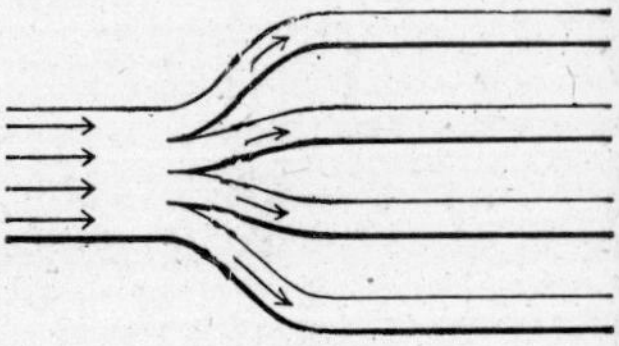

The arithmetical question is "What is one fourth of one fifth?"

$$\frac{1}{4} \text{ of } \frac{1}{5}$$

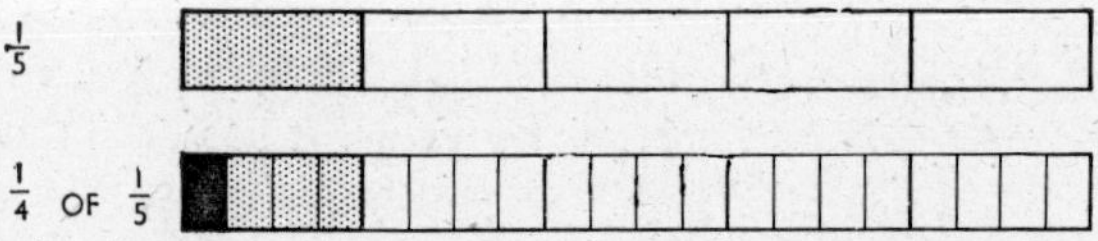

The pictures show that $\frac{1}{5}\times\frac{1}{4} = \frac{1}{20}$

In words: we break down the fifths on which we are operating into convenient smaller portions so that we may extract the piece that is required.

Calculation to give this result can only be as follows:

$$\frac{1}{5}\times\frac{1}{4}\left[=\frac{1\times 1}{5\times 4}\right]=\frac{1}{20}$$

Notice that when two proper fractions are multiplied together their product (the name given to the result of a multiplication process) is less than either of them.

(v) What is the radius of a circular hole $\frac{5}{8}$ in. in diameter?

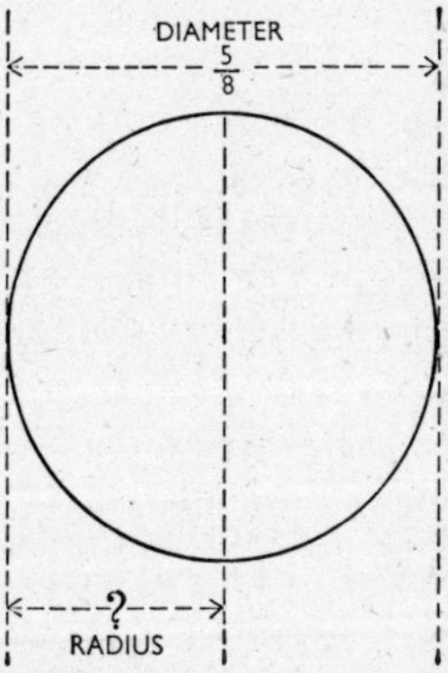

The arithmetical question is "What is one half of $\frac{5}{8}$?"

$$\frac{1}{2} \text{ of } \frac{5}{8}$$

Using the same idea, diagrams may help again.

$$\frac{1\times 5}{2\times 8}=\frac{1\times 5}{2\times 8}=\frac{5}{16}$$

We have again broken down the eighths into smaller bits, sixteenths, so that we may avoid such clumsy language as two-and-a-half-eighths.

The product is again less than either $\frac{1}{2}$ or $\frac{5}{8}$

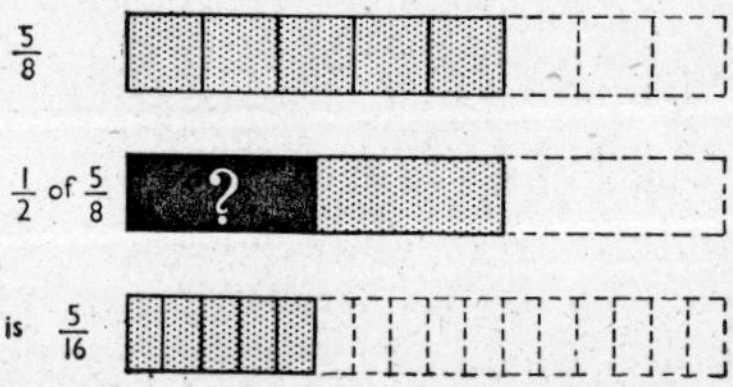

(vi) To find the combined resistance of several resistances in parallel add their reciprocals ($\frac{1}{5}$ is the *reciprocal* of 5) and find the reciprocal of the result.

Example: The combined resistance R of the arrangement in the diagram is given thus:

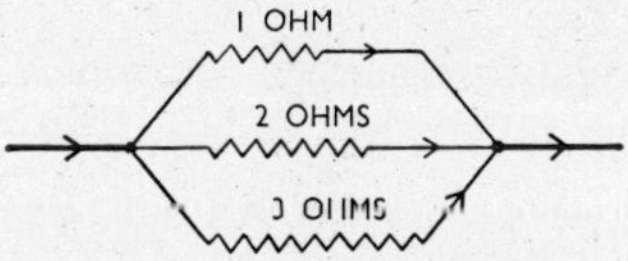

$$\text{Sum of reciprocals} = \frac{1}{1} + \frac{1}{2} + \frac{1}{3}$$
$$= \frac{6+3+2}{6}$$
$$= \frac{11}{6}$$
$$\therefore \quad \text{Combined resistance} = \frac{6}{11} \text{ ohms.}$$

(vii) What voltage must be applied to a $\frac{3}{4}$-ohm resistance to maintain a current of $\frac{2}{3}$ amperes? (volts = amperes × ohms).

$$\frac{3}{4} \times \frac{2}{3}$$

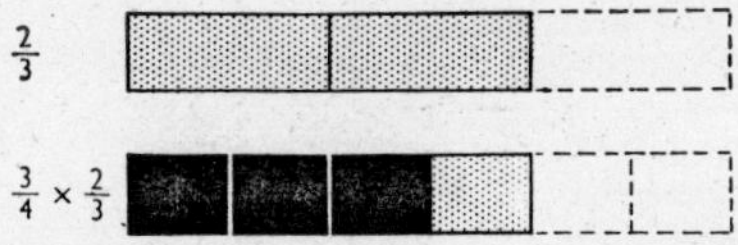

Following the hint of the last example, we may break down the thirds into twelfths to get the result $\frac{6}{12}$, which the diagram shows in the simpler form, $\frac{1}{2}$.

The arithmetic runs as follows:

$$\text{Voltage} = \frac{3}{4} \times \frac{2}{3} = \frac{3 \times 2}{4 \times 3} = \frac{6}{12} \text{ or } \frac{1}{2}$$

At this stage we usually seize the fact that $\frac{3}{3} = 1$, and *cancel* (strike out) the two threes before proceeding

$$= \frac{{}^{1}\not{3} \times 2}{4 \times \not{3}_{1}}$$

Note also that because $\frac{2}{2} = 1$, we may

cancel top and bottom by 2

↓

$$= \frac{\overset{1}{\cancel{3}}\times\overset{1}{\cancel{2}}}{\underset{2}{\cancel{4}}\times\underset{1}{\cancel{3}}} = \tfrac{1}{2}$$

Normally, all these stages are merged into one by cancelling any factors that are common to the numerator and the denominator, and we have, therefore,

$$\text{Voltage} = \frac{\overset{1}{\cancel{3}}}{\underset{2}{\cancel{4}}}\times\frac{\overset{1}{\cancel{2}}}{\underset{1}{\cancel{3}}} = \tfrac{1}{2}$$

The result is again less than either of the proper fractions forming the product.

(viii) On a normal winter evening in a flat, about $1\frac{3}{5}$ units of electricity are used. What is the cost at $2\frac{1}{2}$d. per unit?

$$2\frac{1}{2}\text{ pence} \times 1\frac{3}{5}$$

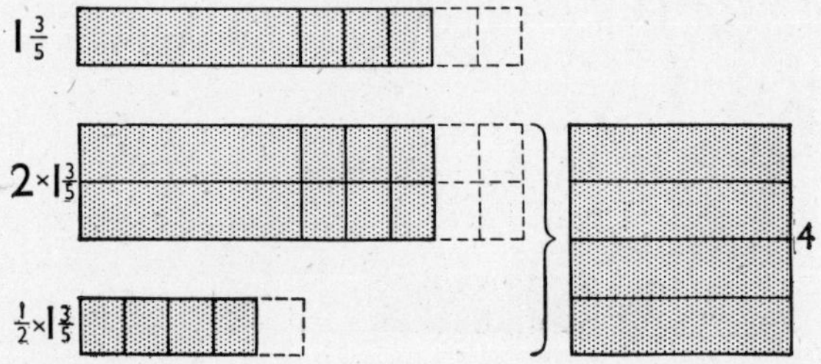

The result of this calculation must be somewhere between $2\frac{1}{2}$ and 5, because $1\frac{3}{5}$ is between 1 and 2.

The diagram enables us once more to get the answer by counting. The simpler method is to proceed by the rules of calculation that have already been devised. We can calculate only when the mixed numbers have been given the form of fractions (improper fractions, because the word fraction means a small portion).

$$\text{No. of pence} = 2\frac{1}{2} \times 1\frac{3}{5} = \frac{\overset{1}{\cancel{5}}}{\underset{1}{\cancel{2}}} \times \frac{\overset{4}{\cancel{8}}}{\underset{1}{\cancel{5}}}$$

$$= \frac{4}{1}$$

$$= 4$$

It will be found rather entertaining to look at a few text-books on arithmetic to find some problems on fractions. There will be plenty of mechanical exercises on the manipulation of fractions, but the problems are usually missing or else they are artificial—"spending one-fifth of my money, and half the remainder" and so on. The reason for this is that the use of fractions is usually incidental to a more complex problem. The later portions of this book will require agility in these matters, otherwise we would not bother to deal with them at all.

(ix) This sort of thing often happens. Divide a half by two

$$\tfrac{1}{2} \div 2$$

There is a variety of ways of reading this:

"Divide a half by two."
"How many twos are there in a half?"
"What must I multiply two by to get a half?"

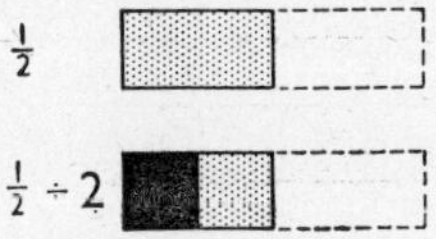

And no one needs the pictures to help them to see the answer, $\frac{1}{4}$.

It will repay us, however, to dwell on the picture for a short time, because it shows

how many of these there are

in this.

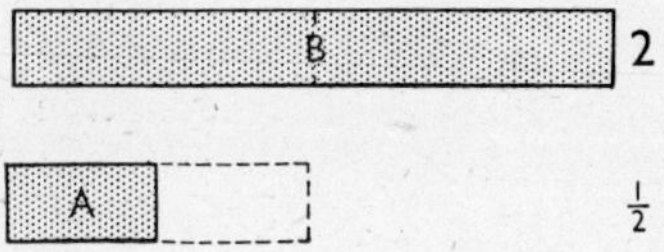

There is only a part of *B* in *A*; one quarter, in fact.

$$\therefore \quad \tfrac{1}{2} \div 2 = \tfrac{1}{4}$$

This question of the translation of the written language of arithmetic into the mother tongue is most important. People who get into a flat spin when they are confronted with

$$\frac{2}{3} \div \frac{1}{3}$$

would not hesitate to answer the question "How many thirds are there in two thirds?"

How many of these are there

in this?

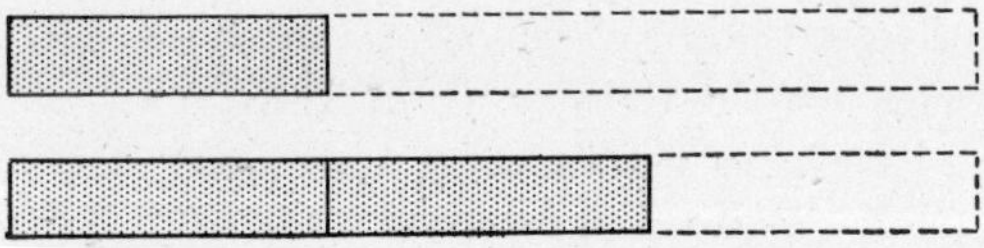

$$\frac{2}{3} \div \frac{1}{3} = 2$$

This is easy because the denominators are alike and may be ignored. In the next example they cannot be ignored.

(x) What current of electricity is carried by a $\frac{3}{4}$-ohm resistance at a pressure of $\frac{2}{3}$ volts? (Amperes = volts ÷ ohms).

$$\text{The calculation will be } \frac{2}{3} \div \frac{3}{4}$$

We can see the answer if we break down both fractions into a finer form.

In $\frac{2}{3}$

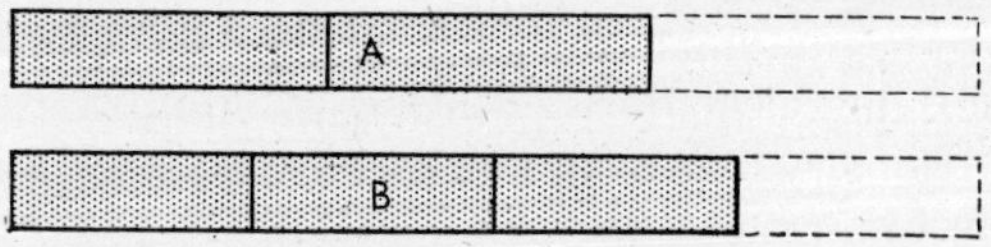

how many of these are there?

Thirds and fourths both break down nicely into twelfths (3 × 4 = 12).

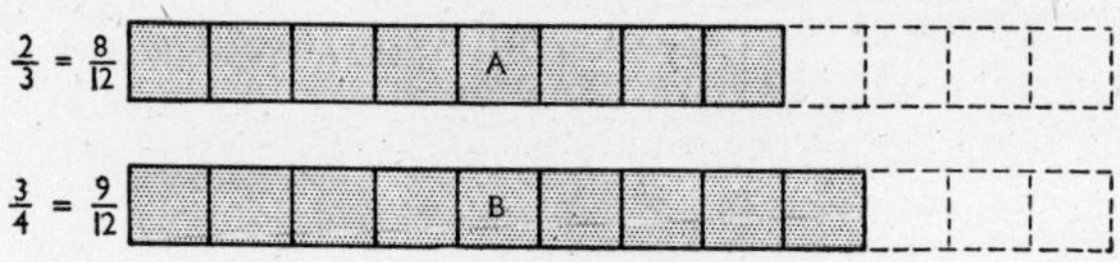

How many B's are there in A? The answer is $\frac{8}{9}$

$$\text{i.e., } \frac{2}{3} \div \frac{3}{4} = \underbrace{\frac{8}{12} \div \frac{9}{12}}$$

and the twelfths may now be disregarded as they are the name common to both quantities

↓

$$= \frac{8}{9}$$

The 8 and the 9 came from the first 2 and 3 in the breaking-down process.

$$\frac{2}{3} \div \frac{3}{4} = \frac{2}{3} \times \frac{4}{3} = \frac{8}{9}$$

Hence, the mechanical rule for division by a fraction (which often confuses rather than clarifies), is invert the divisor and multiply. We do not condemn the rule if its derivation is understood.

(xi) We do a great many sums of this type without much trouble and without recognizing them as the division of fractions. To find what weight of potatoes at 7s. 6d. per cwt. can be purchased for 6s. 8d., for example, we may change the money into pence (90 pence and 80 pence) and proceed to divide 90 by 80. In this case, the fractions are disguised as pence. We can also get the answer by working in pounds.

7s. 6d. (three halfcrowns) = £$\frac{3}{8}$
6s. 8d. = £$\frac{1}{3}$
Weight of potatoes = $\frac{1}{3} \div \frac{3}{8}$

$$\text{Weight of potatoes} = \frac{1}{3} \div \frac{3}{8} \text{ cwt.}$$
$$= \frac{1}{3} \times \frac{8}{3} \text{ cwt.}$$
$$= \frac{8}{9} \text{ cwt.}$$

In the next series of examples and exercises we shall return to the use of ratio, and our experience with fractions will enable us to understand the calculations involved.

We shall make use of illustrations as much as possible, not only to clarify the ideas, but because illustrations are a legitimate, and often a valuable aid to *understanding* the nature of a problem. It will be important, too, for us to bear in mind that every mathematical problem requires *data* (information): the calculation is really a careful process of arranging the information so that it tells us what we want to know. The mathematician is, in fact, a detective; he solves his problem by putting together all relevant evidence in the right manner. We must always extract the information from the problem, therefore, *before* we can hope to solve it.

MAKING A PUPPET THEATRE

The puppets on their set must be a small-scale version of living players on a real stage. Therefore, a good basis to work on is the theatre stage, making allowance for the fact that the theatre stage requires a wide and deep angle of vision, while the puppet stage does not.

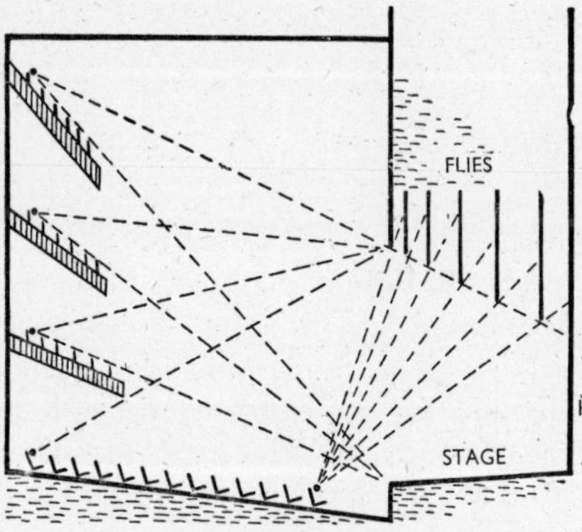

THEATRE (SIDE VIEW)

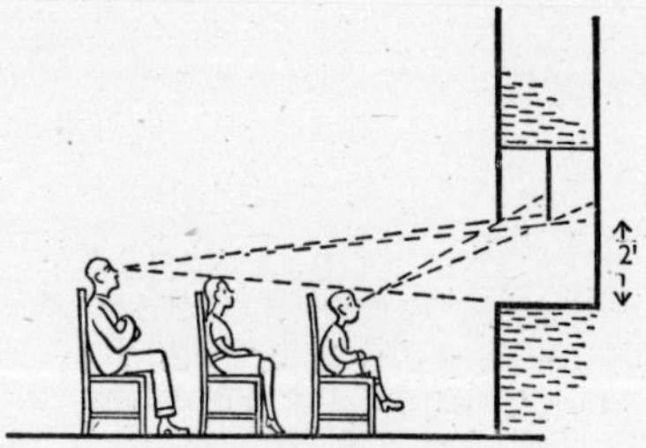

PUPPET THEATRE

Reality

Normal height of large room	12 ft.*	*Information, of which the items starred are essential because they relate reality with puppetry.*
Normal height of humans	5 to 6 ft.	
Normal height of chair seat	18 in.	
Normal height of table	30 in.	

Puppet

Height of stage	24 in.*

$$\text{Scale of puppet set, therefore,} = \frac{24 \text{ in.}}{12 \text{ ft.}} = \frac{2 \text{ ft.}}{12 \text{ ft.}}$$

$$= 1 : 6 \text{ (or two inches to the foot)}$$

This ratio 1 : 6 is the key to the many questions that may arise: it will enable us to give the proper proportions to the replica of actuality, to make the puppets and their environment *proportional* to the real thing. Using the ratio 1 : 6 as our special elastic measure, we may proceed.

Height of adult puppet $= \frac{1}{6} \times$ 6 ft., i.e., approximately 1 ft.

Height of puppet chair-seat $= \frac{1}{6} \times$18in. = 3 in. approximately.

In the same way, the ratio 1 : 6 enables us to convert all other measurements in reality to the measurements we shall need for our puppet theatre.

SCALE DRAWINGS

Drawings of aeroplanes are usually 1 : 72 of the original. Let us find what length in the drawing is required to represent a 30-ft. component.

In this example, the information is already presented in the form we want.

$\therefore$ Length in drawing for 30-ft. component $= \frac{1}{72} \times 30$ ft.

$$= \frac{30}{72} \text{ ft.}$$

and you could find the answer by changing 30 ft. into 360 in., in which case the original multiplication would lead ultimately to division.

However, it always pays to look out for opportunities to cancel: we prefer now to cancel by 6.

Length in drawing for 30-ft. component $= \frac{\overset{5}{\cancel{30}}}{\underset{12}{\cancel{72}}} = \frac{5}{12}$ ft. or 5 in.

MAKING A TRANSFORMER

The A.C. electricity supply is usually maintained at a voltage of between 200 volts and 250 volts. To operate low-voltage apparatus like electric motors for driving models, electric bells and battery chargers, the voltage required may be 4 volts or 12 volts. Transformers are used to obtain from an A.C. supply the particular voltage required for a special purpose.

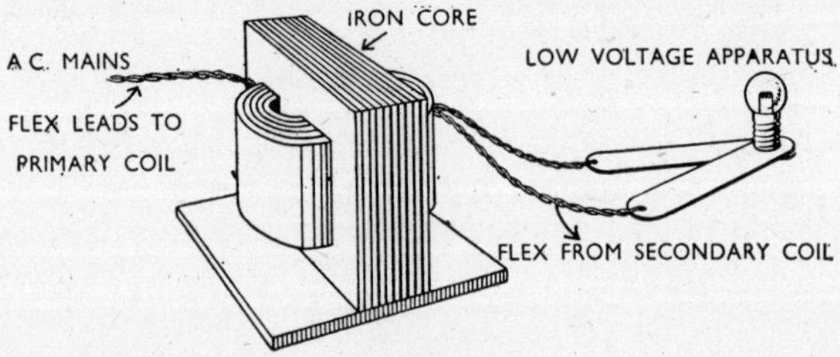

Where the core is a closed magnetic circuit of iron one square inch in section, it is safe to allow eight turns per volt for the primary (input) coil. The ratio of the number of turns in the primary coil to the number in the secondary coil is equal to the ratio of the primary voltage to the secondary voltage.

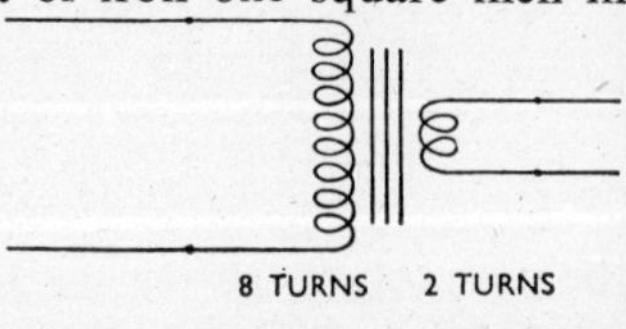

With this information a transformer may be designed to step-down from 240 volts to 4 volts.

1 volt on primary requires 8 turns

$\therefore$ 240 volts on primary requires 8×240 turns

Ratio of voltages required $= 240 : 4$
$= 60 : 1$

$\therefore$ ratio of $\dfrac{\text{primary turns}}{\text{secondary turns}} = 60 : 1$

Since the number of primary turns $= 8 \times 240$

$$\therefore \text{Number of turns on secondary} = 8 \times \overset{4}{\cancel{240}} \times \frac{1}{\underset{1}{\cancel{60}}} \text{ (cancel by 60)}$$

$= 32$

Further matters appertaining to transformer design are considered in other sections of the book.

MAKING AN ELECTRIC CLOCK

An electro-magnet fed from the A.C. mains changes its polarity 100 times per second. Every ·01 second, then, the pole is at full strength and will attract magnetic materials. We can make use of this idea by an arrangement typified in the diagram.

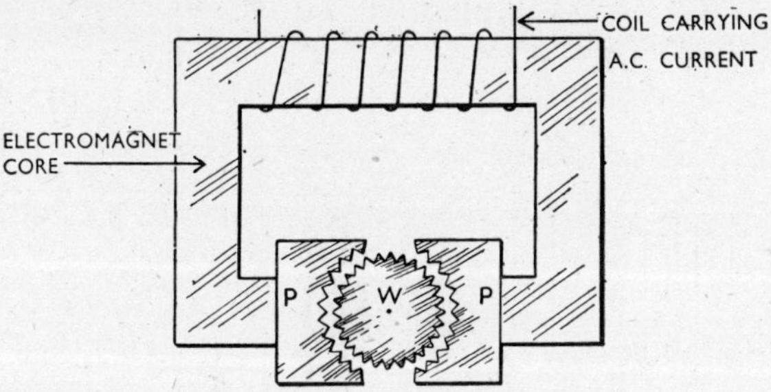

The steel fly-wheel *W* is toothed to match teeth on the insides of the two pole-pieces *PP*. The wheel is given a spin by hand; then, while the magnetic force tends to pull a movable tooth (on wheel) towards alignment with a fixed tooth (on pole-piece), the inertia of the wheel carries it beyond its mark, and the next fixed tooth beyond attracts it, when its full surge of magnetic flux has been built up.

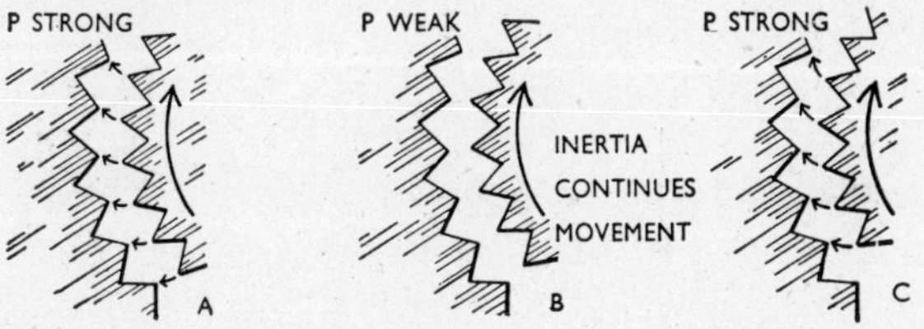

Thus, the speed of tooth-to-tooth movement of the wheel settles down to the rate at which the fixed teeth are brought to full magnetic strength, and in this case it is 100 times per second.

How many teeth would you give wheel *A* so that it will make 2 revolutions per second?

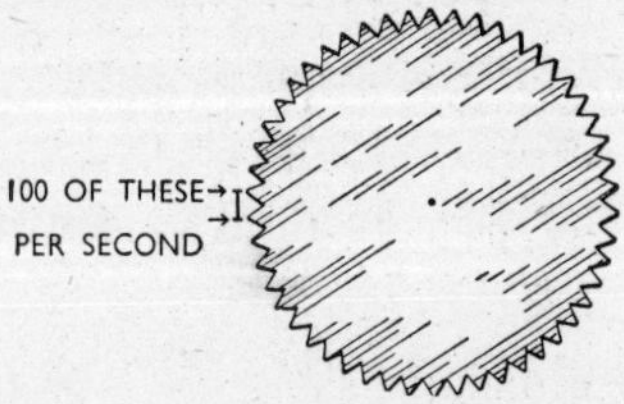

Given: 100 tooth-to-tooth movements in one second
2 revolutions in one second
i.e., 100 tooth-to-tooth movements is equivalent to 2 revolutions, and therefore one revolution involves 50 movements, so the wheel must have 50 teeth.

The teeth should be close together so that the magnetic force is not called upon to act across a great distance—this would weaken its effect.

The same idea can be used for making electric motors for any purpose requiring perfectly constant speed.

HYDRAULIC JACKS

An hydraulic jack has a plunger (at which the effort is applied) of area $\frac{1}{2}$ sq. in. If the effort is to be about 7 lb. what area must be used to give a mechanical advantage of 160 : 1?

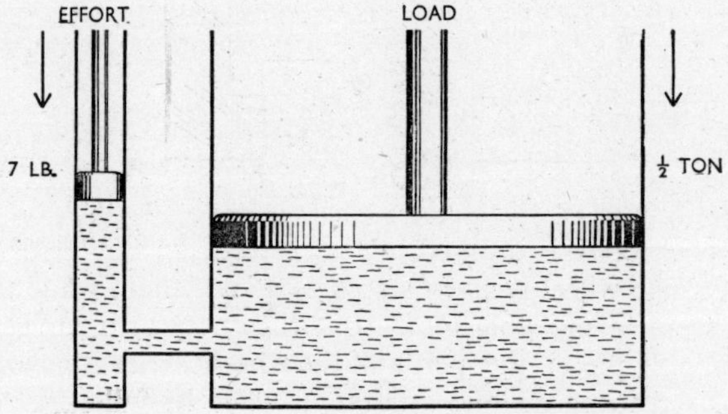

The size of the plunger, in this case $\frac{1}{2}$ sq. in., depends on the pressure which it is desired to transmit.

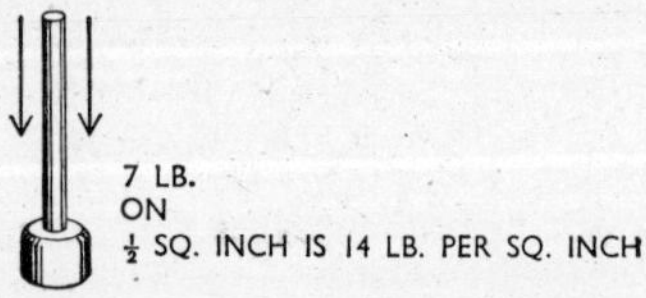

Therefore the load plunger receives an upward thrust from the fluid of 14 lb. per sq. in.

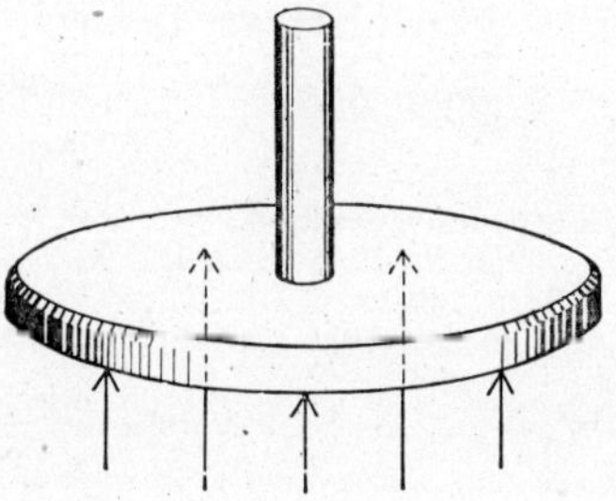

Now the load is to be $7\times\frac{160}{1}$ lb.

∴ The area of its plunger is obtained by finding how many 14 lb. there are in 7×160 lb.

$$\text{Area of load plunger} = \frac{\overset{}{\not{7}} \times \overset{80}{\not{160}}}{\underset{2}{\not{14}}} = 80 \text{ sq. in.}$$

A shorter way of working is to use the idea of ratio immediately.

Ratio of load plunger to effort plunger = Ratio of load to effort = 160 : 1

$$\therefore \text{Area of load plunger} = \frac{160}{1} \times \text{area of effort plunger}$$

$$= \frac{160}{1}\times\frac{1}{2} \text{ sq. in.}$$

$$= 80 \text{ sq. in.}$$

Both roads lead to Rome but the second is the one selected if you know your mathematical topography, i.e., if you have the right feelings about ratio as an elastic measure.

In modern engineering processess, it is sometimes necessary to bring enormous forces to bear. For example, large ingots of steel may require thousands of tons pressure for forging: a blacksmith's hammer would make no impression. However, a machine may enable the smith to do the job.

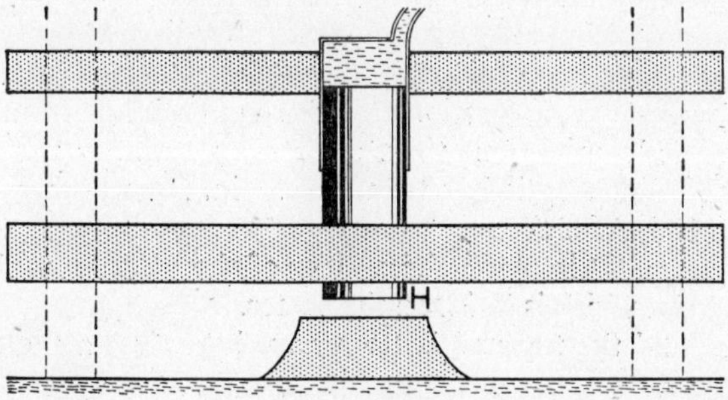

For *H* to be driven down with force of 1,000 tons weight, product of oil pressure and area of plunger must be 1,000 tons.

i.e., if area of plunger is about 2,000 sq. in.

$$\text{pressure of oil per sq. in.} = \frac{1,000}{2,000} = \frac{1}{2} \text{ ton}$$

$\frac{1}{2}$-ton pressure per sq. in. is a big load, but a power-driven motor can easily be designed to generate it. Indeed, a 6,000-ton forging press is in use which uses an effort-pressure of $2\frac{1}{2}$ tons per sq. in.

RATIO

MAKING A POSTER

We are to make a poster. The best way of doing it, the method used by the poster artist, is to sketch it out first on a scrap of paper like this:

This gives a layout and a rough guide to the sizes of lettering. We want to work on a sheet of paper measuring 30 in. × 22 in. Our rough scheme occupies $3\frac{1}{2}$ in. × $4\frac{1}{2}$ in.

Spacing of lines (base line of letters).

We judge by the eye the fractional distance of each line from the top, e.g., the title is a little less than one third of the way down. In the actual poster, we shall strike a line a little less than $\frac{1}{3}$ of 30 in. from the top—say 9 in. (a little less than 10 in.) for the title.

"The Village Hall" is about three-fifths of the way down the sheet, i.e., about 3/5 of 30 in. which is 18 in. on the poster.

When these and the top and bottom have been drawn the others can be placed.

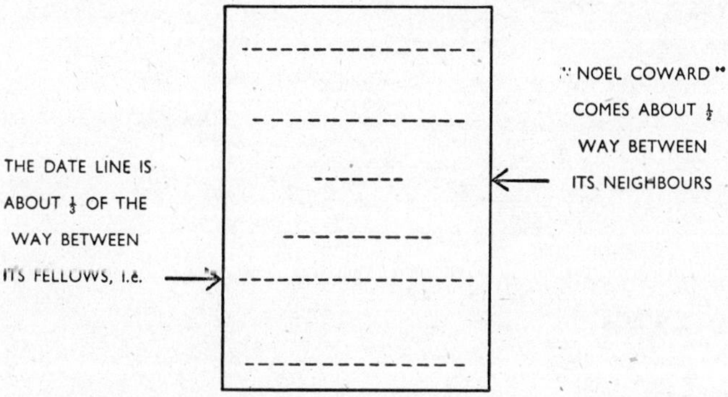
"NOEL COWARD"
COMES ABOUT ½
WAY BETWEEN
ITS NEIGHBOURS
THE DATE LINE IS
ABOUT ⅓ OF THE
WAY BETWEEN
ITS FELLOWS, i.e.

The Size of Letters.

As we are not very clever at freehand lettering, we want tramlines in which to place them, so we need to estimate their gauges. "Blithe Spirit" is about $\frac{1}{3}$ in. high in the sketch; how high must it be in the poster? This is decided by the length-of-line relationship, and, for all lines in our problem this is 22 in. compared with $4\frac{1}{2}$ in., or to use arithmetical language, the ratio $22 : 4\frac{1}{2}$. This ratio can be boiled down roughly to $5 : 1$ because 22 is nearly 5 times $4\frac{1}{2}$.

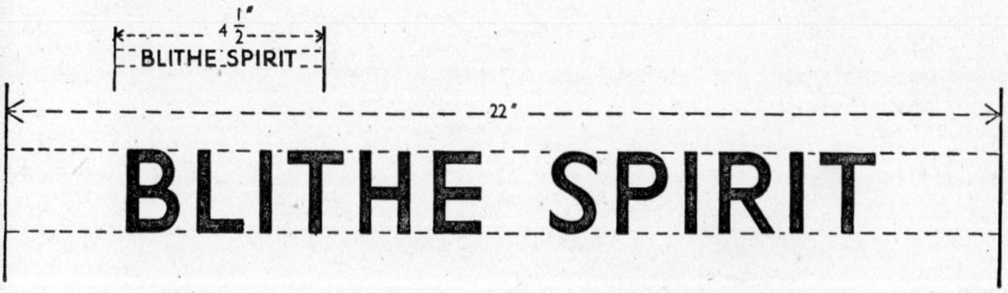
4 1/2"
BLITHE SPIRIT
22"
BLITHE SPIRIT

The diagram shows that if the lengths of the lines are enlarged in the ratio of $5 : 1$, the height of the letters must have the same ratio. Measure and see for yourself that this is so in the diagram. If the poster and sketch were of similar shapes, we might work from the ratio of heights of papers.

"Blithe Spirit" letters, then, must be $5 \times \frac{1}{3}$ in., i.e., $1\frac{2}{3}$ in. high. Similarly, "The Village Hall" letters will be 5 times their height in the sketch, i.e., $5 \times \frac{1}{6}$ in. which is a little less than 1 in.

THE STROBOSCOPE

To check the speed of your gramophone turn-table, make a stroboscope. The usual form is a white disk with a repeated pattern of black triangles marked around its edge. When the turn-table is spinning with the right speed in light from the A.C. electricity supply, the pattern appears stationary. The lamp is actually lighting up 100 times a second, and your stroboscope is turning at such a speed that the pattern has moved on one place between one pulse of light and the next, i.e. in $\frac{1}{100}$ sec. The diagrams explain this.

At one instant the eye, looking at the portion of the disk indicated by the arrow, sees this. The lamp is giving a pulse of full illumination.

A

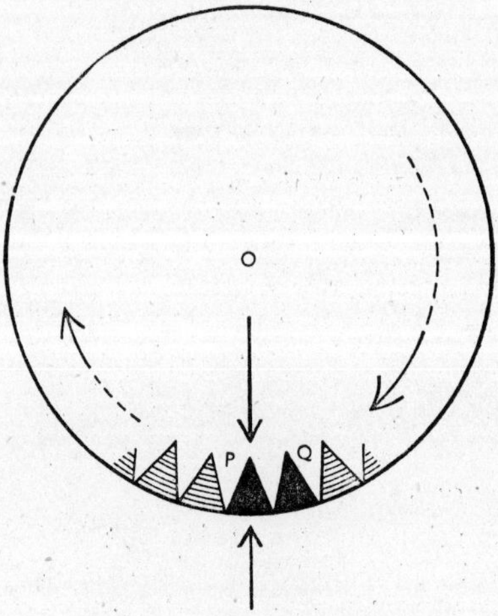

While the disk performs its next shift, the lamp filament is giving weaker light. The image is, therefore, blurred and weak.

B

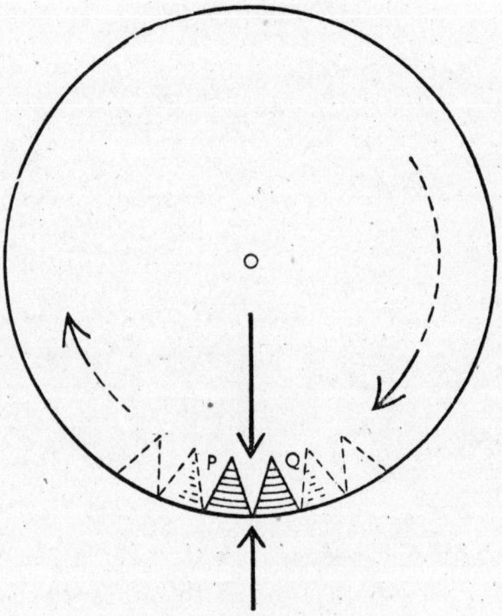

At the next moment of full light the correct speed has brought the next triangle *Q* to the position lately occupied by *P*.

C

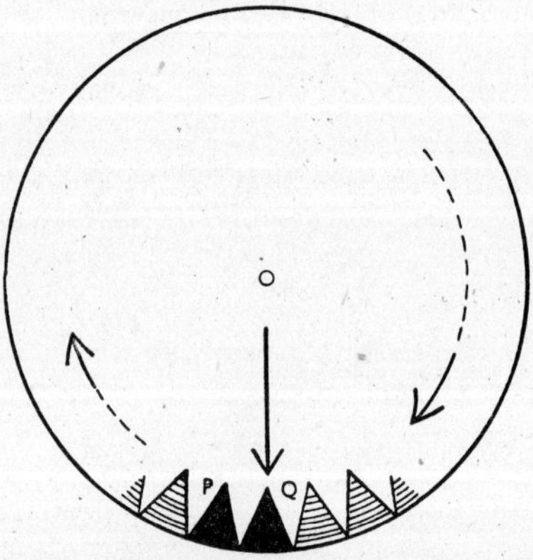

During the constant repetition of this cycle the eye sees the same pattern at each full illumination and is, therefore, unaware of the movement.

If the disk is slightly slower than it should be the stroboscope pattern will appear to idle slowly anticlockwise, whilst an excessive speed gives the same effect clockwise.

For the modern gramophone record, the speed of the turn-table should be 78 r.p.m. (revolutions per minute).

Now we get 100 light pulsations per second, i.e., each pulsation follows the last in $\frac{1}{100}$ sec. The number of revolutions of the disk made in this time will be $\frac{\overset{13}{\cancel{78}}}{\underset{10}{\cancel{60}}\times 100}$, which is $\frac{13}{1,000}$

The distance *PQ*, then, must be $\frac{13}{1000}$ revolutions. In other words, each triangle must be $\frac{13}{1000}$ revolutions from the next. A disk with $\frac{1000}{13}$ equal triangles round its circumference would fulfil the conditions required. Unfortunately, however, this number is not a whole number, but $76\frac{12}{13}$, so we must choose between accuracy, which will result in a pattern that jumps slightly for each revolution of the disk, or a slight inaccuracy following the choice of 77 triangles instead of $76\frac{12}{13}$.

HOME-MADE DIMMERS

You can get a lot of arithmetical and electrical fun out of making dimmers for electric lights. The best way to set about it is to do a few small-scale experiments for a start.

You need a thermometer, a jar or pot and two equal disks of tin arranged like this:

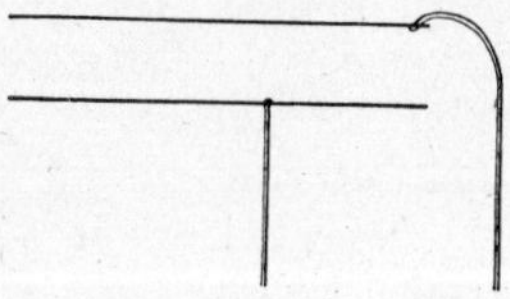

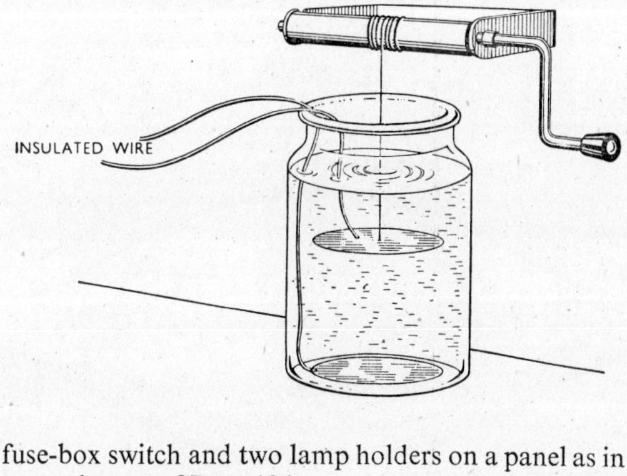

Fix up a fuse-box switch and two lamp holders on a panel as in the diagram that is shown on the top of Page 134.

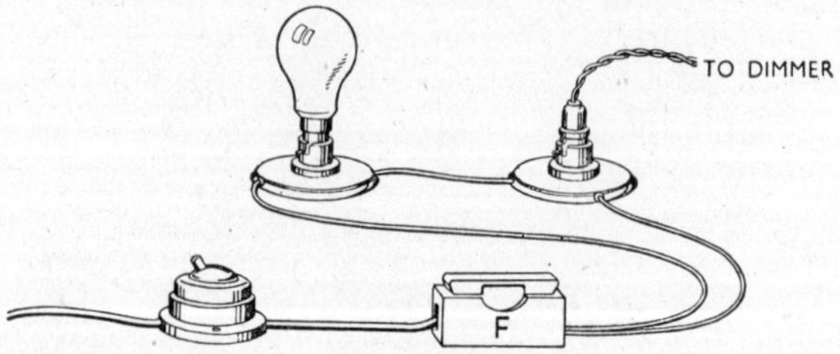

To the water in the pot add strong salt solution a *drop* at a time until the light gives a slight glow with the top disk about halfway down the jar. You can now adjust the strength of the solution until the lamp is at full brightness just before the plates touch, and extinguished just before the top plate reaches the surface.

Not much arithmetic so far. But before you think of using this dimmer for a battery of lamps instead of one—as you might wish to do for stage lighting—you will encounter some arithmetic.

With the thermometer find out the rate at which the temperature of the salt solution rises (so many degrees per minute).

Now repeat the experiment with the same solution for a lamp of much higher wattage, to find out how the *ratio* of lamp wattage is related to the *ratio* of rates of heating, when the lamp filaments are just visible. Electricity is nearly always producing heat when it gives light: our intention is to give it the chance to make more heat, and, therefore, less light—without the dimmer getting too hot. (If you have done any back-stage work with this kind of dimmer, you will know the dreadful suspense of finding the wretched thing nearly at boiling point when the dim-out has still got minutes to run.)

You will find that the rate of heating up in the dimmer is directly proportional to the total lamp wattage, so if your first dimmer boiled in 30 minutes for a 60-watt lamp it will boil in about 3 minutes for ten 60-watt lamps! Remedy—increase the capacity of the dimmer by the same ratio as you increase the wattage it controls.

ELECTRICITY

A current of electricity is shared among three conductors of resistances 2 ohms, 3 ohms and 5 ohms respectively. What fraction of the total load is carried in each conductor?

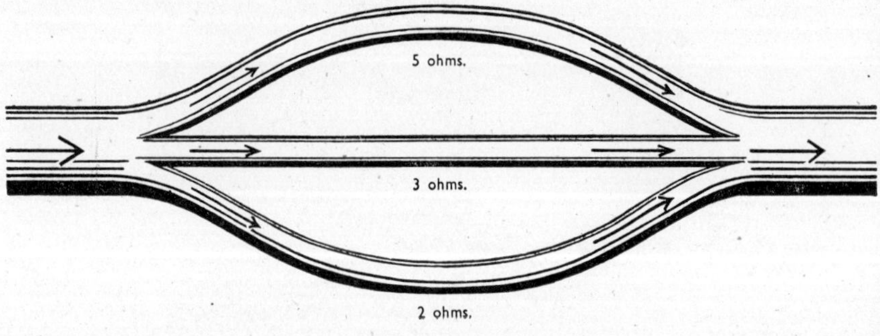

This time, we refer to Ohm's law, which says that

$$\text{current} = \frac{\text{electromotive force}}{\text{resistance}}$$

As the same electromotive force is urging the flow of electricity in each conductor,

$$\text{current in 5 ohms} = \frac{E}{5}$$

$$\text{current in 3 ohms} = \frac{E}{3}$$

$$\text{current in 2 ohms} = \frac{E}{2}$$

$$\text{Total current} = \frac{E}{5}+\frac{E}{3}+\frac{E}{2}$$

$$= E.\left(\frac{1}{5}+\frac{1}{3}+\frac{1}{2}\right)$$

(The full-stop, which is often omitted, indicates multiplication.)

We must break down these fractions into finer fractions all of the same denominator. The most convenient denominator is 30.

$$\text{Total current} = E\left(\frac{6}{30}+\frac{10}{30}+\frac{15}{30}\right)$$

$$= E\,.\,\frac{31}{30}$$

If we think of this as 31 shares of $\frac{E}{30}$, then, clearly the loads will be 6 shares, 10 shares and 15 shares in the 5-ohm, 3-ohm and 2-ohm conductors respectively. This gives the fractions $\frac{6}{31}$, $\frac{10}{31}$, $\frac{15}{31}$ respectively.

A current of electricity is shared by two conductors of resistance 3 ohms and 5 ohms respectively. What fraction will each conductor carry?

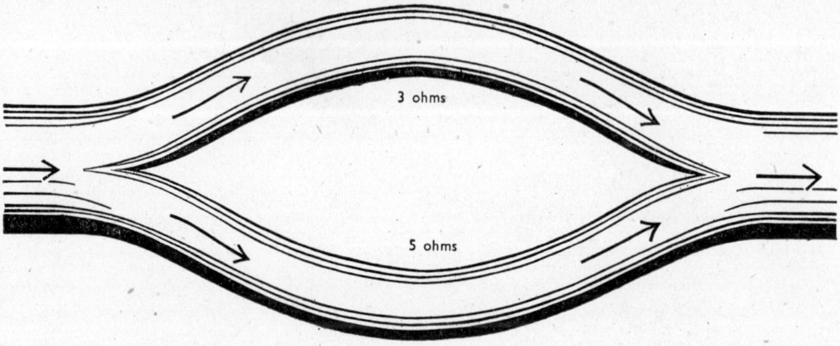

Clearly the current will be shared in the ratio of 5 : 3, and the better conductor (3 ohms) will carry the greater load. We must imagine the main current to be split up (divided) into a number of equal portions that can be shared in this ratio.

Current in 3-ohm conductor	=	5 portions.
Current in 5-ohm conductor	=	3 portions.
∴ Total current	=	8 portions.

This shows that the current is shared thus:—

3-ohm conductor carries $\frac{5}{8}$ of total load.

5-ohm conductor carries $\frac{3}{8}$ of total load.

If you review the ground that has been covered in this chapter you will find that a good deal of attention has been given to fractions and to ratio. Very few mechanical rules of method have been accumulated because they may offer too many pitfalls. We have been profuse with illustrations and experiments because they enable us to feel what we are doing with numbers, to acquire a kind of extra sense in handling them.

Now let us note some of the things we have not delved into.

(1) We have assumed you can add, subtract, multiply and divide ordinary numbers.

(2) We have not paid much attention to money problems.

(3) We have not tried to learn how to carry out simple calculations with compound measures of length, weight (avoirdupois, etc.) involving the English tables that we forgot almost before we left school.

(4) We have scouted decimals and percentages.

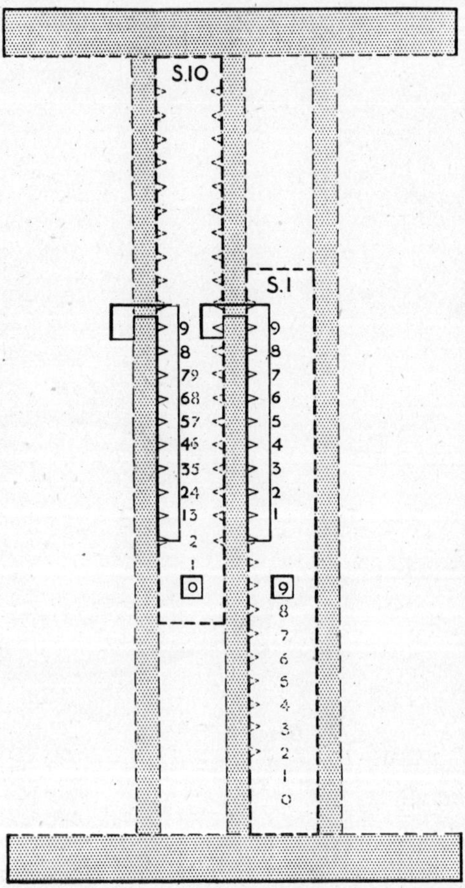

(1) For readers who are not happy about their agility in the four rules of numbers, any game that gives practice (see Chapter II) and a little light entertainment in handicraft may help—making an adding and subtracting machine as the one sketched here.

S_1 and S_{10} are slides, exactly alike with little bites cut out at $\frac{1}{4}$-in. intervals. A pencil point through the long windows can push the slides up or down, the windows at the bottom showing the answer for that column.

Quarter-inch squares ruled on cardboard are the best guide to cutting out.

The shaded portions represent separating strips which hold front and back cards together and serve as a guide to the slides.

First set the slides so that they show 0 in the answer windows.

Now add 2 and 5, i.e., put the pencil opposite 2 and draw the slide down as far as it will go. This shows answer 2.

Now put the pencil in 5 and draw down to the bottom again. This gives the answer, 7.

Suppose you want to add 6. Put the pencil opposite 6 and try to draw the slide to the bottom. It will not go right down because 6 and 7 make more than 9. Push the slide to the top instead and move the pencil over to the left and down, this will carry ten over as 1 in the tens' window and will show 3 in the units' window. Why? When you move from 6 to the top you have taken off 4 from the units answer (10 — 6 = 4) leaving 3 (7 — 4) showing in the window. If you think about this for a moment you will see that you have added ten and subtracted four. Your full answer is now 13.

You can make your adding machine deal with as many columns as you like by giving it as many slides as you like.

Try a few addition sums, and check the machine by working them on paper so that you may be sure you are using it correctly.

Now try one or two simple subtraction sums to see if you can find the technique for subtraction. Then do more ambitious ones, checking on paper until you are sure you are working the machine in the right way.

If you are not sure of the multiplication tables as far as the twelve-times table, write them out and learn them until you are able to give an immediate answer.

It is quite simple to make a cardboard table-machine, and making it and using it gives good table practice.

A fixed card forms the back and carries the tables arranged like the diagram below, each table appearing once vertically and once horizontally.

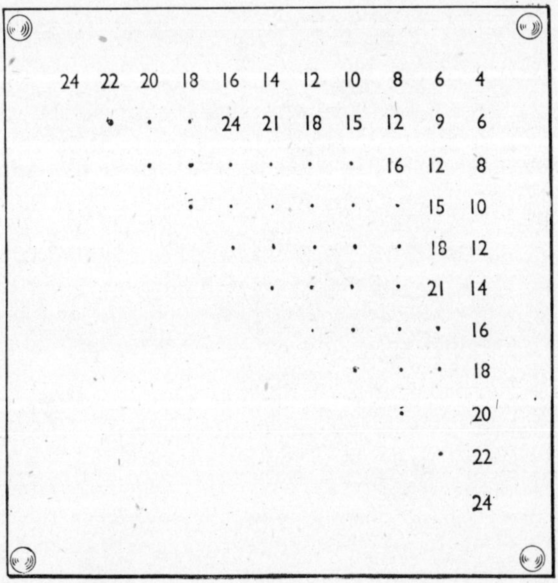

Two long rectangular slides of equal size and shape, each with a long narrow window, are fitted at right angles over the tables. To multiply 6×9 move one slide along 6 spaces and the other 9. The window of the first is now over the six-times table and that of the other the nine-times table, so the windows cross at 6×9 and 54 is seen in the answer window.

You can use the same idea, of course, for making any multiplication tables you like.

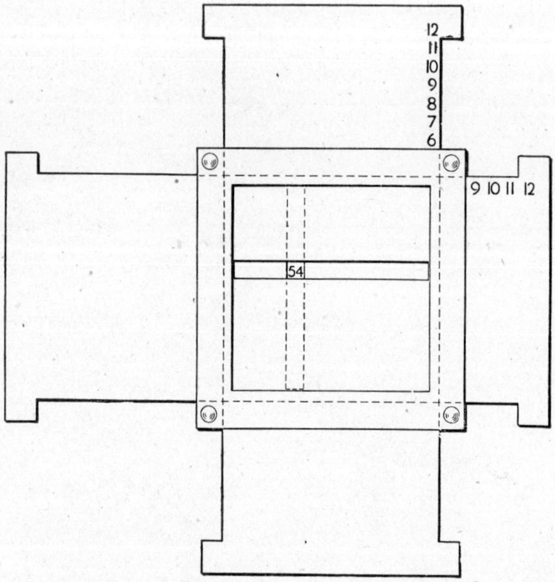

(2) and (3) *Money Problems and Compound Units.*

Nowadays the hard work of money calculations is largely eliminated by the help of ready reckoners of one kind or another. As our aim is to build up a mathematical background rather than a skill at reckoning—which is only one elementary branch of arithmetic—we do not propose to digress into this admittedly important subject.

However, if you absorb the ideas that are being outlined in these early chapters of the book, it is felt that you will have no difficulty in devising your own (the best) methods of reckoning in pounds, ounces, feet, yards, shillings, pence and the rest.

There have been a good many standard methods devised but the bald fact is that *there are no golden rules* for the four rules of compound units: each calculation offers its own best method of treatment, and a good general mathematical sense will help you to spot it very quickly.

(4) *Decimals and Percentages.*

These and further basic operations will be covered in the next chapter. They have been evaded up to now merely for the sake of clarity. One thing has been dealt with at a time.

Exercises

1. The electricity supply is rated at 240 volts. You desire to make decorative festoons of miniature

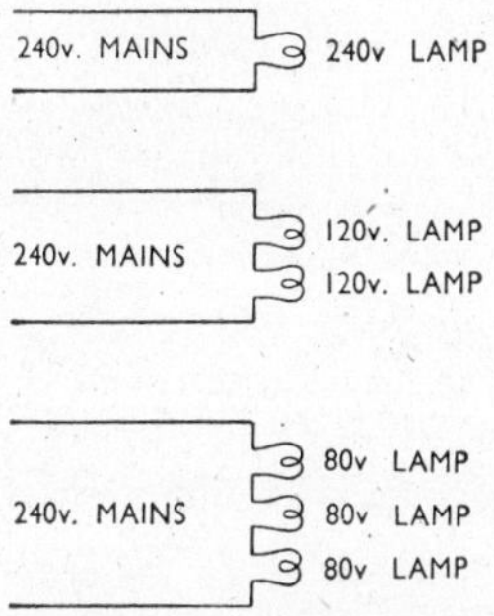

lamps to be run off the mains: how many will you need and of what voltage?

The illustration above shows that the 240-volt mains will light one bulb

rated at 240 volts,

or

two of 120 volts arranged in series,

or

three of 80 volts in series,

and so on, because the voltage (pressure) can be shared.

(i) What voltage would be required for 40 lamps?

(ii) How many lamps of a 4·5 volt rating would be necessary?

2. Devise a set of weights (the fewer the better) capable of giving selections for any weight from 1 lb. to 23 lb. It is advisable to work from the lower end of the scale.

3. Devise a set of weights from which any weight between 1 gm. and 10 gm. may be selected. How many different denominations have been used? Can fewer denominations be used?

4. You want a particular length of cycle chain made up with links of a particular length. How will you find how many links are required for the chain?

5. A printer uses large sheets, which are afterwards cut into smaller sheets. How many pages of print will be produced if one large sheet of paper is folded double three times?

6. How would you find out how many dry cells are needed to replace a 12-volt battery?

7. What would you do to find the length of fencing needed for a triangular plot of ground?

8. Suppose lawn grass-seed should be sown at one ounce to the square yard; what measurements do you make on a rectangular (oblong) plot to be sown, and what will you do with the measurements to find the quantity of seed required?

Note.—Draw sketches to help you with these problems.

9. Find the distances covered in each pedal revolution (*a*) in top gear (*b*) in bottom gear, in the example given on Page 116.

What is the combined resistance of each of the following parallel arrangements:

10. 2 ohms, 3 ohms?

11. 3 ohms, 4 ohms, 5 ohms?

12. $4\frac{1}{2}$ ohms, 6 ohms?
(the reciprocal of $\frac{9}{2}$ is $\frac{2}{9}$).

13. $2\frac{1}{2}$ ohms, 4 ohms, 6 ohms, 10 ohms?

14. What resistance must be put in parallel with a 12-ohm resistance to give a combined resistance of (*a*) 8 ohms, (*b*) 6 ohms, (*c*) 9 ohms, (*d*) 4 ohms?

15. An ammeter (measuring

amperes) is arranged to read one-tenth of the current (measured in amperes). What readings should it give for currents of (*a*) 71 amperes, (*b*) 3 amperes, (*c*) $2\frac{1}{2}$ amperes?

16. A conductor carries $\frac{2}{3}$ of the main load. What current does it carry when the main load is (*a*) 1 ampere, (*b*) $1\frac{1}{2}$ amperes, (*c*) $\frac{1}{2}$ ampere, (*d*) $\frac{3}{4}$ ampere?

17. Fifteen turns of a screw move the head $3\frac{1}{8}$ in. How many turns are needed to move it (*a*) $2\frac{1}{2}$ in., (*b*) $1\frac{1}{2}$ in., (*c*) $1\frac{1}{4}$ in.?

18. In the previous question how far will (*a*) 18 turns, (*b*) 24 turns, move the head?

19. A kilometre is $\frac{5}{8}$ of a mile. What distance in miles is equivalent to $6\frac{2}{5}$ km.?

20. How many turns on the coils of the transformer will be required (assuming 8 turns per volt) for:

(*a*) Stepping-down 240 volts to 6 volts?
(*b*) Stepping-down 200 volts to 12 volts?
(*c*) Stepping-down 250 volts to 10 volts?
(*d*) Stepping-down 230 volts to 8 volts?

21. What number of teeth will give (i) 5 revolutions per second, (ii) 1 revolution per second in the example given on Page 127.

For questions 22 and 23 follow the examples given on Page 128.

22. What effort is required to raise a load of 1 cwt. if the hydraulic jack has a mechanical advantage of (*a*) 25 : 1, (*b*) 49 : 1?

23. The area of the effort plunger is $\frac{3}{4}$ sq. in.: what area is needed on the load plunger to give a mechanical advantage of (*a*) 40 : 1, (*b*) 75 : 1?

24. If you made the choice of 77 triangles instead of $76\frac{12}{13}$ for the gramophone disk described on Page 131, would the disk be running fast or slow for a stationary pattern?

25. The B.B.C. gramophone turntables are run at a speed of $33\frac{1}{3}$ r.p.m. for their own disk recordings. What number of equal triangles would you expect to find on the stroboscope for checking this speed?

26. Before 78 r.p.m. was adopted as the standard speed for gramophone records, 80 r.p.m. was in common use. Design a stroboscope for this speed.

27. Concrete is made from sand and cement in the ratio of $3\frac{1}{2}$: 1. What quantities of each are needed to make up 2 cwt.?

28. What current (amperes) will flow in each of two conductors, 1 ohm and 4 ohms, arranged in parallel if the total load is found to be 3 amperes?

29. Share a current of $1\frac{1}{2}$ amperes between conductors of 1 ohm, 2 ohms and 3 ohms arranged in parallel.

30. Gears of 35 teeth and 16 teeth are in mesh. The speed of the larger wheel is 40 r.p.m.: what is the speed of the smaller?

31. Gunpowder is a mixture of nitre, sulphur and charcoal in the proportions 33 : 5 : 7. If there are 99 gm. of nitre, what weights of sulphur and charcoal should be mixed with it?

32. An empty bottle weighs 8 oz. Full of water it weighs 33 oz. Full of alcohol it weighs 28 oz. What is the density of alcohol relative to that of water?

33. A journey by car took $3\frac{1}{4}$ hours at an average speed of 26 m.p.h. What average speed would be needed to do it in $2\frac{1}{2}$ hours?

CHAPTER V

FURTHER OPERATIONS IN ARITHMETIC

CHAPTER III shows the usefulness of a decimal system that extends to fractions (after a decimal point) derived from our ordinary method of counting and writing in tens. It may be advisable to read it again before going on with this chapter so that you appreciate what decimal fractions are.

The metric system, first introduced in France, is used all over the world, especially by scientists and engineers, because of its simplicity. There is one standard unit for each kind of measure, with greater and smaller groupings of tens or tenths: it is, in fact, a decimal system of measure.

The standard unit of length is the metre, a little more than the English yard. A large distance of travel may be given as 527 Km. (kilometres), which means 527,000 m. (metres). A length of platinum wire might be stated as 12 mm. (millimetres), which means ·012 m. Intermediate groupings are named dekametre (10 m.), hectometre (100 m.), decimetre (·1 m.) and centimetre (·01 m.).

Similarly, weight is measured in terms of the gramme (gm.), volume in terms of the litre (equal to a cubic decimetre). There is not a metric measure of time.

As we pass on now to further basic operations, we should bear in mind that we shall still be dealing with numbers, and the need for clear mental images of what we are doing is the same as before. It should also be remembered that decimals are not a different number language but the old familiar one with an extension of its usefulness.

ADDITION AND SUBTRACTION

(i) Standard blocks are used in the engineering workshop for setting up accurately a thickness that may be required in making a test. The full range of blocks contains four series.

Series A ..	·1001 in. to ·1009 in.	by intervals of ·0001 in.	9 blocks
Series B ..	·101 in. to ·149 in.	by intervals of ·001 in.	49 blocks
Series C ..	·05 in. to ·95 in.	by intervals of ·05 in.	19 blocks
Series D ..	1 in., 2 in., 3 in. and 4 in. ..	.. ..	4 blocks

Thus, a thickness of 3·4567 in. could be made by combining the following selections:

A ..	·1007	in.
B ..	·106	in.
C ..	·25	in.
D ..	3	in.
	3·4567	in.

You should notice two things about this example. First, four blocks only need be used. These blocks are true within certain stated limits, but if we put a great number of them together the many slight inaccuracies might add up to an amount which can no longer be regarded as negligible. The second point to note is that the procedure for selection is to progress from series A to series D in that order.

Here is another example. A thickness of 7·1825 in. is made up as follows:

A	..	·1005 in.
B	..	·132 in.
C	..	·95 in.
D	..	4 in.
		2 in.
		7·1825 in.

Thicknesses less than ·1000 in. may be prepared by setting up two combinations side by side, the difference between which is the thickness required. For example, the step between a ·1008-in. block and a ·1003-in. block is ·0005 in.

(ii) The angle of a conical hole is measured by lowering into it two spheres, one after the other, and then measuring the distance between their centres.

This distance is obtained by measuring the distance of the top of each ball from the same base line.

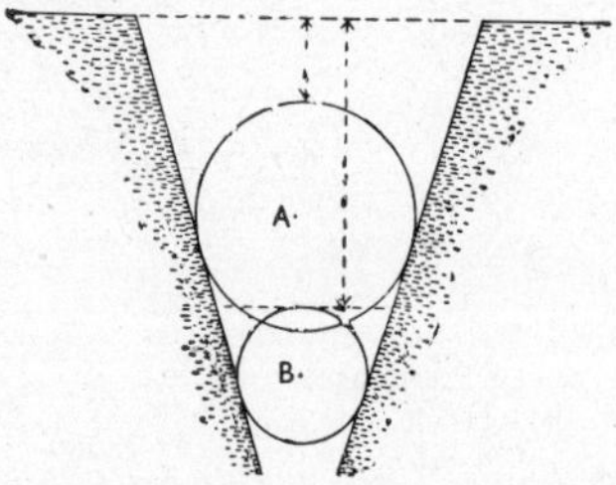

Suppose the large one gives a distance of 1·63 cm.
and the small one gives a distance of 5·22 cm.

The radii of the spheres are known to be 2 cm. and 1·5 cm.

To calculate the result, we need to know the distance between A and B. One way is to find the depths of A and B (by additions) and then to work out their difference. What is your value for AB?

When you have looked into Chapter XI you will find it quite simple to use this result to complete the calculation of the angle of the hole.

VERNIERS

Measuring lengths is an everyday necessity in many walks of life. Yard-sticks, tape-measures, rulers, chain measures, are well known to most of us, and we have little difficulty in laying them against the object to be measured and reading them. Where the measurement must be made to a finer degree of accuracy, however, these instruments may not be of much use. Two components which are to be fitted together may need to be made within small limits of error: they will require something more sensitive than tapes or sticks.

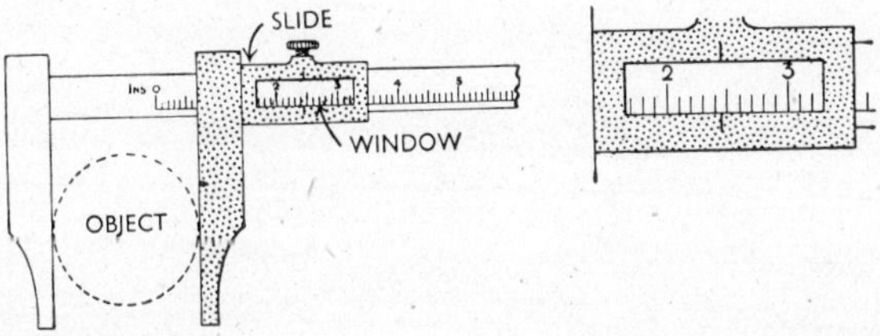

The kind of gauge shown above is better than a plain rule: the window moves over a fixed scale, and a scratch on the side of the window indicates the reading to be taken from the scale. In our example, the reading will be between 2·4 and 2·5. Is it 2·45 or 2·46? The vernier is a refinement that enables us to state the measurement within finer limits. Instead of a single indicator scratch, the side of the window carries a small scale, thus:

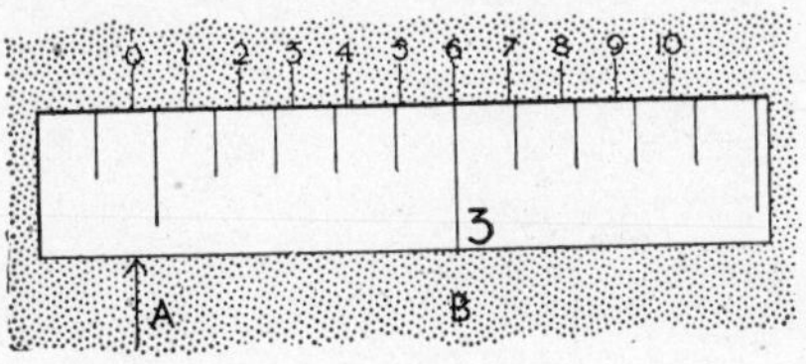

Intervals of ·09 in.

Intervals of ·1 in.

The reading at the arrow is now obtained by finding the marks on the two scales that are coincident, i.e., the point *B*, and reading the number on the small vernier scale at this point, i.e., 6.

This digit is added to the right of those given by the main scale, i.e., 2·4, giving the complete reading 2·46.

The measurement from the left up to *A* will clearly be equal to the distance up to *B* less the distance *AB*. In our example, the reading is, therefore,

$$3{\cdot}00 \text{ inches} - 6\times 0{\cdot}09 \text{ in.}$$
$$= 3{\cdot}00 - 0{\cdot}54 \text{ in.}$$
$$= 2{\cdot}46 \text{ in.}$$

There is a good deal of mathematical exercise involved in making a vernier gauge for oneself, and if you are a handyman you would find many a use for it. You could make one like that suggested by the diagram out of an adjustable spanner, or you might prefer to make one entirely from scratch, in wood or metal. A coarse scale is the best to start on, and inches are good units for this. Afterwards, you might make a centimetre vernier gauge: that would be more of a challenge to your skill as a craftsman.

Take your readings thus:—

(*a*) The nearest lower graduation on the main scale,

together with (*b*) The digit over the graduation line in the vernier which coincides with a line in the main scale.

Then check by calculation as we did in the original example.

(iii) Verniers are not used nearly as widely as micrometers. It is not easy to be sure where the point of alignment lies. The micrometer uses a similar idea, but is much safer to read, and is capable of giving much more accurate readings.

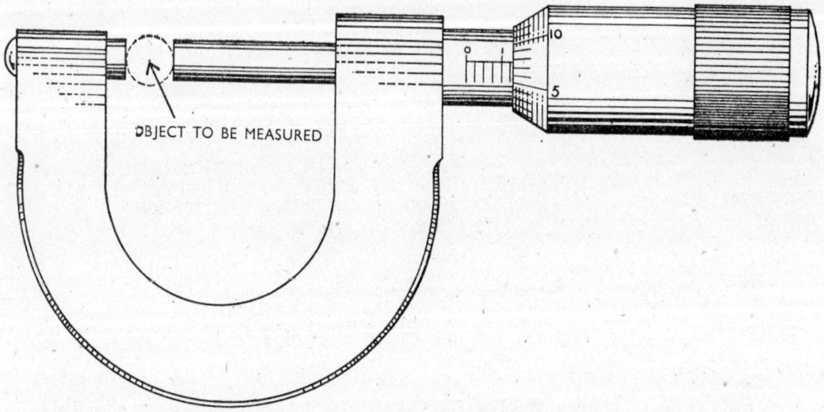

One arm of a U-piece carries a cylindrical arm on which is the main scale: through this arm passes a screw which can be moved up to the object to be measured by turning the knurled end on the right, which moves over the cylindrical arm.

One revolution of the adjustment carries the screw horizontally through exactly one division on the main scale. The reading is found by noting the highest graduation exposed on the main scale and adding to this the further measurement represented by a fraction of an extra revolution of the screw i.e., the same fraction of one interval of the main scale.

Example:

The reading shown here is:

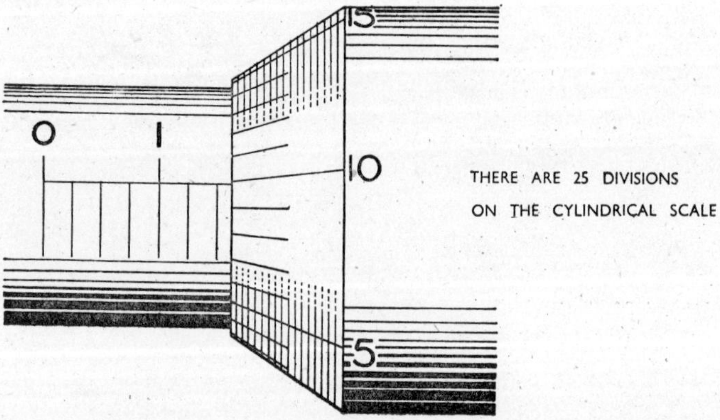

(*a*) Main scale 1·5, because each division is 0·25.
(*b*) Cylindrical scale $\frac{10}{25}$ of ·25, i.e., 0·10
making altogether 1·60 units.

On an engineer's micrometer, these units would normally be tenths of an inch: our reading would then be 0·160 in. Such an instrument, then, will give readings to the nearest thousandth of an inch. The limit of accuracy is determined by the craftsmanship of the maker—not in the personal factor of the man reading the scale, for that is easy.

(iv) How much expansion to a 100 ft. girder will be caused by a rise in temperature of 15°C (coefficient of linear expansion of iron = 0·000012 per 1°C)?

As in all mathematical problems, we must seek information first. The information here is the statement in brackets, namely:

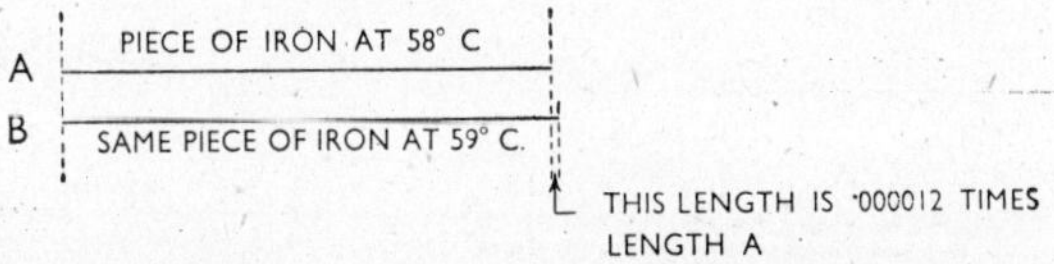

The increase in length of a piece of iron is in the ratio of 12:1,000,000 $\left(\frac{12}{1000000} \text{ or } \cdot 000012\right)$ to its original length when its temperature rises through 1°C.

Having understood the information we can manipulate it to make it yield an answer to our particular question.

Original length = 100 ft.

Expansion for 1°C increase in temperature = 100 × ·000012 ft.

But our rise in temperature is 15°C, so we must increase this answer 15 times.

Expansion for 15°C rise in temperature = 15 × 100 × ·000012 ft.

The answer would obviously be handier as a number of inches.

$$\begin{aligned} \text{Expansion} &= 15 \times \cdot 000012 \times 12 \times 100 \text{ in.} \\ &= 180 \times \cdot 0012 \text{ in.} \\ &= 18 \times \cdot 012 \text{ in.} \\ &= 0 \cdot 216 \text{ in.} \end{aligned}$$

(v) The construction of the Forth Bridge was completed by bolting together cantilevers which had been built out towards each other from adjacent booms.

The engineers had calculated that the expansions caused by the sun would bring the opposing plates together for fastening, but an east wind sprang up at the critical moment. To fasten the west part of the union would probably have resulted in a major disaster by nightfall. The chief engineer ordered rafts of straw and wood to be burned on the east side. This raised the temperature sufficiently to complete the bolting operation.

The chief engineer had to do a rapid calculation. Let us set about it ourselves.

Given:Length of a half span of bridge = 855 ft.
Coefficient of linear expansion of iron = ·000012 per 1°C.
What rise in temperature is needed to close the gap of 2 in.?

Expansion of one half span = 1 in.

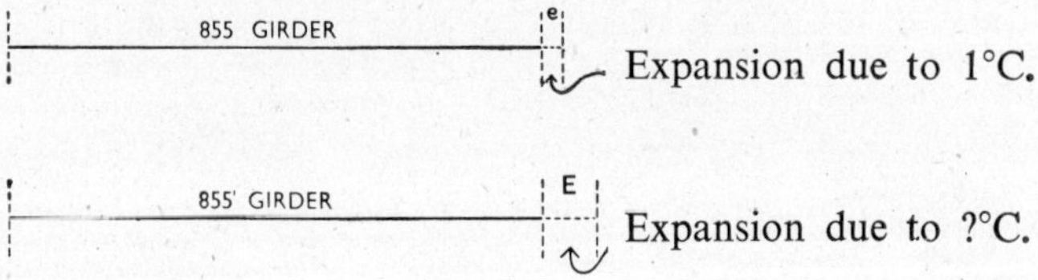

The diagram shows that we must find out how many lengths the same as *e* are contained in *E*.

Expansion of 0·000012×855 ft. is caused by rise in temperature of 1°C.

$\therefore$ Expansion of $\frac{1}{12}$ ft. is caused by $1 \times \dfrac{\frac{1}{12}}{0{\cdot}000012 \times 855}$ °C.

$\therefore$ Rise in temperature required $= \dfrac{1}{12 \times 0{\cdot}000012 \times 855}$ °C.

We must pause here for a moment. We have treated the numbers in our argument just as if they were integers (whole numbers) and now we find ourselves face to face with an awkward-looking expression.

We will estimate the answer approximately:

$$12 \times 855 \times 0{\cdot}000012 \simeq 10{,}000 \times 0{\cdot}000012$$
$$\simeq 1 \times 0{\cdot}12$$

and $$\frac{1}{0{\cdot}12} \simeq 8,$$

giving the rise in temperature required = 8°C.

The chief engineer had to decide whether he could raise the temperature of the east side of the bridge by this amount in time to save the situation. (We have assumed the gap to be closed was 2 in., whereas it was probably a good deal less than this.)

You may feel dissatisfied with our decision to scout the hard work by approximate working, but you must admit that it is sufficient for this particular problem. Were accurate calculation necessary, we should be able to resort to logarithms or the slide-rule to make the calculation easy. Or, we might do the sum without such aids, thus:

(*a*) Work out the denominator. $12 \times 0.000012 \times 855 = 0{\cdot}12312$
(*b*) Divide 1 by 0·12312,

i.e., divide 100,000 by 12,312, $\dfrac{1}{0{\cdot}12312} = 8{\cdot}12\ldots.$

We have now met decimal fractions in all the usual contexts—addition, subtraction, multiplication and division—and you will notice that we have not laid down any mechanical techniques for dealing with these operations. There is no need for new techniques if you will remember that decimal fractions are in every respect like ordinary integers: the decimal point is only omitted from whole numbers because we can understand without its help. Full-stops are left out of posters, press headings, chapter headings, etc., for the same reason, although they are indispensable in literature.

The working for (i) $\frac{0{\cdot}05 \times 27}{3{\cdot}2}$ is precisely the same as for (ii) $\frac{500 \times 2{\cdot}7}{0{\cdot}032}$, and for (iii) $\frac{5 \times 27}{32}$ and the three answers will contain the same pattern of figures, 421875.

The size of the result is then decided by examining the question of size separately.

(i) $\frac{27}{3{\cdot}2}$ is roughly 9, and $9 \times 0{\cdot}05 \simeq 0{\cdot}45$,

giving the answer 0·421875

(ii) $\frac{2{\cdot}7}{0{\cdot}032} = \frac{270}{3{\cdot}2} \simeq 90$,

and $90 \times 500 = 45{,}000$,

giving the answer 42,187·5

(iii) $\frac{5 \times 27}{32} \simeq 5$, giving the answer 4·21875

This approximate working for the size of the answer is done quite easily after a little practice without writing. It is so important that you should be facile in doing it that we give you some examples before going on.

$$2{\cdot}89 \times 51{\cdot}5 \simeq 150 \quad (3 \times 50)$$
$$35{\cdot} \times 0{\cdot}24 \simeq 7 \quad (35 \times {\cdot}2)$$
$$\frac{86}{9{\cdot}3} \simeq 9 \quad (86 \div 9)$$
$$\frac{25{\cdot}2}{0{\cdot}52} \simeq 50 \quad (250 \div 5)$$
$$\frac{0{\cdot}036}{4{\cdot}25} \simeq 0{\cdot}009 \quad ({\cdot}036 \div 4)$$
$$\frac{7{\cdot}25}{0{\cdot}0064} \simeq 1{,}200 \quad (7{,}000 \div 6)$$

Where numbers are very large or very small we save ourselves a lot of writing by a kind of shorthand, which also enables us to estimate the sizes of results of calculations with certainty. We shall consider the matter a little later in this chapter.

SHORT METHODS

Multiplying and dividing by numbers which are simply related to the integral powers of 10 (i.e., 100, 1,000) can be carried out quickly without written working.

$$\text{Regard } 25 \text{ as } \frac{100}{4},$$

$$125 \text{ as } \frac{1{,}000}{8}.$$

Then multiplication and division by these numbers will involve the use of a one-figure instead of a two- or three-figure operation.

Examples: 25×353

$$= \frac{35{,}300}{4} = 8{,}825 \quad \text{(Rough working: } 20\times400=8{,}000)$$

$125\times62{\cdot}75$

$$= \frac{62{,}750}{8} = 7{,}843{\cdot}75 \quad \text{(Rough working: } 120\times60=7{,}200)$$

$827\div25$

$= 8{\cdot}27\times4 = 33{\cdot}08$ (Rough working suggests answer to be between 30 and 40)

$173{\cdot}75\div125$

$= 0{\cdot}17375\times8 = 1{\cdot}39$ (Rough working suggests answer to be between 1 and 2)

Similarly: $33\frac{1}{3}$ should be regarded as $\frac{100}{3}$ and

$16\frac{2}{3}$ should be regarded as $\frac{100}{6}$, and so on.

Give yourself a few similar exercises: work by the short method, and by the long method if you feel you need a check on your accuracy.

Again, one may find that the multiplier is annoyingly approximate to a number which would give easy mental working. In such cases, it may be worth while to multiply by the desirable number and correct the result by the necessary difference.

Example: 998×37

This is done mentally by two stages:

$$(1{,}000\times37) - (2\times37)$$

From 37,000 take away 74: this gives 36,926.

After a little practice, results to this kind of sum can be written down without much mental effort.

$$99\times85 \;(= 8{,}500 - 85) = 8{,}415$$

The value of a short method is that it will save time and labour. If you find yourself groping for a short method and fumbling in applying it, then it is not, in fact, a short method, and you would have been wiser to calculate your result by the humdrum routine. We suggest you entertain yourself with exercise 8 appearing at the end of the chapter, so that you may become familiar with the principles underlying some common short cuts. Afterwards, you will find it easier to detect occasions for using them.

HOW TO TACKLE MATHEMATICAL PROBLEMS

In the work that has been done so far we have made use of any device which might help us towards the goal. The secret of success in arithmetic is to look at the problem as one of those little challenges of life that abound in every working day. The calculation is only incidental to the fundamental task of appreciating the nature of the problem.

The lorry driver who is to pick up a load of granite and deliver it on a new housing estate is troubled very little by manipulation of the various controls (steering wheel, clutch, accelerator, brake, choke, etc.) by means of which he carries out his task. His main preoccupation is that of appreciating the general problem and organizing his resources towards smooth working.

So it must be with the mathematical assignment. There is no room for misgivings as to whether the job can be done: we must make it our first business to understand the problem and our many small arithmetical skills will then enable us to carry out the manipulations involved.

We repeat the sequence advised in Chapter IV:

(1) To read the problem carefully and to understand it as a problem.

(2) To arrange the information given so that it points towards the solution.

(3) To resolve the calculation by the simplest methods.

We hope you will have noticed two evidences of care in the examples so far considered.

(*a*) To use arithmetical language correctly throughout the argument.

(*b*) To use diagrams and sketches properly labelled to help us to see the nature of the problem.

The reader is advised most earnestly to make tidy and methodical layout of the question a matter of strict habit. If you are working in shillings do not tire of writing *s.* for shillings every time a number of shillings is involved; otherwise you may well find yourself putting £ or pence later on in the proceedings. Put in the operative signs ; $\times$, $=$, $+$, and so on at every stage of working, and state clearly what your working is to yield. A sketch is of no use without labels. You may be inspired by it at one moment and baffled the next unless you label it in your moment of inspiration.

(vi) A floating body displaces an amount of water equal in weight to itself (1 cu. ft. of water weighs 1,000 oz.).

What depth of canvas bag of average area 300 sq. ft. would be required to float a 30-ton tank for crossing a stream?

$$1{,}000 \text{ oz. needs } 1 \text{ cu. ft.}$$

$$\therefore \quad 30 \text{ tons or } 30\times 2{,}240\times 16 \text{ oz. needs } \frac{30\times 16\times 2{,}240}{1{,}000} \text{ cu. ft.}$$

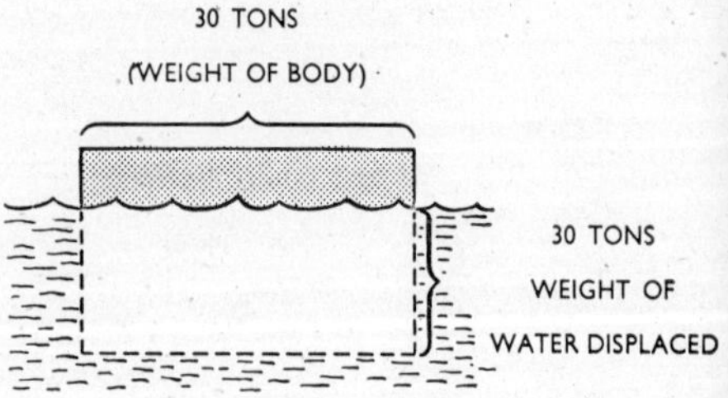

(Leave the main labour of calculation in the hope of cancellation later on.)

$$\text{Depth} = \frac{\text{Volume}}{\text{Area}} = \frac{\cancel{30}\times 16\times 2{,}24\cancel{0}}{1{,}000\times \cancel{300}}\text{ ft.}$$
$$= 16\times{\cdot}224\text{ ft.}$$
$$= 3{\cdot}6\text{ ft.}$$

Thus we could feel safe in making a box-shaped canvas bag for the purpose if its depth were, say, 4 ft. 6 in. But, of course, the problem of stability would need to be solved as well.

RATES AND SPEEDS

A good many of life's little problems require us to consider quantities of different kinds at the same moment. For example, these statements are incomplete and, therefore, meaningless.

The rocket rushed along at the terrifying speed of 2,200 ft.

Today's price of milk is 4d.

The thermal contraction of lead between setting and cooling is $\frac{1}{2}$ in.

The petrol consumption of my car is 25 miles.

We have only to add per second, per pint, per foot and per gallon and the clouds disappear.

This way of tying one kind of quantity with another is called rate. When we say that the rate of progress in building in a city is 30 houses per week, this means that the more weeks we consider, the more thirties of houses are built.

A few problems will show that where we are concerned with rates the arithmetical instrument used is usually ratio.

Examples.

How long will it take to build 2,500 houses in the city just quoted, if the rate of building is increased to 36 per week?

36 houses in 1 week
2,500 houses in ? weeks

We need to know how many times 36 is contained in 2,500, for each 36 represents one week.

$$\text{Thus, time taken is, } \frac{\overset{625}{\cancel{2{,}500}}}{\underset{9}{\cancel{36}}} = 69\tfrac{4}{9}\text{ weeks.}$$

The round answer will be 70 *weeks.*

When we refer to speeds, we usually consider the distance covered in one unit of time.

For example:

(*a*) A car travels at 60 miles per hour.
(*b*) A meteor travels at 10 miles per minute.
(*c*) Light travels at 186,000 miles per second.
(*d*) A snail travels at 4 feet per hour.
(*e*) A wheel revolves at 2,000 revolutions per minute.

The same procedure holds good for the other rates; the second quantity is one unit of its kind, thus; 25 miles per gallon, 3 gallons per hour, 2s. 6d. per hour, 20 oz. per pint.

Now it frequently happens that a rate involves two variables of the same kind.

Discount in sale	=	2s. in the pound.
Birth rate	=	16·3 per 1,000 people.
Water content	=	7 parts in 10 by weight.
Wastage of material in a job	=	6 oz. in 1 lb.
Rate of profit for retailer for a certain class of goods	=	3d. in 1s.
Efficiency of a machine	=	13 out of 20.

It makes comparisons and calculations much easier in most of these cases to express the two quantities as a fraction of standard form.

(vii) In a sample operation prior to large-scale production, it was found that to make a component weighing $3\frac{1}{8}$ oz., $5\frac{1}{2}$ oz. of steel were needed. What is the rate of wastage?

$$\text{Wastage out of } 5\tfrac{1}{2}\text{ oz.} = 5\tfrac{1}{2}\text{ oz.} - 3\tfrac{1}{8}\text{ oz.}$$
$$= 2\tfrac{3}{8}\text{ oz.}$$

This could be given as an answer, but it would be unwieldy.

As a ratio, the wastage could be expressed $\dfrac{2\frac{3}{8}}{5\frac{1}{2}}$

$$\text{or rate of wastage} = \frac{19}{44} \text{ (19 out of 44)}$$

and this would tell the same tale with better effect.

In the form of a decimal, this ratio would be 0·432:1 (to three significant figures).

As we have already noted, it will be much easier to compare this rate with a similar one if they are both in decimal form. We may even improve on this, however,

$$\frac{0{\cdot}432}{1} = \frac{43{\cdot}2}{100}$$

and, written in the more familiar form, 43·2%, this becomes a highly convenient way of expressing the rate of wastage.

Percentage, then, is a particular form of fraction in which the denominator is fixed at one hundred (cent).

(viii) Which gives the more light, an 80-watt lamp rated at 85% efficiency, or a 100-watt lamp at 65% efficiency?

80-watt lamp gives 85% of 80 watts in the form of light.

$$= \frac{\overset{17}{\cancel{85}}}{\underset{20}{\cancel{100}}} \times \overset{4}{\cancel{80}} = 68 \text{ watts.}$$

100-watt lamp gives 65% of 100 watts.
$= 65$ watts.

So the 80-watt lamp gives more light.

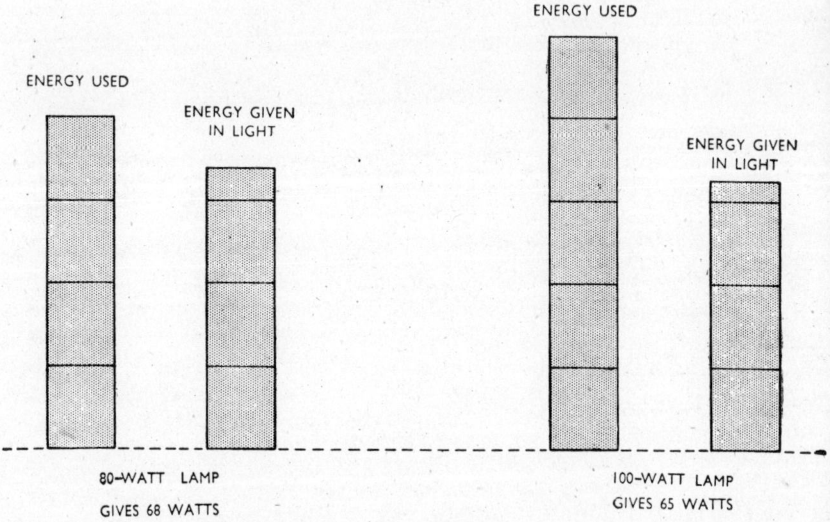

(ix) To find the percentage proportion of water present in certain crystals a sample was weighed, dehydrated and re-weighed. From the given readings find the result.

Weight of container empty	=	4·250 gm.
Weight of container and crystals	=	6·085 gm.
Weight of container + residue	=	5·305 gm.

(*a*) We need to know the weight of crystals and
(*b*) The weight of water that has been removed.

CRYSTALS CONSIST OF POWDER AND WATER

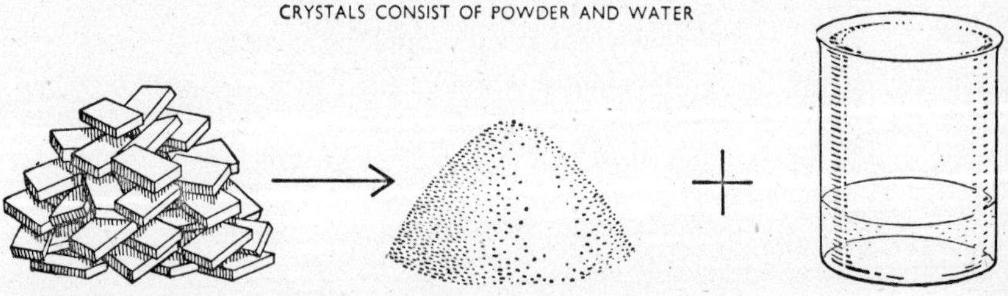

(*a*) Weight of crystals $= 6{\cdot}085 - 4{\cdot}25$ gm.
(*b*) Weight of water $= 6{\cdot}085 - 5{\cdot}305$ gm.

The subtraction calls for no new skill—we set the working out in columns as when dealing with whole numbers.

$$\text{Fraction of water present} = \frac{{\cdot}78 \text{ gm.}}{1{\cdot}835 \text{ gm.}} = \frac{780}{1{,}835}$$

for a ratio still has the same value if we magnify both parts in the same way.

The value of the fraction is ascertained quickly by the help of logarithms or a slide-rule (see Chapter X); of course, it can be worked out by direct division, but four figures rather deter one from this unnecessary labour.

$$\text{Fraction of water present} = \frac{780}{1{,}835} = 0{\cdot}425$$

And as 0·42 and 42% are precisely the same thing,

$$\text{Percentage of water present} = 42{\cdot}5\%$$

Having embarked on this ingenious extension of the number system which we learned as infants, we may as well follow it up to find out if it has any other advantages.

(x) *A* and *B* are arguing about their relative prowess in batting. *A* has totalled 283 runs in 22 innings, while *B's* performance is 270 in 21 innings; neither performance is very good.

Their arithmetic took them to these results for their averages:

A: $12\frac{19}{22}$ runs per innings.
B: $12\frac{6}{7}$ runs per innings.

But neither would confess that his was lower than the other's. Which is the greater, $\frac{19}{22}$ or $\frac{6}{7}$?

We are going to seize on the fact that $\frac{19}{22}$ is not really the end of the division sum. It has been left half finished simply because *A* and *B* did not know how to finish it. We will go forward with our superior knowledge that 19 can be given an endless train of noughts provided we put in a point to mark the end of whole numbers. We then work out the sum:

$$\frac{19{\cdot}00000\ldots\ldots\ldots\ldots \text{ as far as you like.}}{22}$$

and get 0·8636, that is, *A*'s average is 12·8636
and 0·8571, that is, *B*'s average is 12·8571
thereby settling the dispute beyond doubt in favour of *A*.

We have opened up an important field of arithmetic. The old familiar vulgar fractions, with their fraction line an ever-present challenge to our powers of division, can be transformed to the more sensible decimal system and brought under a more convenient discipline.

You will have no difficulty in accepting the following conclusions:

$\frac{1}{2} = 0{\cdot}5$ $\qquad \frac{3}{5} = {\cdot}6$
$\frac{1}{4} = 0{\cdot}25$ $\qquad \frac{5}{8} = {\cdot}625$

and it will repay you to work out a fair number of ruler fractions in decimal form and memorize those that are in common use.

You may be a bit puzzled by $\frac{1}{3}$: we write its decimal form $0{\cdot}\dot{3}$ (point 3 recurring) to save ourselves from the boredom of repeating the 3 for the rest of our days.

It is not uncommon for a vulgar fraction to lead to a recurring decimal. Here are two more:

$$5/12 = 0{\cdot}4166\ldots\ldots \text{ or } 0{\cdot}41\dot{6}$$

$$1/7 = 0{\cdot}\dot{1}4285\dot{7}$$ (the same group of figures recur, hence the two dots)

The more significant figures we consider, the more accurate is our calculation.

SHORTHAND FOR VERY LARGE AND VERY SMALL NUMBERS

(xi) The distance of the earth from the sun is 93,000,000 miles, which may be written thus:

$$\begin{aligned} 93{,}000{,}000 &= 93\times 1{,}000{,}000 \\ &= 93\times 10\times 10\times 10\times 10\times 10\times 10 \\ &= 93\times 10^6 \text{ (ninety-three times ten to the sixth).} \end{aligned}$$

This 10^6 is called the sixth power of 10, and the small six is called the index, because it shows what power is being used.

These powers of ten are very useful for expressing large and small numbers. Look at this series:

(*a*) 10,000 1,000 100 10..........

which we may now write:

(*b*) 10^4 10^3 10^2 10^1.........

The index is telling us of a certain treatment of 10 which is to be considered.

See if you can write down the next few terms of series (*a*) and then the next few of the equivalent series (*b*).

You probably had no difficulty in continuing thus:

..........100 10 1 0·1 0·01 0·001

.... 10^2 10^1 10^0 10^{-1} 10^{-2} 10^{-3}

The negative power, therefore, is instructing us to divide 1 by a power of ten instead of multiplying 1 by a power of ten—as in the first part (i.e., the whole number part) of the series.

Each of the following magnitudes is restated in this notation as a whole number multiplied by a power of 10.

Coefficient of linear expansion of glass (per °C) = 0·0000087

$= 87\times 10^{-7}$

Cosmic ray wave-length $= 0{\cdot}00000000000005$ in.
$= 5 \times 10^{-14}$ in.

Age of the earth $=$ 2,000 million years
$= 2 \times 10^{9}$ years.

Age of life on the earth $=$ 300 million years
$= 3 \times 10^{8}$ years.

Not only are these powers of 10 a useful arithmetical shorthand, they enable us to put awkward-looking calculations into a happier perspective.

(xii) The Forth Bridge has an overall length of 8,295 ft.; it is made of steel, which has a coefficient of thermal expansion of 0·000012 per 1°C. What elongation may be expected between temperatures of 10°C and 23°C?

Expansion for 13°C rise in temperature

$$= 8{,}295 \times {\cdot}000012 \times 13 \text{ ft.}$$
$$= 8{,}295 \times 1{\cdot}2 \times 10^{-5} \times 13 \times 12 \text{ in.}$$
$$= 8{\cdot}295 \times 10^{3} \times 1{\cdot}2 \times 1{\cdot}3 \times 1{\cdot}2 \times 10^{2} \times 10^{-5} \text{ in.}$$
$$= 15{\cdot}53 \times 10^{5} \times 10^{-5} \text{ in.}$$
$$= 15{\cdot}53 \text{ in.}$$

(This multiplication was carried out with a slide-rule.)

The actual procedure for working from the second line is to calculate, regardless of sizes, to get 1,553, the pattern of the answer, and then, mentally, to collect up the powers of ten, thus:

$$8{,}295 = 8{\cdot}295 \times 10^{3}$$
$$12 = 1{\cdot}2 \quad \times 10^{1}$$
$$13 = 1{\cdot}3 \quad \times 10^{1}$$
$$0{\cdot}000012 = 1{\cdot}2 \quad \times 10^{-5}$$

The continued product, then, $= 15{\cdot}53 \times 10^{(3+1+1-5)}$
$= 15{\cdot}53$ in.

We are reminded again of the fact that the multiplication and division of decimal fractions is carried out just as for whole numbers. The decimal point must be placed in the result by examination.

(xiii) We want to make a mercury-in-glass thermometer, which makes mercury under thermal expansion move along a capillary tube. Our special purpose is to cover a range of temperature of 50° F with good big markings.

With a stem 10 in. long we should then have 0·2 in. $\equiv$ 1°F, and we could measure to about 0·1°F.

We will find out what length on the scale for 1°F would be needed if the bore of the capillary tube were ·00001 sq. in. in area and we were using 1 cu. in. of mercury (Fig. *A* on page 156).

Since the coefficient of apparent expansion of mercury in glass is 0·000087 per 1°F., the total apparent expansion of 1 cu. in. for 1°F=0·000087 cu. in. (Fig. *B*)=1 sq. in.×0·000087 in

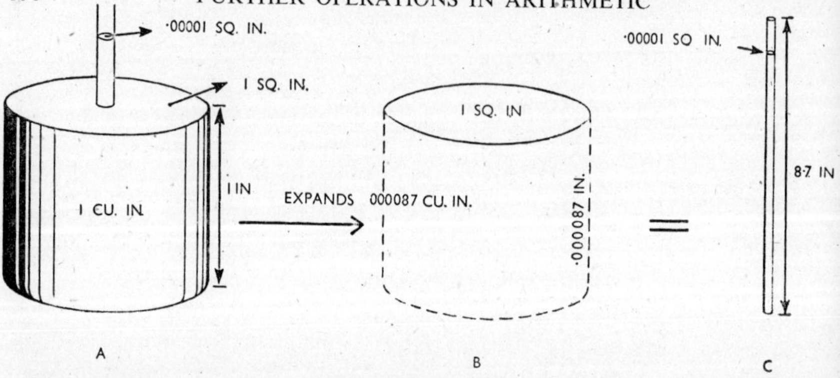

Now if this expansion is to be squeezed into a very narrow tube (Fig. *C*) it will occupy a greater length, in this case 8·7 in., because $0{\cdot}000087\times 1 = 8{\cdot}7\times 0{\cdot}00001$.

In other words, a bulb containing 1 cu. in. of mercury would cause a rise of 8·7 in. in a capillary tube of 0·00001 sq. in. bore for every rise in temperature of 1°F. This would require a stem 50 times as long, i.e., 435 in., to cope with a temperature range of 50°F.

If we want the thermometer scale to be 0·2 in. ≡ 1°F, instead of 8·7 ≡ 1°F, we must reduce the amount of mercury to $\frac{0{\cdot}2}{8{\cdot}7}$ of the 1 cu. in. we were just using, or use a larger bore. A bulb containing 0·023 cu. in. of mercury will meet our requirements.

THE KINDS OF NUMBER WE HAVE MET SO FAR

We have now gone a long way from the simple integers 1 to 9: we have been carried along by necessity born of experience, and have met fractions, decimals and percentages. To make sure that you have understood and appreciated the family tree of arithmetic, we will consider this matter calmly and carefully before going on.

Beside the integers, such as 7, 31, 582, 1,765, numbers are more frequently a mixture of whole numbers and fractions, or fractions alone, such as $\frac{1}{4}$, $3\frac{1}{2}$, $294\frac{7}{8}$, $76\frac{3}{11}$.

The fractional bits that crop up in calculation and measurement are so varied that often it is not easy to see how one bit compares with another (e.g., $\frac{1}{4}$ and $\frac{3}{11}$). Again, these vulgar fractions contain two parts instead of one part like the well-behaved integers; and they are an ever-present challenge to our power of division.

Therefore, we extend the decimal relationship used among the integers to these awkward fractional bits, and call them decimal fractions instead of vulgar fractions. Here are the vulgar fractions from above in their new decimal form:

$$0{\cdot}25,\quad 3{\cdot}5,\quad 294{\cdot}875,\quad 76{\cdot}\dot{2}\dot{7}$$

A vulgar fraction can be transformed into a decimal simply by carrying out the division sum implied; $\frac{1}{4}$ means 1 divided by 4. If it is necessary to express a decimal fraction as a vulgar fraction, we can do so at once by promoting the figures to whole-number rank and giving them a denominator (which must be a power of 10) to show that they are in reality of humble status after all.

$$\cdot 25 = \frac{25}{100} \quad \text{which can be simplified by cancelling,}$$

$$\text{and } 294{\cdot}875 = 294\frac{875}{1{,}000} \quad \text{which also can be simplified by cancelling.}$$

Ratios have the appearance, and often the effect, of vulgar fractions, and when they are used to operate on other numbers, they are always fractions used as multipliers. They may, therefore, have the form of decimals.

$$\text{Ratio of 3 to 4} \equiv \frac{3}{4} \equiv \frac{\cdot 75}{1}$$

We may include the denominator 1 because a ratio is essentially a comparison of *two* numbers, and without the 1 we should only see one number.

The standard denominator 100 is extremely useful for conveying information about ratios and certain kinds of rate. Ratios and rates expressed in this standard form are known as percentages.

For example, a 55% government grant on certain expenditure of a local authority means that:

(*a*) The government pay £55 out of every £100 expenditure.
(*b*) The government pay 55 pence of every 100 pence expenditure.
(*c*) The government pay 11 shillings of every £1 expenditure and so on.

The important thing to remember about 55% is that it contains two numbers which are both under consideration: the 100, though not there to be seen in figures, is none the less important. If you always remember to think of $12\frac{1}{2}\%$ as $\frac{12\frac{1}{2}}{100}$, or $12\frac{1}{2}$ per 100, you are not likely to have any difficulty with percentages.

To sum up this little aside, look at these statements, and see if you agree that they are true:

$$\frac{1}{8} = 0{\cdot}125 = 12{\cdot}5\% \text{ or } 12\tfrac{1}{2}\%$$

$$\frac{3}{2} = 1{\cdot}5 = 150\%$$

$$40\% = \frac{40}{100} \text{ or } \frac{2}{5} = 0{\cdot}4$$

MATHEMATICS OF THE SIMPLE PENDULUM

(xiv) Make a simple pendulum by suspending a weight of some regular shape on a very light thread, fastened to a nail or hook.

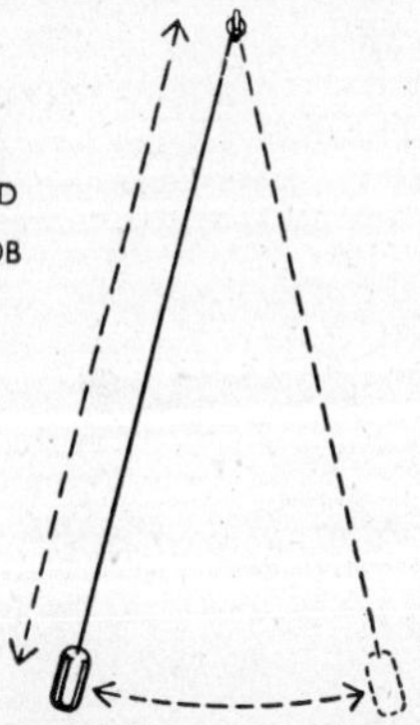
LENGTH MEASURED
TO CENTRE OF BOB
AN OSCILLATION IS ONE COMPLETE
TO-AND-FRO MOVEMENT

Let it swing freely through a small angle, and find the time taken for one oscillation. You will find that, provided the angle is not large, the period of oscillation is always the same.

INFLUENCE OF LENGTH

Now find the period for different lengths of the pendulum, and see if you can find what mathematical relationship there is between length and period. As you might not succeed in making any satisfactory discovery, we suggest you proceed in this way.

Measure the period for a short length, say 1 ft.

Then repeat for a length twice as great, and again for a length three times as great. Put your results in a table and you will get this:

	Length in ft.	*Time for 20 oscillations in sec.*	*Period in sec.*
(*a*)	1	22	1·1
(*b*)	2	31	1·55
(*c*)	3	38	1·9
(*d*)	4	42	2·1

Clearly, the period increases when the length is increased, but not by any of the simple relationships we have met previously. There is only one pair of results that seem to hint at a relationship—namely (*a*) and (*d*).

Length in ft.	*Period in sec.*
1	1·1
4	2·1

Do you agree that the ratio of the periods here (allowing for our inaccuracies of measurement) might be 1:2? If so, ratio of lengths 1:4 is not unrelated to the ratio 1:2 of periods. Test this theory by repeating the experiment for two fresh lengths of pendulum, of which one is four times the other. You will find that the ratio of periods is again 1:2.

Now find the periods for two lengths with the ratio 1:9. This was done and the following results obtained:

	Length	*Period*	
Ratio 1:9	8 in.	·9 sec.	Ratio 1:3
	72 in.	2·7 sec.	

Are 2 and 4 related in the same way as 3 and 9? Diagrams reminiscent of Chapter III give us a clue

For two simple pendulums, then, the ratio of the lengths is equal to the ratio of the squares of the periods.

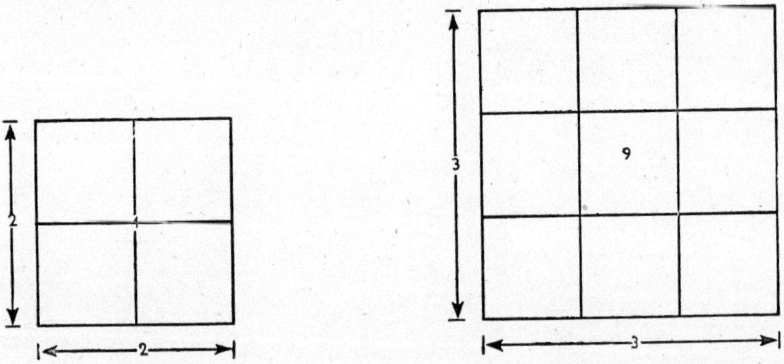

4 is the SQUARE of 2 AND 9 is the SQUARE of 3

Looking back at (*a*) and (*b*) in the first table of results, then, it would be found that the ratio of the square of 1·1 to the square of 1·55 is 1:2. Test this for yourself and then test the validity of the law with other selections from the table.

Squaring, then, is a special kind of multiplication. It is not confined to problems of area, but is needed to a surprising extent in pure, as well as applied, mathematics. We will think about it in a simple way.

(xv) The following figures tell the same tale about equilateral triangles.

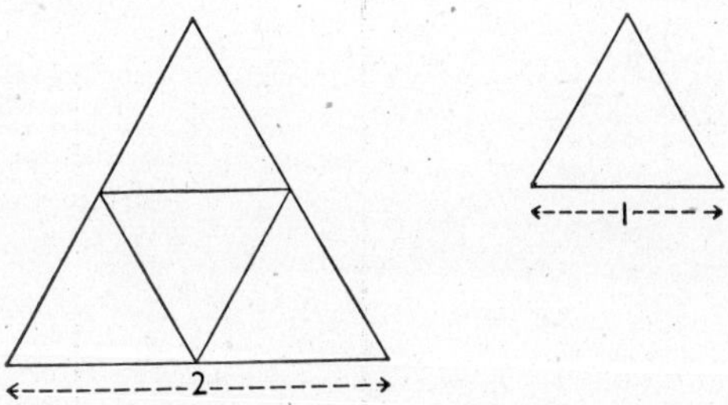

When the ratio of the sides is 2:1 the ratio of the areas is 4:1, i.e., the square of 2:1. The square of 2 is written 2^2.

Similarly, if the ratio of sides is 3:1, the ratio of the areas is 3^2:1, i.e., 9:1, as shown by the picture appearing on top of page 160.

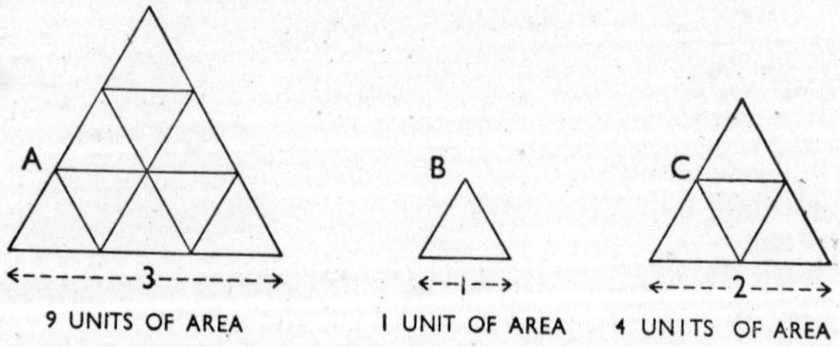

Considering A and C, ratio of sides $= 3:2$; therefore, ratio of areas $= 3^2:2^2$, i.e., $9:4$.

If you have followed so far you will see that for any figures of similar shape, the ratio of areas is the square of the ratio of linear (length) measurements.

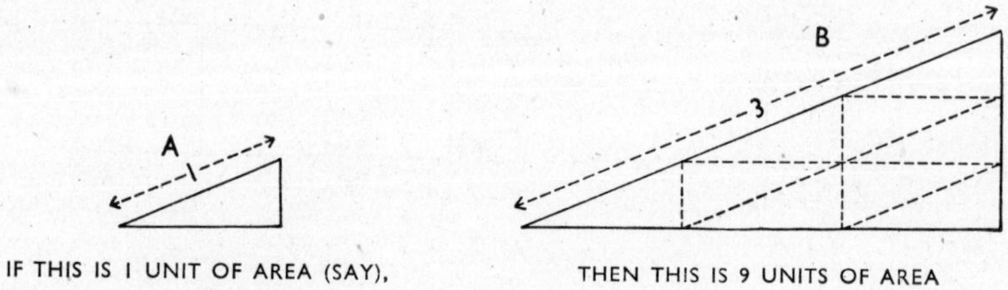

Ratio of corresponding sides $= 3:1$
Ratio of areas $= 3^2:1$
$= 9:1$

Which would be the better bargain, one square foot of plywood for one shilling or a two foot square of the same material for two shillings?

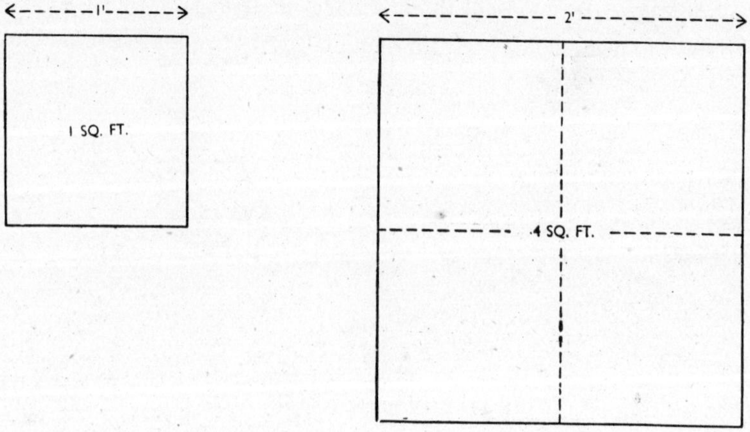

(xvi) The water supply to the workshop was carried in 1-in. piping, and was not adequate. An extra 1-in. pipe was considered as a remedy, and the replacement of the old one by a 2-in. pipe was also suggested. How would each of these improvements affect the water supply? A diagram like this

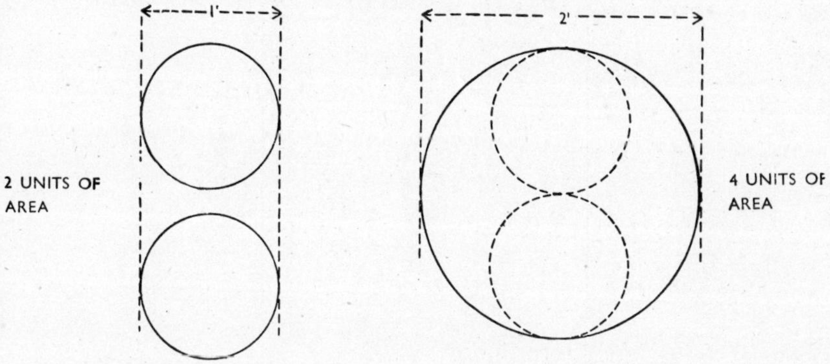

helps, but does not satisfy us as the preceding figures did, because we are not able to fit the small circles exactly into the large one. However, you will now be prepared to accept the mathematical conclusion that the 2-in. pipe will deliver four times as much water as the 1-in. pipe. You could slice four 1-in. circles into narrow strips and paste them together to fill in the 2-in. circle if you wanted to clinch the argument.

The squaring operation originates with the square (figure) but is now of importance purely as an operation, like the four rules.

We are not troubled by the squares of fractions in vulgar or decimal form. A square with a side of $\frac{1}{2}$ in. has an area of $\frac{1}{2}\times\frac{1}{2}$ sq. in.

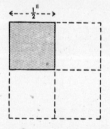

or $(\frac{1}{2})^2$ sq. in., which is clearly $\frac{1}{4}$ sq. in.

$$\text{Similarly, } \left(\frac{3}{4}\right)^2 = \frac{9}{16}$$

$$\left(3\frac{1}{3}\right)^2 = \left(\frac{10}{3}\right)^2 = \frac{100}{9} = 11\tfrac{1}{9}.$$

$$(0{\cdot}8)^2 = 0{\cdot}64$$

$$(0{\cdot}05)^2 = 0{\cdot}0025$$

We are faced with a more puzzling proposition when our problem demands calculation in the opposite direction. If we need to make a square hole with cross-sectional area of 5 sq. in., we must be able to mark out the job, and this will bring us to the question:

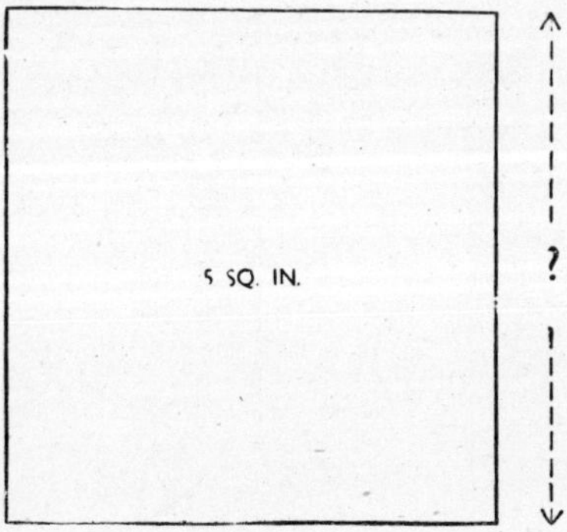

"Of what number is 5 the square?"

We know that the number we are looking for is greater than 2 because the square of 2 is 4. We also know that it is less than 3 because the square of 3 is 9.

One way of finding this elusive number known as the square root of 5, is to try squaring our guesses between 2 and 3 until we hit on the best result. The task is rather like division only more complex. Fortunately we can resort to the labour of others in the form of a table of square roots (or we may use logarithms or a slide-rule, as indeed we shall in Chapter X).

The tables tell us that the square root of 5 is 2·236 (to four significant figures). If you are sceptical you should take the trouble to multiply 2·236 by 2·236 and see what you get.

Using symbols, $\sqrt{5} = 2{\cdot}236$

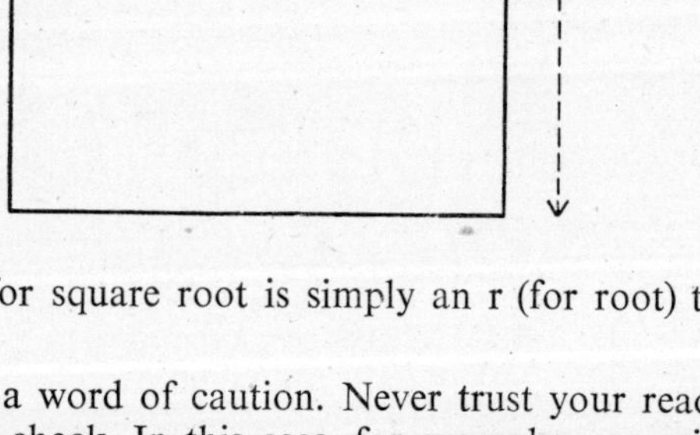

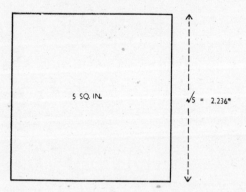

The sign $\sqrt{\ }$ for square root is simply an r (for root) that has got a bit distorted.

We must add a word of caution. Never trust your reading from a table without a rough check. In this case, for example, you might have alighted on 70·71, or 0·2236, or ·7071, as the answer. You were able to select the right one because our preliminary search for the answer established that it must be between 2 and 3.

CUBES AND CUBE ROOTS

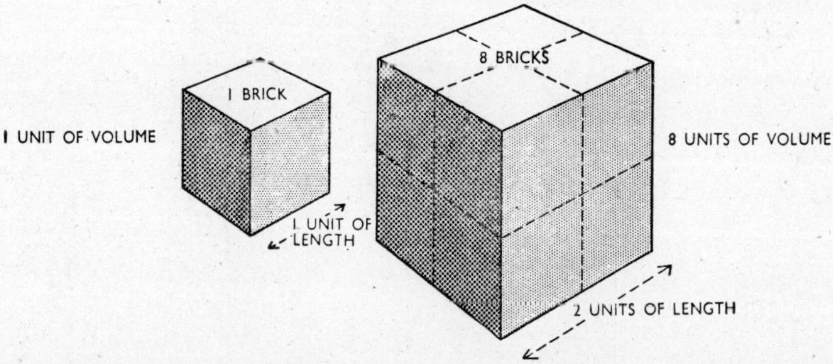

(xvii) A child's cubical building bricks can be used to find how volume grows in relationship to length.

$$\begin{cases} \text{Ratio of edges (lengths)} = 1:2 \\ \text{Ratio of volumes} = 1:2\times2\times2 \\ \qquad\qquad\qquad\quad = 1:8 \end{cases}$$

8 is called the *cube* of 2, written thus:

$$2^3 = 8$$

In the same way, you would need 27 bricks to make the next sized cube.

If ratio of edges is 1:3, ratio of volumes $= 1:3^3$

Once again, we must note that the cuboid shape does not end the matter.

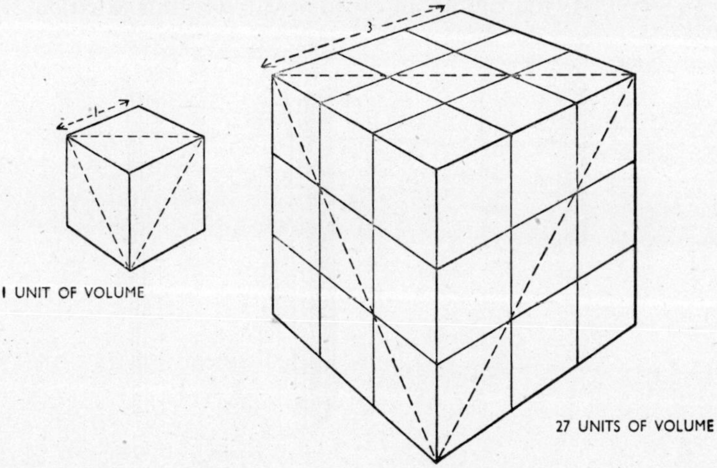

If we cut off a corner along the plane formed by the dotted lines shown in the illustration we may give our figures a different form.

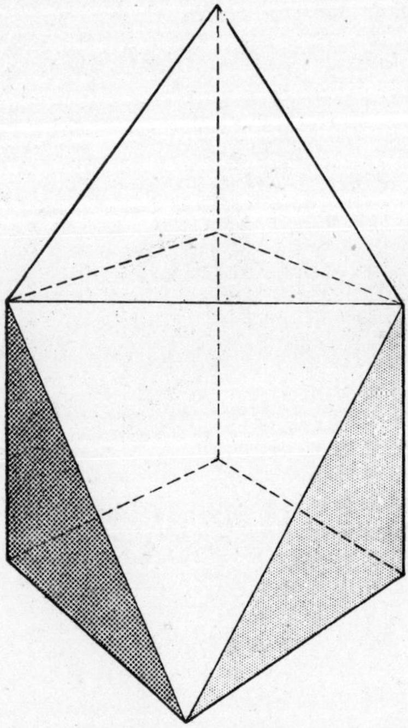

Provided the figures are similar, i.e., of *exactly* the same shape, the ratio of volumes will equal the ratio of the cubes of corresponding lines.

If you can find two round tins of which one is twice as tall *and* twice as wide as the other, you can do an experiment to test this assertion.

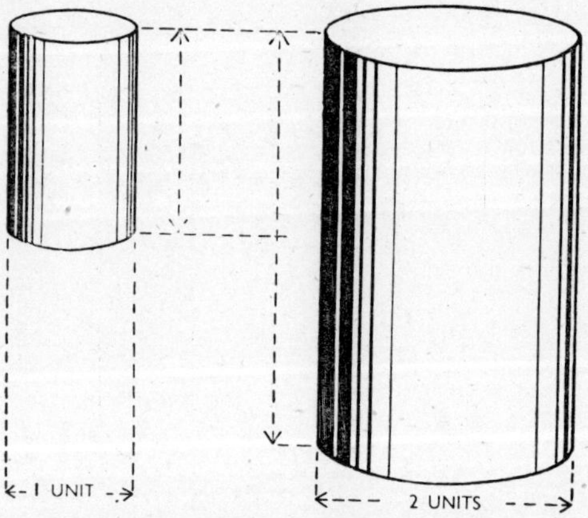

Find out how many smaller tins full of water are required to fill the larger. It should need eight.

NOTE: Three-dimensional figures are similar only when one is an exact enlargement of the other. A tall salmon tin and a squat salmon tin are not similar.

(xviii) A little experimenting with water in jars will give you practice in this new operation of cubing. Get any two jars of similar shape, find how many times one is wider or taller than the other (i.e., the ratio of their linear dimensions), cube the result and then test this ratio of their volumes that you have calculated, by finding out how many times the capacity of the bigger jar is greater than that of the smaller jar.

It was tried with a 1-lb. jam jar and a 2-lb. jam jar. The 2-lb. jar was 5 in. high (and $2\frac{7}{8}$ in. wide) and the 1-lb. jar 4 in. high (and $2\frac{1}{4}$ in. wide). This gave a ratio of approximately 5:4 for the linear dimensions; the volumes, therefore, should have the ratio $5^3:4^3:1$ approximately.

$$\text{Ratio of volumes} = \frac{5^3}{4^3} = \frac{125}{64} = \frac{2}{1} \text{ approximately.}$$

This result compliments our calculating ability, verifies the mathematical law we are considering, and vindicates the jam manufacturer.

We must mention cube roots. Suppose we want to cast a lead cube with a volume of 10 cu. in.

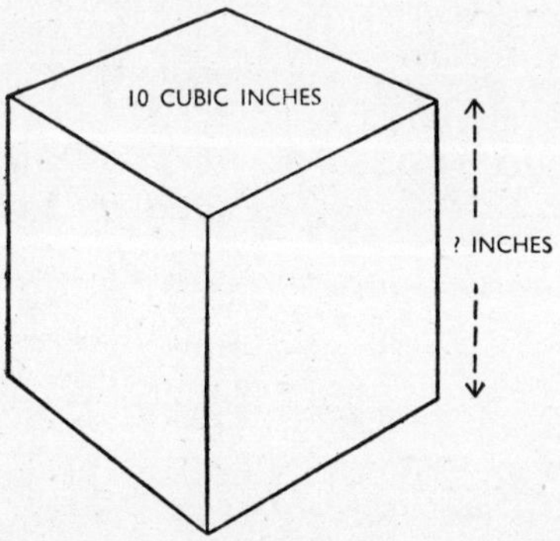

The length of the edge when cubed must give 10. The number we seek is called the cube root of 10.

$$\text{Length of edge} = \sqrt[3]{10} \text{ in.}$$

We can say that the answer will be between 2 and 3, but an accurate calculation would be agonizing. Fortunately we can get the answer quite easily with the help of logarithms. It is approximately 2·15 in.

Exercises

1. The weight box of a chemical balance uses the following patterns for quick recognition:

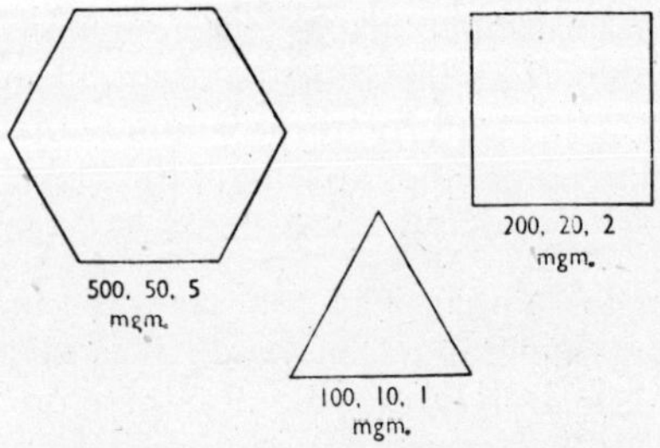

What is the total weight on the scale pan in each of the following pictures?

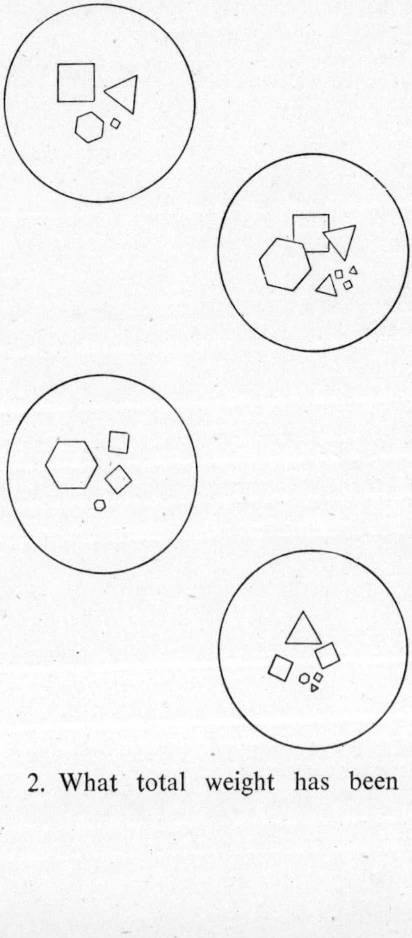

2. What total weight has been removed from the weight box in each of the following pictures?

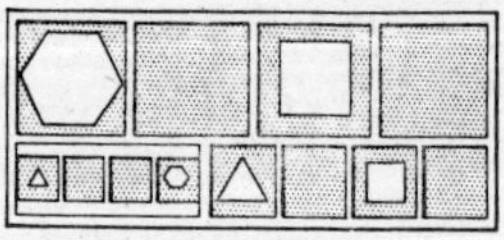

a

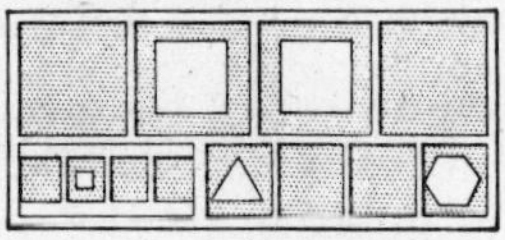

b

3. What thickness is offered by each of the following combinations of standard blocks?

(*a*) ·1003 in., ·127 in., ·85 in., 4 in.

(*b*) ·1002 in., ·135 in., ·6 in., 2 in.

(*c*) ·1008 in., ·141 in., ·25 in., 3 in. and 4 in.

4. What combinations would you select for each of the following thicknesses?

(a) 4·7645 in. (b) 1·5125 in.
(c) 5·3875 in. (d) 9·1093 in.
(e) 1·0825 in.

5. Using as few blocks as possible, suggest pairs of combinations for giving thicknesses of ·045 in., ·0225 in., ·0133 in., ·0625 in. and ·1234 in.

6. We suggest again that you try making a micrometer. One was made which consisted mainly of a long screw of 50 threads to the inch. Two units brazed on to the U-piece carried it through the cylindrical scale. Here are one or two problems encountered:

(*a*) What axial distance of movement was given by one revolution of the screw of the micrometer?

(*b*) What intervals were we to

select for the graduations on the main scale?

(*c*) How many equal divisions were on the cylindrical scale?

(*d*) Suppose we were to make one to measure centimetres, by using a screw with 20 threads to the centimetre; find the answers to (*a*), (*b*) and (*c*) in this case too. We admit that the scales would not be ideal in this case, but they present the kind of arithmetical problem you will meet in practical work.

NOTE: It is essential to zero instruments of this kind before taking readings on any occasion. Zeroing is adjusting the screw till the jaws are closed and taking the reading: it *should* be zero, but it may not be.

(*e*) Suppose you have taken some readings—0·873, 1·128, 1·080, 0·302—and then realize you have not zeroed. You do so and find that the zero reading is 0·002. What will your corrected readings be?

7. What is the rough answer for each of the following:

(*a*) $3{\cdot}92 \times 41{\cdot}3$ (*d*) $256 \times {\cdot}19$

(*b*) $\frac{785}{8{\cdot}1}$ (*e*) $\frac{3{\cdot}6}{{\cdot}013}$

(*c*) $\frac{0{\cdot}27}{3{\cdot}1}$ (*f*) $\frac{412}{{\cdot}039}$

8. Give rough answers to the following multiplication exercises:

(*a*) 98 × 21 (*f*) 99 × 10·2
(*b*) 99 × 719 (*g*) 34 × 19·9
(*c*) 49 × 13 (*h*) 1·9 × 3·5
(*d*) 201 × 42 (*i*) 5·9 × 1·5
(*e*) 37 × 999 (*j*) ·29 × 1·8

9. The air in a room has an average weight of ·08 lb. per cu. ft. What weight of air is there:

(*a*) in a room measuring 10 ft. by 12 ft. and 8 ft. 6 in. high?
(*b*) in a room twice as long?
(*c*) in a room of twice each of these measurements?
(*d*) in a room measuring 8 ft. 6 in. by 10 ft. 6 in. by 9 ft. 3 in.?

10. A transformer core is made up of many thin stampings of soft iron painted on one side for insulating against eddy currents. How many stampings are needed for a 1 inch core if the thickness of one stamping is ·014 in.?

The stampings are arranged in pairs, thus:

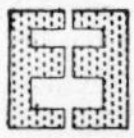

11. Express the following as percentages:

Dividend of two shillings in the pound.
Error of ·05 inches in measuring 3·25 inches.
Birth-rate of 16·3 per 1,000 of population.
Road fatalities of 16,000 in a population of four million.

12. Express the following percentages as fractions:

40%, 15%, $12\frac{1}{2}$%, $62\frac{1}{2}$%, $66\frac{2}{3}$%, $\frac{1}{2}$%, ·1%

13. What are the squares of the following:

(*a*) 1·1 (*b*) ·7 (*c*) $\frac{2}{3}$ (*d*) $\frac{1}{5}$
(*e*) $1\frac{1}{2}$ (*f*) ·03 (*g*) ·012 (*h*) $2\frac{1}{2}$

14. What are the square roots of 81, ·01, 1, ·16, 1·44, ·04, ·0025, $2\frac{1}{4}$, $6\frac{1}{4}$

15. What are the approximate square roots of

3·9, ·24, 150, 14·4, ·008

16. Estimate the cube roots of the following numbers:

(*a*) 64, (*b*) 1,000, (*c*) 729, (*d*) 125, (*e*) ·008, (*f*) 1, (*g*) ·125, (*h*) ·000001, (*i*) 1,000,000

CHAPTER VI

FORMULAE

It is known to many people that children at school, when they have finished arithmetic, begin to learn algebra. Comparatively few people know the use to which algebra can be put, or why anybody should bother to learn it. It would be very interesting to ask a number of children who had just started to learn algebra what good it might be to them.

You do not get much enlightenment from looking into an algebra text-book of the traditional kind. On the first page there appear signs x, y and z. These signs are new to you, but they seem to have known each other a long time; there are all kinds of relations between them, and rules for what you may do to them and what you may not do, all of which have to be faithfully observed. The further you go into the book, the more xs, ys and zs you meet, and the less you find of anything else. After you have glanced through the whole book, you still have no idea of what these xs, ys and zs are, how anybody ever came to think of them, or how all the facts that are (apparently) known about the behaviour of these mysterious letters came to be discovered.

This point seems worth looking into. How was algebra started? Who invented it? Why? Algebra did not exist in the time of the cavemen. Somebody must have been the first to use algebra. What led to its use, and how did the first person to use it know what to do? If we can discover how algebra came about, it should help us to understand the subject more easily.

It is not possible to give the life story of the man who started algebra, because the beginning was too long ago. It is possible, however, to explain quite simply what algebra is and how it came about.

Algebra, as we know it today, is first and foremost a system of abbreviations.

Abbreviations are very useful, and everyone tends naturally to use them; to say B.B.C. instead of *The British Broadcasting Corporation*, or N.U.D.A.W. instead of *The National Union of Distributive and Allied Workers*. It conveys the essential idea, and saves a lot of time.

Take a collection of words, such as:

> At the battle of Hastings in 1066, the Saxons, under the leadership of Harold, were decisively beaten by the Norman invaders under the banner of William, usually known as William the Conqueror, who thereby became King William the First of England.

If you want to remember that, all you need write in your notebook is:

Hastings, 1066. Saxons (Harold) v. Normans (Wm. I, "Conq.") 2. (The 2 indicates that the home team were beaten.) That contains all the essentials of the statement: it takes far less time to read; and by cutting the statement down to this bare form you help yourself to remember it.

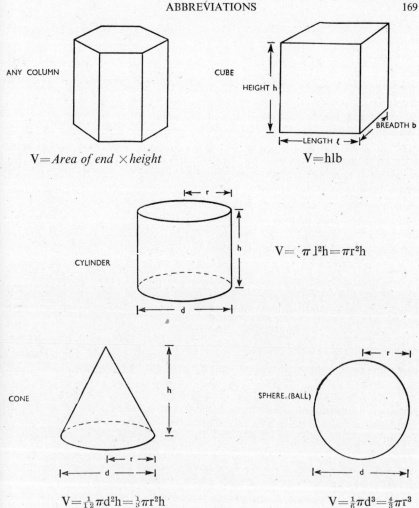

ANY COLUMN

$V = \textit{Area of end} \times \textit{height}$

CUBE

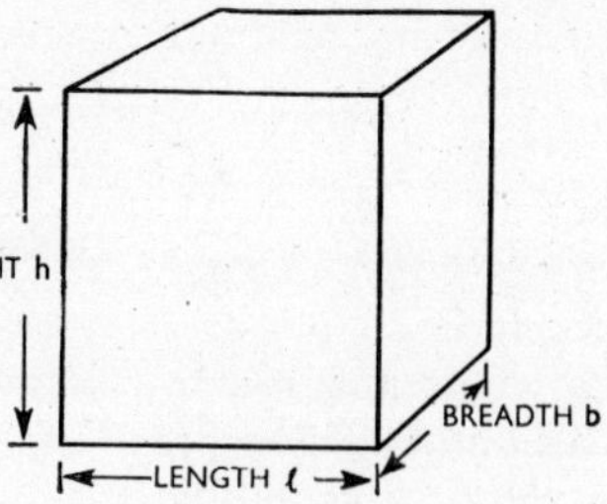

$V = hlb$

CYLINDER

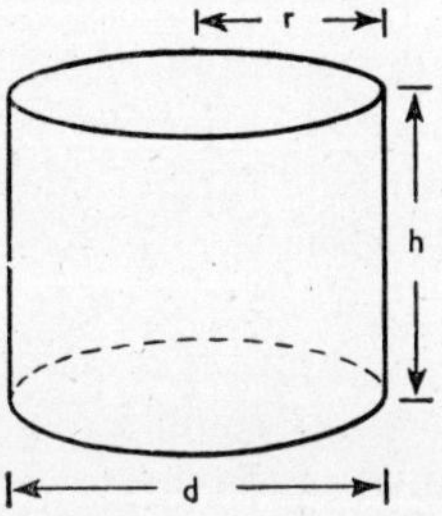

$V = \frac{1}{4}\pi d^2h = \pi r^2h$

CONE

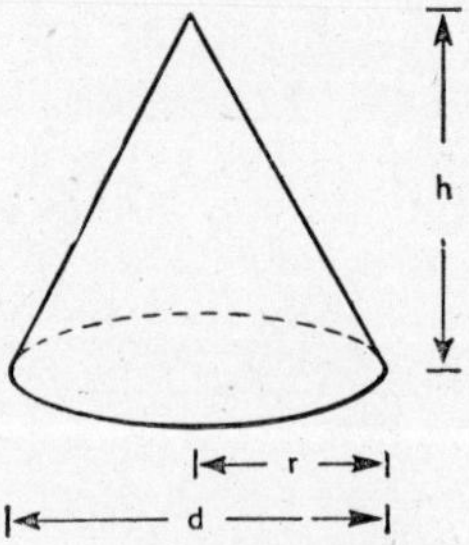

$V = \frac{1}{12}\pi d^2h = \frac{1}{3}\pi r^2h$

SPHERE (BALL)

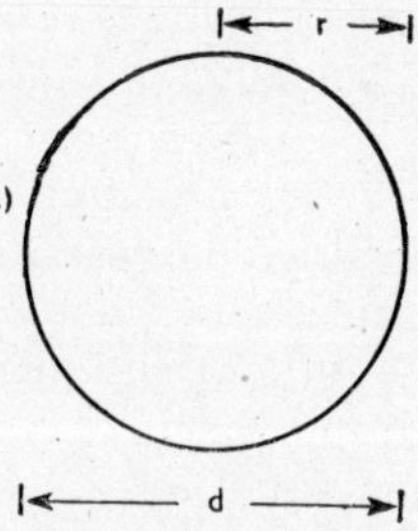

$V = \frac{1}{6}\pi d^3 = \frac{4}{3}\pi r^3$

MENSURATION BY FORMULA (1) VOLUMES

In each of the five cases above, V *stands for the volume of each object.*
π *is approximately* 3·14, *or* $3\frac{1}{7}$.

Schoolchildren are not usually encouraged to use abbreviations. (In some schools permission had to be obtained to shorten anything or use the sign for ditto.) This is a mistake. In writing things out in full, you tend to waste all your time and energy in *writing:* you have less chance to think what you are writing about.

Anyhow, if you want to discover algebra for yourself, you should give free rein to your desire to use abbreviations. The desire to avoid unnecessary writing was one of the main things that led to algebra in its modern form.

This brings us to another question. We use abbreviations when we want to make a note about something. But what is there to be said about numbers? What is there worth making a note of?

There are, of course, such truths as $2 + 2 = 4$, and $3 \times 5 = 15$, but these belong to arithmetic. We do not need any special signs to write these statements down. Algebra begins where arithmetic leaves off. What can it be about?

Let us imagine you know all about arithmetic, that you can make any calculation. If this is too much to ask, let us imagine instead that you have a set of calculating machines, one for adding, another for subtracting, one for multiplying and one for dividing; if you like, we may add to these machines for doing all the other operations of arithmetic—finding squares and square roots, H.C.F. and L.C.M., and so on. With this collection of machinery you can make any calculation in arithmetic.

It may seem that there is no more to know. But yet, with all this collection of machines, you could not (without further knowledge) answer any of the simple practical questions that follow.

What horse-power is necessary in a locomotive to haul a 600-ton train at a steady speed of 40 miles an hour on the level?

A plank ten feet long, one foot wide and two inches thick is used as a bridge across a small stream. What is the largest weight that can safely be taken across it?

How many turns of wire should be put in the primary of a mains transformer, if the core contains one square inch of iron and the mains voltage is 240 volts?

What weight can be safely lifted with a steel cable two inches thick?

Your calculating machines would not help you with any of these questions, because you would not know how to begin. You would have to be told in each case by what method to work. What rule connects the weight and speed of a train with the horse-power of the engine? What rule connects the measurements of a plank with the weight it will bear? What rule gives the number of turns necessary for a transformer? What rule connects the thickness of a steel cable with the weight it can support?

Arithmetic tells you nothing about any of these. All these things had to be found out in the first place by experiment. From the experiments certain working rules were found. And last of all, these rules gradually were put into shorter and shorter form, until at last they reached the extremely short form used in modern algebra.

In order to understand algebra, it is best to go through all this for yourself —to make experiments, to spot the rules, to write them down, and then make suitable abbreviations.

All the questions asked above could be answered by experiment, but unfortunately they all require rather expensive equipment. Most of us are not in a position to run locomotives and measure the horse-power developed, or to wind a great variety of coils and notice which go up in smoke when connected to the mains. The strength of planks might be investigated with miniature planks, and the snapping of wires might also be investigated in miniature.

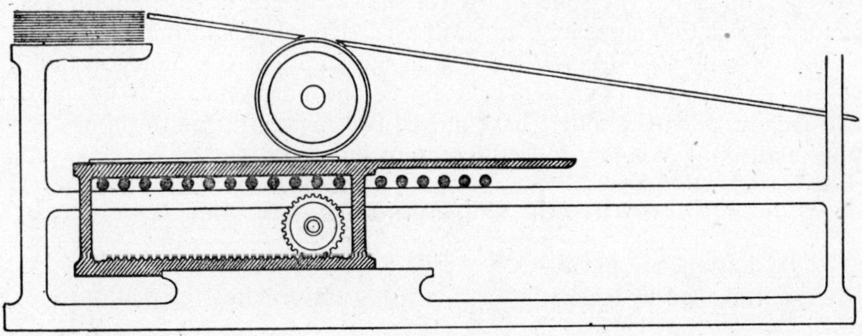

A DIAGRAMMATIC ILLUSTRATION OF THE MOVABLE PLATFORM AND ROLLERS OF A PRINTING MACHINE

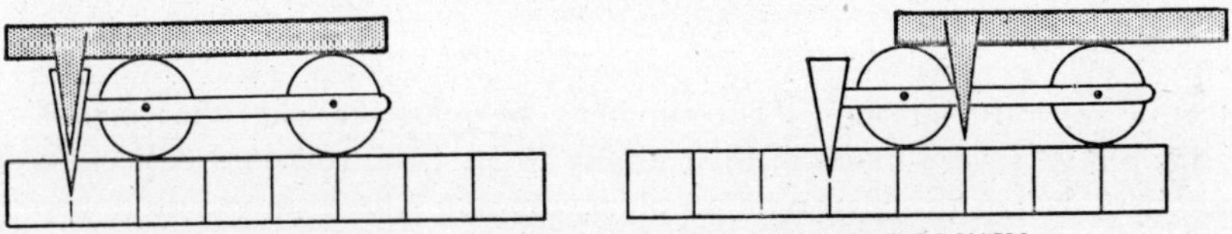

A PIECE OF APPARATUS TO SHOW HOW THE PLATFORM OVERTAKES THE ROLLERS

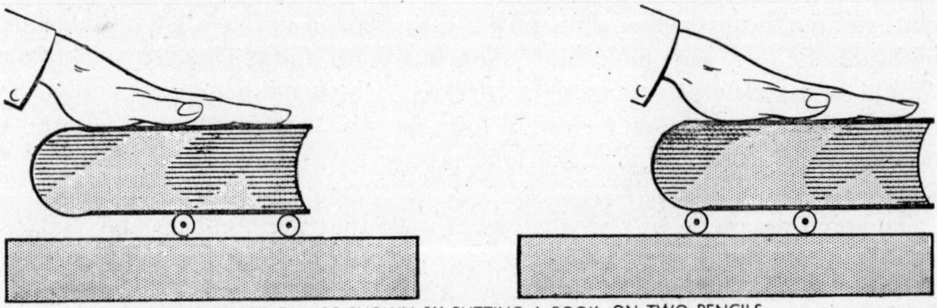

THE SAME EFFECT CAN BE SHOWN BY PUTTING A BOOK ON TWO PENCILS.

It seems desirable to mention one or two very simple experiments that you can carry out for yourself without difficulty. These experiments are, perhaps, not so practical as the experiments suggested above, but on the other hand they are simpler to perform. The type of reasoning is just the same in both cases; the practice you get with these simple experiments will be of value to you when you come to deal with actual problems.

The first experiment was suggested by the behaviour of some printing presses at Odhams Press. It is very noticeable that, when a movable platform runs on rollers, the platform moves farther than the rollers. You can test this for yourself by putting a book on top of a couple of pencils, as shown in one of the illustrations above, or you may prefer to make the more formal piece of apparatus also shown above.

As you can see from this figure, or by trying the experiment for yourself, the moving platform overtakes the rollers.

A scientifically minded person is never content just to say, "The platform moves farther than the rollers." He (or she) will want to have a more exact picture of what is happening, and will ask, "How much farther?"

The obvious way to answer this is to measure and see. You will find, if you try it, that when the rollers have moved one inch the platform has moved two inches: when the rollers have moved two inches, the platform has gone four, and so on. We may collect the results in a table like this:

MOTION OF A PLATFORM ON ROLLERS

Distance in inches travelled by rollers.	Distance in inches travelled by the platform.
1	2
2	4
3	6
4	8
5	10
6	12

Now we must interpret these numbers; we must see what they mean.

People vary very much in their ability to spot the rule in a collection of numbers such as this. To some people it comes in a flash: others do not seem able to see anything, however long they look. It seems possible that the ability to detect *pattern* in a set of numbers is the essential thing that a mathematician must have. This power may depend on having a certain kind of brain. People who have no feeling at all for finding patterns in things should hesitate before choosing a career in which mathematical knowledge is essential. There are many useful jobs for which no mathematics at all is necessary. You may regard the table above as a good test of the type to which you belong.

To some people it will be obvious at once that the numbers above are in

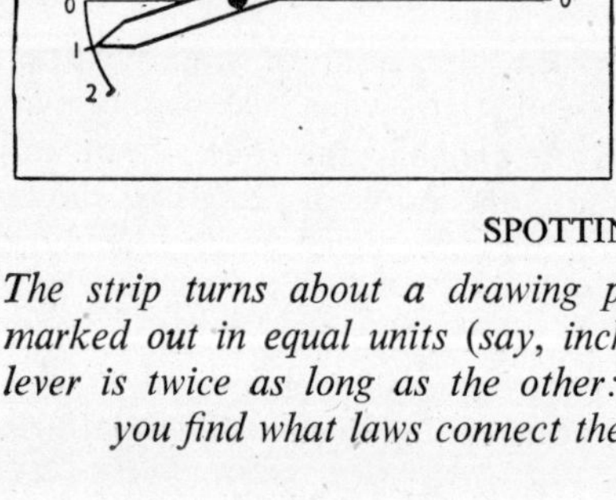

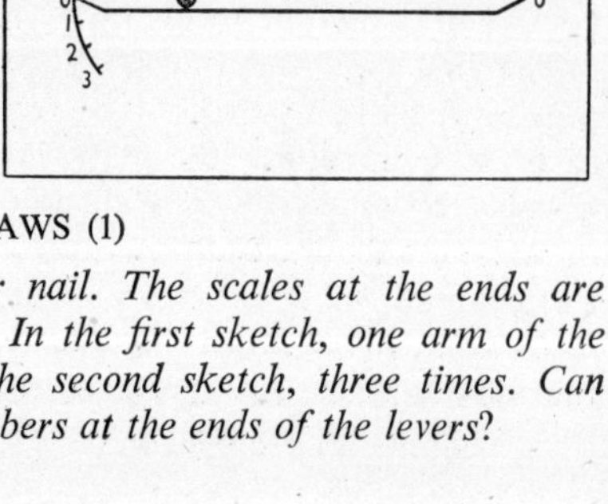

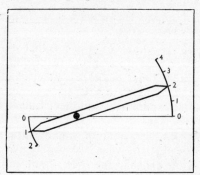

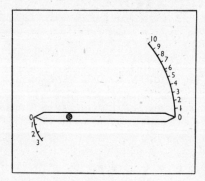

SPOTTING LAWS (1)

The strip turns about a drawing pin or nail. The scales at the ends are marked out in equal units (say, inches). In the first sketch, one arm of the lever is twice as long as the other: in the second sketch, three times. Can you find what laws connect the numbers at the ends of the levers?

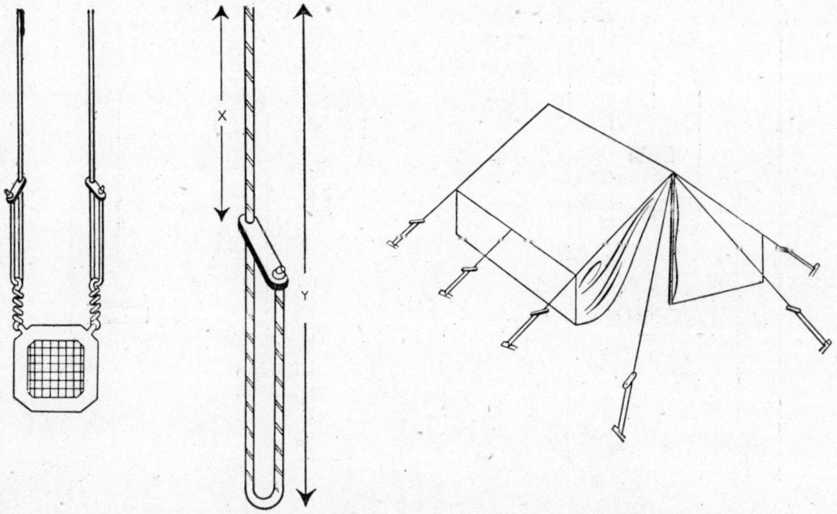

SPOTTING LAWS (2)

This device is used for adjusting the guy ropes of tents, and also for suspending microphones at the B.B.C. Can you discover what law connects x *and* y?

fact the two-times table: the distance travelled by the platform is twice the distance travelled by the rollers.

Others will spot the law in a rather different form. They will say, "Yes, I can see a rule. The numbers 2, 4, 6, 8, 10, 12 go up by two each time."

This is perfectly true, but it is not yet such a complete answer as the previous one. For there are other sets of numbers that go up by two each time—1, 3, 5, 7, 9, 11 for instance, or 56, 58, 60, 62, 64, 66.

So it is not a complete answer to the question, "What is the rule connecting the numbers in the two columns of the table?" It merely tells us that for every *extra* inch the roller goes, the platform goes two *extra* inches. This certainly leads us in the right direction; it suggests that the two-times table may be *something to do with* the answer.

This property, of going up by twos is, therefore, a valuable clue to the correct answer, but it is not itself the answer. This is mentioned because people often spot this clue, and stop there.

Now let us return to the rule we have discovered, "The platform goes twice as far as the rollers."

In order to make this into part of algebra, all we now have to do is to find the shortest possible abbreviations.

It is not obvious just how to do this. There are, in fact, various ways still used. At the time when modern algebra was being developed (roughly from A.D. 250 to A.D. 1600 and particularly A.D. 1500—1600) all sorts of different systems were used. Some had one advantage, some another. The whole thing grew gradually, and you will find, if you start inventing abbrevia-

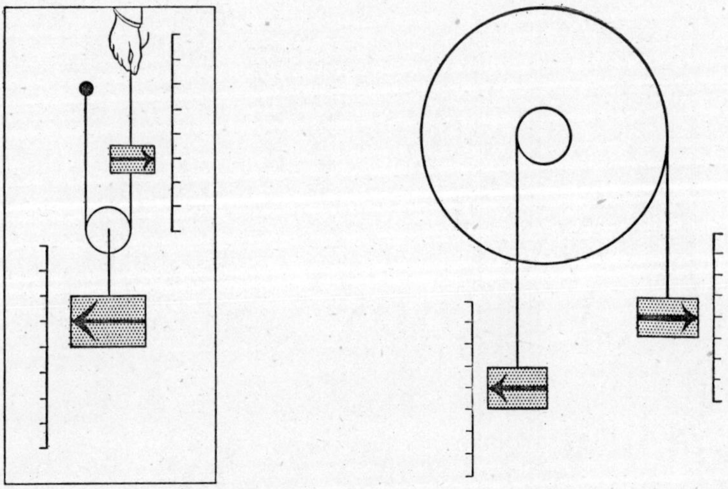

SPOTTING LAWS (3)

Here are two easily made mechanical contrivances. They are a pulley and wheel and axle. What laws connect the distances through which the weights move?

tions, that your abbreviations will gradually get shorter and shorter, as you keep using them.

We might begin with our statement in the form:

The distance the platform goes is twice the distance the rollers go.

We might shorten this to

Platform distance is twice rollers' distance

or

Platform distance = 2 × *rollers' distance*

which might become shortened still further to

P. dist. = 2 *R. dist.*

or finally to

$P = 2R$,

which is the form used in modern algebra, as a rule. (You may occasionally meet other forms, for instance

$d_p = 2d_r$ where *distance platform goes* has been shortened to d_p, and *distance rollers go* has become d_r.)

In an engineer's sketch book, all that we have said in the last page or two might be summed up by this diagram:

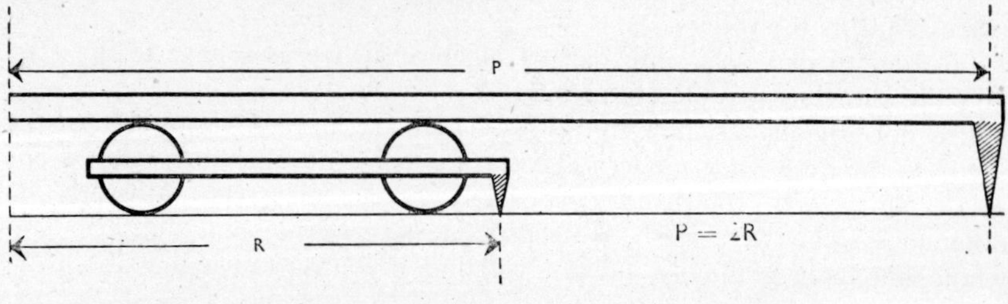

A rule expressed by means of letters, such as $P = 2R$, is known as a formula. The plural of formula is usually taken to be formulae (not formulas); formula is a Latin word, and the old Latin plural has become part of the English language.

Some formulae are found by experiment, in much the way that we found the formula for the platform and rollers.

Other formulae can be found purely by reasoning. A simple, but very useful example, is the theory of gear wheels. Suppose we have a small gear wheel—called the pinion—meshing with a larger wheel, which is simply called the gear wheel.

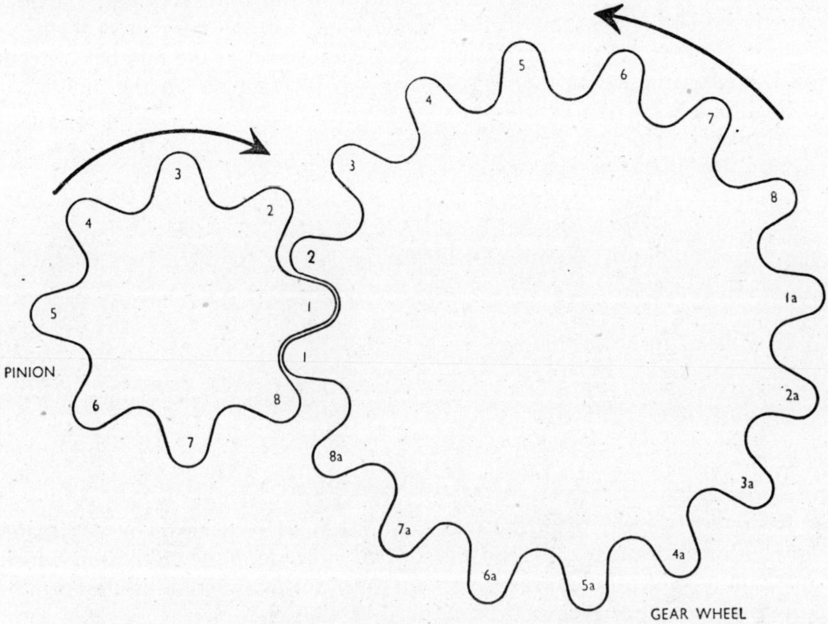

We are now asked, "Supposing you know the number of teeth on the pinion, and the number of teeth on the gear wheel, how would you work out the number of times the pinion must turn to make the larger wheel turn once?"

It is usually best to begin by considering a particular example—say the one illustrated above, in which the pinion has 8 teeth and the gear 16. Let us consider what happens.

At the instant shown above, the tooth marked 1 on the pinion is pressing the tooth marked 1 on the wheel. In a moment or two the tooth marked 2 on the pinion will be pressing on the tooth marked 2 on the wheel. We go round the two wheels, writing the numbers in as we go, to show the teeth that will come together later on.

By the time we have reached 8, we have marked all the teeth of the pinion, but not all those of the gear. Since the tooth 1 on the pinion follows the tooth marked 8, we must go through the numbers again. This is shown by the teeth marked 1*a*, 2*a*, 3*a*, 4*a*, 5*a*, 6*a*, 7*a*, 8*a*. These teeth are pressed by the corresponding teeth of the pinion, on the pinion's second time round. When they have all been done, we are back where we started.

So it requires two revolutions of the pinion to make the gear wheel turn once.

We might state the argument briefly like this; each time the pinion turns, it presses 8 teeth of the gear wheel round. There are 16 teeth on the gear wheel. To make these 16 teeth pass round, therefore, requires 16 ÷ 8 revolutions of the pinion.

There is nothing special about the numbers 8 and 16 (except that 8 divides exactly into 16). The same *method* would apply for any number of teeth.

In the answer 16 ÷ 8, the 16 was there because it was the number of teeth on the gear; the 8 was there because it was the number on the pinion.

So the general rule is:

Answer = Number on gear wheel ÷ number on pinion.

Now for the abbreviations.

A for "Answer".
G for "Number on GEAR WHEEL".
P for "Number on PINION".

Our rule becomes

$$A = G \div P.$$

It is usual to write this as

$$A = \frac{G}{P}, \quad \text{or} \quad A = G/P$$

USING FORMULAE

It should be clear from the two examples just given how you can make up your own formulae. You must first of all understand the method by which a certain type of problem is solved: you must put that method in the form of a general rule: and then you bring in abbreviations.

The advantage of a formula is that it allows division of labour to take place. A scientist investigates the strength of steel rods, or the electric current that will melt a copper cable. He puts what he discovers into a rule, which is most conveniently expressed by a formula. The engineer who designs practical equipment need not understand all that the scientist does; he may simply use the *method* on the word of the scientist that the results will be correct. There are dangers in working too much like this to rule of thumb, but we none of us have time to learn everything, and occasionally we all have to take somebody's word that it just is so.

Now let us consider how to make use of a formula that has been discovered by someone else.

Suppose you wish to cross a deep canyon by means of a rope and pulley, as shown on page 177. The rope is 40 ft. long, it sags 3 ft. in the middle, and you weigh 140 lb. (10 stone). With what force will the rope pull at the supports on the side of the canyon?

$$P = \frac{WL}{4s}$$

L = *Length of rope*
W = *Weight*
s = *sag*

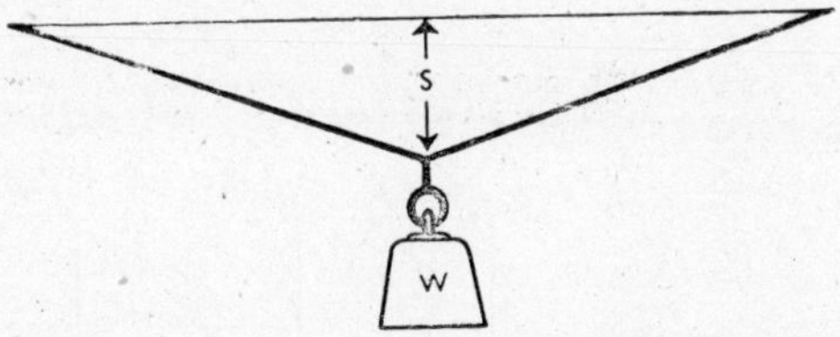

You might think that, since the rope is supporting a 10-stone weight, it would be sufficient if the supports were strong enough to stand a pull of 140 lb. If you thought this, you would soon find yourself at the bottom of the canyon. Actually, the pull is very much greater. (You can test this by the experiment shown on page 179.) The formula for the pull is:

$$P = \frac{WL}{4s}$$

where P means the pull on the supports, in pounds.
W your weight in pounds.
L the length of the rope, in feet.
s the sag in feet.

In a formula, it is always understood that, when two letters are put next to each other without any sign, a multiplication is to be understood. The reason for this is, perhaps, that the multiplication sign, $\times$, looks very much like the letter x, and might get mistaken for it. So, in algebra, multiplication signs are usually left out. This is a bit confusing at first, so perhaps while we are explaining this formula, we may write the letters very large and put very small multiplication signs in, so that there will be no chance of mistaking one for the other.

The formula would then look like this:

$$P = \frac{W \times L}{4 \times S}$$

This formula shows us the pattern of the calculation we are going to make. It means that

$$\text{the pull is} \left(\begin{array}{c} \text{something times something} \\ \text{divided by} \\ \text{four times something} \end{array} \right)$$

We might put it a bit more definitely by putting spaces, with instructions for what is to go in them, like this:

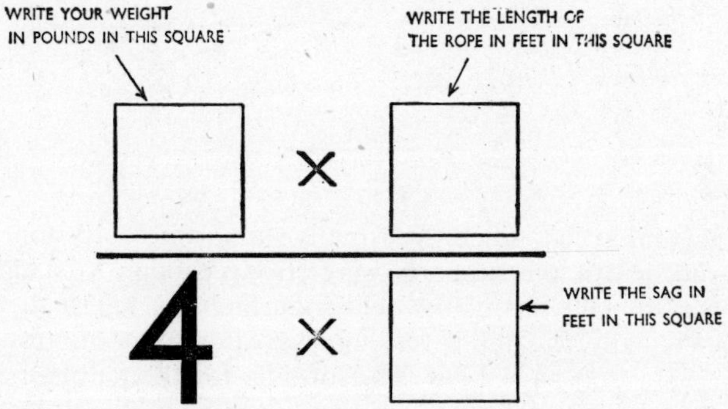

This diagram shows what the formula really means, and what a formula does for you. A formula gives you instructions; it tells you what to write down, how to begin the sum. It says to you, "You see this *W*? Well, that is the *place* where the weight should be written. And this *L* is where the length of the rope should be. And the sag goes where that little *s* is. Then it is up to you to work the answer out for yourself. When you have completed the work, the result is the pull, shown by the letter *P*."

One way of making sure that you are using a formula correctly is to write the formula in pencil, and then ink in, over each letter, the number it stands for.

To finish off the canyon question is now just arithmetic. We fill in the

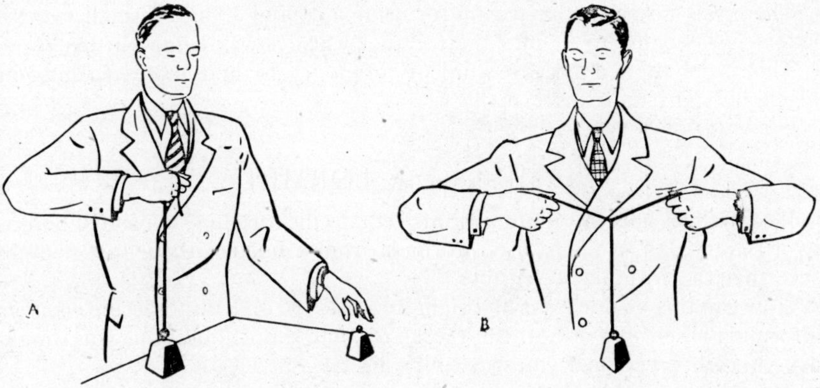

AN EXPERIMENT ON THE STRENGTH OF CABLES

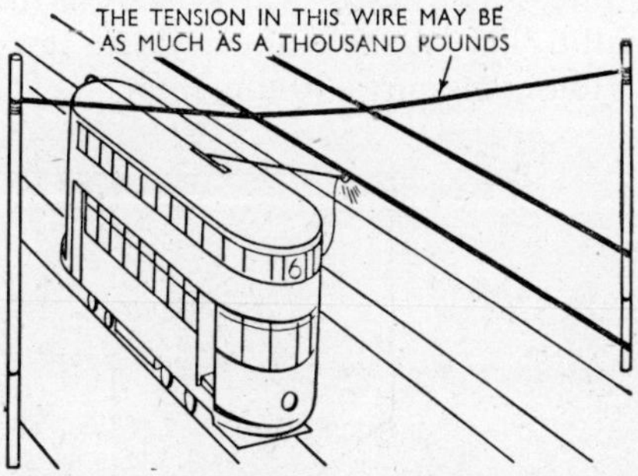

THE TENSION IN THIS WIRE MAY BE AS MUCH AS A THOUSAND POUNDS

Take a string, or cotton thread, and find what weight is just enough to break it, when the string hangs vertically, as at A. *Now take a weight one-half or one-quarter as large, and with the same kind of string, try to support the weight as at* B, *with the upper string nearly straight. Although the weight is smaller, the upper string will break, before the position at* B *can be reached. Wires from which overhead tram-wires hang must be strong enough to hold a weight much greater than that of the tram-wires, owing to this magnifying effect.*

numbers that were given at the beginning of this problem, and we find

$$\text{the pull} = \frac{140 \times 40}{4 \times 3} = 466 \text{ lb. roughly.}$$

So the rope would have to be strong enough to stand a pull not far off five-hundred pounds, which is worth knowing.

You may wonder if there is any reason for sometimes using large letters such as W and L, sometimes small letters such as s.

There is no difference in meaning between capital and small letters. We are making up our own abbreviations. It would make no difference if we said w was to stand for the weight in pounds. We could even use some other letter altogether, such as x or Y. All that matters is that once we have chosen a meaning for a letter, we stick to it.

The reason why L was used for the length in the formula above, rather than l, was because the manuscript was typed and, on some typewriters, the same key is used for l and the figure 1. If l had been used the printers might have had difficulty in distinguishing between the figure and the letter.

There was no particular reason for using a capital W and a small s; these letters just seemed to fit into the formula when it was being written.

This is mentioned because students often try to find more meaning in algebraic signs than there really is.

EXAMINING A FORMULA

It sometimes happens that misprints get into the formulae in printed books, so it is very dangerous to use a formula from a book without first making sure that the formula is sensible.

How can this be done? At first sight it looks very difficult to decide whether a formula is sensible or not. But there are some simple questions you should ask yourself every time you use a formula.

The first question is, "Does it give an answer roughly the right size?"

Take an example of this. Often in a factory a large block of steel has to be lifted. You have such a block in front of you. Should you send for a small trolley, capable of carrying a few pounds, or for a 1-ton crane, or for a 3-ton crane, or a 10-ton crane?

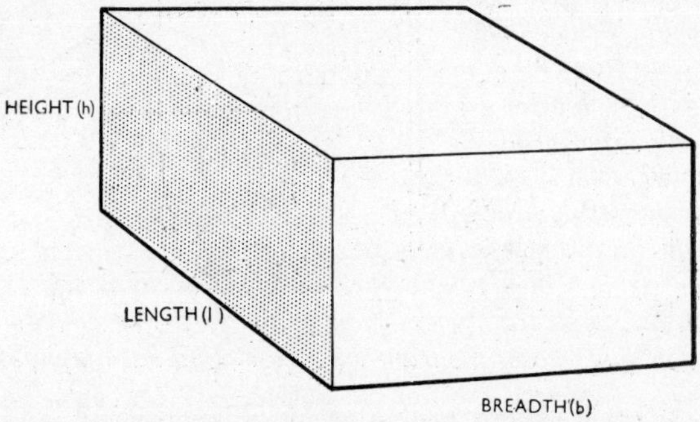

Suppose someone tells you that the weight in pounds is given by multiplying together the height, length and breadth of the block, all these being measured in feet. In symbols this would be $W = hlb$.

If you are wise, you will check this rule before using it. You think to yourself, suppose the block were one foot high, one foot wide, one foot long. Then, according to this formula, it would weigh one pound. But the pound weight on a set of kitchen scales is made of iron, which weighs roughly the same as steel, and it is far smaller than a cubic-foot block. So the formula gives us an answer that is ridiculously small.

In fact, a cubic foot of steel weighs something in the neighbourhood of 500 lb.—say, just under $\frac{1}{4}$ ton. The correct formula would be:

$$\text{weight} = 500\, hlb \text{ lb. roughly.}$$
$$= \tfrac{1}{4}\, hlb \text{ tons roughly.}$$

You will notice that we say *roughly*. It would, of course, be possible to work out the weight much more accurately—so many tons, hundredweight, quarters, stones, pounds and ounces. But this would be much harder to do, and it would be no better *for the purpose in hand.* No factory keeps one crane for lifting a weight of 3 tons and a different crane for lifting 2 tons 18 cwt. There are many sizes and patterns of cranes in common use, but certainly a factory will only use a few standard sizes, so the question will be, "Is it safe to use the 5-ton crane, or must we send for the 10-ton one?" Anything in between 5 and 10 tons would, in these circumstances, have to go on the 10-ton crane. It would not matter whether it was 6 tons, or 7 tons 14 cwt., or 9 tons 2 cwt. 3 qrs. 1 stone 5 lb. $3\frac{1}{2}$ oz. Since it does not matter, why bother to work it out? You will be using harder numbers, and more likely to make a mistake in consequence.

One point we must be careful about. When we give a rough answer, the mistake should (unless it is very small indeed) be on the safe side. Actually, a cubic foot of steel weighs rather less than 500 pounds (490 pounds about), and 500 pounds is rather less than $\frac{1}{4}$ ton ($\frac{1}{4}$ ton is 560 pounds), so that in fact the steel block would really weigh less than the formula shows. It does not matter putting less weight on a crane; putting too much might have serious results. Our formula errs on the side of safety.

Another question we may ask about a formula is, "Does it vary in the proper way?" First, an explanation of what is meant here by vary. Take the example we have just considered and suppose that, as the result of a misprint, the formula were given to us as:

$$W = \frac{1}{4}\frac{hb}{l} \text{ tons,}$$

that is, as a quarter of the height times the breadth *divided by* the length (instead of *multiplied by*).

According to *this* formula we should have the following results:

Height	Breadth	Length	Weight
1 foot	1 foot	1 foot	$\frac{1}{4}$ ton
1 foot	1 foot	2 feet	$\frac{1}{8}$ ton
1 foot	1 foot	3 feet	1/12 ton

But here something is obviously wrong. The longer the block is, the less the rule makes it weigh. We know the longer the block is, the more it would weigh. So there is something wrong with the rule as given. Varying the length makes the weight vary in the wrong direction.

After some practice with formulae, or if your arithmetic is good, you will be able to recognize such a mistake without needing to try particular values, as we have just done. You will see straight away that dividing by the length makes the weight vary in the wrong direction. But if your arithmetic is not so good, you should stick to the method we have just used.

DIFFERENT TYPES OF FORMULA

Earlier the question was asked, "What weight can safely be taken across a plank bridge of specified size?" The formula for this question* is as follows.

* To be exact, the quality of the wood ought to be carefully specified. With particularly good wood the formula might perhaps be $\frac{7}{8}\ bd^2/L$; with particularly bad wood $\frac{1}{2}\ bd^2/L$, or even less. This formula applies to average wood.

A plank L feet long, b inches broad, d inches thick (d for depth), will safely carry a weight of W cwt. if

$$W = \frac{3bd^2}{4L}$$

This is the first formula we have had containing a sign such as d^2. The sign d^2 is spoken in words as d squared. You may remember from the chapter on arithmetic that 10^2 was used to mean 10×10, and that 10^3 stood for $10 \times 10 \times 10$. It is exactly the same in algebra.

For instance, if the plank is 10 ft. long, 12 in. wide and 2 in. thick, we must

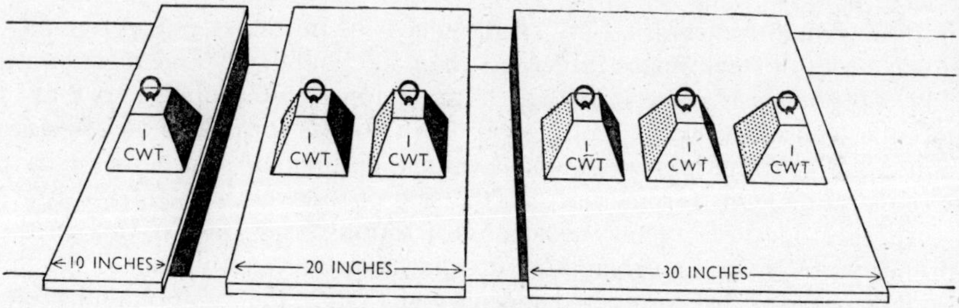

Here is shown the effect of changing the breadth of a plank bridge. You will notice that the diagram shows the length and thickness the same each time.

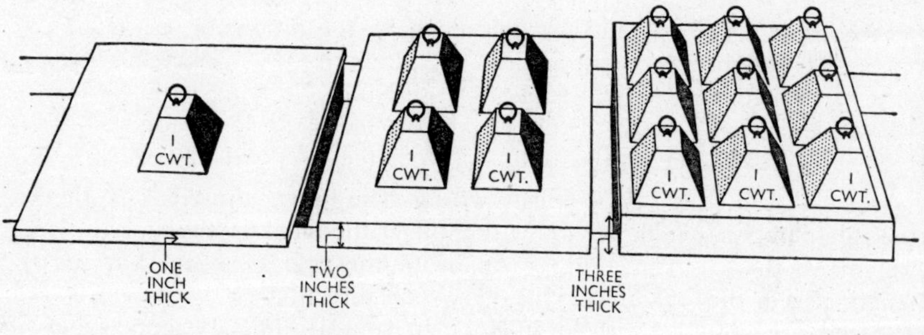

Here the thickness varies while the length and breadth are kept the same.

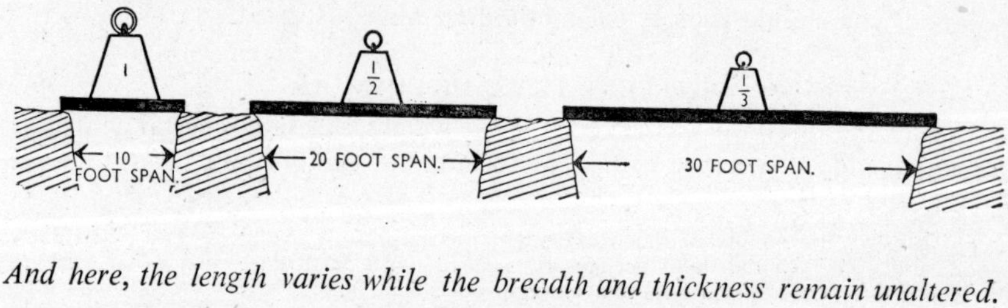

And here, the length varies while the breadth and thickness remain unaltered.

put 10 where L stands, 12 for b, and 2 for d. We should, thus, obtain the expression:

$$\frac{3\times 12\times 2^2}{4\times 10}$$

In this 2^2 means what it always means in arithmetic, 2 squared; that is, 2×2.

Working the sum out, we find the answer 3·6; so the plank would carry about $3\frac{1}{2}$ cwt. safely.

In the old days, instead of writing d^2 they used to write dd, so this formula would have been written:

$$W = \frac{3bdd}{4L}$$

This form is perhaps simpler to understand. You can see straight away that the safe weight on the bridge is $\frac{3}{4}$ of the breadth times the depth times the depth, divided by the length.

With the present way of writing *d squared* as d^2, students tend to mix it up with $2d$. There seem to be people who find it very hard to see things in their correct order. As children they know that "cat" is spelt with C, A and T, but they are equally likely to write it ACT or ATC or CTA. For people like this it must be very hard to distinguish between $2d$ and d^2, and it is difficult to help them. But even students who do not have this particular difficulty in seeing positions often mix the two up.

Perhaps it will help to study the table below, in which n stands for any number, and the values of $2n$ and n^2, $3n$ and n^3 are given. By looking through this table you can make sure that you have the right idea of the meaning of these signs.

A good way to make sure that you understand is to put this table away,

SIGN	n	$2n$	n^2	$3n$	n^3
NAME IN WORDS	*Any number*	*Twice the number*	*The number squared*	*Three times the number*	*The number cubed*
	0	0	0	0	0
	1	2	1	3	1
	2	4	4	6	8
	3	6	9	9	27
	4	8	16	12	64
	5	10	25	15	125
	6	12	36	18	216
	7	14	49	21	343
	8	16	64	24	512
	9	18	81	27	729
	10	20	100	30	1,000

Many things grow by equal steps, like this.

For instance, the length of a cycle tyre is proportional to the size of the wheel —the tyre is shown straightened out.

The weight of a stone block is proportional to its length.

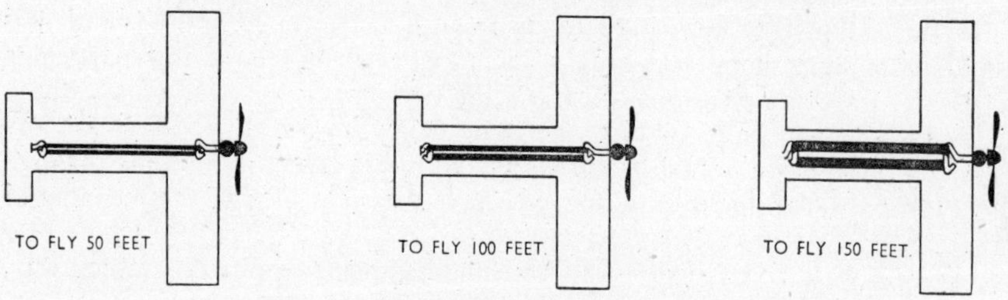

The distance a model aeroplane will fly is proportional to the weight of rubber used to turn the propeller.

The distance a spring is compressed is proportional to the weight on it.

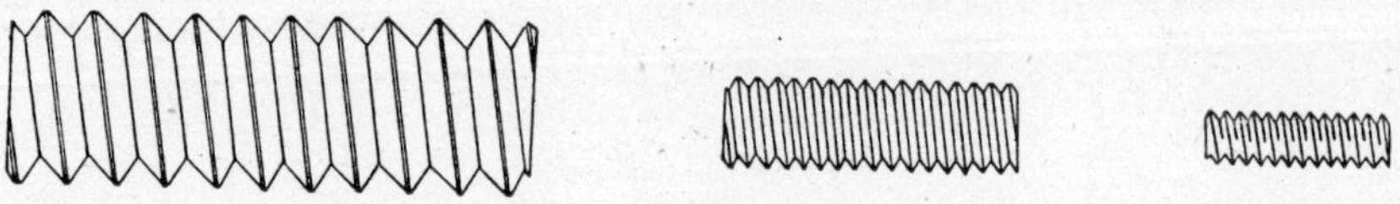

The depth of the Vs in a screw is proportional to the distance between the threads.

EXAMPLES OF DIRECT VARIATION

$v=kx$ *where* k *is some fixed number.*

and then work out for yourself a table like this one, and see if you get the same numbers.

You can buy tables quite cheaply which contain, among other things, the squares and cubes of numbers—not only whole numbers, but also numbers between, such as 6·37 and 1·94. You should use such tables to save arithmetic, but you must be quite sure of the algebraic signs for *n squared* and *twice n*, otherwise you may use the wrong table. Also, in order to understand what you are doing, you should understand what n^2 and n^3 mean, so that you could work them out for yourself if no tables were available.

It is one thing to be able to work out the value of a formula such as $W = \frac{\frac{3}{4}bd^2}{L}$; it is quite another thing to *feel* what it means, to see how it behaves, how it grows or shrinks. This feeling is the most important thing; once you get it you will lose all fear of formulae. So let us take some examples of formulae, and try to see what they mean.

The formula for the strength of a plank bridge will be quite a good one to start with. There is one inconvenient thing about this formula, the fraction $\frac{3}{4}$. It is always good to make examples as simple as possible, so let us just drop this $\frac{3}{4}$, and take $W = \frac{bd^2}{L}$. (We might justify this by supposing that we had exceptionally good wood for the plank, or we might just say it is convenient to drop the $\frac{3}{4}$ and that is why we are doing it, in order to get *some idea* of how the formula behaves.)

Now we examine in turn the different measurements. How does the strength depend on the breadth of the plank? How does it depend on the thickness? How does it depend on the length?

First of all, the breadth b. Suppose the plank is ten feet long and one inch thick, that is, $L = 10$, $d = 1$. We consider different breadths, say 10 in., 20 in., 30 in. Working these out in turn, we find that when $b = 10$, $W = 1$; when $b = 20$, $W = 2$; when $b = 30$, $W = 3$.

This means that a plank 10 in. wide will support 1 cwt.
a plank 20 in. wide will support 2 cwt.
a plank 30 in. wide will support 3 cwt.

This is a very simple way of behaving—as the breadth goes up in equal steps, the weight also goes up in equal steps. When breadth is doubled, weight is doubled. The weight varies *directly as* the breadth.

It is quite different when we come to consider the thickness of the plank. If we take a definite length, say 10ft. as before, and a definite breadth, say 10 in., and take the thickness, d, as being in turn 1 in., 2 in. and 3 in., we find:

when the plank is 1 in. thick it will carry a load of 1 cwt.
when the plank is 2 in. thick it will carry a load of 4 cwt.
when the plank is 3 in. thick it will carry a load of 9 cwt.

Here the thickness goes up in equal steps, but the strength goes up quicker and quicker. On page 182 you will notice that the weights are arranged in squares to illustrate this case. This shows why we say that the strength of the plank varies as the *square* of the thickness.

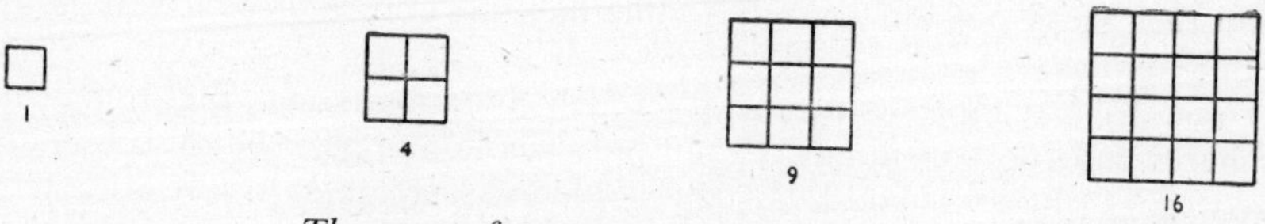

The area of a square grows in this way.

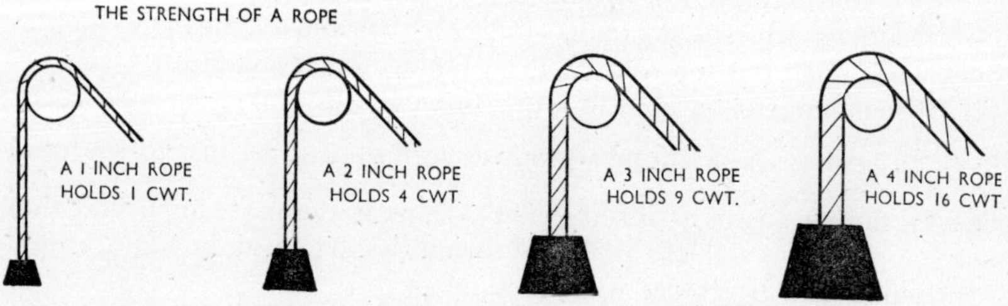

A 1 INCH ROPE HOLDS 1 CWT.
A 2 INCH ROPE HOLDS 4 CWT.
A 3 INCH ROPE HOLDS 9 CWT.
A 4 INCH ROPE HOLDS 16 CWT

Other things also grow the same way: for instance, the strength of a rope.

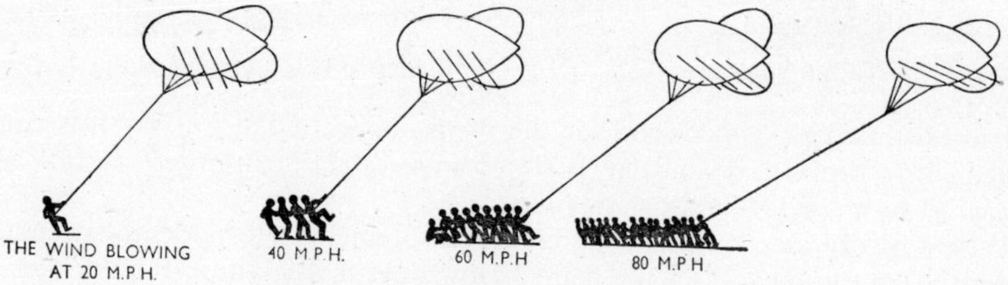

THE WIND BLOWING AT 20 M.P.H.

The pressure of the wind.

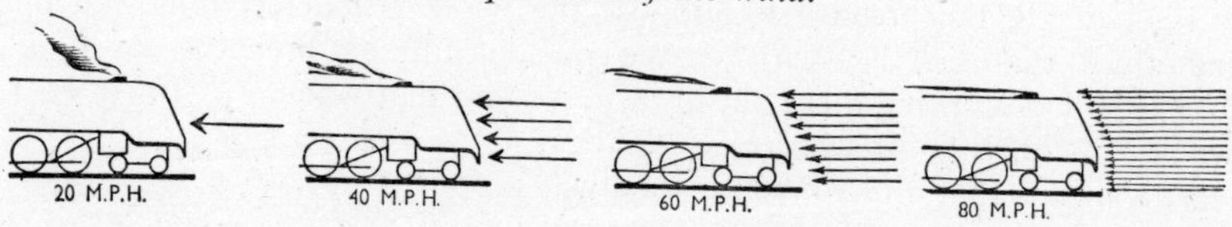

The air resistance to a locomotive.

THIS PENDULUM SWINGS ONCE A SECOND. IT IS ABOUT 39 INCHES LONG.
THIS ONE ONCE EVERY TWO SECONDS. IT IS FOUR TIMES AS LONG AS THE FIRST.
THIS ONE, ONCE EVERY THREE SECONDS. IT IS NINE TIMES AS LONG AS THE FIRST.
THIS ONE, ONCE EVERY FOUR SECONDS. IT IS SIXTEEN TIMES AS LONG AS THE FIRST.

The length of a pendulum.

EXAMPLES OF THE SQUARE LAW

$y = kx^2$ *where* k *is some fixed number.*

Finally, we can fix the breadth and thickness of the plank—say breadth 10 in., thickness 1 in.—and try the effect of varying the length of the plank. We find:

when the length is 10 ft. the plank will support 1 cwt.
when the length is 20 ft. the plank will support $\frac{1}{2}$ cwt.
when the length is 30 ft. the plank will support $\frac{1}{3}$ cwt.

Here, again, is something quite different. The longer the plank is, the less weight the bridge will carry. That is quite reasonable; if there were an island in the middle of the stream so that we could use two short planks instead of one long one, we should expect the bridge to be stronger.

The term *inverse variation* is used to describe this third type of behaviour.

Note that all the information contained in the figures on page 182 has been obtained from the formula itself. We have not quoted any books on bridge building. We have simply put numbers into the formula, and tried the effect of varying them one at a time.

In some of the self-contained illustrations examples are given of formulae, in which squares, cubes and other powers occur. Every time you meet a formula, you should try putting particular values into it, until you discover which (if any) of these examples it behaves like. With experience, it is possible to see at a glance how a formula behaves.

SQUARE ROOTS

It may happen that a formula contains a square root. For instance, there is a formula for the rate at which water comes out of a small opening:

$$G=2LH\sqrt{H}.$$

In this formula, G means gallons each minute.
L is the length of opening in inches.
H is the height of water in inches.

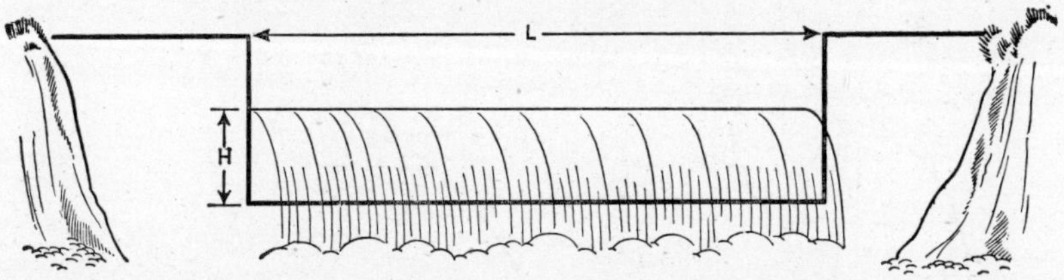

Let us examine this formula, and see if the square root sign, $\sqrt{}$, causes any trouble. Suppose the opening is 12 in. wide, and the water surface is 4 in. above the bottom of the opening. That is, $L = 12$ and $H = 4$. The number of gallons each minute will be:

$$G = 2 \times 12 \times 4 \times \sqrt{4}.$$

This result has been obtained simply by writing 12 for L, and 4 wherever H stands, and putting in multiplication signs, as usual, when there is no sign already between the letters.

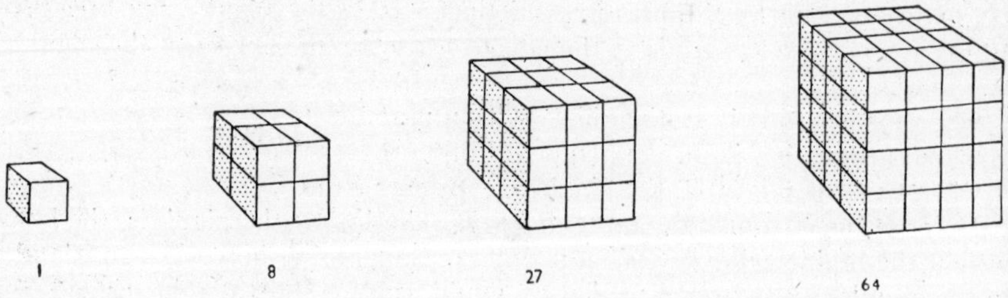

The volume of a cube grows like this.

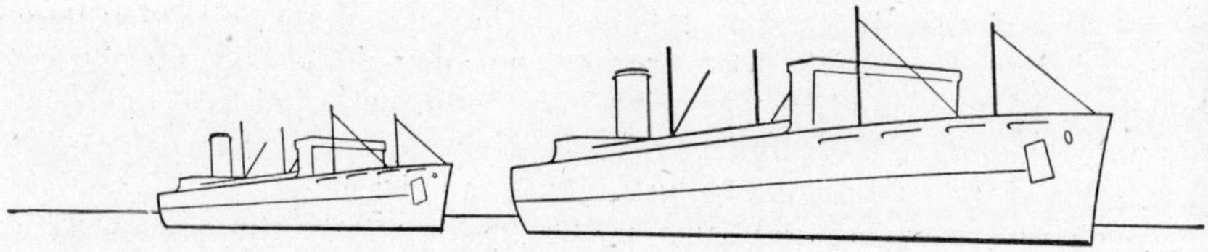

Any solid body grows in the same way. If the scale of a ship is doubled,

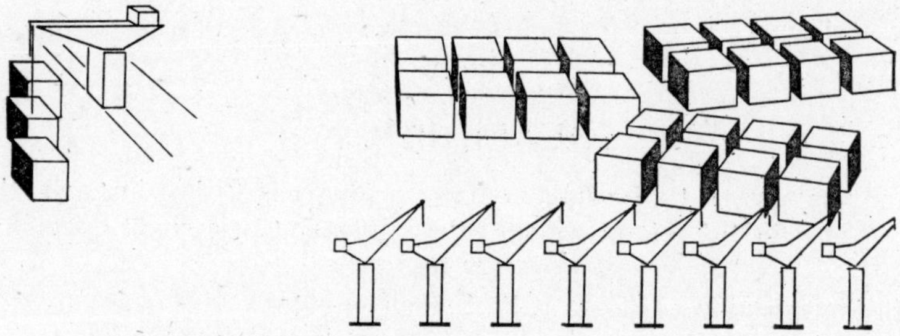

the cargo it can carry is multiplied by 8.

Other things vary in the same way. If the speed of the wind doubles, a wind-driven generator will produce eight times as much power.

EXAMPLES OF THE CUBE LAW

$v = kx^3$ *where* k *is a fixed number.*

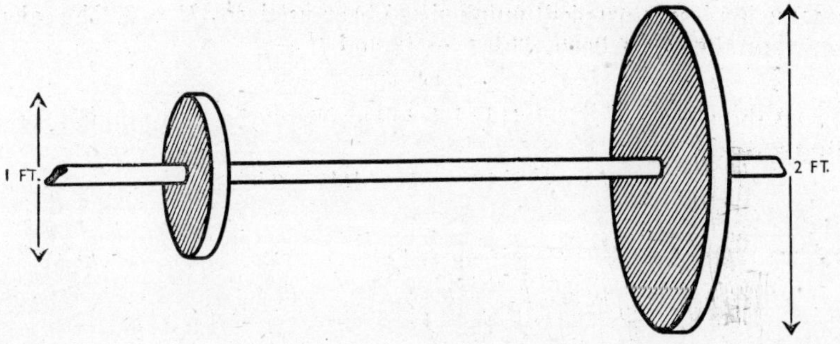

The energy of a Flywheel. Sixteen times as much energy is stored in the flywheel having double the diameter.

The strength of a Support. If the thickness of a bar is doubled, the load it can carry is multiplied by sixteen. The weight that a bar can bear on its ends comes into many practical questions—for instance, the design of bicycle handlebars.

EXAMPLES OF THE FOURTH POWER LAW ($y = kx^4$)

The fourth power law is not very common. Two examples only are given.

We now come back to arithmetic. What is the meaning of $\sqrt{4}$? There is one very quick way of settling this question.

As $\sqrt{\ }$ stands for the square root of, and as there is a table of square roots in the book of tables, we can simply look up this table, and see what it gives for the square root of 4. It gives 2. So we may replace $\sqrt{4}$ by 2. Accordingly:

$$G = 2 \times 12 \times 4 \times 2$$
$$= 192.$$

So 192 gallons a minute would flow through the opening.

Of course, in the above calculation, we were fortunate in having $H = 4$, because the square root of 4 is exactly 2. The arithmetic would have been the same if a less convenient number had been used, say $H = 2$. The calculation would then have been, with $L = 12$ and $H = 2$:

$$G = 2 \times 12 \times 2 \times \sqrt{2}.$$

From the tables, $\sqrt{2}$ is 1·414. 1·4 will probably be near enough for our purpose. So:

$$G = 2 \times 12 \times 2 \times 1{\cdot}4 = 67{\cdot}2.$$

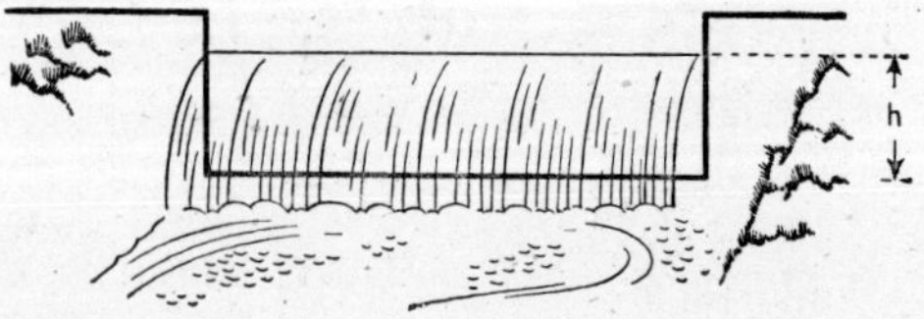

The rate at which water flows over a weir is proportional to $h\sqrt{h}$.

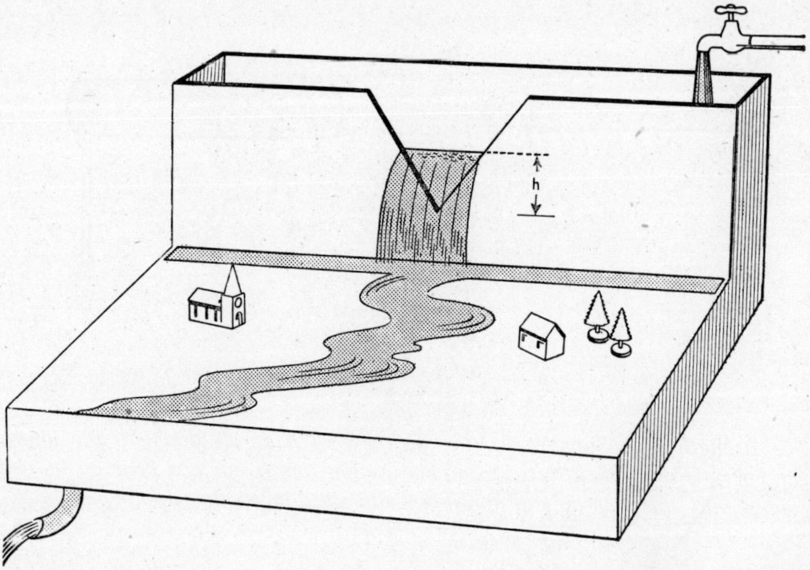

Rate at which water flows over a triangular slot is proportional to $h^2\sqrt{h}$. *This fact is made use of to measure the rate at which water flows. Effect of proposed alterations to rivers, locks, etc., is investigated by means of models, into which water is allowed to flow at a rate corresponding to flood conditions.*

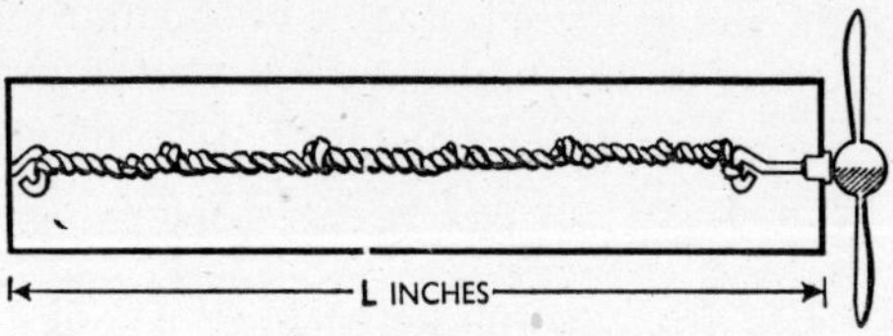

The number of turns a rubber motor will stand is given by:

$$N = \frac{4L\sqrt{L}}{\sqrt{W}}$$

where W *ounces is the weight of rubber per skein.*

EXAMPLES OF LESS USUAL TYPES OF VARIATION

Therefore, if the head of water in the opening stayed steady at 2 in., roughly 67 gallons a minute would be flowing through it.

Of course, it is as well to know that 2 is the square root of 4 because $2 \times 2 = 4$, and 1·414 is the square root of 2 because $1{\cdot}414 \times 1{\cdot}414 = 2$: in short, that a table of square roots is a table of squares written backward. But this belongs to arithmetic and has already been dealt with in Chapter V.

PYTHAGORAS' THEOREM

An important application of square roots is Pythagoras' Theorem. Some of the uses of Pythagoras' Theorem will be explained in Chapter VII, on Geometry. It is also of use in the study of electricity (power supply), and in most parts of more advanced mathematics it is mentioned again and again.

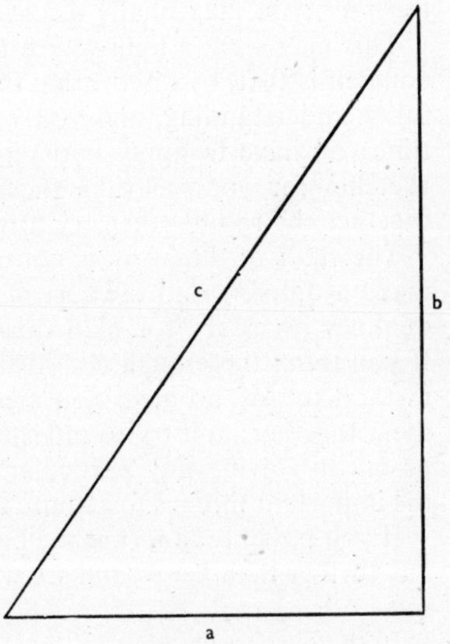

This theorem deals with a question such as the following. If you can reach a certain town from your home by going 30 miles East and then 40 miles North (which nobody would do in practice, of course), how far is the town from your home in a direct line?

Is there a simple way of working this out, without actually making a drawing? Is there a formula?

If there is a formula, three things must come into it. There must be the two distances we are given, one to the East and the other to the North. For short, we will call these a and b. There must also be the distance we are trying to find, the length of the direct route. Call this c. Is there a simple rule giving c in terms of a and b?

There is, in fact, such a rule. The rule is quite simple. Finding this rule is rather like finding the answer to a riddle: it is all right once you get started on the right track. But the right track is not obvious at a glance.

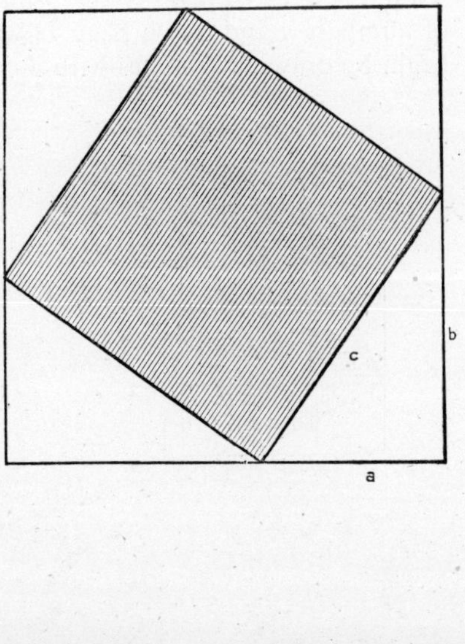

We therefore propose to give one or two clues. If you can find the rule for yourself with the help of these clues, it will do you good.

The first, and most important, clue is that you should begin by drawing the square on the side c, and complete the figure shown here.

This may seem an extraordinary thing to do—as we said, the way to find an answer to a riddle is not obvious.

The second clue is this. The shaded square has sides of length c. If we knew the area of this shaded square, we could find the length of the side c. (For instance, if the area of the shaded square were 36, the side would have to be 6, since 36 is 6×6.) Again, not too obvious as a method for finding c.

The third clue; if you look back to Chapter III, you will find that we there found the areas of some tiled squares, very much like the shaded square we have in mind now. In fact, on pages 78 and 79, a broad hint was given about finding a simple rule. This simple rule (if you have spotted it) was based on the sketches on page 78, and in these sketches you may notice that b is always 1. By drawing corresponding sketches with the side b of length 2, or 3, or 4 you may be able to discover rules for these cases, and, putting all these rules together, you may finally discover the rule that holds for any a and any b.

This may seem a long way round to an answer. The value of doing it for yourself is that, by discovering the answer for yourself, you will gain a much fuller understanding, and you will be confident of what you are doing any time you have to apply Pythagoras' Theorem. Do not be in a rush. Draw sketches for yourself (like those on page 78); count the squares; collect together the results; then try to spot some simple rule.

The value of this work is not only in the result you find at the end. It will make a difference to the sort of person you are; it will develop in you the qualities necessary for mathematics or any kind of scientific investigation. If you think these qualities worth having, you should try to apply the same method to any problem you meet. Make sketches and calculations; collect them together; and try to interpret them for yourself. (Whether you succeed or fail in solving any particular problem unaided is of minor importance; the important thing is to acquire the habit of looking into things for yourself.)

If you possibly can, shut the book at this stage—or at any rate do not read any further than here—and see what you can make of this question for yourself.

In the paragraphs that follow, we shall outline the solution of this problem.

First of all, we draw sketches, similar to those on page 78, for a wide variety of numbers a and b. On page 78 we have enough cases with $b = 1$. We can begin by drawing sketches with $b = 2$, such as these:

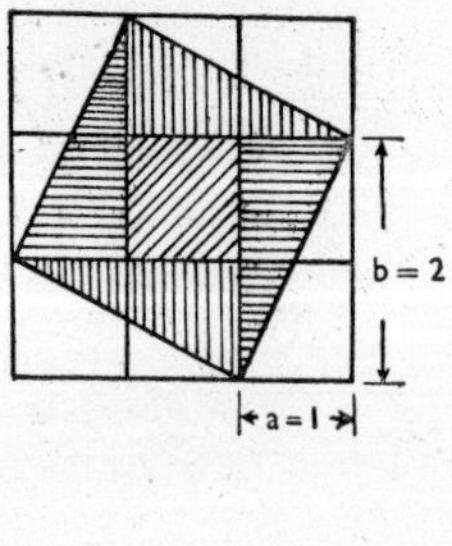

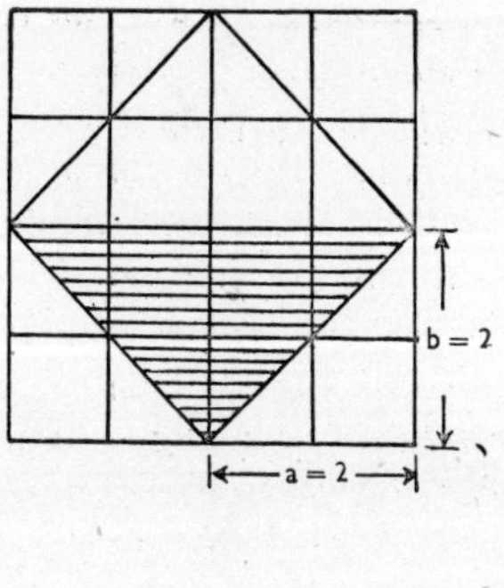

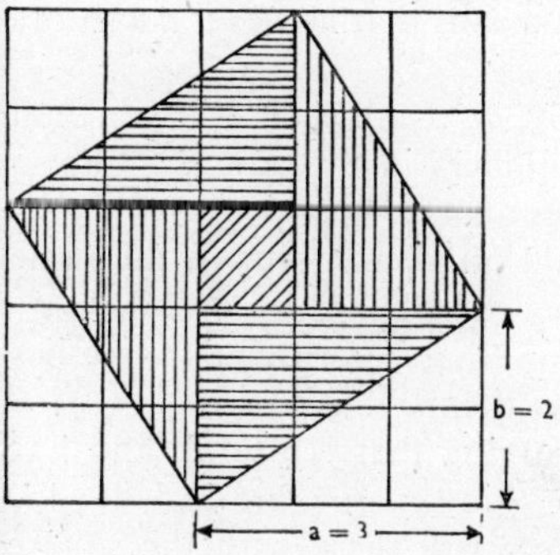

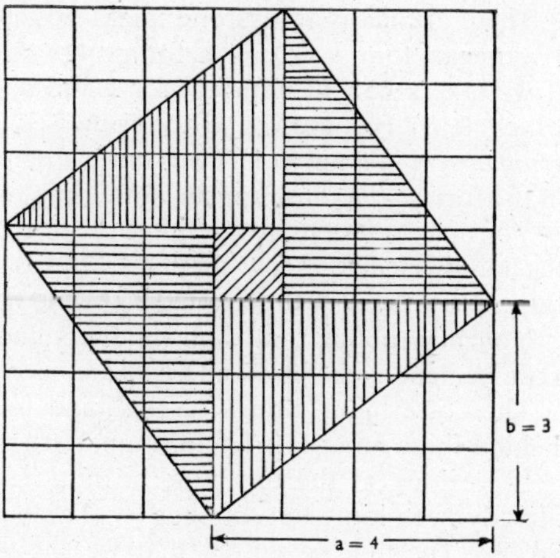

Then we sketch cases in which $b = 3$.

We may go on, making sketches with $b = 4$, $b = 5$ and so on.

Then we have to consider each sketch, and find how many small squares would be needed to cover over the shaded square. The way of doing this has already been explained in Chapter III.

For instance, when $a = 1$ and $b = 1$, we find that two small squares cut up will cover the shaded square. When $a = 2$ and $b = 3$, thirteen are necessary.

We may collect all the results together in the form of a table, like this:

TABLE FOR AREA OF SHADED SQUARE (c^2)

	$b=1$	$b=2$	$b=3$	$b=4$	$b=5$	$b=6$
$a=1$	2	5	10	17	26	37
$a=2$	5	8	13	20	29	40
$a=3$	10	13	18	25	34	45
$a=4$	17	20	25	32	41	52
$a=5$	26	29	34	41	50	61
$a=6$	37	40	45	52	61	72

Here we have enough numbers to look at. What do they mean? Is there any simple rule behind them?

There are many things one might notice. For instance, the same number, 17, appears for $a=1$, $b=4$ as for $a=4$, $b=1$. Similarly, for the other numbers. If we take a pair of numbers for a and b, it does not matter which is a and which is b. The answer is the same. (In official language, the formula is *symmetrical* in a and b.) This is quite a help. It means that however a appears in the formula, b must appear in the same way.

You may notice that the numbers in the row $a=2$ are each 3 larger than the numbers in the row for $a=1$, and the numbers in the row $a=3$ are 5 larger than those in the row $a=2$; and so it goes on.

You may notice that even numbers and odd numbers occur in the same arrangement as the black and white squares on a chess board.

There are many things of this kind to show that some regular law lies behind these numbers. There is a pattern about them.

If we look at the top row, we notice something that is useful, and has already been hinted at on page 78. The numbers in this row are 2, 5, 10, 17, 26, 37. The hint suggested that we should compare these with the square numbers 1×1, 2×2, 3×3, 4×4, 5×5, 6×6, that is to say, 1, 4, 9, 16, 25, 36. If we put these sets of numbers close to each other, like this:

2	5	10	17	26	37
1	4	9	16	25	36

we notice that the top numbers are always one more than the corresponding numbers below.

The formula for the square numbers is b^2.

So the formula for the top numbers must be $b^2 + 1$.

This gives us a rule for the top row.

Since it helped us to compare the top row with b^2, let us try comparing the next row with b^2. It may help again.

The second row;	5	8	13	20	29	40
b^2	1	4	9	16	25	36

MENSURATION BY EXPERIMENT (1)

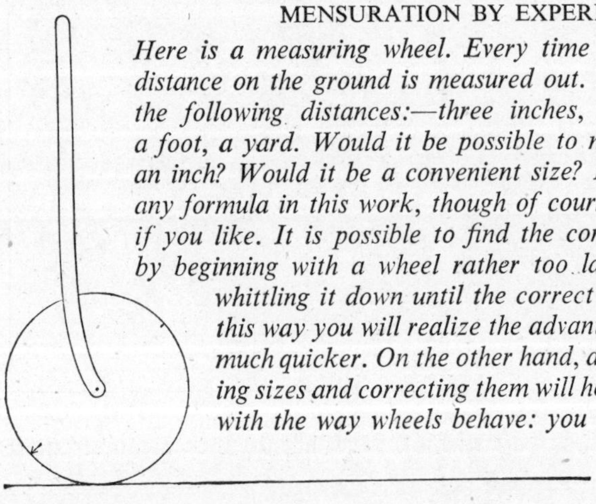

Here is a measuring wheel. Every time it goes round, a certain distance on the ground is measured out. Make wheels to measure the following distances:—three inches, six inches, nine inches, a foot, a yard. Would it be possible to make a wheel to measure an inch? Would it be a convenient size? It is not necessary to use any formula in this work, though of course you can use a formula if you like. It is possible to find the correct sizes for the wheels by beginning with a wheel rather too large for the purpose and whittling it down until the correct radius is found. Doing it this way you will realize the advantage of a formula which is much quicker. On the other hand, actual experience of guessing sizes and correcting them will help you to become familiar with the way wheels behave: you will understand when you come to use the formula $C=2\pi r$.

The rule here is also a simple one. Each number in the upper row is 4 more than the number below it.

So the numbers in this row are given by the formula $b^2 + 4$.

This idea will work again and again. Trying it on the third row we find the formula $b^2 + 9$. The fourth row is $b^2 + 16$. The fifth is $b^2 + 25$: the sixth is $b^2 + 36$.

Here we have six different rules for the six different rows. Can we combine all six into one rule for the whole lot?

We put the six rules together and look at them.

The rule for the first row, in which $a = 1$, is $b^2 + 1$.
The rule for the second row, in which $a = 2$, is $b^2 + 4$.
The rule for the third row, in which $a = 3$, is $b^2 + 9$.
The rule for the fourth row, in which $a = 4$, is $b^2 + 16$.
The rule for the fifth row, in which $a = 5$, is $b^2 + 25$.
The rule for the sixth row, in which $a = 6$, is $b^2 + 36$.

In each case, the rule is of the type:

$$b^2 + \text{some number}.$$

If we can find a rule for the some number, our problem will have been completely solved.

Here the square numbers 1, 4, 9, 16, 25, 36 again supply the solution.

When a is 1, 1×1 is added to b^2.
When a is 2, 2×2 is added to b^2.
When a is 3, 3×3 is added to b^2.
and so on.

The number added is always the same as:

$$a \times a, \text{ or } a^2.$$

So the rule is $b^2 + a^2$. You can check this result by taking particular numbers for a and b, and seeing that it does work: it always gives the number of squares needed to cover the shaded square.

But the shaded square has side c. So its area must be c times c, that is, c^2.

Accordingly, $c^2 = b^2 + a^2$, which is Pythagoras' Theorem.

Since the square of c is $b^2 + a^2$, c must be the square root of $b^2 + a^2$. We may write this:

$$c = \sqrt{a^2 + b^2}.$$

It may be helpful to illustrate this result by an example.

If a town is 6 miles East and 8 miles North, how far away is it in a straight line?

The work is quite short.

a is 6.	$6 \times 6 = 36$	This is a^2.
b is 8.	$8 \times 8 = 64$	This is b^2.
Add.	100	This is $a^2 + b^2$.
Take the square root	10	This is $\sqrt{a^2 + b^2}$.

10 miles away is the answer.

Here the numbers are very simple. If the numbers are complicated, a table of squares and a table of square roots can be used. Then you only have one addition to do for yourself by actual calculation.

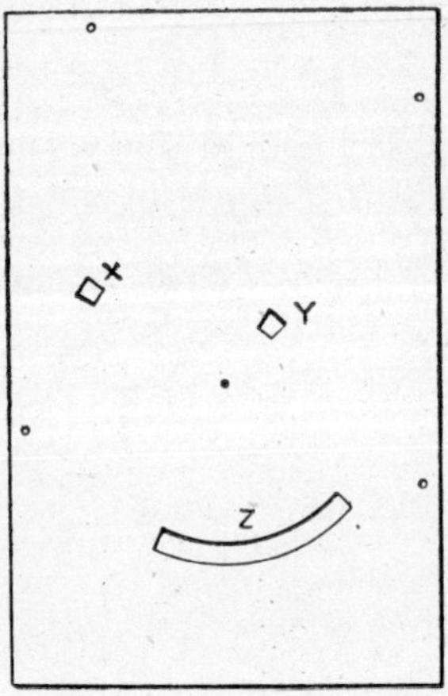

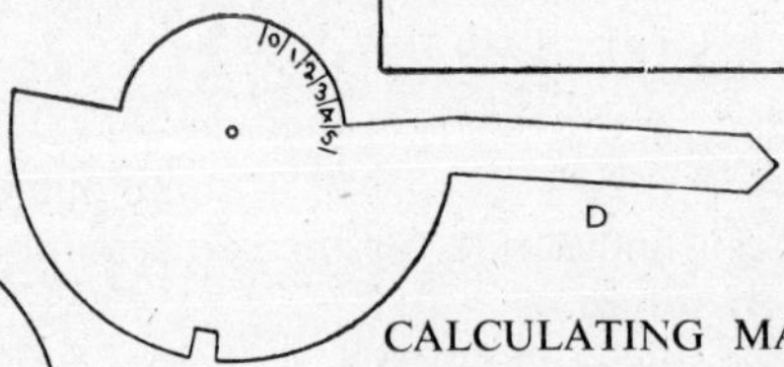

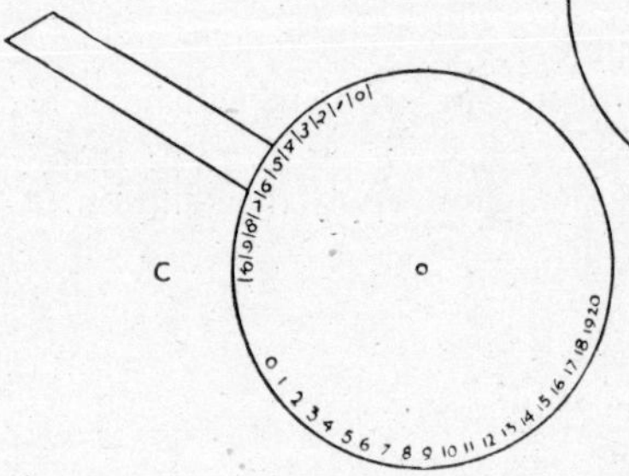

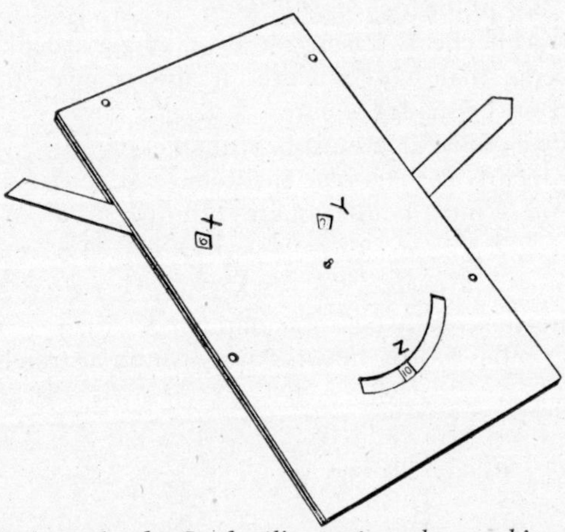

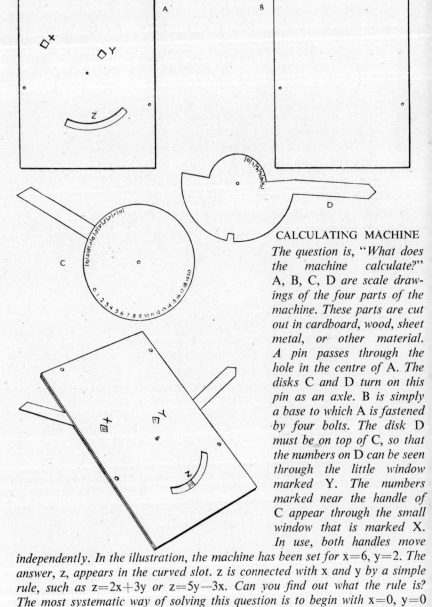

CALCULATING MACHINE

The question is, "What does the machine calculate?" A, B, C, D *are scale drawings of the four parts of the machine. These parts are cut out in cardboard, wood, sheet metal, or other material. A pin passes through the hole in the centre of* A. *The disks* C *and* D *turn on this pin as an axle.* B *is simply a base to which* A *is fastened by four bolts. The disk* D *must be on top of* C, *so that the numbers on* D *can be seen through the little window marked* Y. *The numbers marked near the handle of* C *appear through the small window that is marked* X. *In use, both handles move independently. In the illustration, the machine has been set for* $x=6$, $y=2$. *The answer,* z, *appears in the curved slot.* z *is connected with* x *and* y *by a simple rule, such as* $z=2x+3y$ *or* $z=5y-3x$. *Can you find out what the rule is? The most systematic way of solving this question is to begin with* $x=0$, $y=0$ *and study the effect of varying* x, *while keeping* $y=0$. *Then keep* $x=0$ *and vary* y. *You should now be able to find the rule.*

Pythagoras' Theorem, then, is one that takes a good deal of discovering: but once it is known, it is easy to apply.

SIMPLIFYING A FORMULA

It often happens that a rule is first discovered in a rather long and complicated form. It may be possible to find a shorter and simpler rule that leads to the same result. This is known as *simplifying* a formula.

Sometimes it is not possible to find a simple rule that leads to exactly the same result, but it may be possible to find a simple rule that gives a result near enough for practical purposes. This is known as *finding an approximation* to the formula.

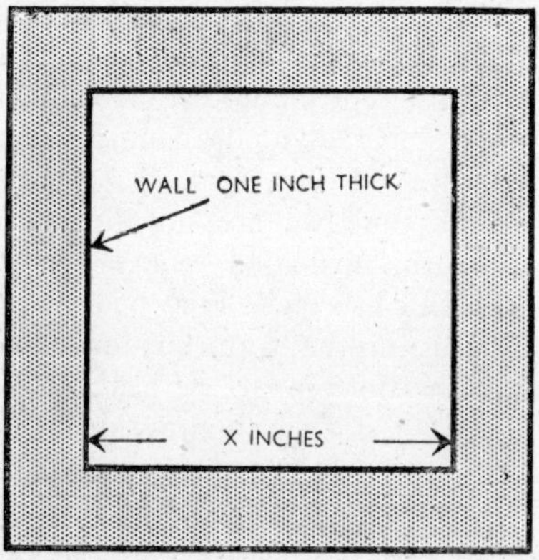

In the next few pages we shall consider examples of each of these.

First, an example in which a rule is made more simple, and exactly the same answer obtained.

Suppose we have a hollow metal container, which when cut through would look like the sketch here. For some reason (perhaps in order to calculate the weight of the metal) we want to know how many square inches there are in the shaded area. How are we to find this?

Let us begin by taking a particular example. Suppose x is 5, so the inside measurement of the container is 5 in. As there is one inch of wall to be added to this at each end, the outside measurement will be 7 in.

The number of squares in the sketch is 7×7, that is 49. But of these 5×5 are empty, unshaded. So the number of shaded squares is $49-25=24$.

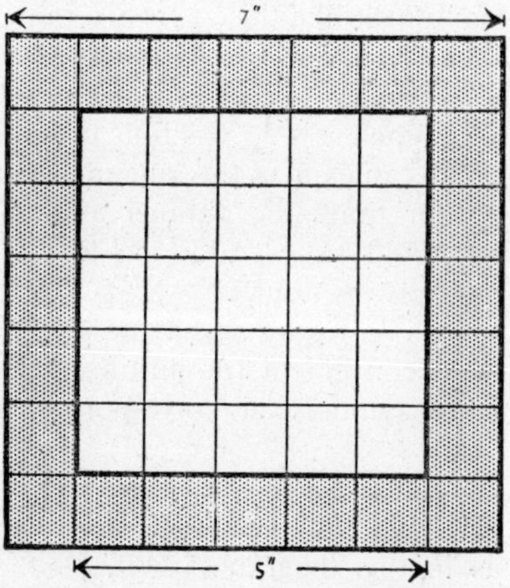

We found this number by working out $7\times7-5\times5$, or 7^2-5^2.

Now we can see what the result will be for any number x, just by going through the same steps.

The inside measurement is x in.

The outside measurement is found by adding 2 to this, so it is $x+2$ in.

The total number of squares, shaded and unshaded, will be found by multiplying this last result by itself—that is, it will be $(x+2)^2$.

Of these x times x, or x^2, will be unshaded.

So the number of shaded squares will be $(x + 2)^2 - x^2$.

If you feel there is any doubt about this result, you can check it by sketching the figures for $x = 1$, $x = 2$, and so on, and verifying that the number of shaded squares does agree with the number given by this rule. (In doing algebra one should check continually, so as to keep one's feet on the ground.)

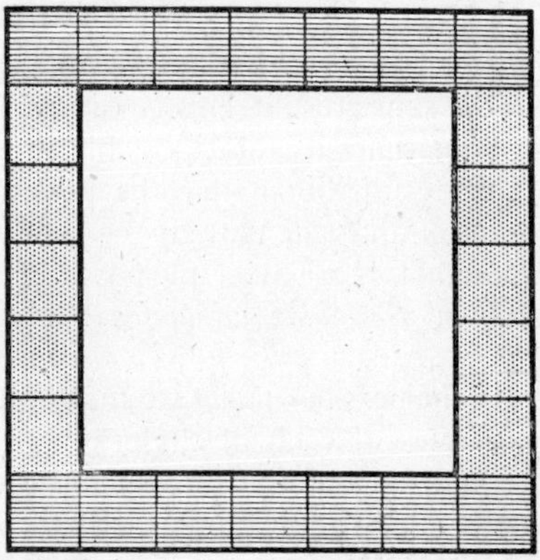

Calling A the area of the shaded part, we have $A = (x + 2)^2 - x^2$.

This rule is not very complicated, but it is not in its simplest form, as we shall see.

You will see for yourself that we might have counted the shaded squares by a different method. For instance, we might have divided them up like the diagram on the right.

This time we are not bothering to count the unshaded squares (so x^2 will not come in). There are 7 heavily shaded squares in the top row, and another 7 at the bottom, so we have $2 \times 7 = 14$ dark squares. Then there are two lots of 5 dotted squares at the sides, $2 \times 5 = 10$. Altogether we have $14 + 10 = 24$ shaded squares, the same answer as before.

If instead of considering 5 we consider x, so that 5 is replaced by x and 7 by $x + 2$, we are led to the rule:

$$A = 2(x + 2) + 2x.$$

Here we have a rule that looks quite different from the first one, but always gives the same answer.

This rule again is not in its simplest form. You can see this if you work out the first few cases, like this:

x	1	2	3	4	5	6
A	8	12	16	20	24	28

The numbers that turn up for A always come from the 4 times table. We may put it like this:

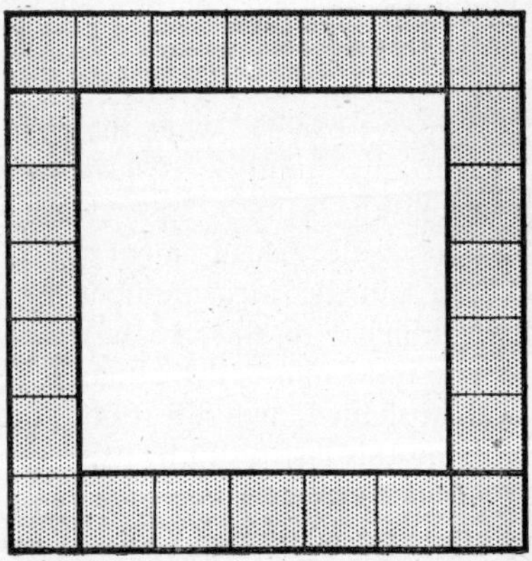

When x is 1, A is four times 2.
When x is 2, A is four times 3.
When x is 3, A is four times 4.

We can express this rule in words, "A is four times the number after x", or we could say, "Add one to x. Then multiply by four".

This last way of saying the rule is most convenient for putting into algebraic symbols; it corresponds to:

$$A = 4(x + 1).$$

You can see the meaning of this rule, if you divide the shaded squares up as in this diagram.

This shows that the shaded squares consist of four lots of 6 each, and $4 \times 6 = 24$.

With x instead of 5, there will be four lots, each containing $x + 1$ squares. So the three formulae,

$$A = (x + 2)^2 - x^2$$
$$A = 2\,(x + 2) + 2x$$
$$A = 4\,(x + 1)$$

all agree with each other; all lead to the same result. The third one is the simplest to work out.

As you can see, it is easy for a simple rule to appear disguised as a complicated one. Nearly all the algebra in the text-books aims at showing you how to simplify any formula you may meet, by definite rules, so that you will not need to potter about looking for a simplification, as we have just done with this problem. (Pottering should always be kept in reserve though, as a means of checking results, and of solving problems that the text-books do not deal with.)

In Chapter IX, the methods of text-book algebra, formal algebra, will be explained.

APPROXIMATE FORMULAE

An example of an approximate formula happened quite naturally while this book was being written. It was readily agreed that a hot-wire ammeter was an easy thing for anyone to construct, and that it might be a good thing to explain the theory of it. The hot-wire ammeter is discussed in greater detail in the Geometry chapter. It may consist of a stretched wire with a small weight hung from the middle point. When the wire is heated by an electric current, the wire expands, and sags in the middle. The question that arises is, "How much has each half of the wire expanded?" We suppose the distance d from the middle point of the wire to the end to be known, and the sag s to have been measured.

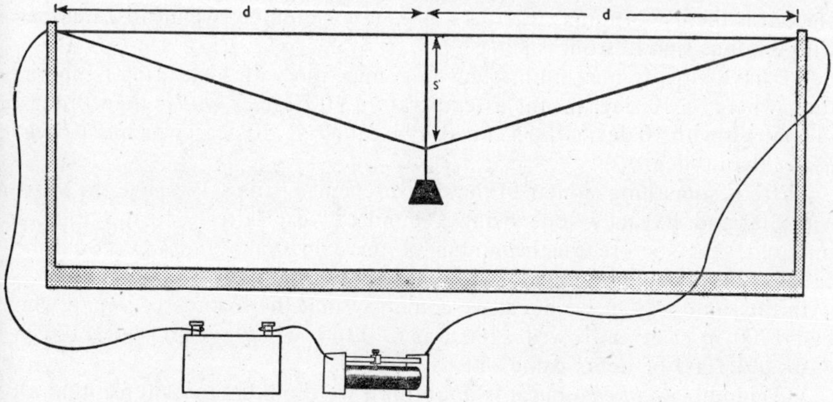

Two mathematicians made a few calculations about this. When they compared notes, they found they had used different formulae. One had used a formula that comes quite easily from Pythagoras' Theorem, according to which each half of the wire expands a distance

$$\sqrt{d^2 + s^2} - d.$$

The other had used a formula that was much simpler. Instead of the expression above he had:

$$\frac{s^2}{2d}$$

which looks quite different.

If you compare these, say for $d = 10$, $s = 1$, the first one gives:

$$\begin{aligned} \sqrt{100 + 1} - 10 &= \sqrt{101} - 10 \\ &= 10.050 - 10 \quad \text{by table of square roots} \\ &= 0{\cdot}05. \end{aligned}$$

The second formula gives:

$$\frac{1^2}{2 \times 10} = \frac{1}{20}$$

As 1/20 is the same as 0·05, the two formulae lead to the same result, and the working is much easier in the second case. This shows the advantage of an approximate formula.

It should be noted that the approximate formula *only works when the sag* s *is small compared to the distance* d.

The first formula is exact, and works for all values of s and d.

As the sag in a hot-wire ammeter is nearly always small, the approximate formula is very suitable for this problem.

If very accurate tables of square roots were used, it would be found that the approximate formula and the exact one gave results that were slightly different.

MINUS NUMBERS

One of the things that most people meet for the first time when they do algebra is the use of minus numbers. By a minus number we mean a number with a minus sign in front, such as -7, or $-2\frac{3}{4}$, or $-3{\cdot}17$.

We have already met minus signs in connection with measuring temperature, where -10 deg. meant a temperature 10 degrees *colder* than 0 deg., in contrast with 10 deg. (which can also be called $+10$ deg.) which is 10 deg. *hotter* than 0 deg.

There is something similar in the measurement of time. We have the years A.D. 100 and 100 B.C.—one being a hundred years after, and the other a hundred years before the beginning of the Christian era. A.D. could be called +, B.C. could be called —, if we liked.

In the same way, if we liked, we could say that the fortune of a man who had £200 in cash and owed £100 was + £100, while a man with £100 in cash and £200 of debts came out as — £100.

We could *if we liked*—but it is doubtful if we should. You will feel that all these examples are rather trivial and forced. They do not look likely to lead to any very startling discovery. And in fact, while they may be con-

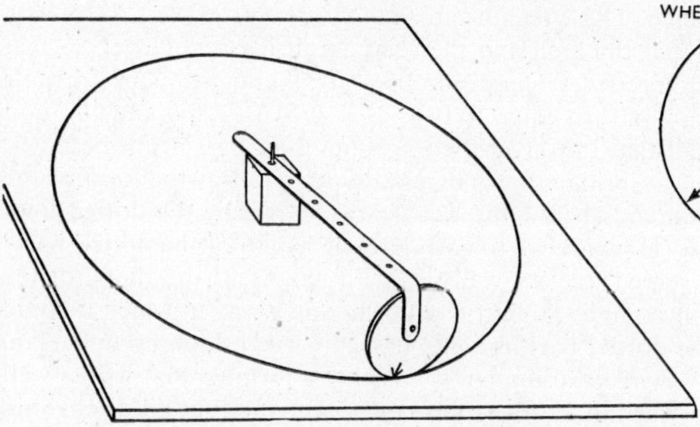

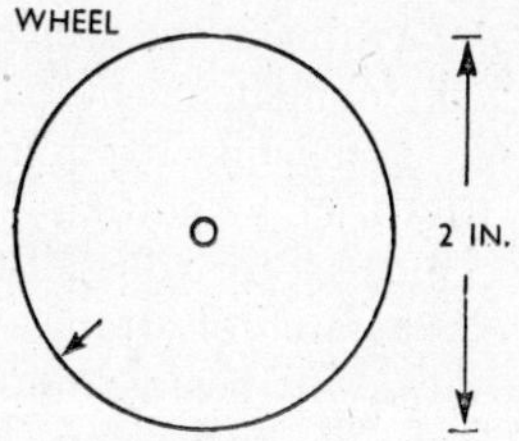

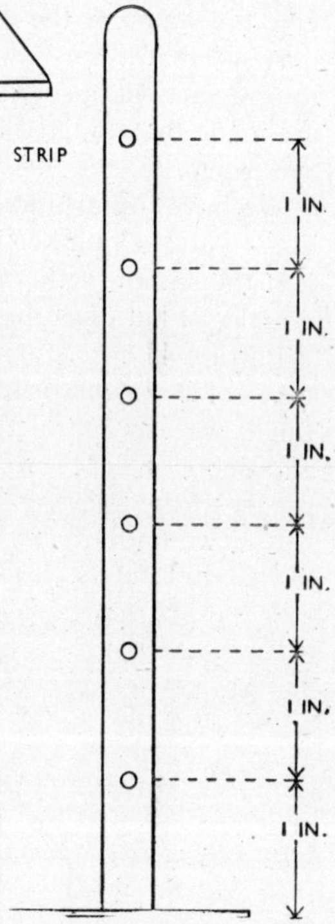

MENSURATION BY EXPERIMENT (2)

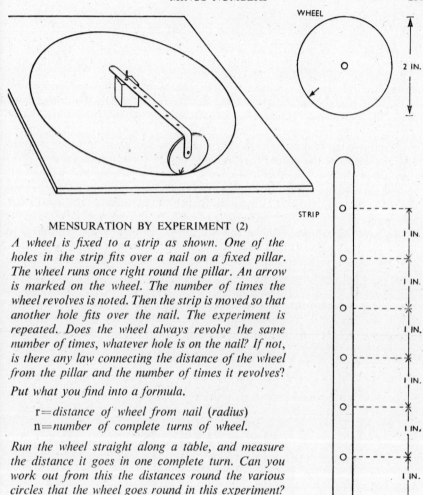

A wheel is fixed to a strip as shown. One of the holes in the strip fits over a nail on a fixed pillar. The wheel runs once right round the pillar. An arrow is marked on the wheel. The number of times the wheel revolves is noted. Then the strip is moved so that another hole fits over the nail. The experiment is repeated. Does the wheel always revolve the same number of times, whatever hole is on the nail? If not, is there any law connecting the distance of the wheel from the pillar and the number of times it revolves?

Put what you find into a formula.

r=*distance of wheel from nail (radius)*
n=*number of complete turns of wheel.*

Run the wheel straight along a table, and measure the distance it goes in one complete turn. Can you work out from this the distances round the various circles that the wheel goes round in this experiment?

venient as illustrations, they are none of them the reason why mathematicians are interested in minus numbers.

Minus numbers were discovered, very gradually, by people who were working at algebra. At first people did not like the idea of minus numbers at all. For instance, if they had a formula like $y = 10 - x$, and x was to be 20, the formula would give $y = 10 - 20$.

Today we would say, 10 — 20 is — 10, but in the early days mathematicians just said, "You cannot take 20 from 10" and left it at that.

Gradually, it came to be recognized that some sense could be got out of expressions like 10 — 20.

Look for instance at the sketch of an arched bridge on page 202. The lengths of the upright bars connecting the steel arch with the road or railway are written in the sketch. These lengths are 0, 9, 16, 21, 24, 25, 24, 21, 16, 9, 0. (The noughts mean that the arch and the road are at the same level, so that no connecting bar is needed.) These numbers are found from the formula $10x - x^2$, by putting x in turn equal to 0, 1, 2, 3, 4, 5, 6, 7, 8, 9 and 10. You can check for yourself that this gives the set of numbers just mentioned.

The arch of a railway bridge does not usually leave off at the level of the railway. It begins and ends below the railway, as shown by the dotted lines in the diagram below. How are we to calculate the length of the dotted bars?

Our formula has served us very well so far, in giving us the shape of the bridge above the railway line. Might there not be some way in which it could give the shape of the dotted part as well? It seems worth looking into. You may say that it is a very risky argument to say that a formula that works well in one part will also work in another part. It certainly is—but all discoveries are made by taking risks. Let us admit that this is a risk, and take it with our eyes open.

We have found the lengths of the bars above the line by taking x equal in turn to all the numbers from 0 to 10. There is an obvious guess to be made—that the length of the next bar (the first dotted one) will be found by taking $x = 11$. What does this lead to?

Putting 11 for x in the formula $10x - x^2$ gives $10 \times 11 - 11^2$, which is $110 - 121$. In the ordinary way of arithmetic we cannot take 121 from 110. But if we use one of the illustrations we had earlier—say a man with £110 and debts of £121—we shall argue that the man is £11 in debt, which corresponds to the answer —11.

Can we find any way of making sense of this answer? The number 11, we

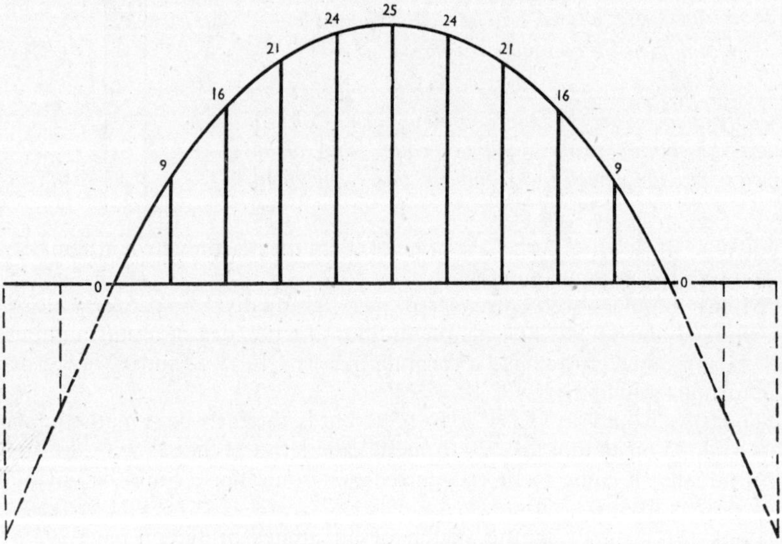

THE SHAPE OF AN ARCHED BRIDGE

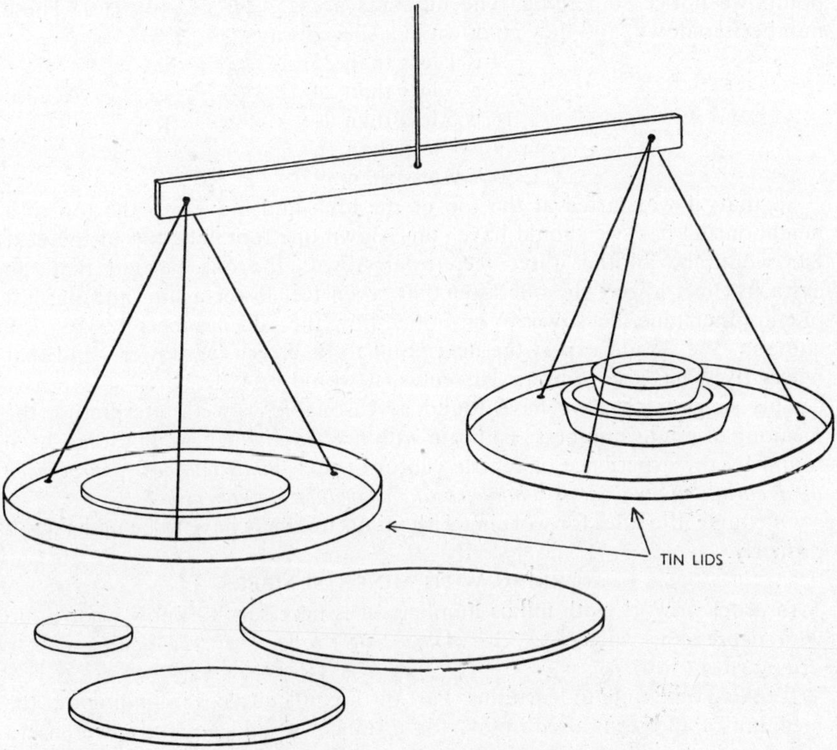

MENSURATION BY EXPERIMENT (3)

To carry out this mensuration problem, cut out some circular disks from a sheet of metal, so that all disks have the same thickness. The disks are of convenient sizes, such as one inch, two inches, three inches and four inches across. The one-inch disk is weighed. Now can you make a guess at what the two-inch disk will weigh? Weigh it and compare the result with your guess. Now guess the weight of the three-inch disk, and check this guess. Continue in this way until you are able to find the law which connects the weight with the size. If metal disks are not available, small tins filled with water may be used. Or you might try your hand at making paper containers and filling these with water. If manufactured scales are not available, home-made scales can be constructed quite easily and they will be found to be very accurate.

might guess, gives the length of the dotted bar. The only meaning we can give to the minus sign is that this bar goes *down* while all the bars without minus signs go up.

This is a possible explanation, but it is only a guess, and we should like to find some way of checking it.

If we look at the numbers on the bars as they go away from the highest point, we notice something. The numbers are 25, 24, 21, 16, 9, 0. These numbers go down, and they go down in a special way.

24 is 1 less than 25
21 is 3 less than 24
16 is 5 less than 21
9 is 7 less than 16
0 is 9 less than 9

So that, if we started at the top of the arch and moved to the top of a neighbouring bar, we should have come down one foot. The top of the next bar would be another three feet lower down; the one beyond that, an extra five feet lower; the one after that seven feet lower again and the last one another nine feet lower. You notice how the odd numbers 1, 3, 5, 7, 9 come in. We should expect the next point to be eleven feet lower—and that is exactly what, according to our guess, it would be.

This suggests that we have found a reasonable way of interpreting the meaning of minus numbers. To begin with it was only a guess, but it has been found by the experience of several centuries that *minus numbers can be used in algebra, and give just as reliable results as ordinary numbers.*

Of course, the rules for working with minus numbers have to be understood properly.

WORKING WITH MINUS NUMBERS

In order to work with minus numbers, it is necessary to know what to do with expressions such as $-3+4-8$, or $(-1)+(-2)$, or $5\times(-2)$, or $(-3)\times(-4)$.

It takes some time to learn this. Part of the difficulty lies in finding out the meaning of the signs used. Why, for instance, should anybody ever use a sign like $+(-2)$? We think of $+$ and $-$ as opposites. What are they both doing in front of the same number?

The answer is that we are dealing with algebra. Suppose you had the formula $10+x$ and you wanted to put $x=-2$. x we can think of as a space to be filled, since $10+x$ means 10 plus something, or $10+(\quad)$. Now the something is to be -2, so we put -2 in the empty space. This gives us $10+(-2)$, and we have the $+$ and $-$ signs sitting next to each other.

What should this mean? Perhaps the best way will be to consider various values of x.

If x is 4, $10+x$ is 14
If x is 3, $10+x$ is 13
If x is 2, $10+x$ is 12
If x is 1, $10+x$ is 11
If x is 0, $10+x$ is 10

The numbers we obtain go down steadily by ones, 14, 13, 12, 11, 10. Here is a simple rule. On the same principle as before, we guess that a simple rule is not likely to break off suddenly. The next numbers we expect to be 9, 8, 7, and so on.

The numbers for x are also going down by ones; they are 4, 3, 2, 1, 0. If they go down any more they will begin to be numbers below sea-level,

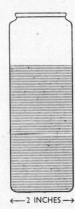

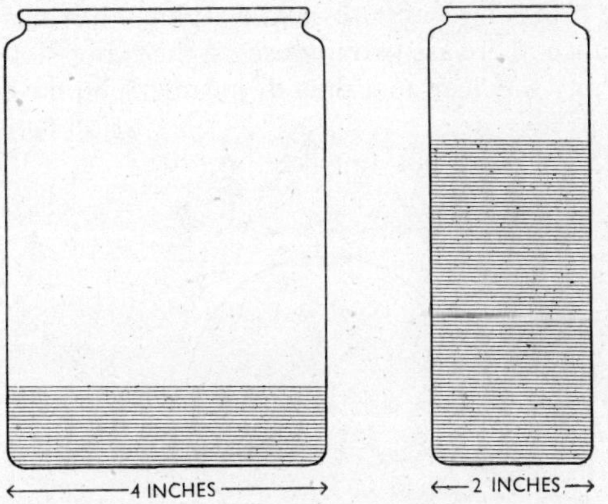

MENSURATION BY EXPERIMENT (4)

Two glass jars are found, one being roughly twice as broad as the other. The same quantity of water is poured into each jar. The height of the water in the two jars is compared. You might think the water would be twice as high in the jar that is half as broad, but you will find it is not so.

minus numbers. The number after 0 will be -1; the number after that, -2, and so on. Accordingly, we have:

If x is -1, $10+x$ is 9
If x is -2, $10+x$ is 8
If x is -3 $10+x$ is 7

So we must take it that $10+(-2)$ is 8. Thus $10+(-2)$ seems to mean the same thing as $10-2$ in arithmetic.

It may help you to think of + as meaning *and*, ordinary numbers as meaning money in pounds, and minus numbers as being *bills* or *debts*. So $10+(-2)$ could be interpreted as £10 *and a debt of* £2, which is as good as £8.

If you meet the expression $10-(-2)$ you will have to think of the first minus sign as meaning *take away*, *destroy*, or *cancel*. $10-(-2)$ might then be interpreted as "Here is £10 for you, and I am tearing up this bill for £2 that you owe me". This is as good as being given £12.

But how do we know that this illustration is correct? How do we make it up? It is done the same way as before. $10-(-2)$ comes originally from putting $x=-2$ in $10-x$, and we try to find a meaning for it that will make it fit smoothly in with the results:

when x is 4, $10-x$ is 6
when x is 3, $10-x$ is 7
when x is 2, $10-x$ is 8
when x is 1, $10-x$ is 9
when x is 0, $10-x$ is 10

Here you can see that, as the numbers at the beginning go down by one, the numbers at the end go up by one. So the next two lines will be:

when x is -1, $10-x$ is 11
when x is -2, $10-x$ is 12

These two examples, on finding $10+(-2)$ and $10-(-2)$, show how to *add* and *subtract* a minus number.

We can make rules to save arguing it out each time. $10+(-2)$ we saw was the same as $10-2$. So $+(-\quad)$ can be replaced by $-$.

$10-(-2)$ was 12, which is the same as $10+2$. So $-(-\quad)$ may be replaced by $+$.

This is sometimes stated in the rule, "Two minuses make a plus". But this rule is rather dangerous. For instance, there are two minuses in the expression 10 — 2 — 3, but this does not in any way lead to a plus. It means "You have £10, and here are bills for £2 and £3".

The rule would apply if a bracket were put in, like this, 10 — 2 (— 3).

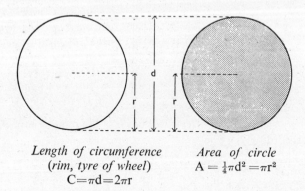

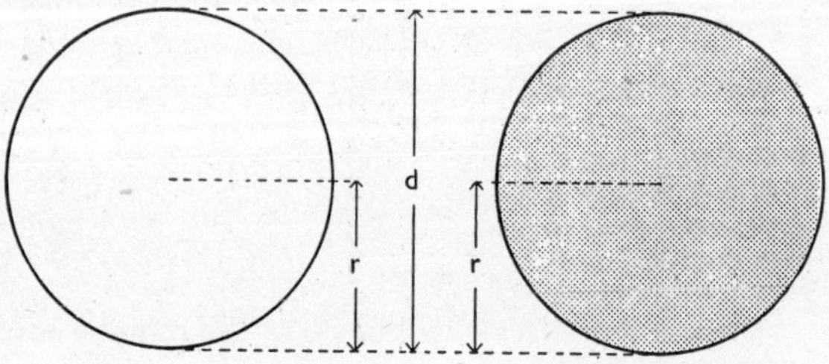

Length of circumference
(rim, tyre of wheel)
$C = \pi d = 2\pi r$

Area of circle
$A = \frac{1}{4}\pi d^2 = \pi r^2$

These two results are often confused with each other. It may help to remember that areas are measured in square feet, *so* d squared *and* r squared *come into the formulae for areas.*

Another way of seeing the result is to remember that the area of a circle takes up about three quarters of the square *containing the circle.*

π *is approximately* 3·14 *or* $3\frac{1}{7}$

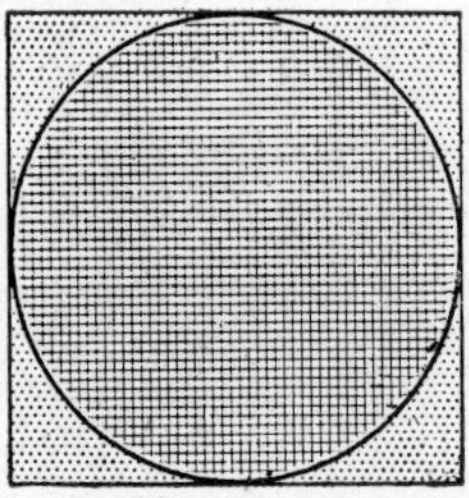

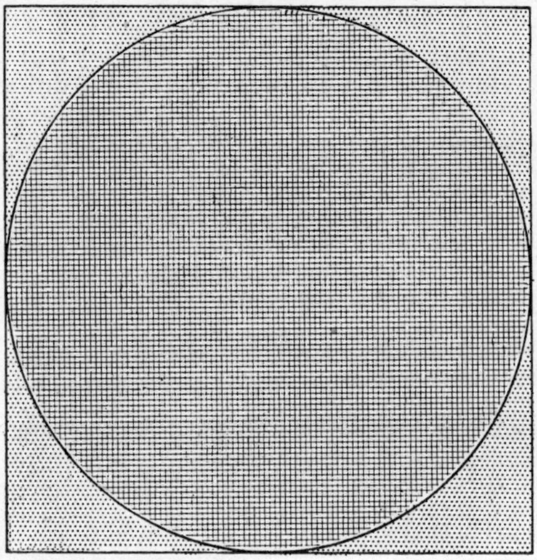

Area of square $= d^2$

Area of circle $= \frac{\pi}{4}d^2 = \frac{3}{4}d^2$ *roughly*

MENSURATION BY FORMULA (2) CIRCLES

This would mean "Here is £10 and I am tearing up 2 bills each for £3"—quite a different story.

It is unfortunate that two things should look so much alike, and have such different meanings. It is not surprising that students find difficulty with this minus business.

The only advice we can give is to say, "Take note, this is a very fiddling business; do not try to rush it; if you want to learn algebra, you must work examples with plus and minus signs until it becomes second nature with you to do the right thing."

One fairly interesting and very instructive way of getting this practice is by drawing lots of graphs. The picture of the railway bridge on page 201 is a graph, and in Chapter VIII the whole subject of graphs will be gone into. Graphs are very useful for checking work. *When a graph has a sudden bend in it, it nearly always means that a mistake has been made.*

Sometimes you will notice things about graphs that help you to spot the right answer. For instance, in our railway bridge you are sure to notice that the same numbers occur whether you leave the top of the arch to the right or to the left. Either way, you get the numbers 25, 24, 21, 16, 9, 0. This property is not likely to leave off suddenly. The number after 0, going to the right, is -11. So, going to the left, -11 should also occur next to 0, in fact for $x = -1$.

The best way to learn algebra is to play about with numbers and formulae, discovering your own laws, making your own mistakes and finding them out later. That is how nearly all good mathematicians began their studies—finding things out for themselves.

To return to the rules for work with minus numbers. We have dealt with addition and subtraction of minus numbers. We still have to consider multiplication and division.

Rules for these processes can be discovered by the same kind of argument as we used earlier. The principle is again to find some rule that works for ordinary numbers, and so arrange things that it works for minus numbers as well.

For instance, you can check for yourself that $x-2$ multiplied by $x-4$ is the same as $x^2 - 6x + 8$, when x is any number bigger than 4.

If x is 5, $x - 2$ is 3
$x - 4$ is 1
$x^2 - 6x + 8$ is $25 - 30 + 8 = 3$, which is 3×1.

The answers are the same for any other number above 4, so we may write:

$$(x-2)(x-4) = x^2 - 6x + 8.$$

We have only checked this for x bigger than 4. What happens if we try numbers less than 4?

Taking $x = 1$, we have $x - 2$ is -1
$x - 4$ is -3
$x^2 - 6x + 8$ is $1 - 6 + 8 = 3$.

So, if the rule found above is still to be true, we must take -1 times -3 to be 3.

In the same way, if we try taking $x = 3$, $x - 2$ is 1, $x - 4$ is -1 and $x^2 - 6x + 8$ is -1.

$$A = ab$$

$$A = bh$$

$$A = \tfrac{1}{2}bh$$

$$A = \tfrac{1}{2}(a+b)\,h$$

$$A = \sqrt{s(s-a)(s-b)(s-c)}$$
where $s = \tfrac{1}{2}(a+b+c)$

$$A = \tfrac{1}{4}\pi d^2$$
$$= \pi r^2$$

Shaded area $= \tfrac{1}{4}\pi(D+d)(D-d)$
$$= \tfrac{1}{4}\pi(D^2 - d^2)$$

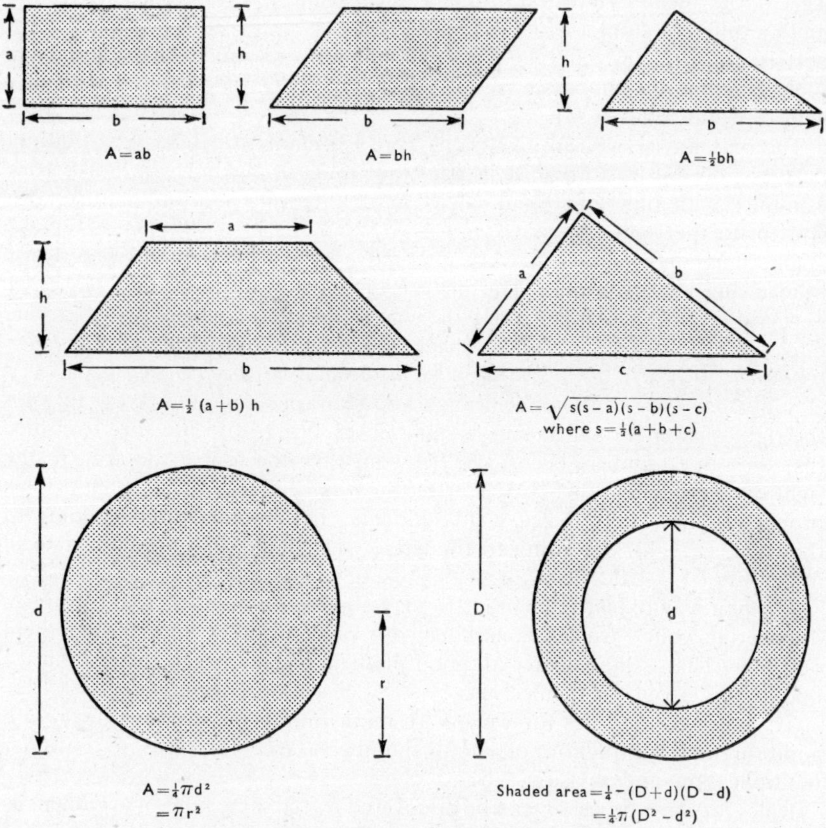

MENSURATION BY FORMULA (3) AREAS

In each case, A *stands for the shaded area.* π *is approximately* $3{\cdot}14$ *or* $3\tfrac{1}{7}$.

So it seems that 1 times -1 is -1.

It is usual to speak of ordinary numbers as *plus*, so that 6 and $+6$ have the same meaning.

We can put the results just found into a rule.

Minus times minus is **plus**.
Plus times minus is minus.

For instance, if we want to calculate $(-7) \times (-8)$, we first say seven eights are 56. Minus times minus is plus, so the result must be plus. So the answer is $+56$, or simply 56.

In the same way, to find $(-6) \times (10)$, we first write down 60, since that is 6 times 10. As we are dealing with minus times plus, the result must be minus. So we put a minus sign in front of the 60, and the answer is, accordingly, -60.

You will meet minus numbers next in Chapter VIII on graphs, and that chapter will probably help you to understand what minus numbers are for. You will also meet them in Chapter IX. When you are reading Chapter IX, you will probably find it desirable to read through this explanation again.

In the meantime, it will probably be sufficient if you remember (1) that minus numbers are just as good as ordinary numbers for putting into a formula in algebra, (2) that minus numbers may be represented as being *downwards* or *backwards*, (3) that there are special rules for adding, subtracting, multiplying and dividing minus numbers. (The division rules are not learnt separately; they follow from the rules for multiplication given above.)

In the next chapter, which is on geometry, you will not need to use minus numbers.

Exercises

In order to use algebra, and to follow further work in Chapter IX, you will need to be thoroughly familiar with algebraic symbols. It is, therefore, important to do a large number of examples, such as the following. Make similar examples for yourself.

1. If l stands for the length of a wooden block in inches,
   b stands for the breadth in inches,
   h stands for the height in inches,

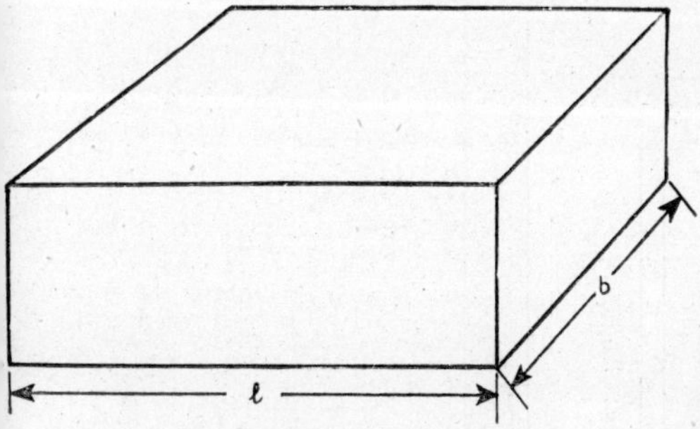

write in algebraic shorthand
   (i) the length multiplied by the breadth;
   (ii) the length times the breadth times the height;
   (iii) the length added to the breadth;
   (iv) the breadth taken away from the length;
   (v) the height divided by the length;
   (vi) twice the length added to twice the breadth;
   (vii) the breadth times the height times the height again;
   (viii) the result of number (vii) divided by the length;
   (ix) the result of number (vi) multiplied by the height.

2. Work out the formulae (i) to (ix) of question 1 for a block of length 10 inches, breadth 4 inches, height 3 inches.

3. Work out the formulae (i) to (ix) of question 1 for $l = 12$, $b = 5$, $h = 7$.

4. Find $2lb + 2hl + 2hb$ for $l = 5$, $b = 4$, $h = 3$. To what problem about a block of wood is this the answer?

5. If n stands for any whole number, express in algebraic symbols (i) double the number; (ii) half the number; (iii) one more than the number; (iv) the number multiplied by four, with three then added; (v) the number multiplied by itself; (vi) the number multiplied by the number that is one less than it;

(vii) the square root of the number;
(viii) a hundred divided by the number.

6. Work out $(n + 1)^2$ and $n^2 + 1$ (i) for $n = 1$, (ii) for $n = 2$, (iii) for $n = 3$.

Is $(n + 1)^2$ the same as $n^2 + 1$ for every number n?

7. Work out $(n + 1)^2$ and $n^2 + 2n + 1$;

(i) for $n = 1$, (ii) for $n = 2$, (iii) for $n = 3$.

Is $(n + 1)^2$ the same as $n^2 + 2n + 1$ for every number n?

8. If x stands for any number whatever (whole number, fraction, etc.), work out $x^2 - \frac{1}{4}$ for the following values of x: 1, $1\frac{1}{2}$, 2, $2\frac{1}{2}$, 3, $3\frac{1}{2}$.

Can you guess what x must be to make $x^2 - \frac{1}{4}$ equal to 42?

9. A strip is bent into the form shown in the diagram. Find a formula for the total length of the strip. Check your formula by taking $x = 3$, $y = 1$, $w = 2$, $z = 3\frac{1}{2}$. (All measurements are in inches.)

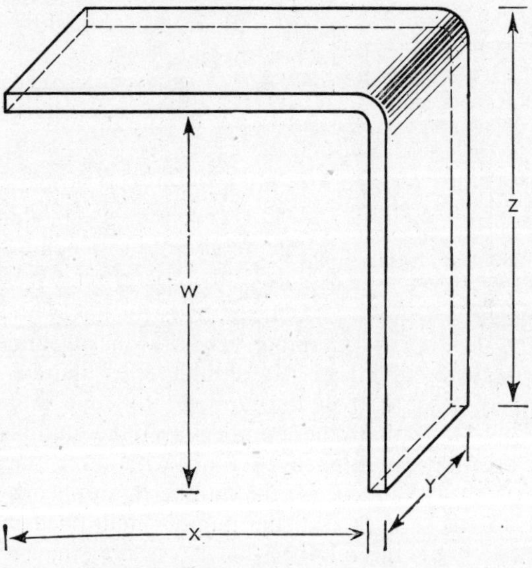

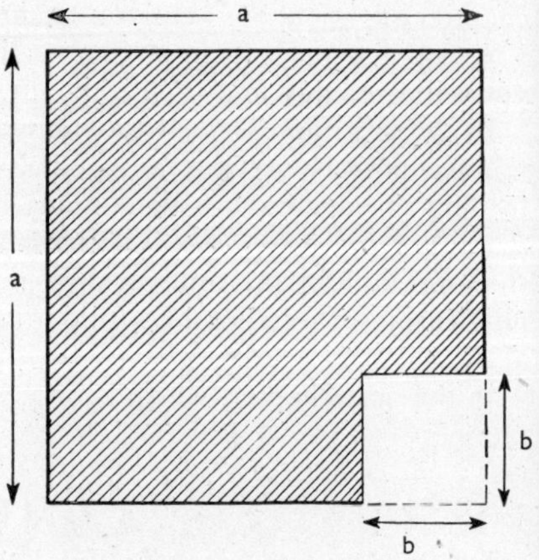

10. A little square of side b inches is removed from a large square of side a as shown in the above illustration.

(i) What is the area of the original large square?
(ii) What is the area of the piece removed?
(iii) What is the area of the piece left (shown shaded in the figure)?

Questions 11—15 *are to be solved by trial and error.*

11. What value of x makes $2x + 1$ equal to 15?

12. Can you find two different values of x that make $20x - x^2$ equal to 75?

13. Can you find *roughly* how large x must be to make $x^2 + x$ equal to 73?

14. *Roughly* how large must x be to make $x^2 + 2x$ equal to 42?

15. A building contains x bachelors, y spinsters, z childless

married couples. How many people in all?

16. The shaded area of question 10 can be cut like this:

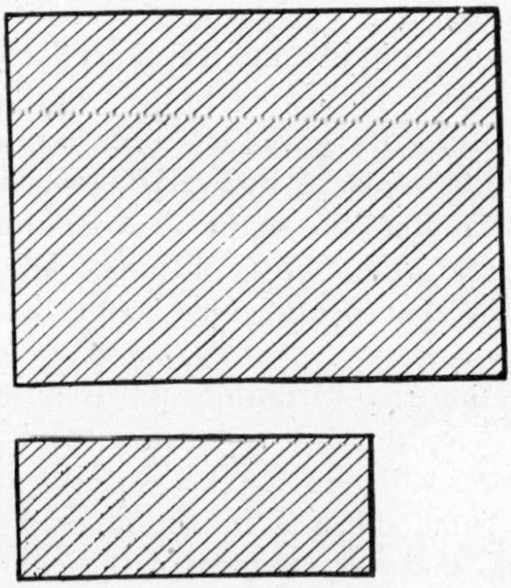

and the pieces put together to form a rectangle, like this:

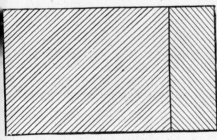

Find formulae containing a and b to represent (i) the height of this rectangle, (ii) the breadth, (iii) the height times the breadth (= the area).

17. The formula found in 16 (iii) represents the same area as the formula found in 10 (iii). The values of the two formulae ought always to be the same. Test this by taking particular values for a and b, such as $a = 5$ and $b = 2$.

Is it true that $a^2 - b^2 = (a - b)(a + b)$ whatever numbers a and b are?

18. Two wheels touch as shown.

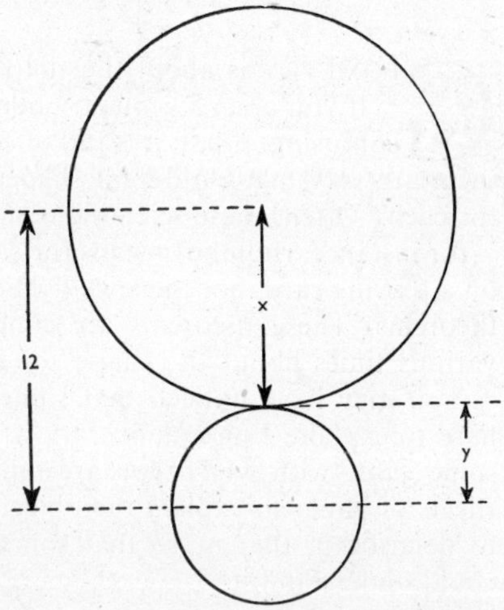

(i) The radius of one wheel is 5 times that of the other; (ii) the centres of the wheels are 12 inches apart.

Express the statements (i) and (ii) in the form of algebraic equations.

19. Can you guess, or calculate, the numbers x and y in question 18?

20. x, y, z are three numbers; x is bigger than y and y is bigger than z.

Taking any three numbers you like for x, y and z, work out $x - y$, $y - z$ and $x - z$.

Is $x - z$ equal to the sum of $x - y$ and $y - z$ for the numbers you have chosen? Is it always true?

21. x, y and z being as in question 20, find $y - z$ and subtract the result from x.

Also find $x - y + z$.

Are the two results the same?

Is it true that $x - (y - z)$ is always equal to $x - y + z$?

22. If n is a whole number, is $n(n + 1)$ always an even number?

CHAPTER VII

GEOMETRY

GEOMETRY is about the shape of things.

If you open a geometry book you will probably find it very dull and confusing. First, it is full of strange names. This is due to the fact that there are very many different shapes, and a scientific name has been found for each. Often, these scientific names could be replaced by everyday words —for instance, rhombus means the same as diamond (the shape of a diamond on a playing card, not the jewel). Then, there are whole hosts of things called theorems. These theorems are simply truths that people have noticed at various times about the shapes of things.

You may have noticed that something quite easy to understand is often hard to explain. For instance, try writing down a description of how to play some game with which you are familiar. You will find it takes sheets and sheets of paper to explain the object of the game and how it is conducted— to describe it, that is, so that someone who had never heard of the game could understand it.

It is the same with the study of shapes. Many things that are quite easy to see are very hard to write down, and require sentences full of long words to explain them accurately.

It will help you to understand geometry if you imagine that you have been told to sit down and write a book about the shapes of things. You would have to decide first of all what shapes were sufficiently important to be included at all, and you would have to decide on names for these shapes. Then you would have to think what there was to be said about these shapes.

It would be very hard to decide what to write, if you just sat down to think about shapes in general. In actual fact, geometry books did not start by people sitting down and thinking. Long before that stage was reached, people had been doing things and making things for many hundreds of years. And in the course of making things, it had been noticed that certain shapes kept cropping up, and that these shapes were particularly suitable for certain purposes.

Geometry in the main is about the shapes used in practical trades, engineering, carpentry, pottery, and so forth. There are other shapes which may be of interest from an artistic point of view—the shapes of clouds, the shapes of animals, the shapes of men and women. Geometry does not at the moment deal with these latter shapes, however. One day it may do.

The way in which simple shapes arise in practical life may be illustrated equally well by the most modern engineering project, or by the earliest productions of primitive man.

Let us consider a few examples of practical problems that call for some understanding of shapes, and have led to special names being invented.

In most machines, one part slides over another. For instance, the piston of a steam-engine or a motor-car slides backwards and forwards in the cylinder.

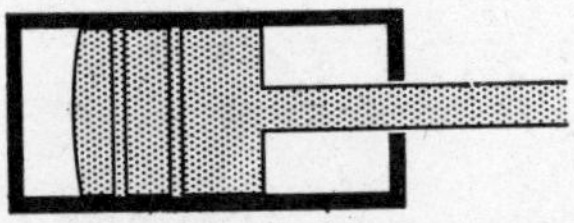

It will not do to have just any shape for the piston and the cylinder. Suppose, for instance, they were made like this :

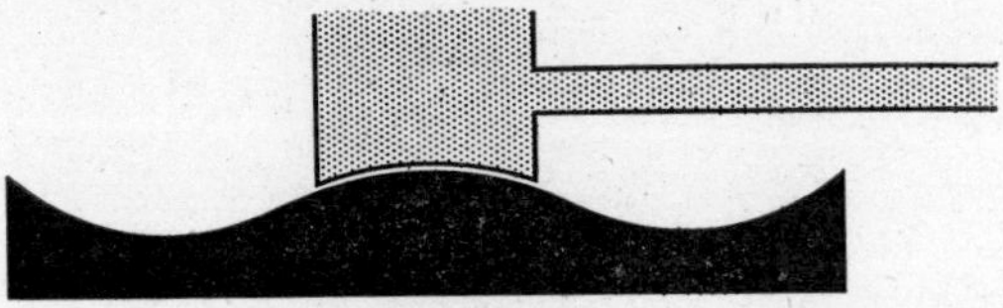

The shapes fit together in this position all right, but the moment the piston moves,

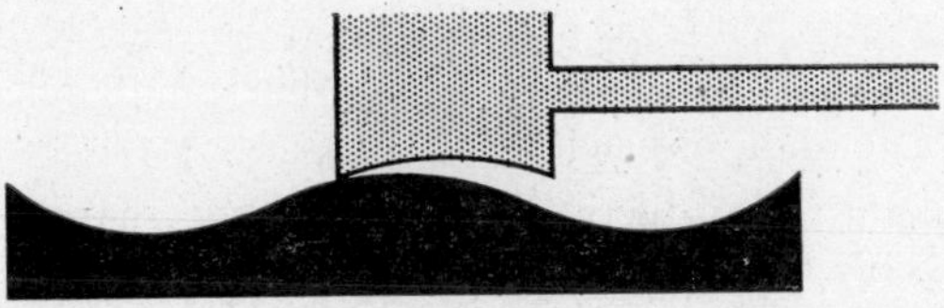

the two no longer fit together.

As everybody knows, the walls of the cylinder and the sides of the piston must be straight.

There is another kind of motion that often happens, namely, turning. A wheel has to turn on its axle. If we had a wheel and axle like this :

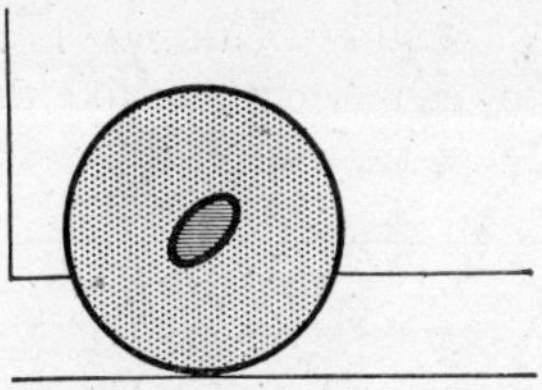

it would be impossible for the wheel to turn at all. Axles are always made to be circular in section.

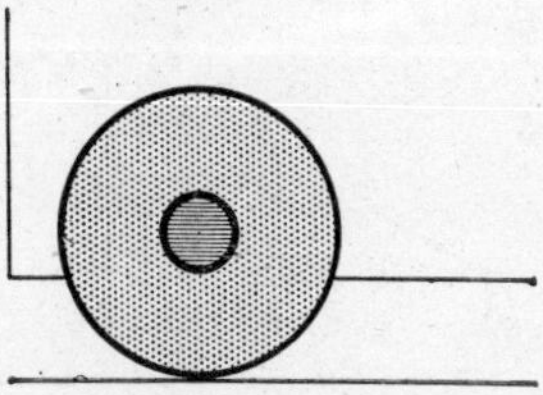

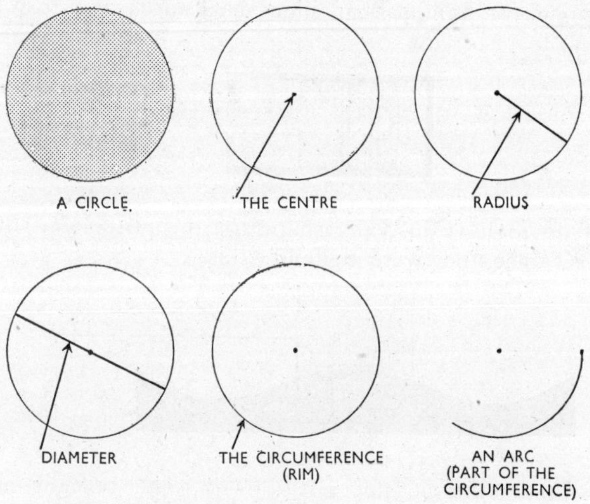

NAMES OF THINGS CONNECTED WITH A CIRCLE

There are no other shapes, besides straight lines and circles, suitable for objects that have to slide on each other.

Perhaps one ought to say there are no other *flat* shapes that will do, because it is possible to have a shape like the thread of a screw, or the surface of a ball, for sliding objects. And even these shapes are closely connected with circles.

Nearly every machine must, therefore, be based on straight lines and circles, and it is not surprising that geometry is very much concerned with these two shapes.

Straight lines are not only important for things that move. Often, straight lines come into the fitting together of things. For instance, if you bend up the figure shown below, you get something like the corner of a box.

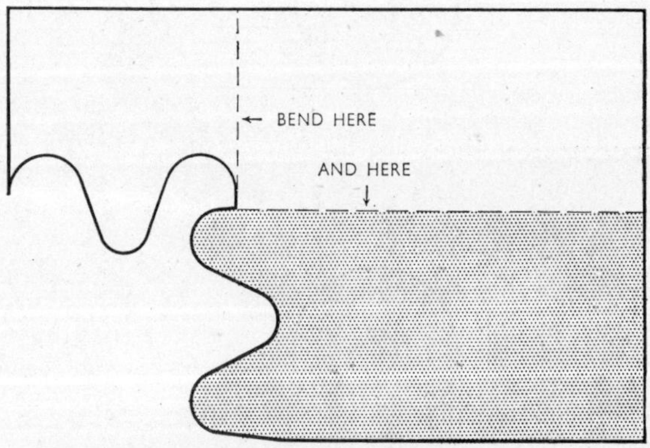

But it is not a satisfactory box corner. It looks like this :

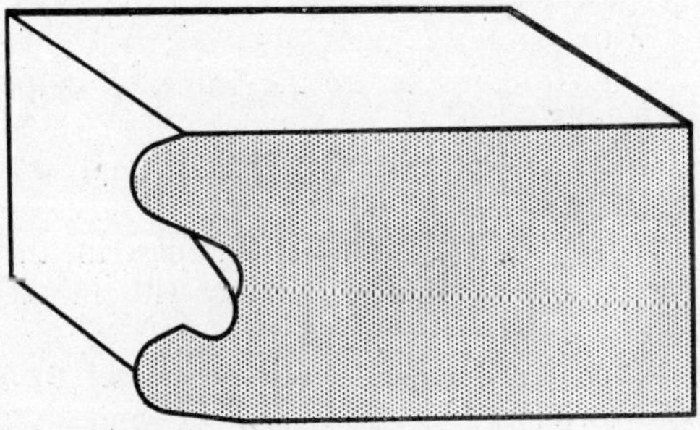

The edges do not fit together and the only way to make them fit neatly is for each side to be straight. Wherever two flat surfaces meet together, you always find a straight line. You may have noticed that the only way to bend a piece of paper, or sheet metal, so as to get flat surfaces, is by folding along a straight line.

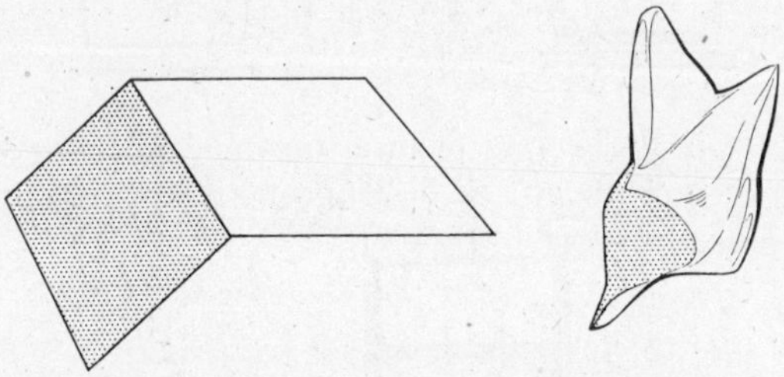

The official name for a flat surface is a plane, so we may put what we have noticed above into learned language by saying, two planes can meet only in a straight line.

The straight line and the circle are both easy to construct. Straight lines are usually drawn with rulers. A straight line can also be obtained by stretching a string as tightly as possible.

A circle can also be made without any apparatus more elaborate than a couple of pegs and a piece of rope. The illustration shows this being done.

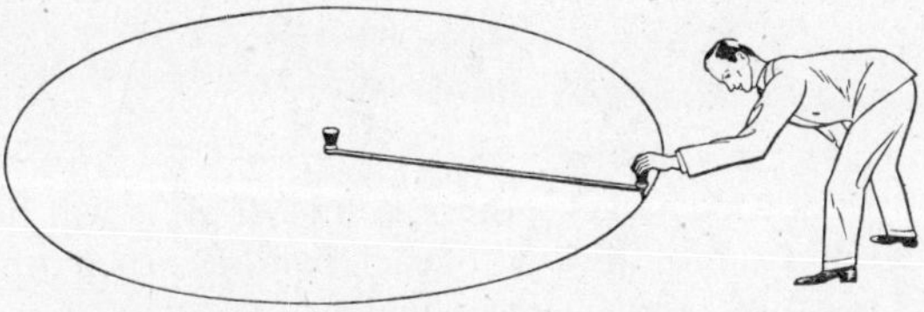

MARKING OUT A CIRCLE FOR A TENT, OR A FLOWER BED

One may use a similar device on a smaller scale when drawing on paper, or compasses or dividers may be used.

The point at the middle of the circle is called the centre. The length of the rope between the peg at the centre and the peg that goes round the rim is called the radius of the circle.

The circle and the straight line are the only two shapes that come into elementary geometry (Euclid).

A surprising variety of shapes can be made simply by putting together straight lines and circles.

Accordingly, our next job is to find words to describe the different ways in which these shapes can be arranged—one line with another, one circle with another, a line with a circle.

First of all, two lines may be parallel. Parallel lines are very important in practical life, as for instance, in railway lines or windows. A window would be no use if it were this shape,

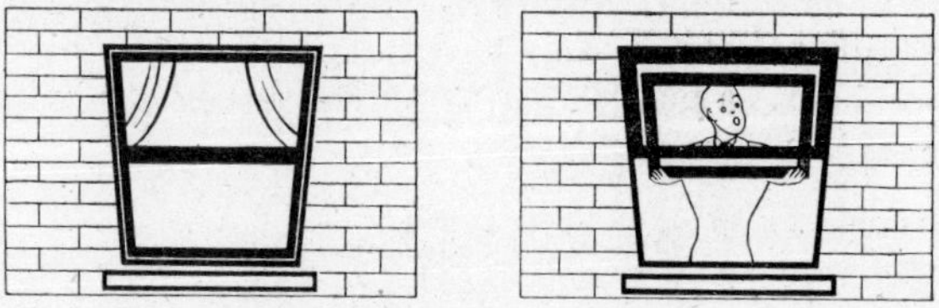

as you can see from the second picture showing somebody opening it.

If the window is to slide up and down properly, the sides must be like this:

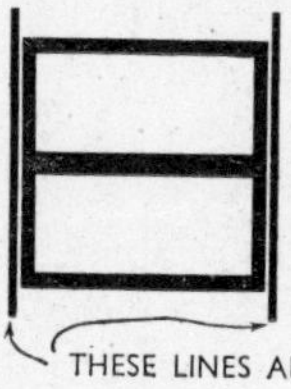
THESE LINES ARE PARALLEL

Other applications of parallel lines are to be found in the cylinders of engines, the rails on which overhead cranes run, the lines on a piece of writing paper, the sides of drawers in furniture, the edges of a brick—to mention only a few.

Now let us consider what happens when two lines are not parallel. Here we have a number of pairs of lines :

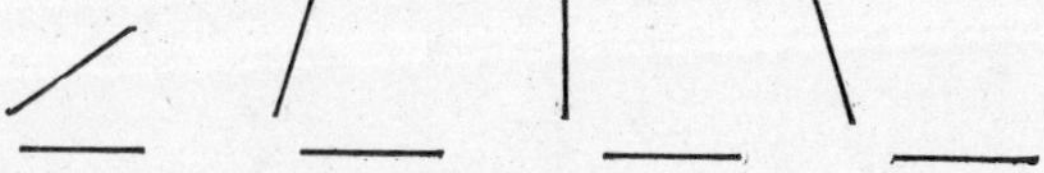

These lines do not meet each other, so first of all it will be convenient to make the lines longer, until the lines of each pair meet each other. (In scientific language, this is called *producing* the lines.)

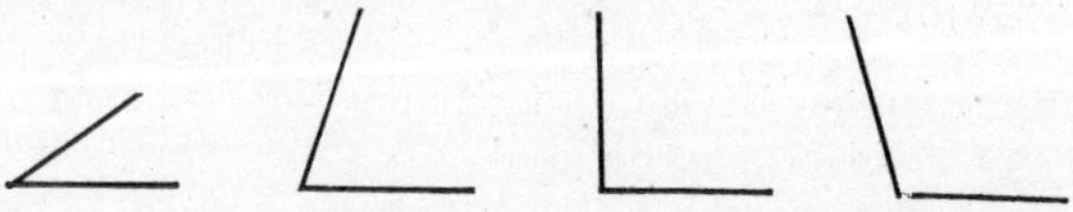

THE NAMES OF SHAPES

The words describing these figures are used to show how many sides a figure has. If a field has four straight sides, it is a quadrilateral, whatever its shape may be. In the same way, anything with three straight sides is a triangle. The names are not too easy to learn. Triangle means "three-angle" (Latin); quadrilateral means "four sides" (Latin); pentagon means "five angles" (Greek); hexagon means "six angles" (Greek). All these shapes may be referred to as polygons ("many angles").

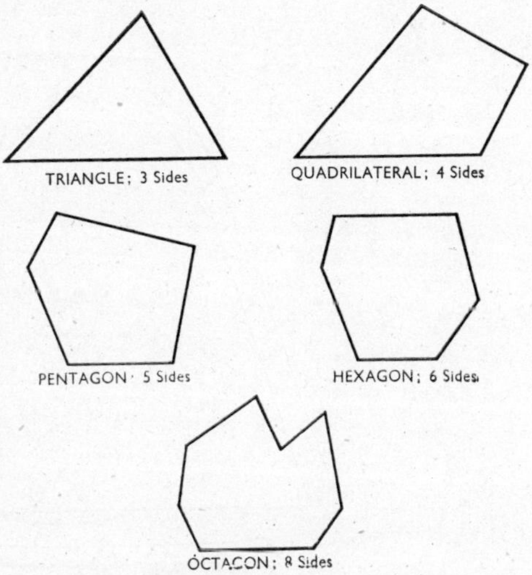

When two lines meet like this, they are said to form an *angle*. As you can see, the four angles are quite different in appearance. The first one is something like the point of a chisel, which you certainly could not say of the last. The third, which looks like the corner of a table or a book, has a special name. It is called a right angle. When two lines make a right angle, they are said to be perpendicular to each other.

It is necessary to have some way of describing these different angles. To take a military example, a man working an anti-aircraft gun receives his orders by telephone. It is no use for the officer at the telephone to say, "Now lads, these aeroplanes are coming over ever so high up, so put a really steep angle on your guns." If he said that, the guns would be pointing in all kinds of different directions.

The illustration on page 218 shows how this problem is solved. There is a scale, marked into ninety divisions, on the gun. A pointer moves on this scale. When the pointer is at 90, the gun is pointing straight up at the sky. When the pointer is at 0, the gun is flat. The numbers between 0 and 90 correspond to the positions of the gun in between.

These divisions are known as degrees, and the same system of measuring that is used for anti-aircraft guns is used for angles generally.

The round scale with angles marked on it is known as a protractor.

Sometimes it is necessary to use angles larger than 90 degrees. We may see this with the same example of anti-aircraft guns. We know how the correct elevation of the gun is obtained, but there is still the question of the direction in which the gun should point—north, south, east, west or in some direction between.

The illustration on page 219 shows the arrangement used. Again we have a pointer travelling round a dial, but the dial is now not a quarter of a circle but a full circle. The figure 0 corresponds to north, 90 to east, 180 to south, and 270 to west. From west to north, the numbers still increase. After 360

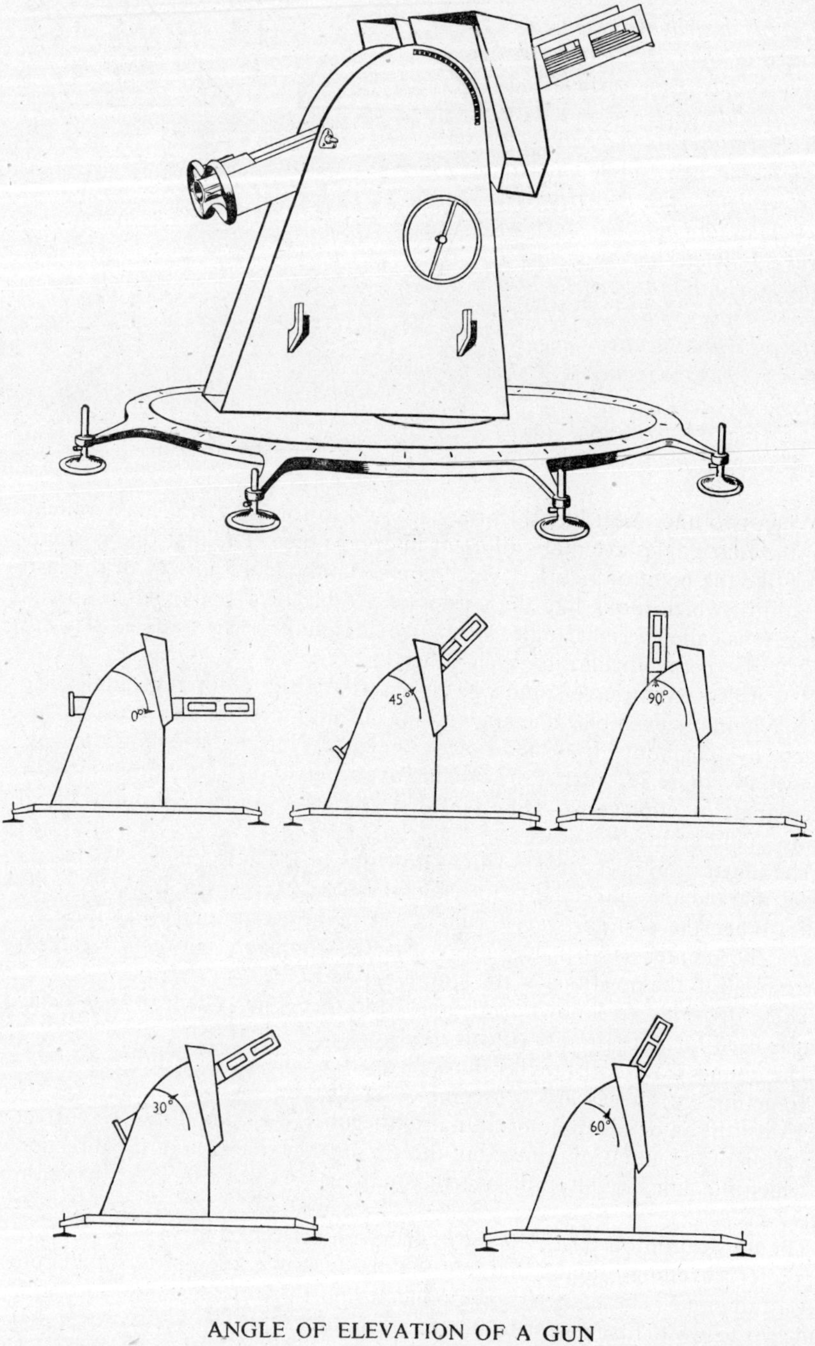

ANGLE OF ELEVATION OF A GUN

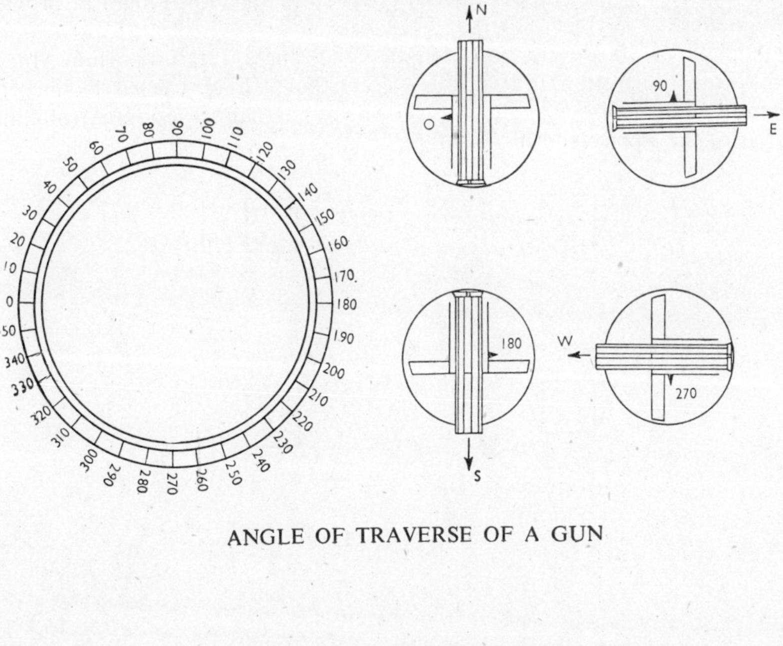

ANGLE OF TRAVERSE OF A GUN

degrees have been passed, one is back again at the starting point, so that 360 is not actually painted on the scale, since its place is already taken by 0.

Sometimes one hears even larger numbers of degrees used. In going once round a circle, you pass over 360 degree divisions, and you can say (if you like) that you have gone through 360 degrees. If you go round twice, you can say you have gone through 720 degrees, and so on indefinitely. Thus the minute hand of a clock goes round 24 times a day, so it turns through 24×360 degrees, i.e., 8,640 degrees a day. We do not often need to use such large numbers of degrees, but occasionally it happens to be necessary.

Angles are of importance when two things have to be fitted together. Look at the three pictures of stoppers in openings. In the first picture, the angle between the opposite sides of the stopper is less than the angle of the opening; in the second one, the angle is the same; in the third one, it is larger. Only the second one gives a correct fit.

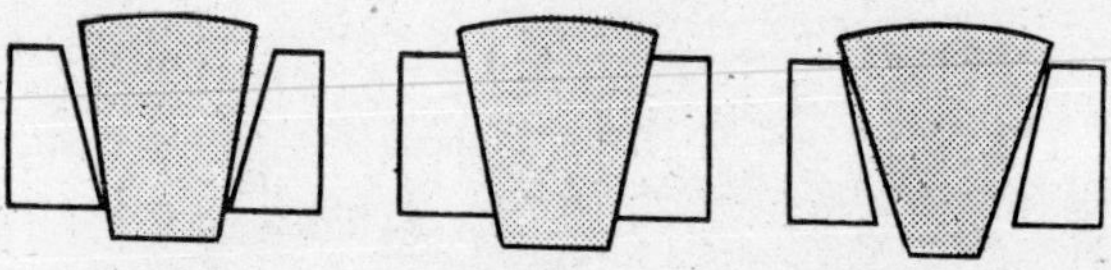

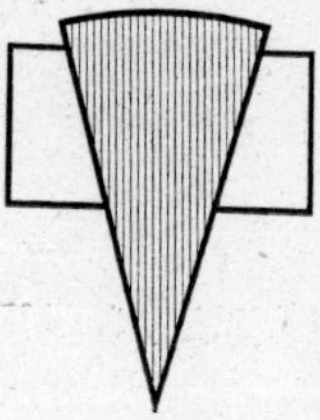

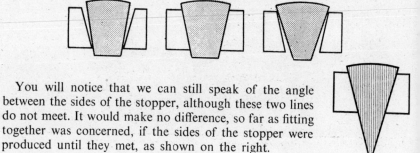

You will notice that we can still speak of the angle between the sides of the stopper, although these two lines do not meet. It would make no difference, so far as fitting together was concerned, if the sides of the stopper were produced until they met, as shown on the right.

In the case of the stopper then, it does not matter how long it is, provided the angles are correct.

Sometimes, however, both lengths and angles are important. In the following illustration the various effects that can be caused by incorrect lengths and incorrect angles are shown, for a spanner gripping (or failing to grip) the square end of a shaft.

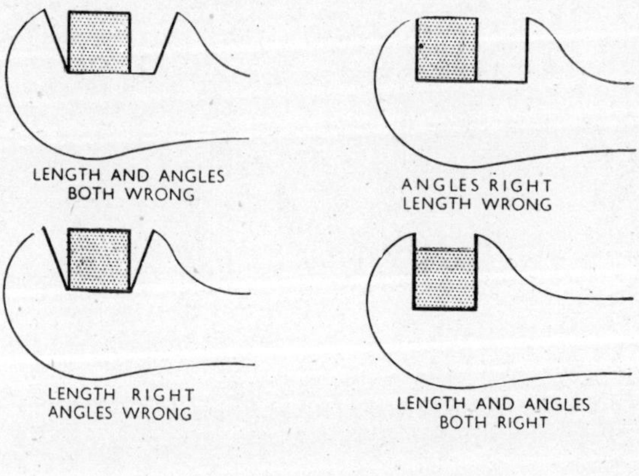

By means of lengths and angles we can specify exactly any shape made up from straight lines. If you know how to measure a length with a ruler and an angle with a protractor, you know enough to make full measurements of any straight-line shape you may meet.

You will find in books various names such as isosceles triangle, rhombus, hexagon, and so forth. These names are convenient labels for certain shapes, but they do not contain any new idea. You could describe the shapes in question without bringing in any new words, if you preferred to do so. Thus an isosceles triangle means simply "a shape made from three straight lines, two of the sides being equal." A rhombus is a figure with four straight sides, all equal. A hexagon is a figure with six straight sides.

These names may tell you either of two things. Some of them tell you how many sides a figure has. Triangle, quadrilateral, pentagon and hexagon, for instance, are names for things with 3, 4, 5 and 6 sides.

Other words may tell you that there is something special about the lengths or angles in the figure. Perhaps two sides are equal in length, or all the sides are the same length, or one angle is a right angle, or all the angles are right angles. This also is a simple enough idea to grasp.

All these names are illustrated on page 222. Some people find it easy to learn these names, others find it difficult. If you find it hard to remember which word is which, it does not mean that you are bad at geometry. To be good at geometry is to understand what shapes *are:* to remember what shapes *are called* is another thing altogether—English, perhaps, or language ability.

It is useful if you can remember these names, though, because you will meet them in this and other books, and you will need to understand what they mean. Some of them—triangle, for instance—will turn up again and again. Others, such as rhombus and pentagon, are not used so often.

Probably the best thing to do is to read on, and turn to the figures on pages 217 and 222, whenever you meet one of these words and have forgotten its meaning. In the course of time you may find you come to know them all. One or two, you may find, tend to cause confusion: if so, you can settle down at some time or other and learn them properly. But do not try to sit down straight away and learn all these names by heart—or, at least, do not worry if you cannot learn them all at once.

We have now done with shapes made from straight lines alone. There is not so much to be said about lines with circles, or circles with circles, and most of it is fairly obvious.

The diagrams at the bottom of page 223 show the various things a line may do to a circle. The line may strike the circle through its centre; it may pass through the circle to one side of the centre; it may graze the circle (in which case it is called a tangent); or it may miss the circle altogether.

The figure on page 225 illustrates the different ways in which two circles can be related to each other. The only point that calls for any remark is the statement that two circles "cross at right angles." We have explained what is meant by the angle between two lines, but the reader may question whether it is correct to talk about the angle between two circles.

It is, in fact, quite possible to talk about the angle at which two circles

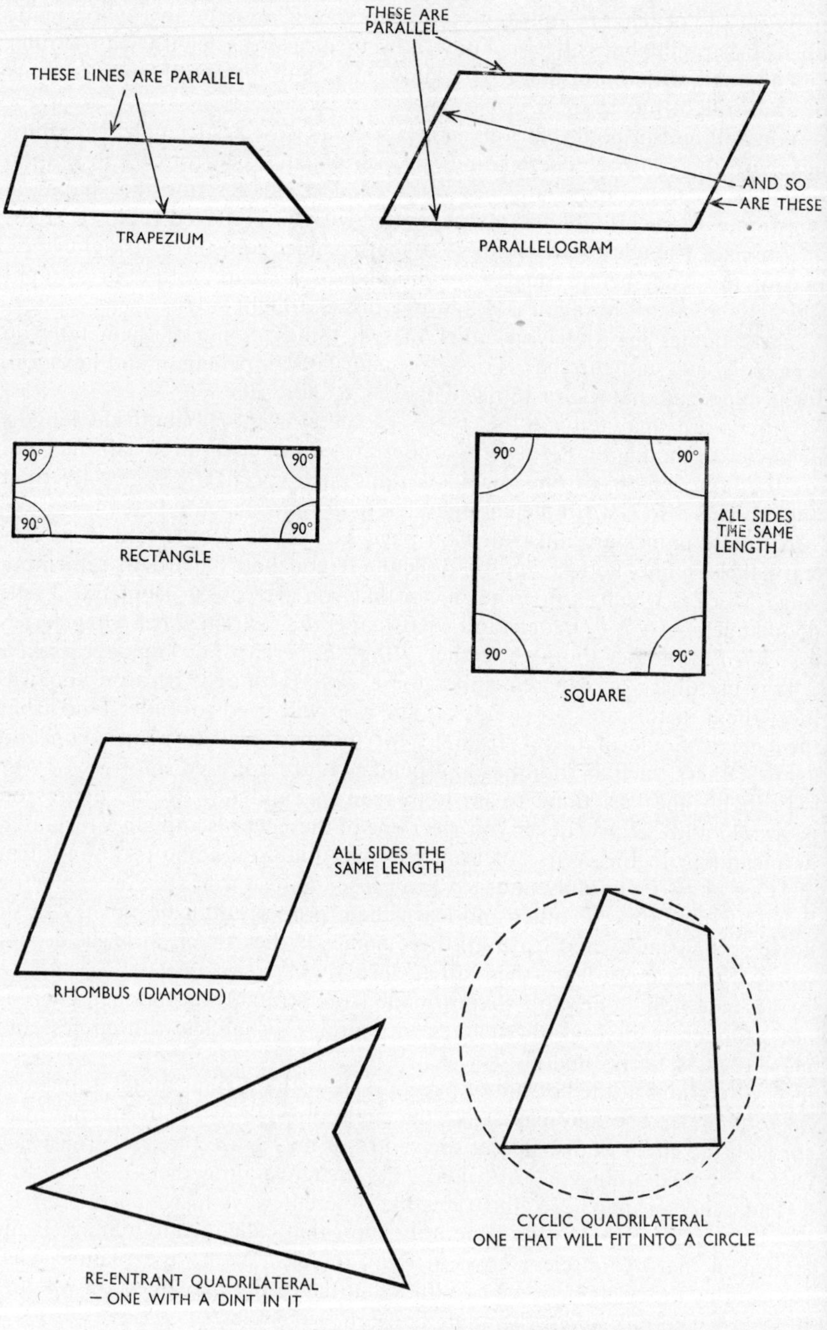

SPECIAL KINDS OF FOUR-SIDED FIGURES (QUADRILATERALS)

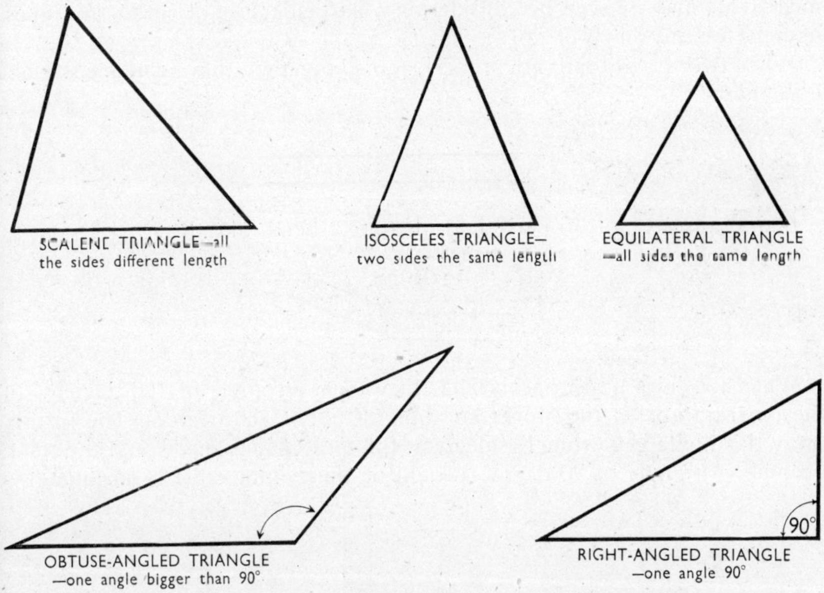
SCALENE TRIANGLE—all
the sides different length
ISOSCELES TRIANGLE—
two sides the same length
EQUILATERAL TRIANGLE
—all sides the same length
OBTUSE-ANGLED TRIANGLE
—one angle bigger than 90°
90°
RIGHT-ANGLED TRIANGLE
—one angle 90°

NAMES FOR DIFFERENT KINDS OF TRIANGLES

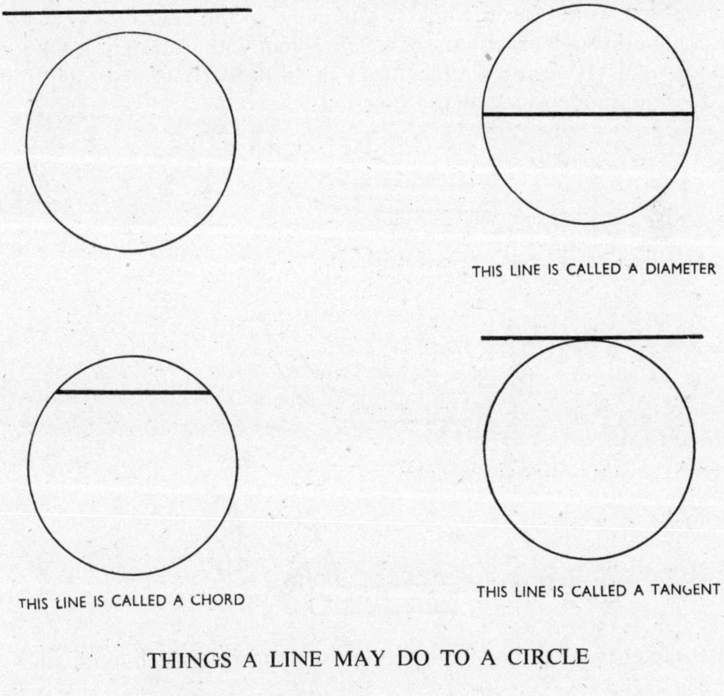
THIS LINE IS CALLED A DIAMETER
THIS LINE IS CALLED A CHORD
THIS LINE IS CALLED A TANGENT

THINGS A LINE MAY DO TO A CIRCLE

meet. This may be seen by considering a particular use of circles and lines, namely for the shape of railway lines.

When two straight rails are properly joined together, they lie in one straight line, thus:

If the rails are not properly laid, there is a bend, like this:

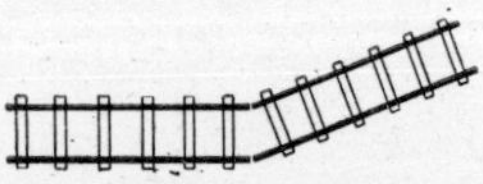

When the lines are properly laid, they form an angle of 180 degrees. In the diagram above, they form an angle of about 160 degrees. The further away this angle gets from 180 degrees, the more dangerous would the track become. An angle of 90 degrees would be quite impossible to negotiate:

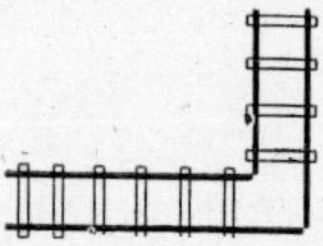

So the angle between the tracks gives us a measure of the seriousness of the bump that would result when a train came to the bend.

We can go through exactly the same argument with a straight track joining a circular track. Here is a circular track fitted properly to a straight one, so as to give no sudden jerk at the junction:

Here is a junction not so well arranged:

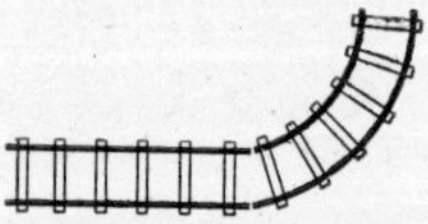

and here is a quite impossible bend:

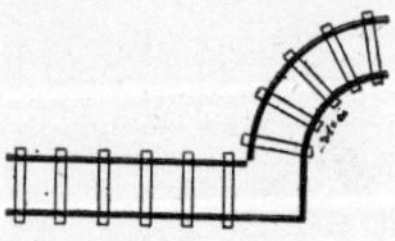

These sketches resemble the previous sketches in which both lines are

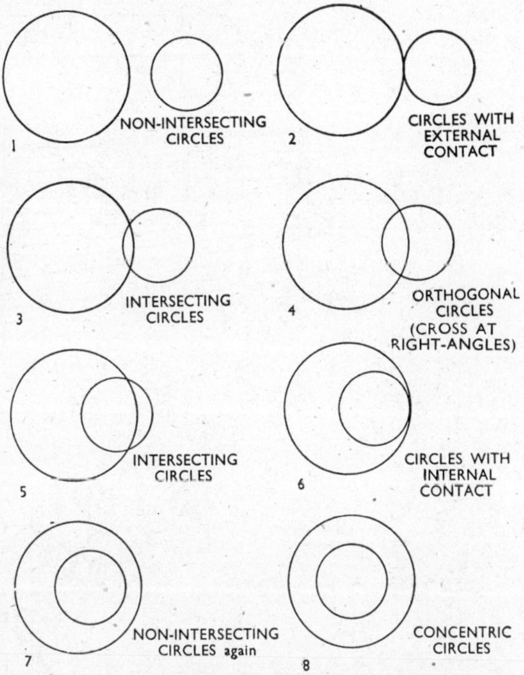

DIFFERENT POSITIONS OF TWO CIRCLES

The figures show various stages of one circle moving towards another, with the scientific names describing the relation between the circles. "Non-intersecting" means that the circles do not cross each other: it does not matter whether one circle is completely inside the other, like 7, *or if it is completely outside, like* 1. *Concentric circles are always used for the bends of railway lines—whether full-size or model—as the distance between the two rails then remains the same. None of the other arrangements is suitable for rails.*

straight, and it seems reasonable that we should be able to say, just as in the previous case, that the rails meet at 180 degrees, at 160 degrees and at 90 degrees.

In fact, if we look only at a very small part of a rail close to the junction, it is difficult to see any difference between the straight and the curved rails. In either case, we have something very much like the three little figures below:

To measure these small angles, we should have to make the lines longer by means of a ruler, and then measure with a protractor. So that, in the junction with the circular rail we should be measuring the angles shown below:

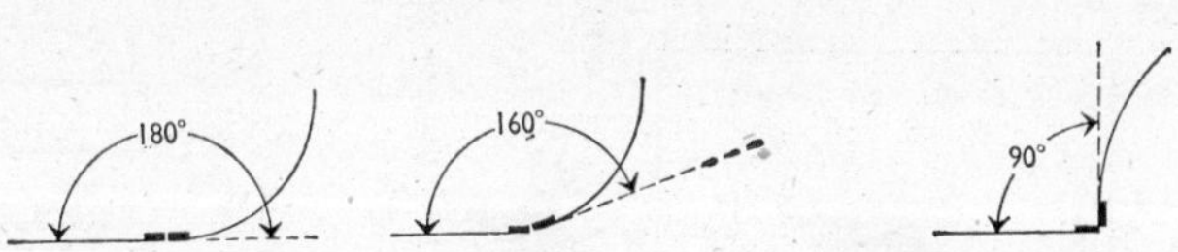

The dotted lines show the *direction* of the curved rail at the point where the two rails meet.

In geometry, we should call these dotted lines the tangents to the circle at the point where the rails meet.

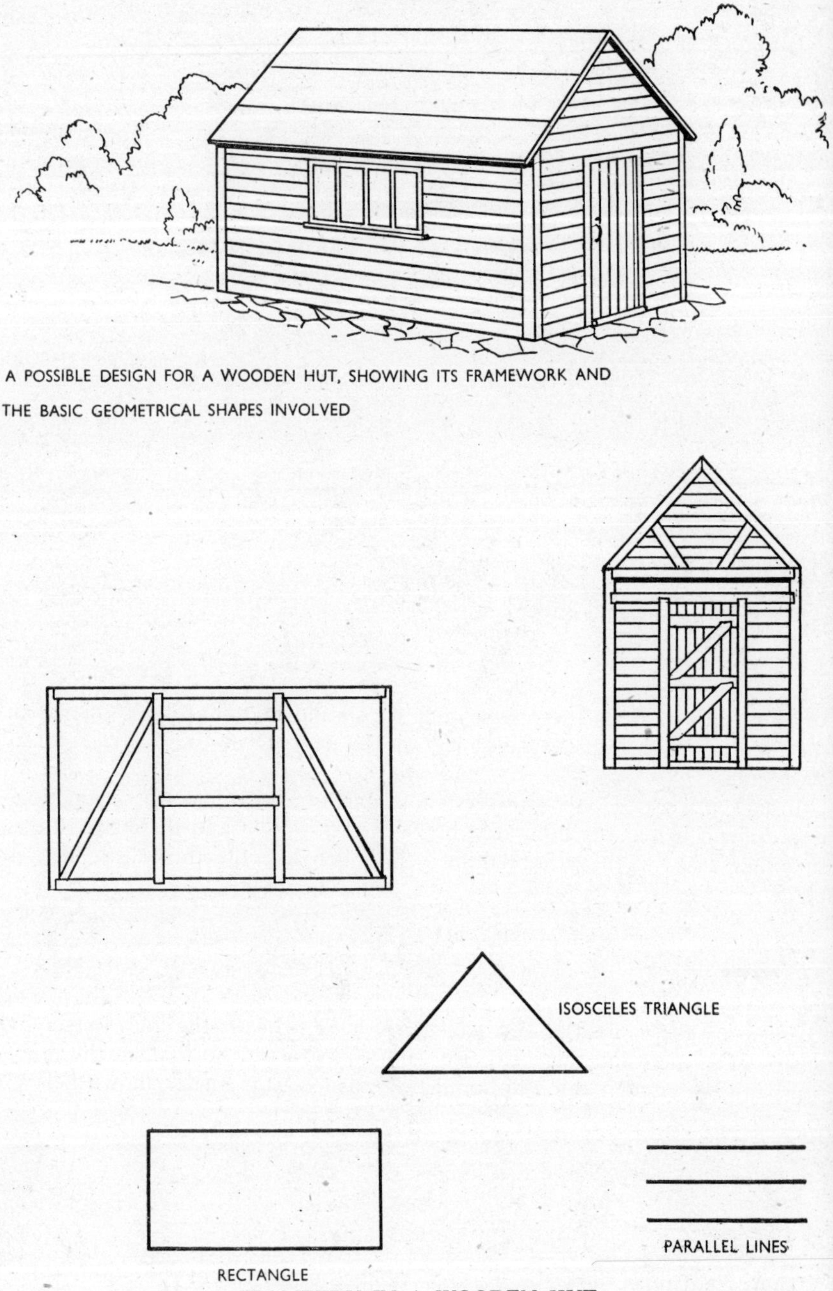
A POSSIBLE DESIGN FOR A WOODEN HUT, SHOWING ITS FRAMEWORK AND
THE BASIC GEOMETRICAL SHAPES INVOLVED
ISOSCELES TRIANGLE
RECTANGLE
PARALLEL LINES

GEOMETRY IN A WOODEN HUT

Here is a possible design for a wooden hut, showing its framework and the basic geometrical shapes involved in its construction.

We can apply the same idea if two circular rails meet at a point. Here are two circular rails, and the small dark **V** shows the angle they make where they meet.

To measure this angle we take a ruler and make the arms of the **V** longer (in other words, we "draw the tangents at the intersection").

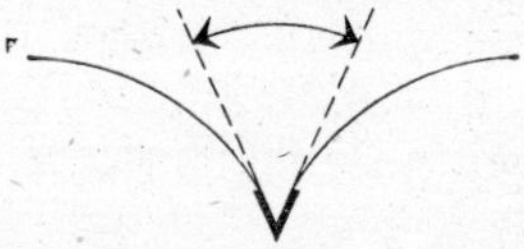

The angle between the two dotted lines is measured with a protractor, and this gives the angle at which the two circles meet.

We now have enough words to give a full description of any drawing made up of straight lines and circles. We can now pass on to consider the various things that people have noticed about straight lines and circles.

OF WHAT USE ARE THEOREMS?

The first question one naturally asks is, "Suppose someone has noticed something about straight lines and circles, of what use is it?"

To read most geometry books you would not think that theorems (geometrical truths) were of any use at all. But we have seen that nearly every machine, nearly everything that is made, depends on the properties of lines and circles. An obvious use of geometry is that it teaches us how to make things the right shape.

For instance, in a certain school, the children go out camping in wooden huts and they build the huts themselves. These huts are made in sections, and then fitted together when the children reach the camp. Obviously, huts in which the sections do not fit together exactly will be very uncomfortable to live in. Each part must be made accurately. How is one to make sure that this has been done?

A simple hut is based on two geometrical shapes—the rectangle and the triangle. The front and back are both rectangles; the roof is made up of two rectangles; the window and door are rectangles. The ends consist of a rectangle with a triangle on top of it.

Now let us consider three theorems from geometry, and see how they would help us in designing and making such a hut.

1*st Theorem. The opposite sides of a rectangle are equal.*

This theorem tells us that the two ends of a rectangle are the same length; and that the top and the bottom are equal in length.

This is fairly obvious, but a large part of geometry just consists in reminding people of things that are fairly obvious.

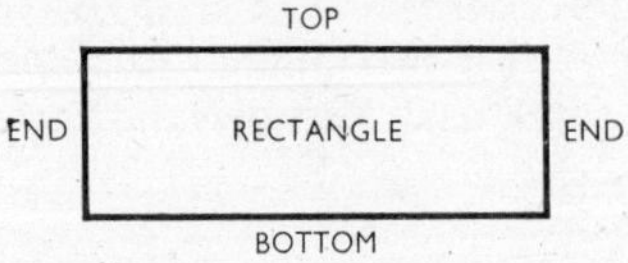

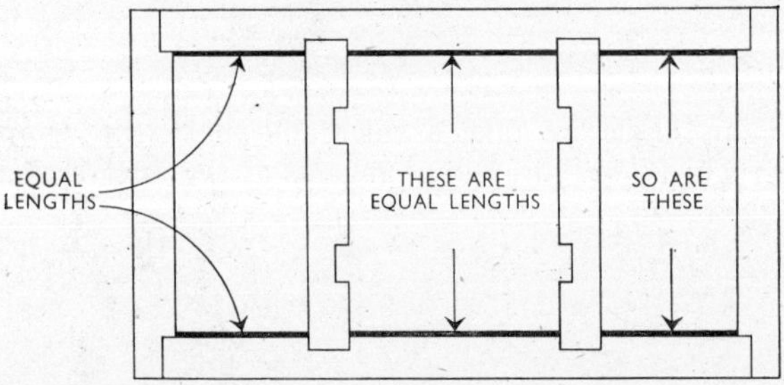

This result helps us quite a lot in designing the frame for the front of the hut. The pieces of wood that support the window divide the front of the hut up into rectangles. For each rectangle we know that opposite sides must be equal. When marking out the places where the joints are to be made, we must check that this really is so. Otherwise the posts will be out of true.

Every joiner knows this and takes it for granted. But not all theorems are so simple and obvious as this one.

2nd Theorem. The diagonals of a rectangle are equal.

The diagonals are the lines that join opposite corners of the rectangle. They are shown dotted in the figure.

This theorem means that a string that just reaches from *A* to *C* should also just reach from *B* to *D*.

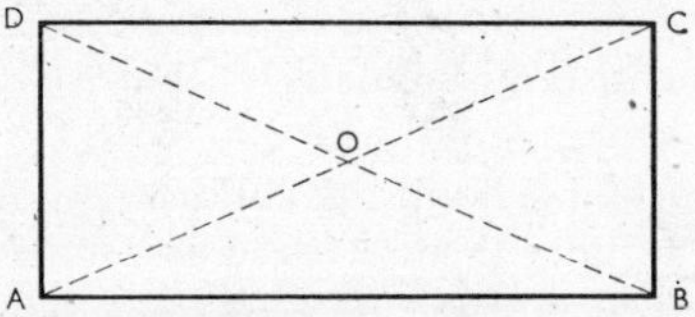

We can therefore check all the rectangles that are used in making the hut by measuring them from corner to corner, and making sure that in each case the two diagonals are the same length.

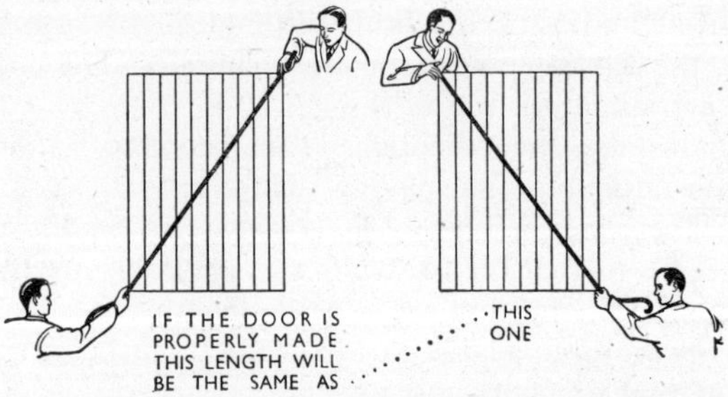

3rd Theorem. The diagonals of a rectangle bisect each other.

Bisect means to chop into two equal pieces. So the place where the diagonals cross should be the middle point of each of them.

In the drawing above of the rectangle *ABCD* with *O* in the middle, this means that the lines *AO* and *OC* should be the same length, and that *DO* and *OB* should be the same length.

This is another way of checking that the rectangles have been correctly made.

We shall, later on, meet still another way of making sure that a rectangle is the right shape, by means of a very surprising result known as Pythagoras' Theorem.

The other shape, besides the rectangle, that came into making the hut was the triangle, which had to appear on the ends of the hut so that the roof could slope.

The end of the hut can have several different shapes. It might be made like this:

or lopsided like this (rather unusual):

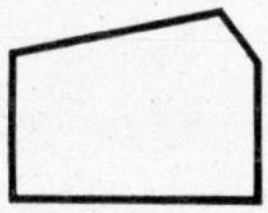

or as we have drawn it on page 226 with the ridge of the roof over the middle of the hut, like this:

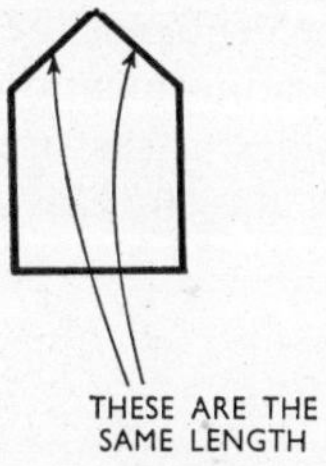

The length of the roof at the front and the back of the hut is then the same.

If we draw a sketch in which *AB* represents the roof at the front, and *BC* the roof at the back, we can say *AB* is equal to *BC*, and the triangle *ABC* is isosceles (has two sides of the same length).

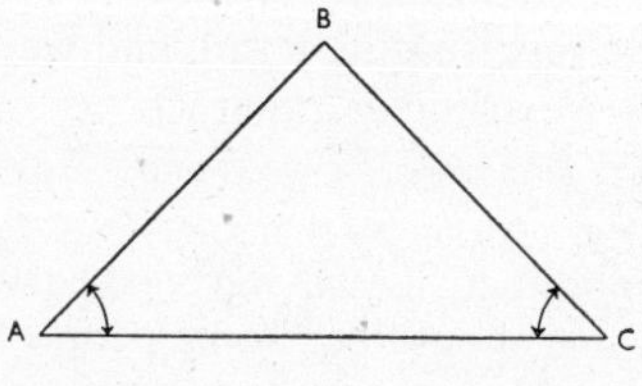

There is a theorem about such triangles.

4th Theorem. Two of the angles of an isosceles triangle are equal.

In the triangle *ABC* drawn below, where the sides *AB* and *BC* are equal, the angles marked in the drawing will be equal. It is convenient to refer to these as the angles *A* and *C*.

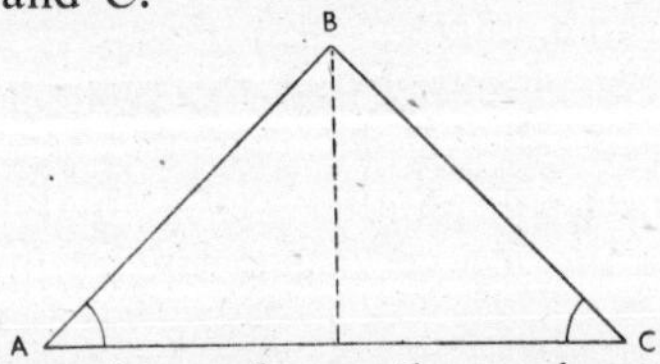

The angles that are equal are always the angles opposite the equal sides. The angle *B* is *between* the equal sides *AB* and *BC*. The theorem does not tell us anything about this angle.

You can see why this theorem is true, by thinking what would happen if the triangle were folded about the dotted line. *A* would come down on *C*. The side *AB* would lie just over the side *BC* which is the same length, and the two angles would lie with one exactly covering the other—so naturally, they must be equal.

We can use this property as an extra way of checking the shape of the ends of the hut. Besides measuring the sides of the roof, *AB* and *BC* and seeing that they are equal, we can also measure the angles *A* and *C*, which also should be equal.

This theorem is also useful when we combine it with the results of other theorems, as we shall see later.

5th Theorem. The tangent to a circle is at right angles to the radius at the point of contact.

This result is illustrated below. The line *PQR* is a tangent to a circle, which it touches at *Q*. *O* is the centre of the circle. Joining *O* to *Q* we get a radius of the circle; this is the radius mentioned in the theorem. The theorem tells us that *OQ* is at right angles to the straight line *PQR*.

It may help you to think of the circle as a wheel resting on a level road.

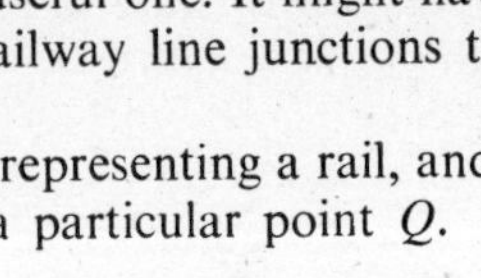

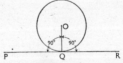

The theorem amounts to saying that the centre of the wheel, *O*, will be directly over the point that touches the road, *Q*.

This theorem is a very useful one. It might have been discovered by someone trying to draw the railway line junctions that we were talking about earlier.

Suppose we have a line representing a rail, and we want to draw a sideline branching off from it at a particular point *Q*.

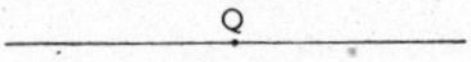

What would you do about it, if you were asked to give a rule for where the centre of the branch line should be? Some people would just sit and stare at the question. That is a mistake. It is much better to have one or two shots at it, and see if we can learn from our mistakes.

Let us begin by putting the point of the compasses at any point A, and drawing a circle through Q. We get this figure.

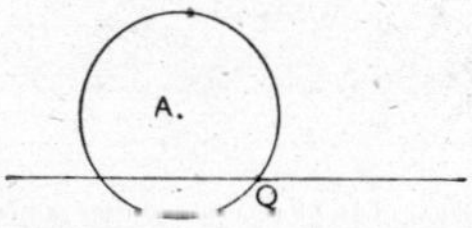

We make another shot, taking the centre at B and get this

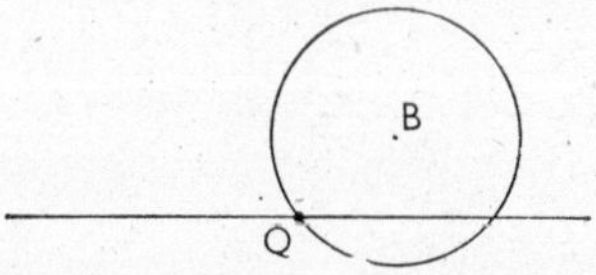

Again we have not got the desired result. If we continue taking pot-shots like this, we might after a little while notice that whenever the centre of the circle was to the left of Q (as at A), the circle cut the line again to the left, and whenever the centre was to the right of Q (as at B), the circle cut the line again to the right. But we want the circle just to touch the line at Q, so that it meets the line neither to the right nor to the left. That means the centre must be neither to the right nor to the left of Q, i.e. it must be exactly above it.

We can, of course, draw many different circles to touch the line at Q, according to the size of the circle we draw. Here are a number of circles, each of which touches the line at Q.

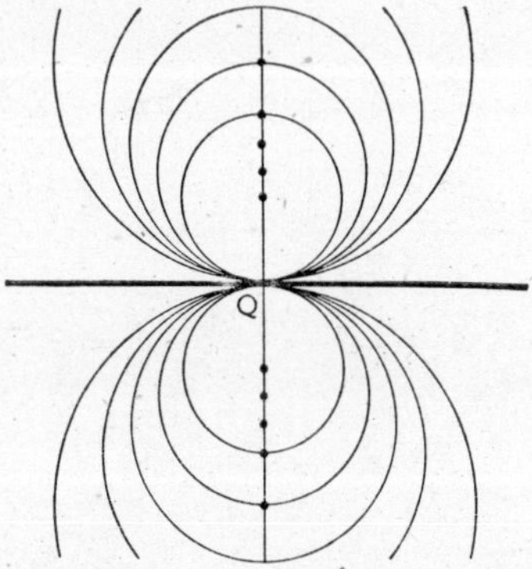

The centres of the circles are shown by the black dots. All the centres are, of course, exactly above or exactly below Q.

All these circles pass through Q in the same direction. That means that

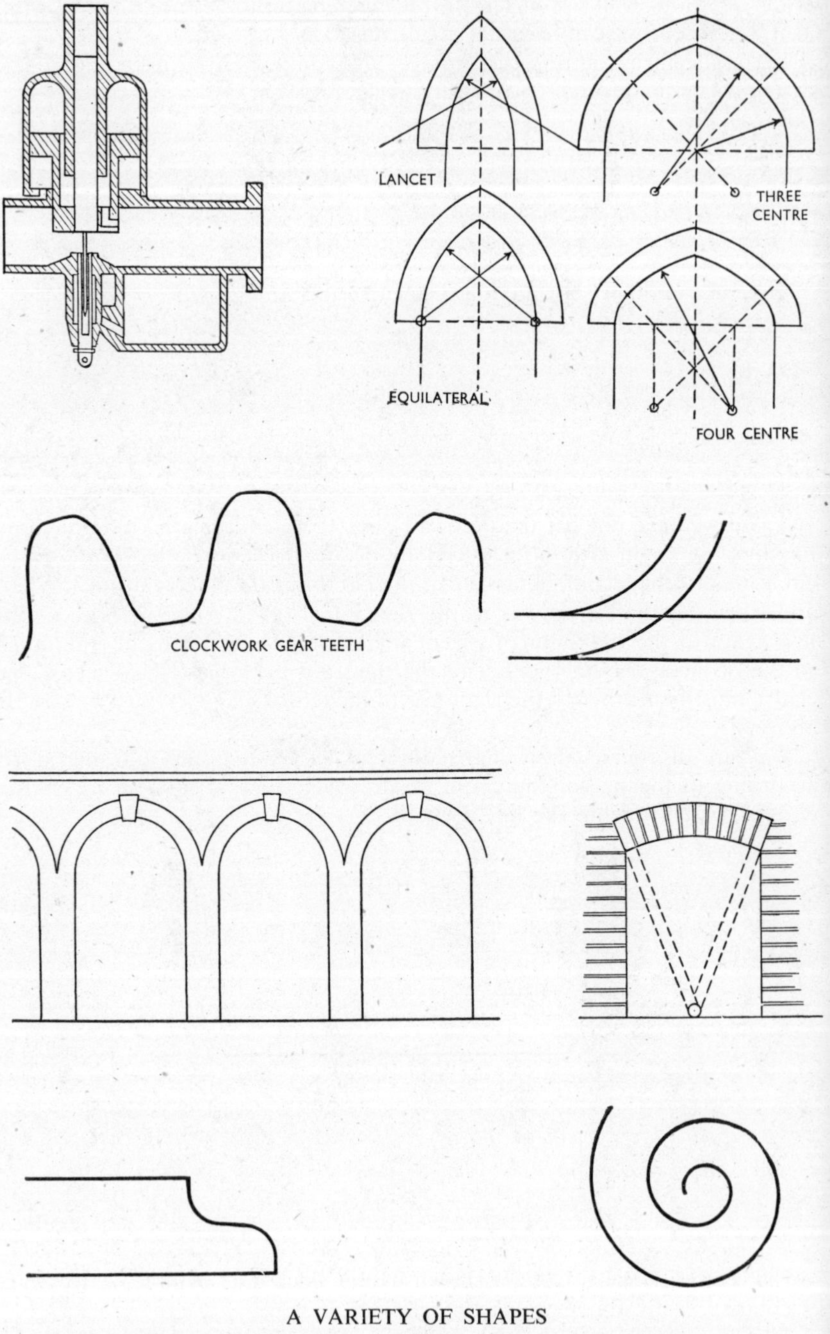

A VARIETY OF SHAPES

These are all made with straight lines and circles only.

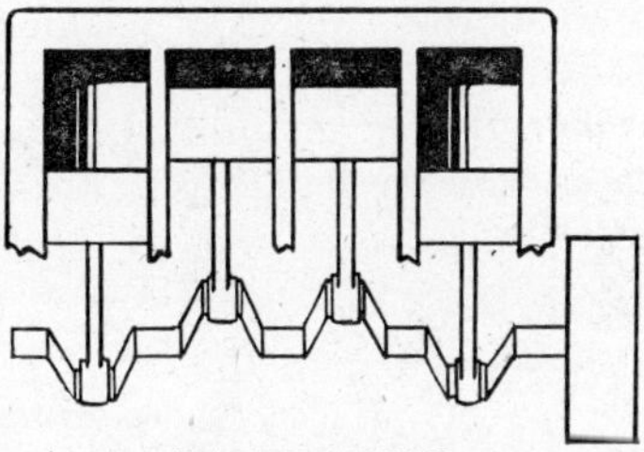

MOTOR-CAR ENGINE

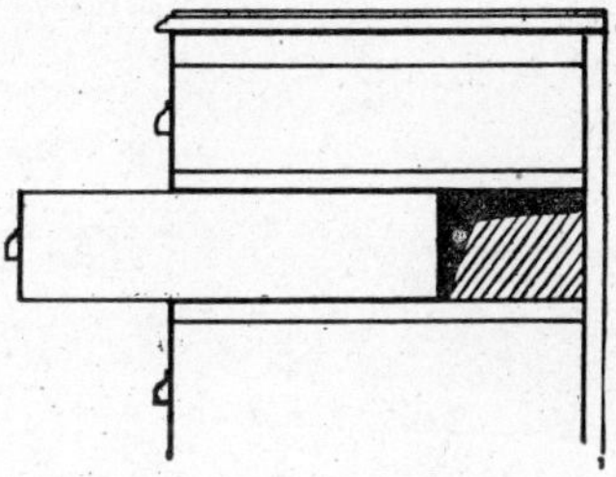

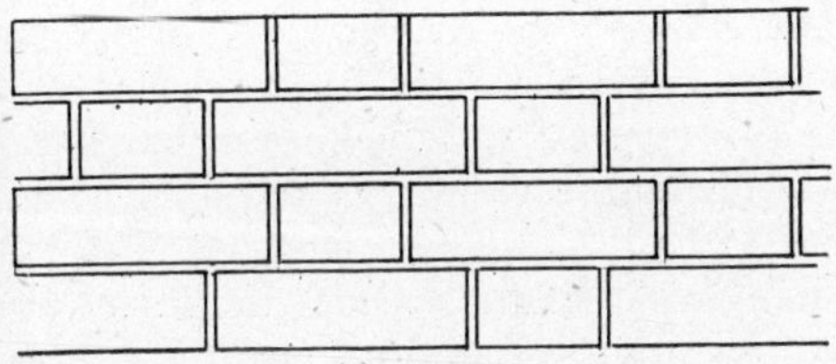

BRICKWORK

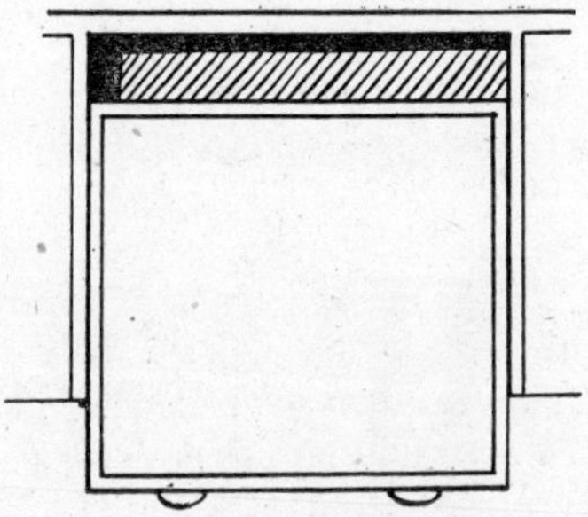

A DRAWER

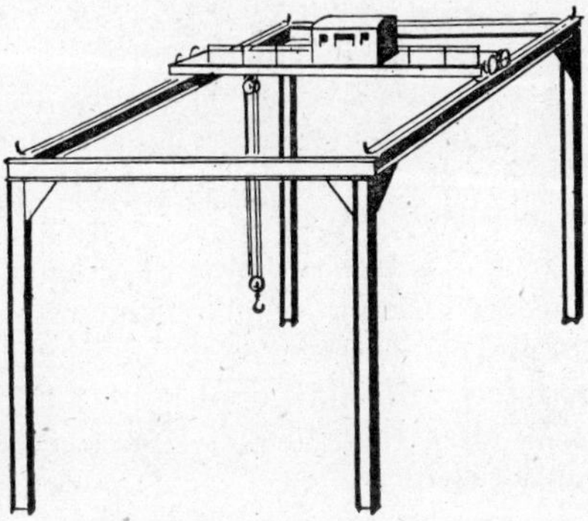

OVERHEAD CRANE

NOTEBOOK

PARALLEL LINES

EXAMPLES OF PARALLEL LINES

In every one of these articles, parallel lines are significant.

we could come into Q along any of these circles and pass out from Q along any other circle without there being any sudden bump.

So this figure not only shows us how to change over smoothly from a straight track to a circular track: it also tells us how to change over from one circular track to another, and obtain figures like these:

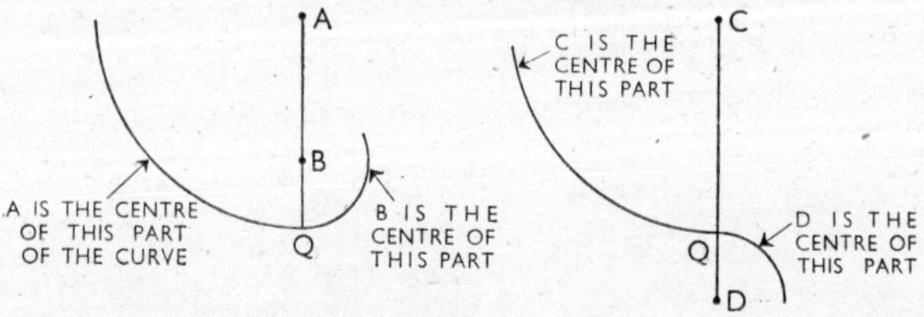

The rule is: *when two circular pieces of railway line have to be joined together, there will be no sudden bump at the join, provided the centres of the two parts of the track are in line with the point where the tracks join.*

In the first figure, A and B are the two centres, and they are in line with Q: in the second figure, C and D are the centres, and they too are in line with Q.

This result is of importance for many other things besides the laying of railway tracks. A circle is the easiest curve to draw, and it is also the easiest curve to cut out of metal. For this reason, many complicated shapes, such as clockwork gears, the cams of motor-cars, or the arches of buildings, are made by fitting together a number of circles. The rule given above must always be observed if it is desired to obtain a smooth curve free from sudden bends. You will see how this principle is applied in the diagram, The Shape of a Cam, on page 236.

We could give many more examples of theorems that have some direct practical use, but perhaps you will be satisfied to have these examples for the moment, as an illustration of the fact that geometry can be useful, and also as showing that geometrical truths, theorems, are things that might be discovered by a workman while doing an everyday job.

In all these examples, we just took one theorem and showed what use could be made of it. It very often happens, however, that in designing something we make use of two or three theorems at once. So it will be more convenient now, instead of giving each theorem separately with some application of it, to go through a list of the main theorems. If a theorem has some direct application, we may make a note of it: but we shall also meet some theorems that are only useful in order to prove other results, and are not of practical value by themselves.

SPECIFICATIONS

We may begin our list with three important theorems known as congruences.

Suppose that for some reason you wanted to have a piece of metal cut out exactly to the shape $ABCD$, and that you asked a friend to do it for you

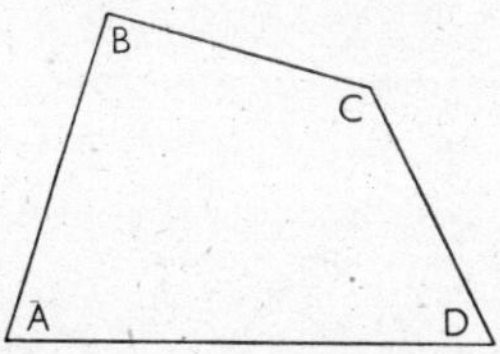

because you had not the necessary equipment. Your friend would want to know the measurements, so as to be sure of getting it the right shape.

There are any number of things you can measure. You can measure the lengths of the sides *AB*, *BC*, *CD* and *DA*. You can measure the angles at *A*, *B*, *C* and *D*. You can measure the diagonals *AC* and *BD*. But how many of these is it really necessary to measure in order to *fix* the exact shape of *ABCD*?

Our theorems are actually not going to deal with such complicated shapes as *ABCD*, but only with triangles. This is no loss, because by drawing a line from *B* to *D*, you can break *ABCD* up into two triangles *ABD* and *BCD*: if you give enough measurements to fix these two triangles, you have fixed the whole thing.

Congruences are, therefore, theorems about how many measurements are necessary to fix the shape of a triangle.

You may find the following way of looking at the problem helpful. The triangle has three corners. Suppose a nut and bolt are to be placed at each corner of the triangle. Call the bolts *A*, *B* and *C*.

To begin with, suppose we know nothing about the triangle. This means the bolts are not fixed in any way. They may be anywhere. So we picture them loose, like this:

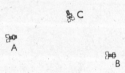

Any information that comes in about the triangle will immediately be shown by fixing these bolts in some way.

Suppose, for instance, we are told that *AB* is 3 inches. We suppose *A* and *B* fixed together by a strip of metal with holes in it 3 inches apart. This will ensure that *AB* is 3 inches. *C* will still be perfectly free. So our bolts will be like this:

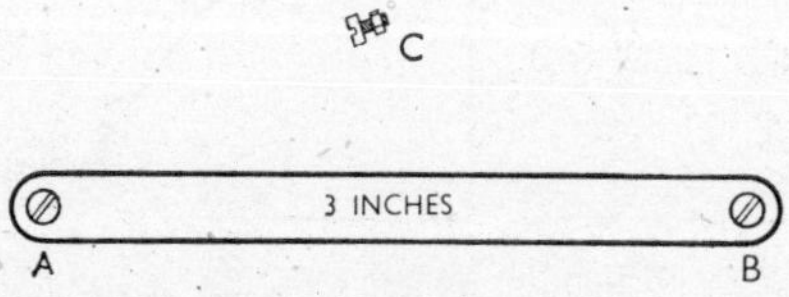

We obviously need more information to fix the shape of *ABC*. Suppose

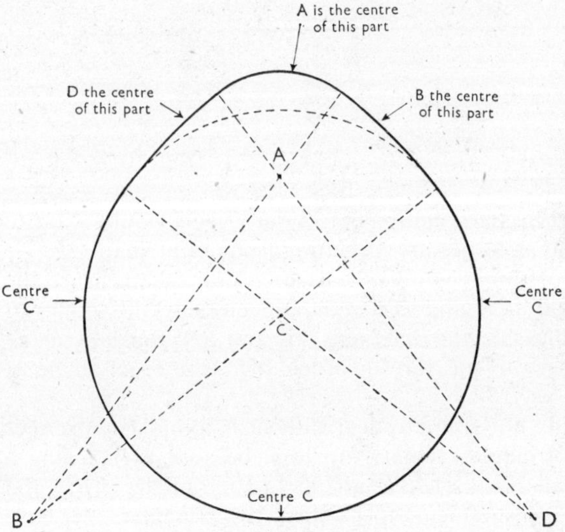

THE SHAPE OF A CAM

This figure shows how a cam can be made by combining together parts of four circles. The greater part of the curve is simply a circle with C as centre. The bulge is made up of small parts of circles with centres at B, A, and D. Each circle passes smoothly into the next.

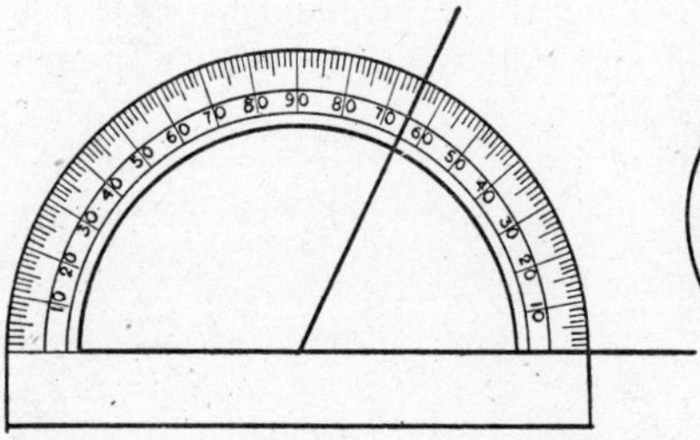

MEASURING AN ANGLE WITH A PROTRACTOR

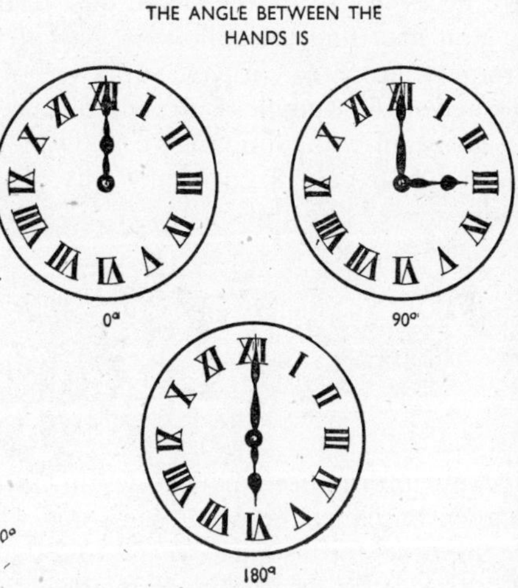

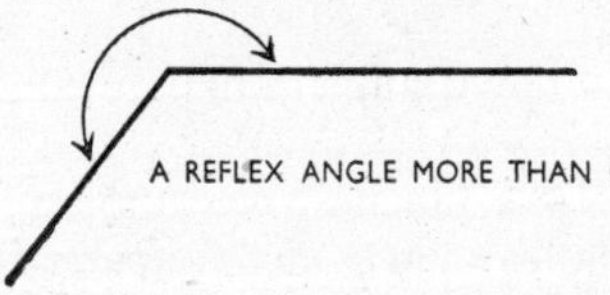

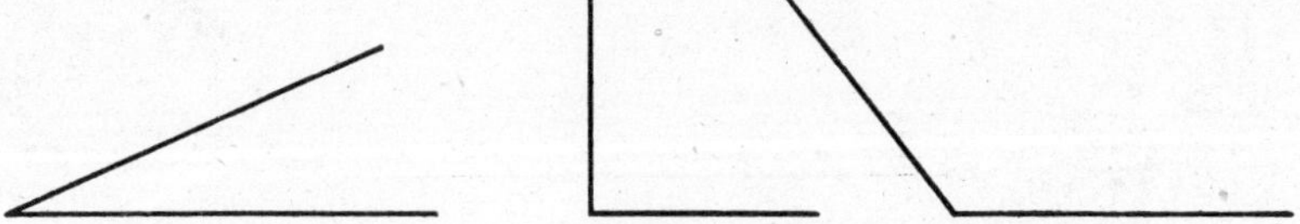

AN ACUTE ANGLE LESS THAN 90° A RIGHT ANGLE 90° AN OBTUSE ANGLE MORE THAN 90°

ANGLES AND THEIR NAMES

we are told AC is $2\frac{1}{2}$ inches. We can represent this by a metal strip joining A to C, thus:

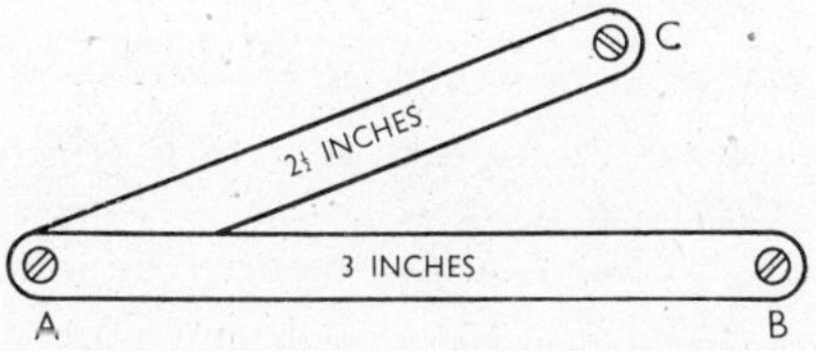

The shape of the triangle is still not fixed, because it is still possible to press the two strips closer together, or to pull them farther apart, i.e. to make the angle at A smaller or bigger.

If we are now told that BC is 2 inches, and put in a strip to make sure that this is so, the shape of the triangle is completely fixed.

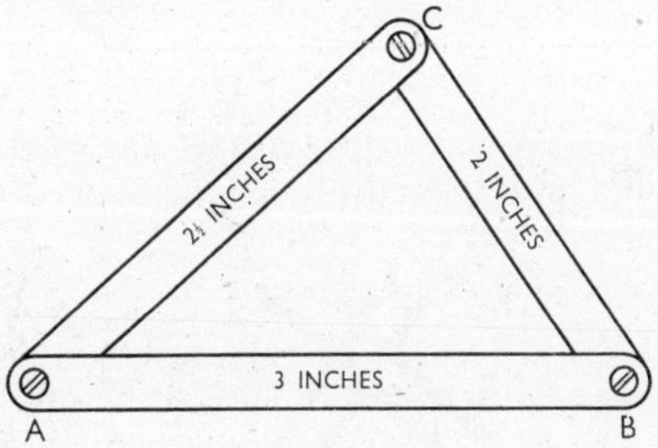

This gives us our 6*th Theorem. The shape of a triangle is completely fixed when the lengths of the three sides are known.* A very obvious result.

There is another way of fixing the shape of the triangle. Go back to the stage when we knew that AB was 3 inches and AC was $2\frac{1}{2}$ inches. Now, instead of being told that BC is 2 inches, we might be told that the angle at A is 41°. We can make it so by putting a wedge, cut to the angle 41°, between the two strips and clamping them in this position.

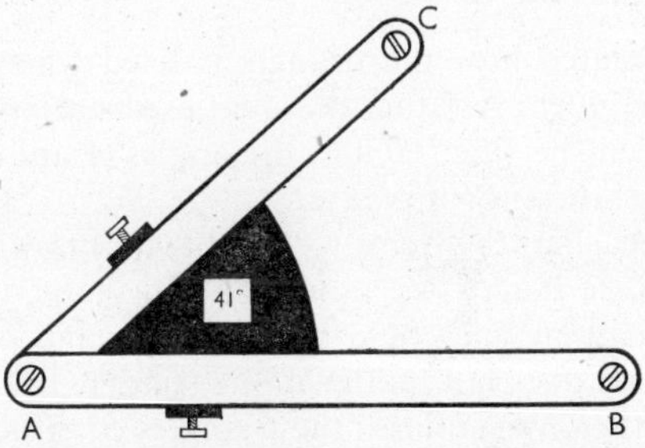

Now, although B and C are not joined directly by a strip, the distance between them is fixed just as definitely as before, and the shape of the triangle cannot be altered. The shape of the triangle has been fixed by giving the length of the sides, AB and BC, and the size of the angle between them, A.

This then is our *7th Theorem. The shape of a triangle is completely fixed by giving the length of two sides and the included angle.*

Still another way of fixing the shape is given by the *8th Theorem. The shape of a triangle is completely fixed by giving the length of one side and the size of two angles.*

To illustrate this, suppose we are told that *AB* is 3 inches, the angle at *A* is 41°, and the angle at *B* is 56°.

Since *AB* is 3 inches, we can start as before, connecting *A* and *B* by a 3-inch strip.

The next step is rather different. At *A* and *B* fix long strips having a slit down the middle, thus:

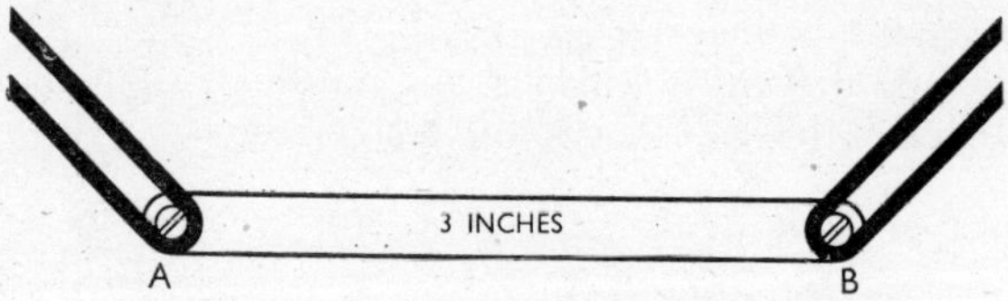

Now put wedges at *A* and *B*, cut to the correct angles, 41° and 56°, and swing the long strips round until they just touch the wedges. Clamp the long strips in this position.

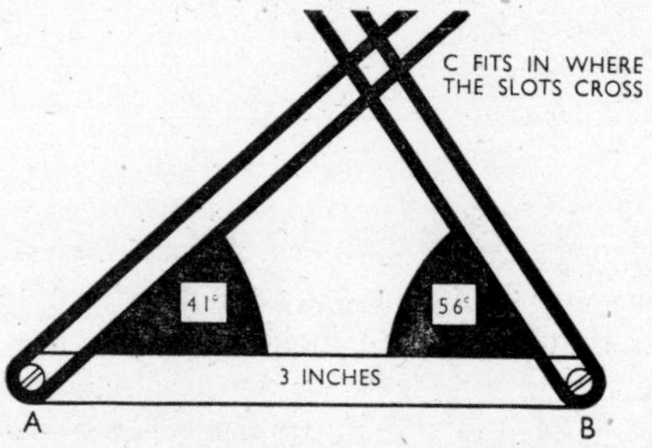

C fits in where the two slots cross. The shape of the triangle is now completely fixed.

We have here illustrated how the triangle is fixed when the side *AB* and the angle *A* and *B* are given. A rather different explanation would have been necessary if it had been the side *AB* and the angles *A* and *C*. You may care to try to find the illustration for this case.

As was mentioned earlier, theorems 6, 7 and 8 are known as congruences. When two triangles have exactly the same size and shape, they are said to be congruent. This means that one could be picked up and put down to cover the other one exactly. It does not matter if one triangle has to be turned over before it will fit the other. We still call the triangles congruent.

In geometry books the sign $\equiv$ is often used for congruent. So, $\triangle ABC \equiv \triangle DEF$ means that "the triangle *ABC* is exactly the same size and shape as the triangle *DEF*."

Such signs are very useful, as the trouble about theorems is that they

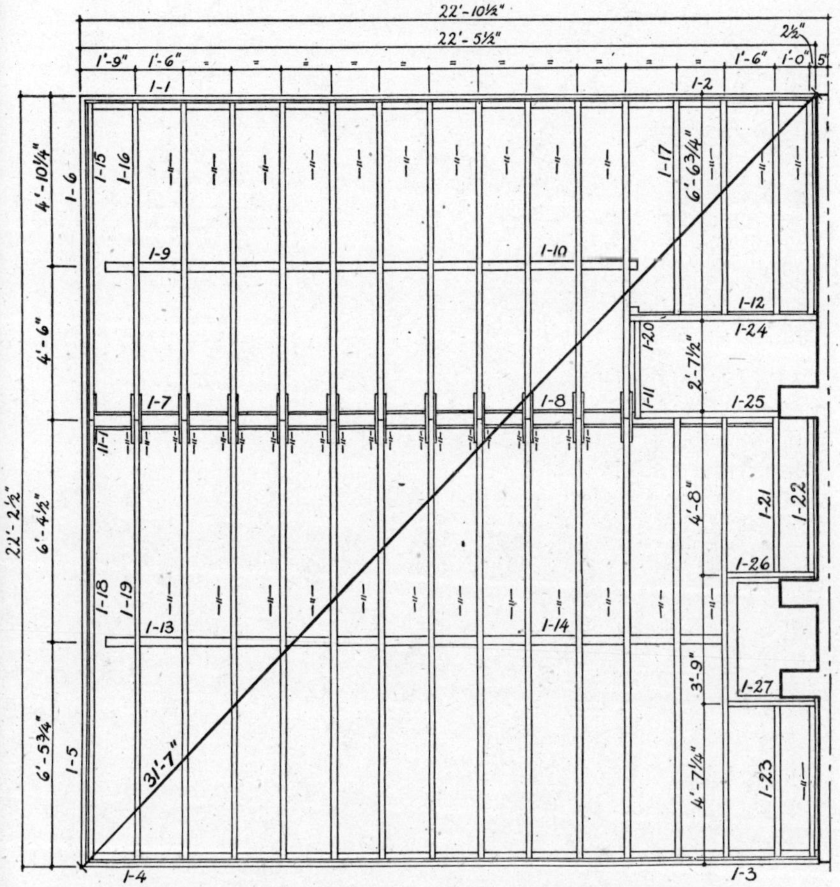

PART OF THE PLANS FOR A PREFABRICATED HOUSE

Note the diagonal measurement, 31 *ft.* 7 *in., found by Pythagoras' Theorem (see page* 248). *It is useful for checking that the foundations are laid properly "square".* (*Reproduced by permission of the Ministry of Works.*)

usually need so many long words to explain them. The best way to remember a theorem is usually by a little sketch, with one or two signs on it.

Very often, if we want to show that two lines are of equal length, we put a little tick on each of them, like this:

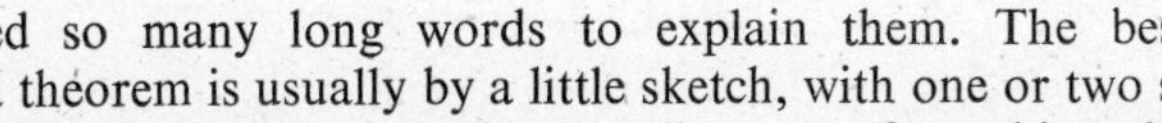

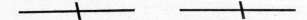

If we have already done this with one pair of lines, and we want to show that another pair are also equal to each other, we may put two ticks on each of the second pair. And so this systematic marking of lines may be continued by using three or four ticks if we find it necessary.

Thus, in the kitelike figure below, the little ticks on the sides are a quick way of indicating that *AB* is the same length as *AD*, and that *BC* is the same length as *CD*.

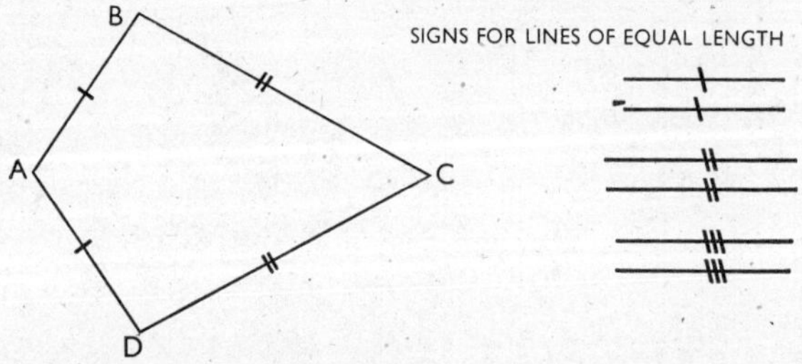

When we want to show that two angles are the same, we put the same sign in each of the two angles—often a little cross, or a little circle, or a letter of the alphabet is used for this purpose.

As an illustration; here is a pattern for making the upper part of a tent, with all the equal lengths and equal angles indicated by signs.

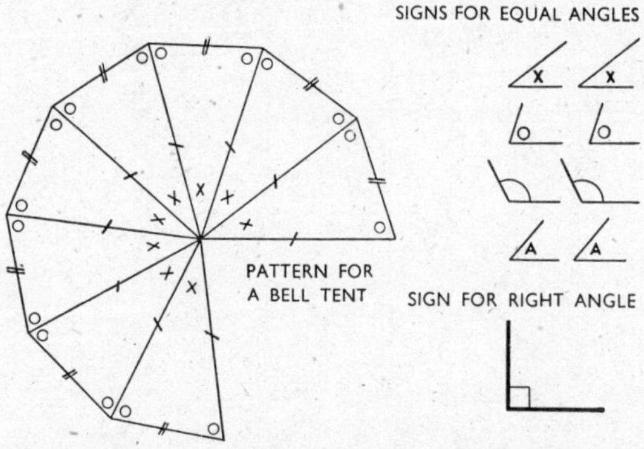

Note the little square sign that is used for marking right angles.

When we are dealing with a triangle *ABC*, it is usual to take the capital letters *A*, *B*, *C* as standing for the size of the angles of the triangle, and the small letters, *a*, *b*, *c* as representing the lengths of the sides. *a* stands for the side *opposite* *A*, as shown in the sketch.

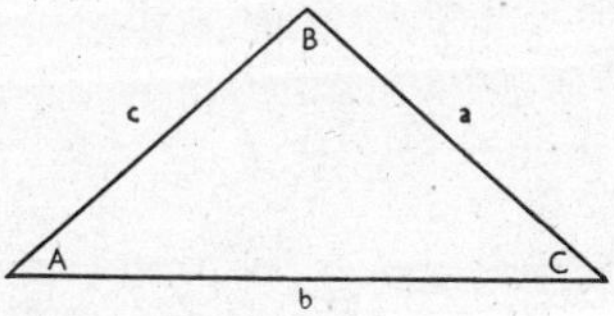

You will see how shortly theorems can be written; for instance, take the 4th, 6th, 7th and 8th theorems, and use these abbreviations.

4th Theorem. If $a = c$, $A = C$.

6th Theorem. A triangle is fixed by a, b, c,

7th Theorem, Or by b, c, A.
8th Theorem, Or by c, A, B.

Here are some more theorems, with the signs used as much as possible. The theorems will also be given in words, so that later on we can refer to them by using these words; but the essential thing is to understand the diagrams. You can omit the statement in words if you like; each theorem seems to bring in a new word, which adds to the difficulty of learning it.

9th Theorem. When two lines cross, the angles marked are equal.

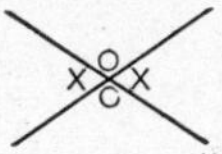

In words; *Vertically opposite angles are equal.*

10th Theorem. The two heavy lines are parallel. The angles marked x are equal.

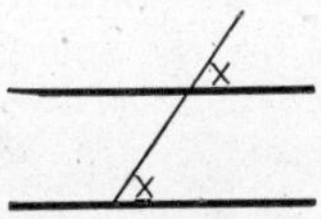

In words; *Corresponding angles are equal.*

11th Theorem. The angles of a **Z** are equal. (The heavy lines are parallel.)

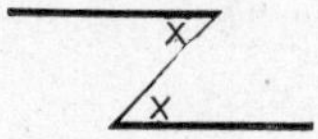

In words; *Alternate angles are equal.* You may notice that this result can be obtained by combining Theorems 9 and 10.

12th Theorem. The angles of a triangle add up to 180°.

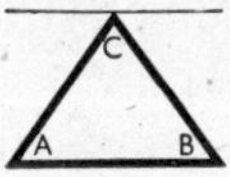

We have to show that $A+B+C$ is 180°. Draw a line through C parallel to

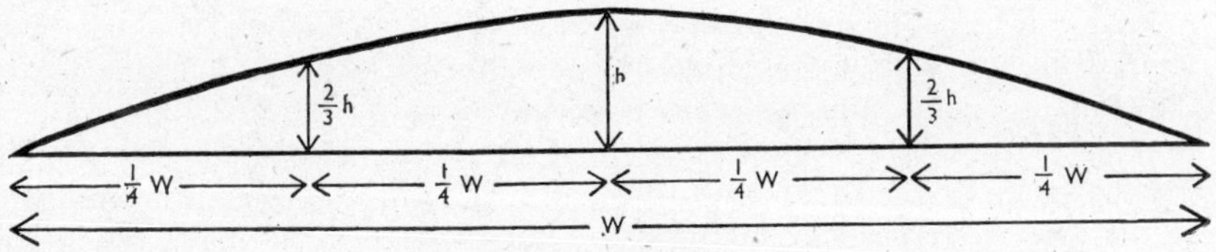

ROAD CAMBER

Here is a sketch showing a standard method of making roads. No words besides the letters W *and* h *are necessary.* W *represents the width of the road, and* h *represents the height at the middle of the road.*

AB, as shown above. If you look at this figure, you will see that it contains two **Z**s—one the right way round, and one back to front.

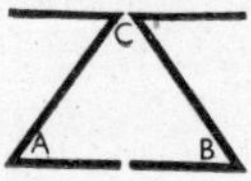

We know from Theorem 11 that both the angles of a **Z** are the same. The lower angle of the left-hand **Z** is *A;* so the upper angle must be *A* as well. In the right-hand **Z**, the back-to-front one, by the same argument both the angles must be *B*. Marking these in, we get the figure:

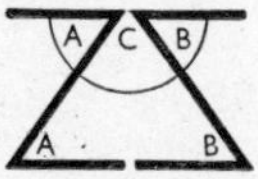

At the top of this figure we have the three angles *A*, *B*, and *C* fitted together so as to have the outside edges in line. Since being in line corresponds to an angle of 180°, this proves that $A+B+C = 180°$, which is what we wanted to show.

Most of our other theorems we have just stated, without giving any proof. But in this case, we have shown that the theorem follows from what we already know. This is known as *proving* the theorem. Many hundreds of years ago, Euclid arranged the theorems of geometry in such a way that certain things (known as axioms) were taken for granted, and everything else was proved to follow from these. People have very different views on whether it is a waste of time or not to bother with proofs. Euclid's way of doing things, proving every result that you use, is, of course, much longer than just noticing certain results to be true. It is a mistake to start learning geometry from Euclid, because you will feel that you are not getting anywhere. You need to have some idea of what geometry is about and what you can do with it before you bother about formal proofs. But there are two reasons at least why it is worth while to spend some time learning Euclid's way of going about it.

First, you will find that proving a result helps to tie it up with the other results, and makes it easier to remember. The figures drawn on page 241, and the proof that goes with them, may help you to understand just what the angles adding up to 180° means, and to remember this result.

Second, when someone shows you a drawing of some object, you may find yourself in doubt about some question—is this line equal to that one?—are these angles equal? You can remove that doubt if you can find some way of proving that the things in question either are, or are not, equal.

It has been noticed that boys who had had plenty of workshop training, so that they were used to handling and making things, still had very queer ideas about the shapes of things. To understand properly, one needs both theory and practice in close connection with each other.

To understand proofs of theorems, then, is a very definite advantage. Understanding does not mean clogging up one's head with all kinds of unnecessary details. Nearly every proof depends on some quite simple idea.

The proof we have just given of Theorem 12, for instance, is quite simple. The important thing is to see the simple, underlying idea. Sometimes there are all kinds of details that have to be filled in, and there may be masses of words and symbols in the full proof. This is not the important thing about the proof.

Proofs are rather like inventions. The modern locomotive is a complicated thing. To understand it, you must go back to the original idea, which was the simple one of making things move by steam. All the complications were added later, to overcome particular snags that arose in practice. Proofs grow in much the same way.

There are two useful results that we can get by combining Theorem 12 with Theorem 4. These deal with the shapes of two special triangles, the isosceles right-angled triangle, and the equilateral triangle. Both of these are shapes used for many purposes.

The name isosceles right-angled triangle means (i) that one angle of the triangle is a right angle, (ii) that two of the sides are equal. Both of these facts are marked in the figure. (Why is the right angle assumed to be between the two equal sides? Could it be in any other position?)

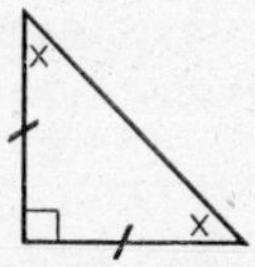

Since two sides are equal, by Theorem 4 the two angles marked x are equal.

By Theorem 12 the angles of the triangle add up to 180°. The right angle accounts for 90° of this, so that 90° is left to be divided between the two angles marked x. Each of the x angles must, therefore, be 45°.

Hence, *if two sides of a right-angled triangle are equal, the angles of the triangle must be* 90°, 45° *and* 45°.

This also works the other way round; if the angles are 90°, 45° and 45°, the two sides must be equal.

An illustration of this will be given later, in the design of a marquee.

An equilateral triangle is a triangle with all three sides equal. Using the abbreviation explained earlier, we may say $a = b = c$. Again we make use of Theorem 4, which says that when two sides are equal, the angles opposite them are equal. But here all the sides are equal. So all the angles must be equal. (This is very reasonable, because there is nothing to distinguish one side from another. So there is no reason why any of the angles should be different from the others.) So $A = B = C$. The three angles together add up to 180°. So each of them must be 60°.

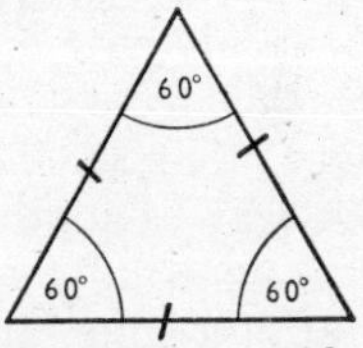

Each angle of an equilateral triangle is 60°.

It follows from this that six equilateral triangles can be fitted together at a point. For six times 60° makes 360°, which is the number of degrees in a complete turn. Six equilateral triangles fitted together give the figure below.

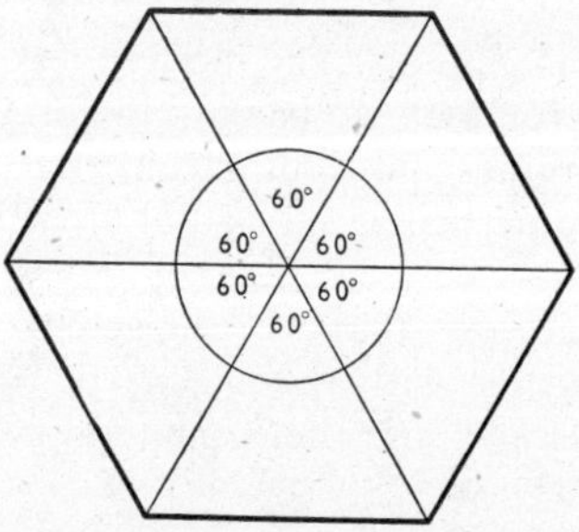

Three equilateral triangles fitted together at a point give us an angle of three times 60°, that is 180°, the angle that corresponds to a straight line. This property is used in one form of girder bridge. In the figure below you will notice that, except at the ends, three triangles meet at each point, and in this way the 180° of the straight edge is made up.

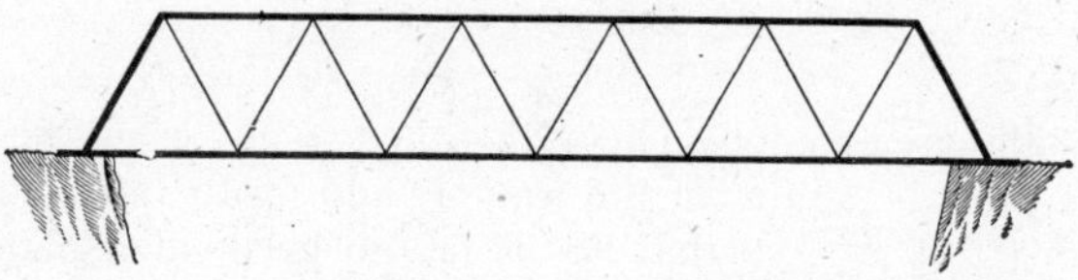

13*th Theorem. The opposite sides of a parallelogram are equal.*

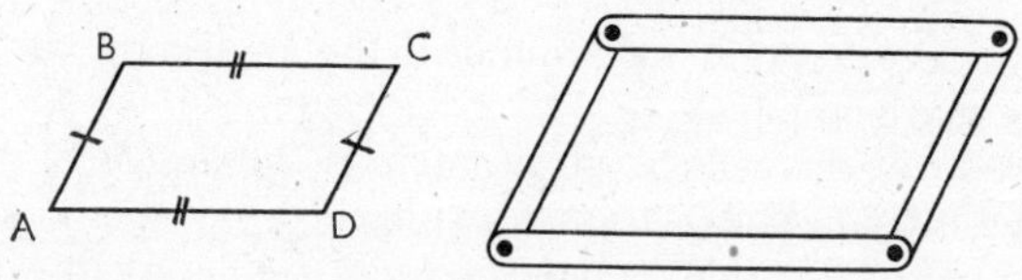

The left-hand drawing shows this result as it would be shown in geometry. The right-hand drawing shows how it is applied in mechanisms; when two pairs of equal rods are linked together in this way, the opposite sides always stay parallel. The illustrations on page 247 show some applications of this idea.

The theorem itself is not hard to prove. The proof depends on Theorems 11 and 8. The diagonal *AC* is drawn, and it is then shown that the two triangles *ABC* and *CDA* are identical.

14*th Theorem.* This might be called the *Enlargement Theorem.* It is the theorem that underlies the design of cinema projectors, telescopes, microscopes and cameras. The simplest way to approach it is by considering how shadows are formed.

If a little figure is held in front of a lamp, and its shadow allowed to fall on a screen, the shadow on the screen will be a true enlargement of the figure,

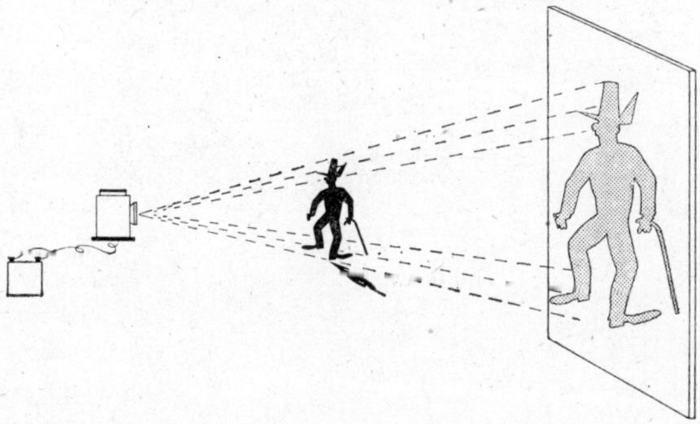

provided the screen is parallel to the little figure. (Otherwise, there will be distortion.)

If the screen is three times as far from the light as the little figure, the shadow will be three times as large.

If the screen is fifty times as far away, the shadow will be fifty times as large as the figure. The accuracy of screw-threads is, in fact, examined by means of a kind of magic lantern which throws an image of the screw, enlarged fifty times, on to a screen, so that one-thousandth of an inch becomes one-twentieth of an inch—large enough to be seen easily.

We obtain the theorem in its geometrical form if we replace the little figure by a straight line, AB, and its shadow by a parallel line CD. A point O corresponds to the light.

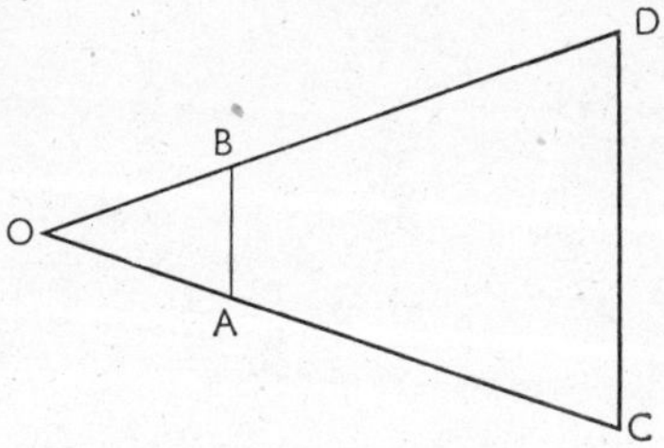

We know

if OC is 3 times OA, CD is 3 times AB.

if OC is 50 times OA, CD is 50 times AB.

if OC is any number of times OA, CD is the same number of times AB.

Using n as short for any number we may say:

if OC is n times OA, CD is n times AB.

OD will also be n times OB.

We may sum this up by saying that, if AB is parallel to CD, the triangle OCD is the triangle OAB enlarged n times.

The triangles OAB and OCD are known as *similar triangles*. They have the same angles (that is, the same shape), but they differ in scale.

15*th Theorem. Pythagoras' Theorem.* This is perhaps the most surprising theorem there is. A good many of the theorems we have considered so far,

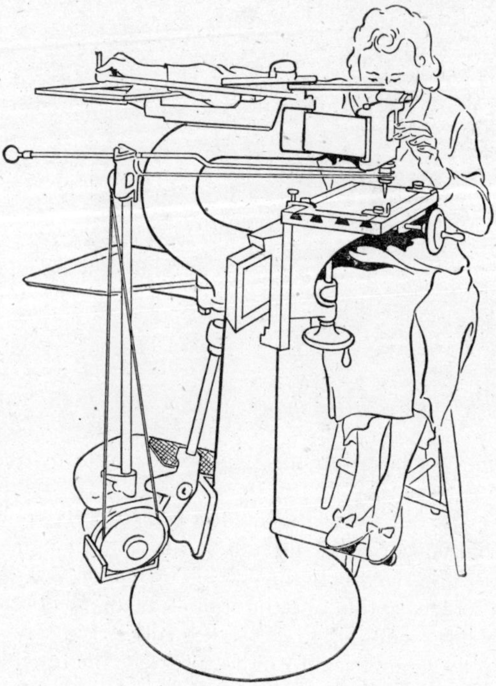

AN ENGRAVING MACHINE

This is a development of the pantograph. As the operator moves the pointer over the large letters on the table, the instrument cuts the same letters, but much smaller, on the object that is being engraved.

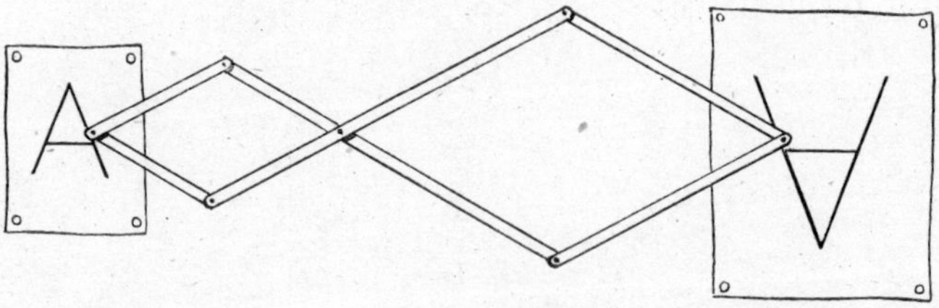

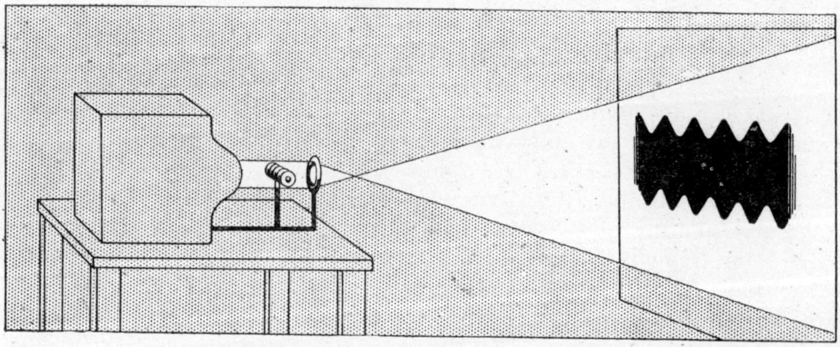

PROJECTOR FOR CHECKING SCREW PROFILES

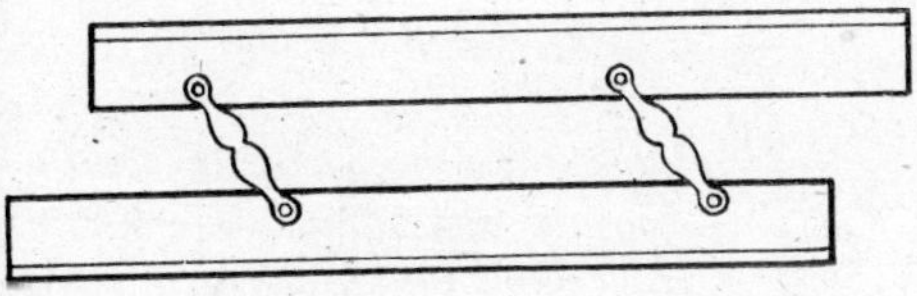

FOR DRAWING PARALLEL LINES

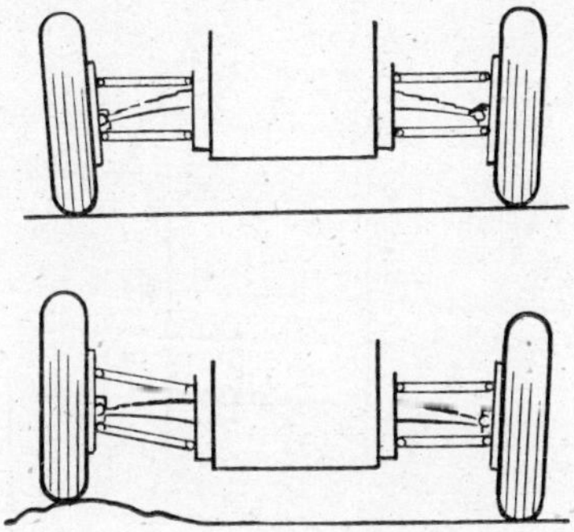

INDEPENDENT SUSPENSION OF MOTOR-CAR FRONT WHEELS

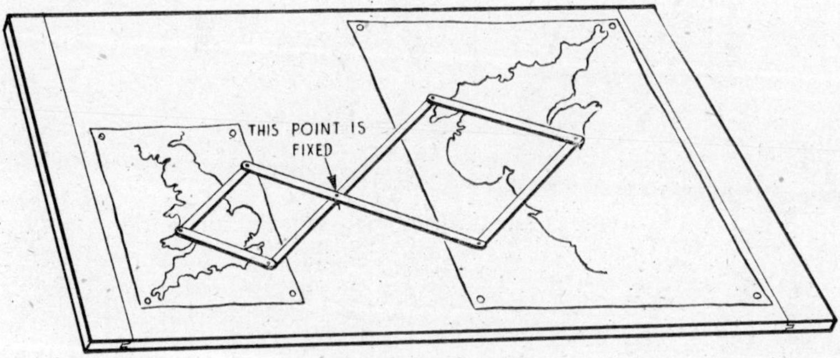

PANTOGRAPH FOR ENLARGING AND REDUCING MAPS AND DRAWINGS
NOTE THAT THE DRAWING APPEARS UPSIDE DOWN

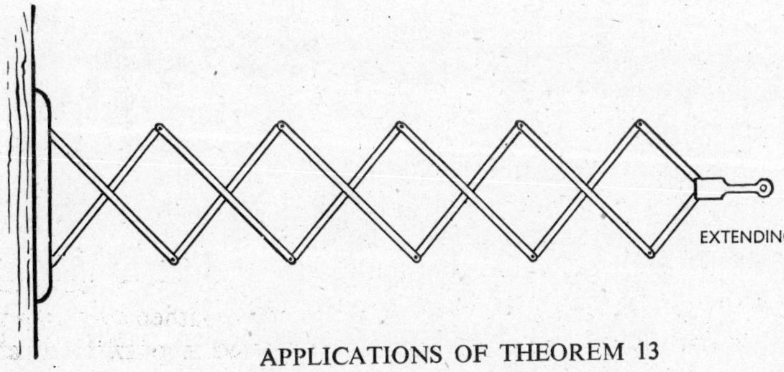

EXTENDING FRAMEWORK

APPLICATIONS OF THEOREM 13

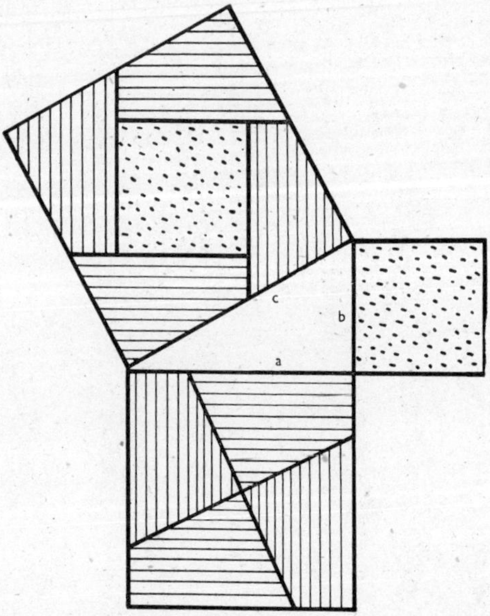

PYTHAGORAS' THEOREM

Pythagoras' Theorem states that the square on c *contains just enough material to make the square on* a *and the square on* b. *One way of cutting up the square on* c, *and making the other two squares is shown here. Another method is explained on page 249.*

such as, for instance, the theorem that the opposite sides of a rectangle are equal, have been quite natural and obvious. You would expect somebody to notice a result like that.

Pythagoras' Theorem is quite different. It is not the sort of thing you would expect anybody to notice. It is somewhat curious that it was ever discovered at all. Yet it was one of the first theorems to be discovered. It probably began with some early Egyptian or Chinese builder noticing that you could get a right-angled triangle by stretching ropes of lengths 3, 4 and 5 units.

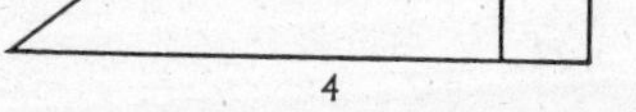

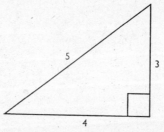

There is no very obvious reason why 3, 4 and 5 should give a right-angled triangle. It is not because 3, 4, 5 are numbers that follow each other. You can see this for yourself by trying other sets of numbers that follow each other, like 2, 3, 4 or 9, 10, 11. They do not give right-angled triangles.

On the other hand, 6, 8, 10 and 5, 12, 13 are not sets of numbers that follow immediately after each other, but they do give right-angled triangles.

People who had some spare time and were interested in mathematics began to think about this, much as today people are interested in puzzles. What

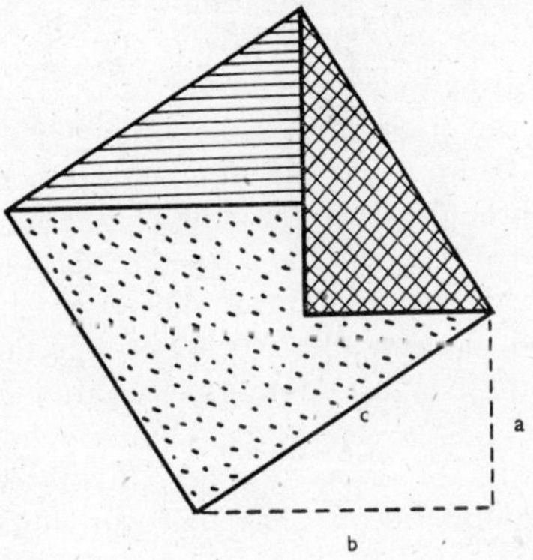

The square on c *is first divided into three parts as shown.*

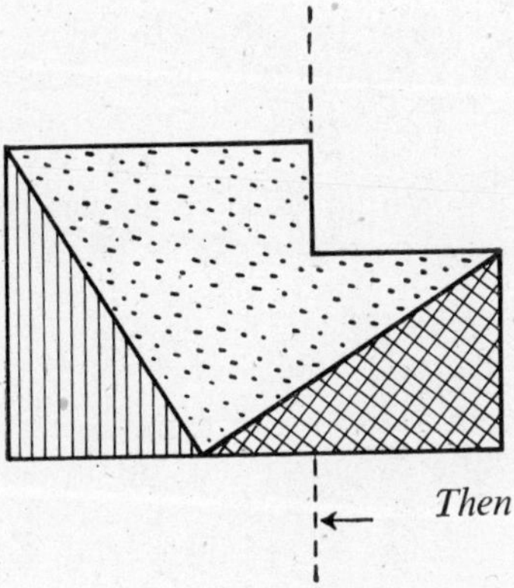

The dotted piece stays still. The other two pieces are moved.

Then a straight cut along this line gives

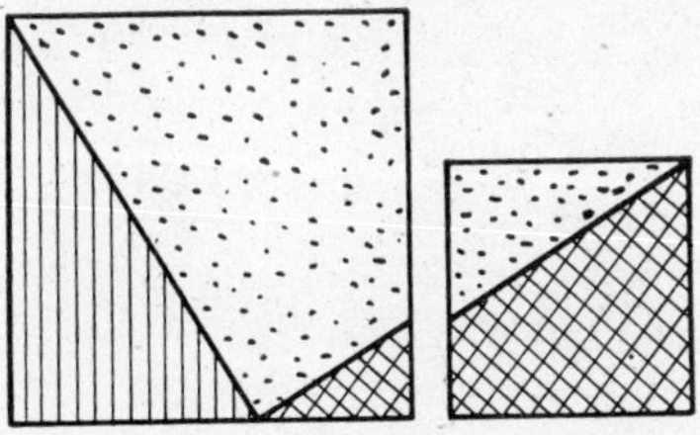

the square on a *and the square on* b.

was there about some sets of numbers that made them give right-angled triangles?

No one knows exactly how the answer to this was discovered. It may have been by considering diagrams like the figures on page 78 in Chapter III, and then drawing conclusions from them, as we did in Chapter V. However it was done, the discovery was eventually made that three numbers a, b, c would do for the sides of a right-angled triangle if $a^2+b^2 = c^2$. This is Pythagoras' Theorem, and we have already discovered it for ourselves in Chapter V.

As a^2 is the area of the square on the side a, and b^2 is the area of the square on the side b, the result means that there is just enough material in these two squares to make the square on side c, if the material is properly cut up and then joined together again. Two ways of doing this are illustrated in the figures on pages 248 and 249. These illustrations may be regarded as giving a proof of Pythagoras' Theorem.

Pythagoras' Theorem is an extremely useful one, and is used in applications of all kinds. Here are one or two examples.

LAYING OUT A TENNIS COURT, OR ANY RECTANGLE

You will not realize how hard it is to do this properly unless you have actually tried doing it. The tennis court is made up of many rectangles, and if you are wrong in one part, you find the mistake getting worse and worse as you fit the other parts on to it.

The method below will apply to any job in which rectangles have to be made—laying the foundations of a house, or marking out a piece of wood or metal.

A tennis court is 78 feet long and 36 feet wide. The difficulty in laying it out is to make sure that the corners are right angles.

It is no good taking a little set-square or protractor and making the right angle at the corner with that. If you do this you will find that any small error of drawing made at the corner will be magnified tremendously by the time you have reached the other end of the court, 78 feet away. (For instance, if your set-square is 6 inches long, any mistake you make will be magnified 156 times. See Theorem 14.)

One way of making sure that the court is properly laid out is to work out the length of the diagonal by Pythagoras' Theorem.

If we take the breadth of the court, 36, as being a, and the length, 78, as being b, the diagonal, c, will be given by $a^2+b^2=c^2$.

Our working will be just as in the examples in Chapter V.

By tables, or calculation,	the square of 36 is	1,296
	the square of 78 is	6,084
Add these.	The square of c is	7,380

From the tables, the number whose square is 7,380 is 85·91.

So the diagonal is 85·91 ft.

This is the same as 85 ft. 10·92 in.

We certainly cannot measure ropes to the nearest hundredth of an inch, so there is no point in keeping this answer to two places of decimals. (In any case, the last figure is probably incorrect.) It will be quite near enough to take the diagonal as 85 ft. 11 in. Even 86 feet would probably give quite a satisfactory tennis court. A mistake of one inch in 86 ft. is very small.

In laying out the boundary of the court we can, therefore, use the measurements below.

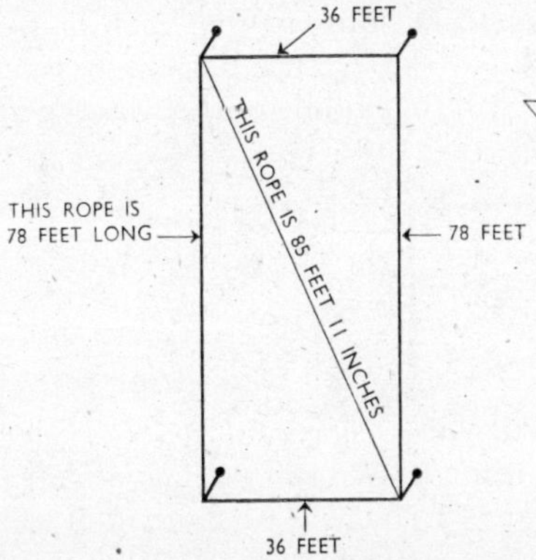

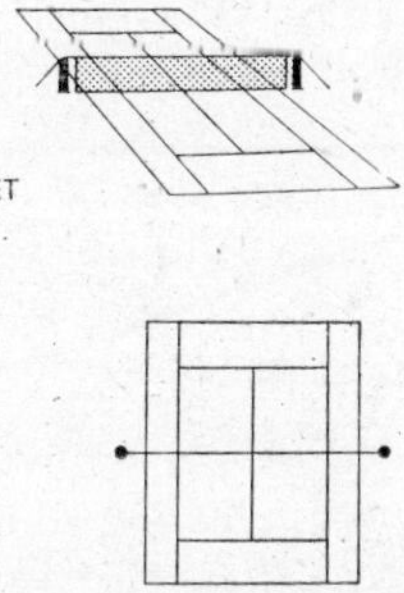

You can check the layout from the fact that the other diagonal also ought to be 85 ft. 11 in., and the diagonals ought to cross each other at their midpoints (Theorem 3).

THE HOT-WIRE AMMETER

Sometimes people say that Pythagoras' Theorem is useless because you could get the answer by drawing to scale. (Actually, there is less work in using Pythagoras' Theorem than in drawing exact diagrams to scale.) Here is an example that could not possibly be done by drawing to scale, because we are dealing with lengths that are far too small to be drawn.

It is well known that an electric current heats a wire when it passes through

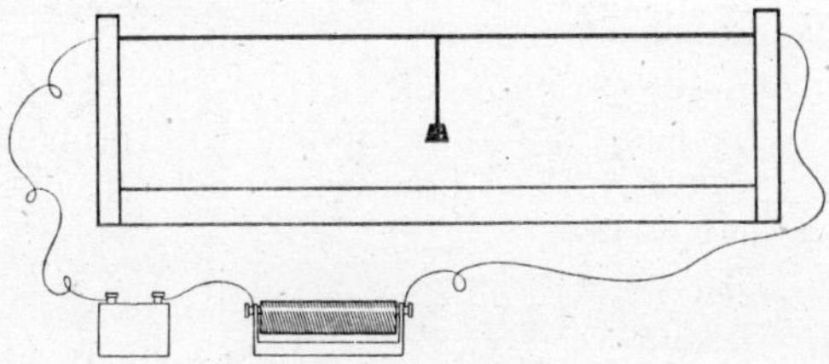

it (as in an electric fire), and that the wire gets longer when it is heated. This effect is used in the hot-wire ammeter, as a way of showing when an electric current is passing, and of measuring how big the current is.

A wire is stretched tight, and a small weight hangs from the middle of it. There is a very definite reason (which will appear in the following paragraphs) for choosing this particular arrangement.

The difficulty in designing any piece of apparatus that depends on metals expanding is that the change in length is very small. Between the hottest day in summer, and an exceptionally cold day in an unusually cold winter, a piece of copper changes its length only by one part in a thousand. It is essential to find some way of enlarging this change, if we are to detect it.

The hot-wire ammeter does not at first sight seem to contain any enlarging device. But actually it has, as we shall now show.

Suppose the stretched wire is 10 in. long, so that each half of it is 5 in. long. Suppose that as the result of an electric current passing, each half stretches by ·001 in. How much will the middle of the wire sag as a result?

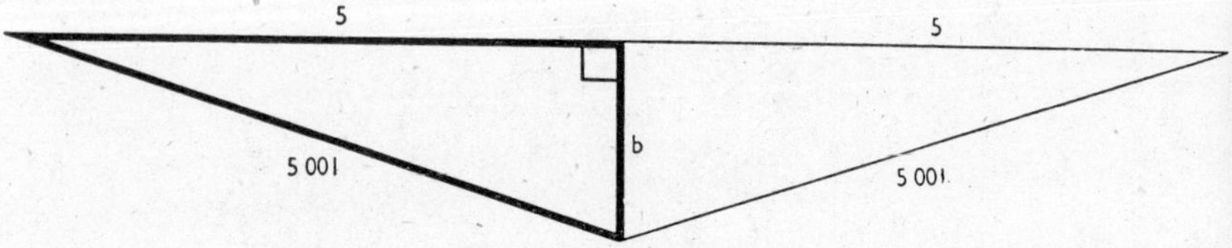

This we can work out by Pythagoras' Theorem; as the sketch shows, we are dealing with a right-angled triangle. We call the sag b in. Then using the formula $a^2+b^2 = c^2$, a is 5, c is 5·001, and b is what we want to find.

Either by tables or by calculation we find

the square of 5 is 25

the square of 5·001 is 25·010.

We know that if b^2 is added to 25 the total is 25·01. So b^2 must be 0·01.

The square of 0·1 is 0·01.

So b must be 0·1.

That is to say, the sag is 0·1 in., or one-tenth of an inch.

When each half of the wire stretches by one-thousandth of an inch, the weight in the middle drops by one-tenth of an inch, which is a hundred times as large.

So the arrangement used in the hot-wire ammeter produces a very large magnification of the effect.

DESIGN AND ERECTION OF A MARQUEE

The standard shape of a circular marquee was chosen in order to make the job of marking out the positions of the tent-pegs as simple as possible. The designer was evidently someone familiar with geometry; this example has been chosen because it shows how several different theorems may come into one practical question.

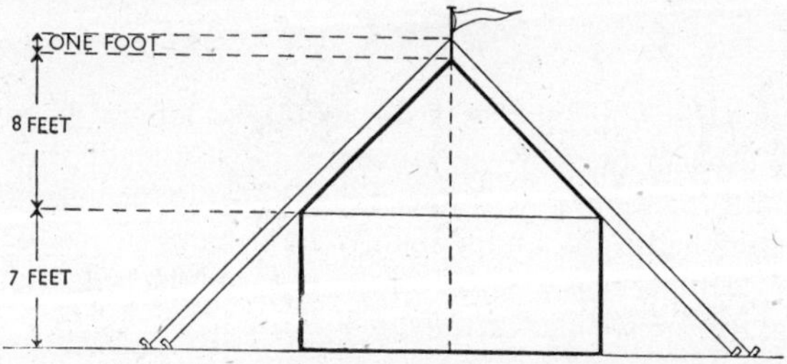

The first point to notice is that the roof and all the guy-ropes slope at an angle of 45°. This angle was obviously chosen by someone familiar with isosceles right-angled triangles. It makes it very easy to work out the various distances on the ground.

These distances are shown in the second diagram. We work them out as follows. First the angles are put in. The angle at *D* is 45°, and the angle at *F* is 90°. So the angle at *A* must be 45°, as we saw earlier.

So in the big triangle *ADF*, we have two angles equal to 45°. It follows from this that the triangle is isosceles, with *AF* and *DF* equal. As *AF* is 15 ft., *DF* must be 15 ft. too. So the tent-peg *D* must be 15 ft. from the foot of the pole.

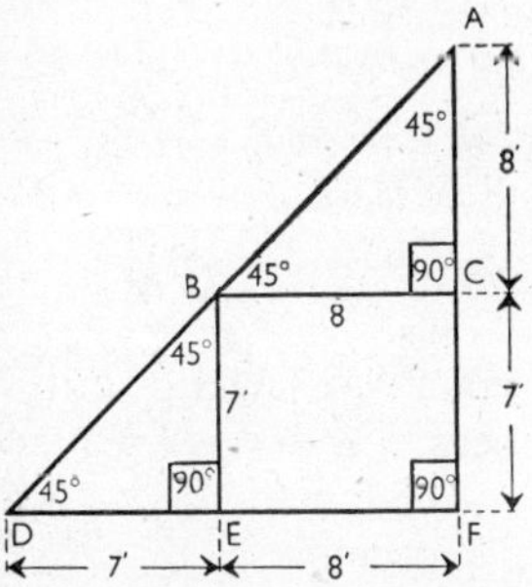

By a very similar argument, we can show that the outer tent-pegs (the ones from which the long ropes go to the tent-pole) must be 16 ft. from the foot of the pole.

The triangle *ABC* is another isosceles right-angled triangle (this follows from its angles, 45°, 45° and 90°). So *BC* and *AC* are equal. *AC* is 8 ft., so *BC* also must be 8 ft.

EF must be 8 ft., because *BCFE* is a rectangle, and opposite sides of a rectangle are equal. So the walls of the tent are 8 ft. from the pole in the middle.

Accordingly the ground plan must be like this:

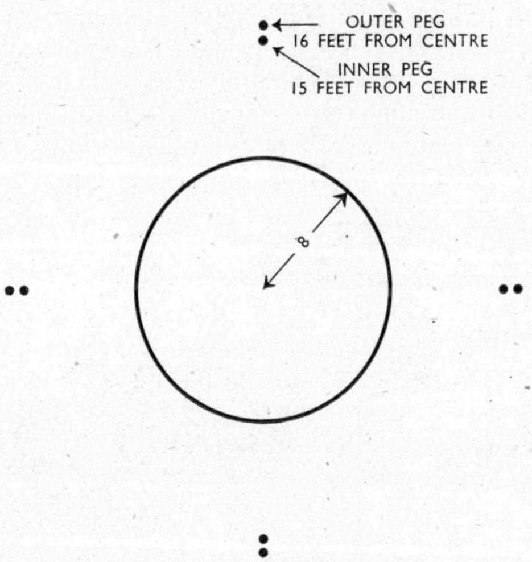

The pegs have to be driven in at the correct positions. For this two ropes are used. One is 16 ft. long, the other 22 ft. 7 in.

First a peg, *O*, is driven in at the place where the centre pole will eventually stand. An outer peg, *P*, is driven in 16 ft. away from *O*, this distance being measured with the shorter rope. Then the 16 ft. rope is fastened to *O* and the

22 ft. 7 in. rope to *P*. The ropes are stretched as shown, and the outer peg, *Q*, is driven in.

The positions of the other outer pegs can be found by continuing in the

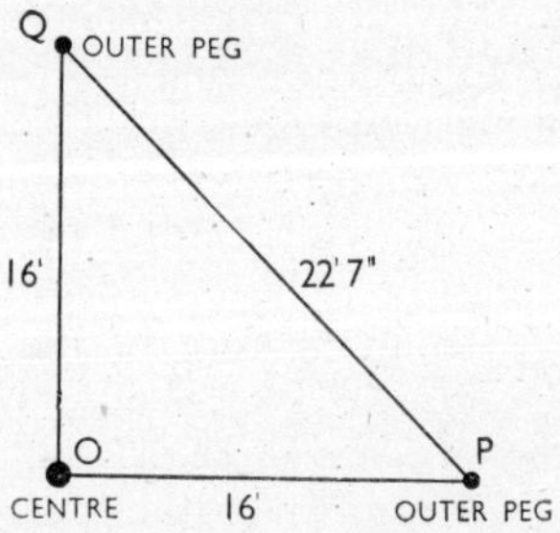

same way. A knot in the 16 ft. rope gives the correct position for the inner pegs.

The length 22 ft. 7 in. is, of course, worked out by means of Pythagoras' Theorem.

Pythagoras' Theorem is also used in making the pattern for the tent. We need to know the length of *AB*, the sloping line of the roof. This is found by applying Pythagoras' Theorem to the triangle *ABC*. We find that *AB* is 11·31 ft., or roughly 11 ft. 4 in.

The wall of the tent is made from a long rectangle, *BEHG*. *HG* fits on *BE* when the tent is made. (We leave out the question of providing doors. These can be put in later, wherever they are required.)

How long should *BG* be? When the tent is complete, *BG* will form the circumference (rim) of a circle. The radius of this circle is to be 8 ft. We saw in Chapter V that the circumference of a circle was $6\frac{2}{7}$ times the radius. So the circumference of the tent is $6\frac{2}{7} \times 8$ ft. 6 times 8 is 48. $\frac{2}{7}$ of 8 is $2\frac{2}{7}$. So $6\frac{2}{7} \times 8$ is $50\frac{2}{7}$. We need not bother to work out just how many inches $\frac{2}{7}$ of a

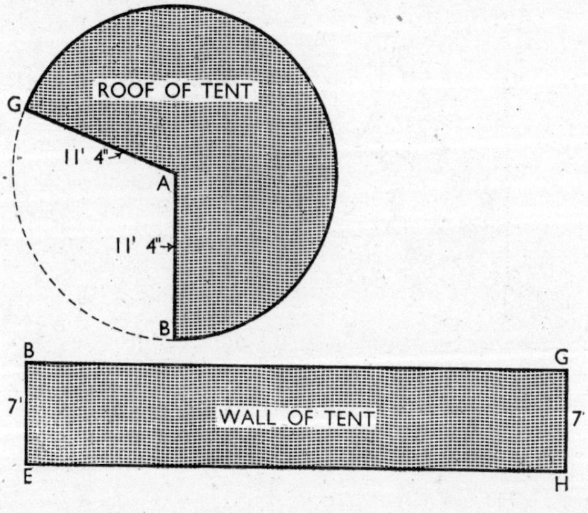

foot is. After all, there will have to be some allowance for hems, so we shall be on the safe side if we take *BG* as being 51 feet.

The last part of the designing, and perhaps the hardest, is to fix the shape of the piece from which the roof is made. This piece is a circle with a **V** cut out from it. When the tent is made, the two sides of this **V** will be joined together. (If you find it hard to see this, cut out a piece of paper to the shape shown, and make a model of the tent roof. Notice how the radius becomes the sloping edge of the roof, which we have called *AB*.)

We have already worked out that *AB* is 11·31 ft. If we took a complete circle of this radius, the circumference would be $6\frac{2}{7} \times 11{\cdot}31 = 71{\cdot}09$ ft. This is too long, because the rim of the roof has to be sewn on to the top of the wall, *BG*, which is only 51 ft. long.

That is why we have to cut a **V** out of the circle. This **V** must be chosen in such a way that the length *BG* left on the rim of the roof is just the same length as *BG*, the top of the wall it fits on to. What angle must this **V** be?

This is a question in proportion, like the question, "If 10 articles cost £15, how many will cost £9?" We would argue, 10 cost £15, one must cost £1½. There are 6 £1½s in £9. So the answer is 6.

The question of the **V**-shaped cut is dealt with in the same way. A complete circle contains 360°. If we divide the circle up into 360 equal parts, by drawing 360 angles of 1° at the centre, there will be the same amount of the rim in each part. Let us first find out how much this will be (this corresponds to finding the cost of one article).

The rim of the complete circle is 71·09 ft. If we divide this rim into 360 equal parts, the length of each part will be 71·09 ÷ 360, which works out at 0·1975 ft.

So an angle of 1° at the centre of the circle corresponds to a length of 0·1975 ft. on the rim.

We want to have a length of 51 ft. on the rim. How many degrees must we take?

This is a problem in division. The answer is 51 ÷ 0·1975, which is slightly over 258. To be on the safe side (as we can always cut material off, but it is not so easy to add it on) and to have a round number, we may take this as being 260°.

Since there are 360° in the whole circle, this means that we have to remove 100°. So 100° is the angle of the **V** that has to be cut out.

It would be as well to make a rough check. 100° is just over a right angle (90°), so we have to cut out rather more than a quarter of the circle. We are leaving a little less than three-quarters. The rim of the whole circle is about 71 feet. Three-quarters of 71 is about 53, which is slightly more than the 51 feet that we want. So the answer seems reasonable enough.

You can make up similar examples for yourself, by varying the shape and size of the tent. A slightly more complicated example is to design a bucket to be cut from sheet metal.

The value of such problems is that they check themselves. If you make a mistake, you find the pieces will not fit together. If they do fit together, you know you have done the work correctly; you need no one to mark your work and tell you it is right, so your confidence in your own reasoning grows.

THE MAIN PROPERTIES OF CIRCLES

Most of the theorems we have had so far come from the first book of Euclid. The only exception is Theorem 5, which is concerned with circles. Circles are dealt with in the third book of Euclid.

The second book of Euclid deals with results that are now obtained by algebra. There is no point in learning these results in Euclid's way, as this method is now out of date, and can be replaced by the methods described in Chapters V and VIII of this book.

The fourth book of Euclid deals with questions that are not of very general interest.

The foundations of geometry are contained in the first and third books. We have not space to discuss in detail the contents of Euclid's third book, so we shall have to be content with giving a brief list of the most important results.

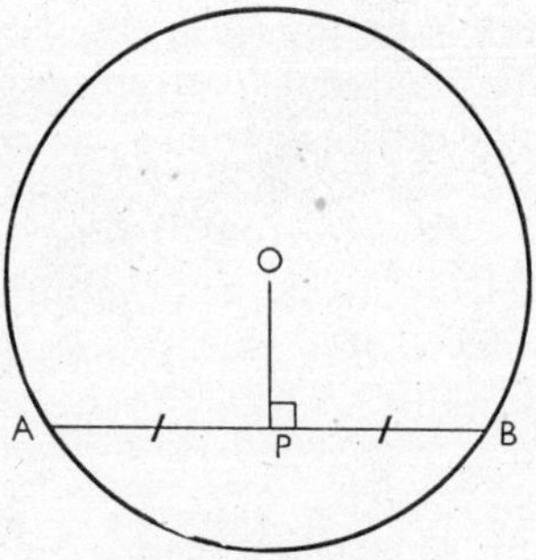

16th THEOREM

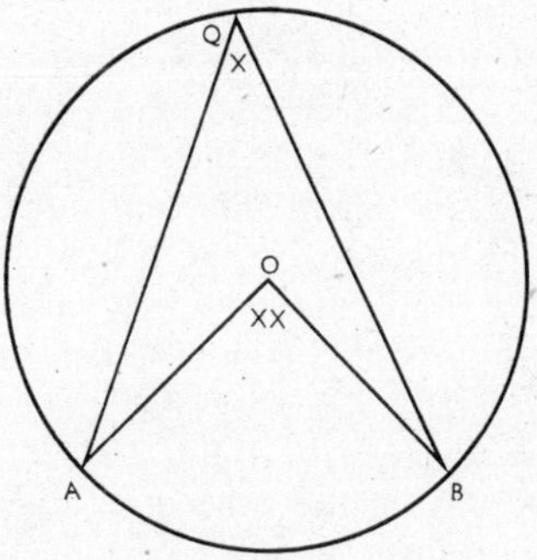

17th THEOREM

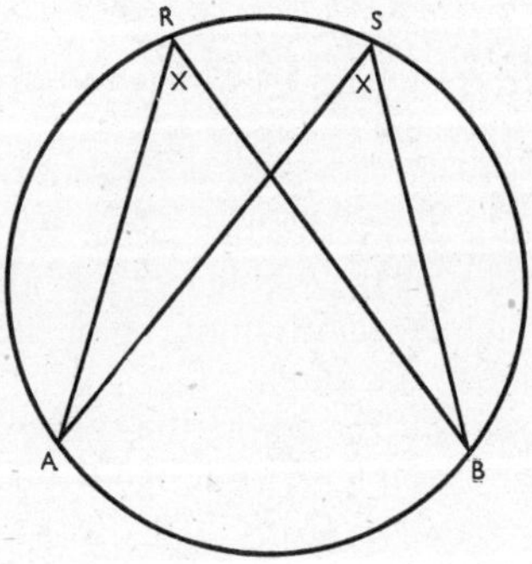

18th THEOREM

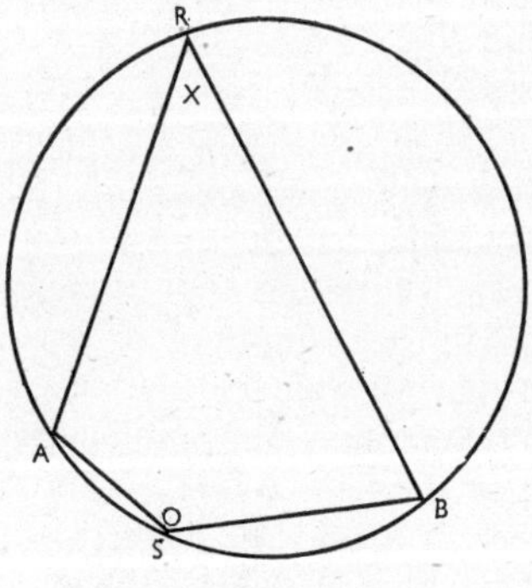

19th THEOREM

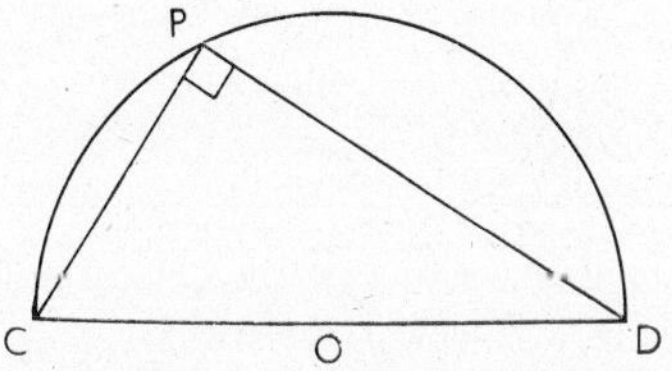

20th THEOREM

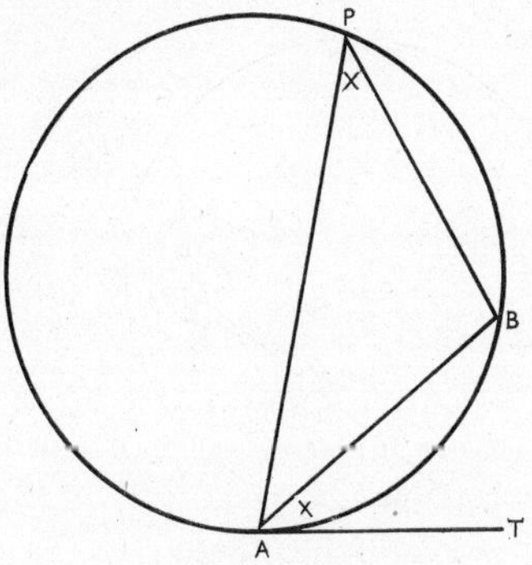

21st THEOREM

16*th Theorem. The perpendicular on to a chord from the centre of the circle bisects the chord.*

O is the centre of the circle. *AB* is a chord. *OP* is perpendicular (at right angles) to *AB*. The theorem tells us that *P* is the mid-point of *AB*.

17*th Theorem. The angle at the centre is double the angle at the circumference.*

A and *B* are any two points on the circle. *O* is the centre. *Q* is any point on the circle. The angle at *Q*, marked *x*, is "the angle at the circumference". The angle at *O*, marked *xx*, is "the angle at the centre". It is twice as large as the angle *x*.

18*th Theorem. Angles in the same segment are equal.*

A, *B*, *R* and *S* are four points on the circle.

The theorem says that the angles marked *x* are equal.

Note that *R* and *S* must be between *A* and *B*, so that the order is *ARSB* or *ASRB*.

If the order were *ARBS*, Theorem 19 would apply instead.

19*th Theorem. The opposite angles of a cyclic quadrilateral add up to* 180°.

That is, the angles marked *x* and *o* add up to 180°.

20*th Theorem. The angle in a semicircle is a right angle.*

O is the centre of a circle. *CD* is a straight line through *O*. *P* is any point on the circle. The angle at *P* will then be a right angle.

21*st Theorem.*

This theorem deals with "*the angle in the alternate segment*".

According to it, the two angles marked are equal.

A and *B* are any two points on the circle. *AT* is a tangent. *P* is a point on the circle.

22*nd Theorem*, dealing with the *products of parts of intersecting chords.*

A, *B*, *C*, *D* are points on the circle. *AB* crosses *CD* at *O*. The theorem states *AO* . *OB* = *CO* . *OD* ((a) in the illustration).

(The dots stand for multiplication. The length *AO times* the length *OB* equals the length *CO times* the length *OD*.)

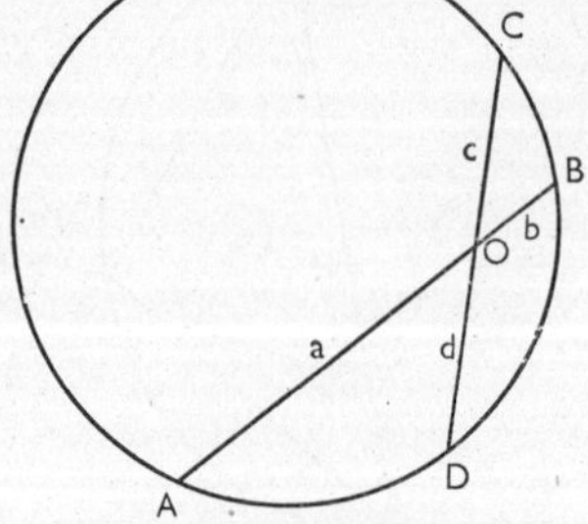

22nd THEOREM
(a)

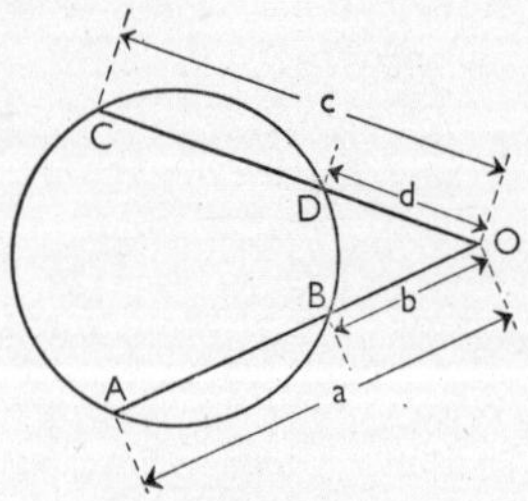

22nd THEOREM
(b)

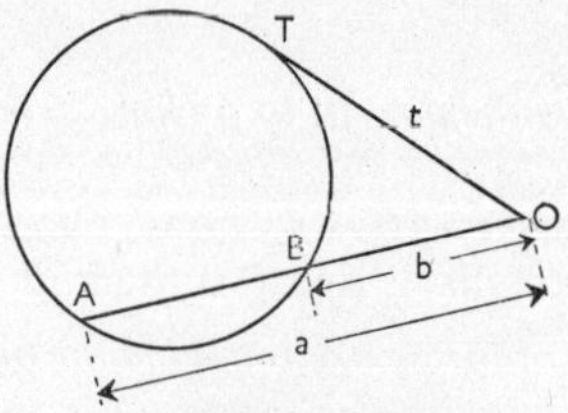

23rd THEOREM

If we use a, b, c, d to stand for the lengths shown, we may write the result more shortly:

$$ab = cd\ .$$

(As usual in algebra, letters standing next to each other are to be multiplied. a times b equals c times d.)

If the lines AB and CD meet outside the circle, the result $AO\ .\ OB = CO\ .\ OD$ still holds. The figure now appears as shown at (b).

As before, $ab = cd$.

23rd Theorem. This is a special case of Theorem 22. If, in (b) of the illustration for Theorem 22, C and D had been very close indeed to each other, the figure would have looked like the figure for Theorem 23. (C and D have met together at the point T.)

c and d have both become equal to t.
Accordingly we have the result:

$$ab = t^2$$

This result holds when the line AB cuts the circle, and the line TO touches the circle at T.

We have now covered the main theorems about straight lines and circles. There are, of course, many particular results that can be shown to follow from these theorems.

If you wish to become an expert at geometry, you will, of course, need to read the books that are written entirely about geometry. In them you will find the proofs of the theorems given here, and exercises to work for yourself. Many points which have just been hinted at here, or stated shortly, in the hope that you will use your own common sense to see exactly what is meant, will be dealt with in greater detail—perhaps in too much detail. It is hoped that this chapter will help as a guide through the masses of details in the larger books, so that you will be able to see what it is all about, and so that you will know what parts to omit and when to read in full.

Exercises

1. What is the name given to this figure?

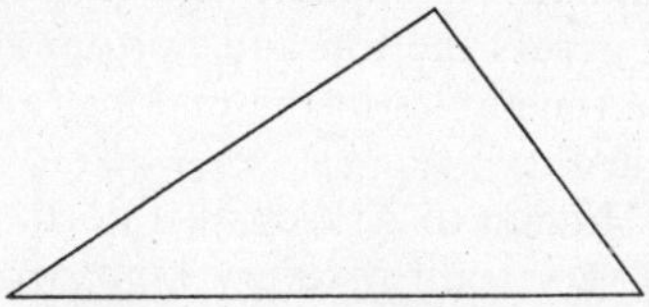

2. What is an isosceles triangle?

3. What is the straight line in this circle called?

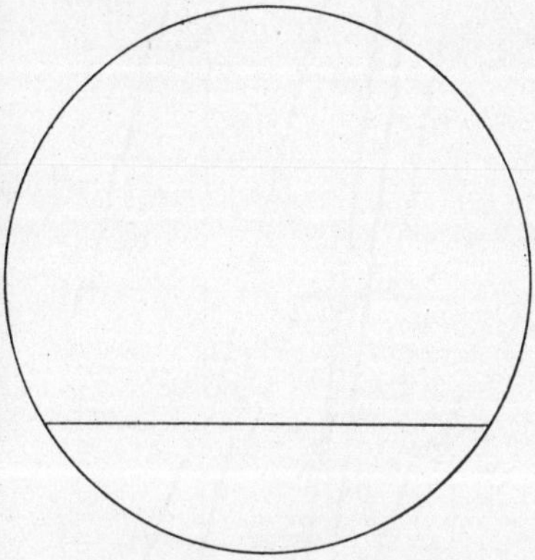

4. How can the accuracy of drawing a rectangle be checked?

5. What is the name given to the angle shown below?

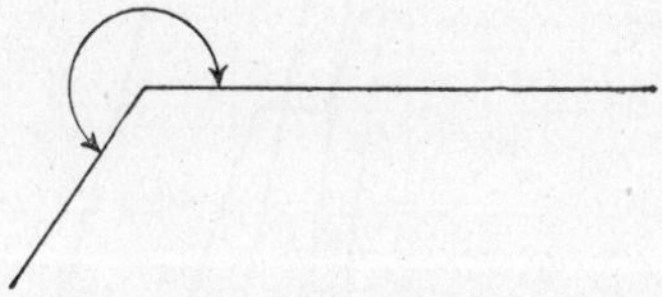

6. If it is three o'clock, what is the size of the angle between the minute and hour hands?

7. If a triangle has one angle equal to 90° and two of the sides equal, what are the sizes of the other two angles?

8. If a triangle has sides in the proportion of 15, 20, 25, what kind of triangle is it?

9. In the figure below OA, OB, OC are equal. AOB is a straight line.

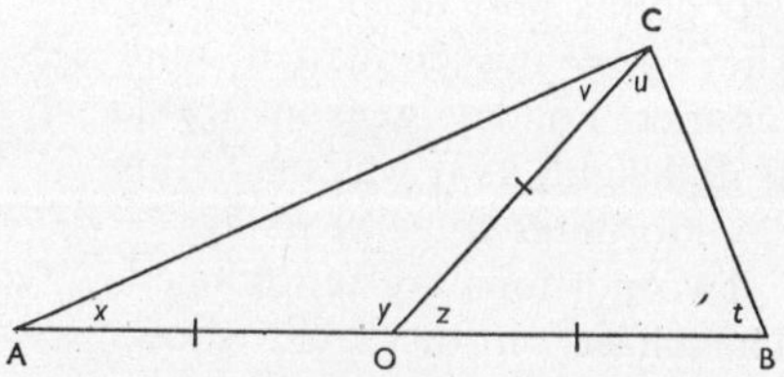

The angles marked are x, y, z, t, u and v (degrees) respectively.

(a) What can be said about x and v?

(b) And about u and t?

(c) If x is 20°, what is y?

(d) What is z, then?

(e) And t and u?

(f) And v?

(g) What is the angle between AC and CB?

(h) If x were changed to something other than 20° (say 30° or 40°), would the angle between AC and CB be the same as before, or would it alter? (Go through the chain of questions (c) to (g) with the new value for x).

(i) Which theorem would give the answer to (h) straight away, and why?

CHAPTER VIII

FIGURES AND FORMULAE INTO PICTURES

IMAGINE that you have two large sheets of graph paper, 44 in. by 30 in., covered with a criss-cross of pencil lines that might make even a spider feel confused. In the margins are the names of railway stations and signal boxes (these last are omitted from the diagram below and the one on page 261, except in two cases near Peterborough), across the top and bottom are times from 12 midnight to 12 noon. They are timetables in the making, and the pencil lines are train paths, as they are called.

These two sheets cover the main line from Hitchin to Arksey, just north of Doncaster, a distance of about 140 miles. Every train of every kind, from Scotch Express to the slowest freight, moving over the lines between these two points and times is shown. They give the congested mid-summer holiday season traffic at its height, as it was on Saturday mornings some years ago.

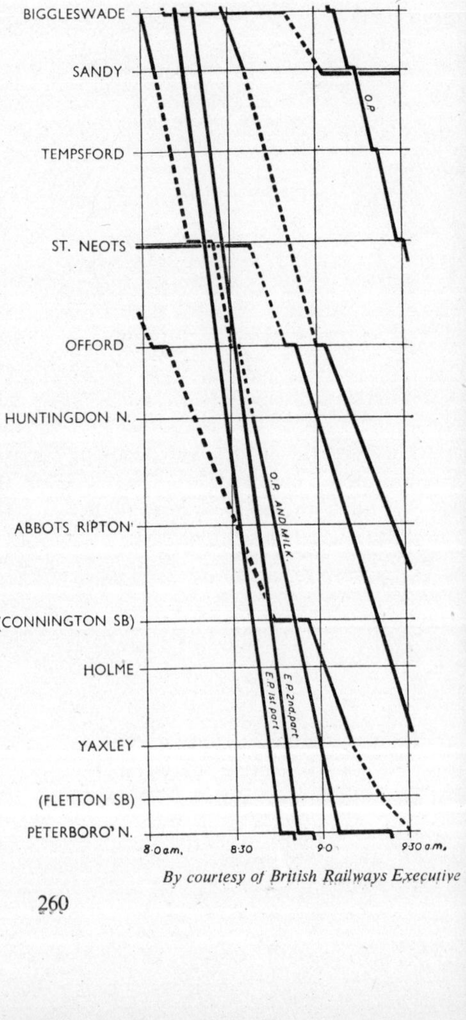

By courtesy of British Railways Executive

Two portions are reproduced. The chart on the right shows down traffic south of Peterborough between 8.30 and 9.30 a.m.—a mixed bag; express, ordinary stopping passenger, and slow freight train. The chart on page 261 is for the up traffic between Grantham and Retford from 10.0 a.m. to noon, and is almost entirely express passenger traffic bringing holiday-makers home in a hurry. (In the original, traffic in both directions is shown on the same chart, one being superimposed on the other. Only one at a time has been shown here to make the diagrams simpler.)

A train path is shown thus: ———, and two of these lines in the same direction must not cross, except at a station, or you will have two trains arriving at the same place at the same time. If, however, one of the trains is on a slow line its path is shown by a broken line: - - - - -, and such a path may cross one of the others, as the trains are on different lines. Stops are shown by a kink in the path:

Now look at the diagrams on the top of page 262 which are self-explanatory and can be left to speak for themselves.

The fact is that, like the rest of the world today, mathematics has taken to going to the pictures. You have only to look at the way facts are presented through pictures, curves or graphs, in newspapers or advertisements, to realize how much more vivid such a method makes them. One glance, and "Ah, I can understand that," you say. The course of an illness, the constitution of the population a generation or two hence, the efficiency of a petrol engine, the shape of a road-corner—all these, and many more, can be brought to life by means of a suitable diagram.

At first these graphs, as they are called, belong to the ABC of the subject. Later they become a powerful tool in the advanced mathematical treatment of the most difficult problems. They are of the greatest practical use and importance, and not merely of theoretical interest or curiosity. They *do* things. They answer questions. Let us look at a few illustrations chosen for their practical serviceability.

Here is one which begins with theory and calculation, a design for an aeroplane wing, with all its problems of streamline, flow and lift. It is a matter for the mathematical physicist, in the first place, who deduces the curves after carrying out his experiments and wind-tunnel tests. His results will be expressed in formulae and equations quite useless in the workshop. What is wanted there is a pattern, not a string of algebraic symbols; shapes, not letters.

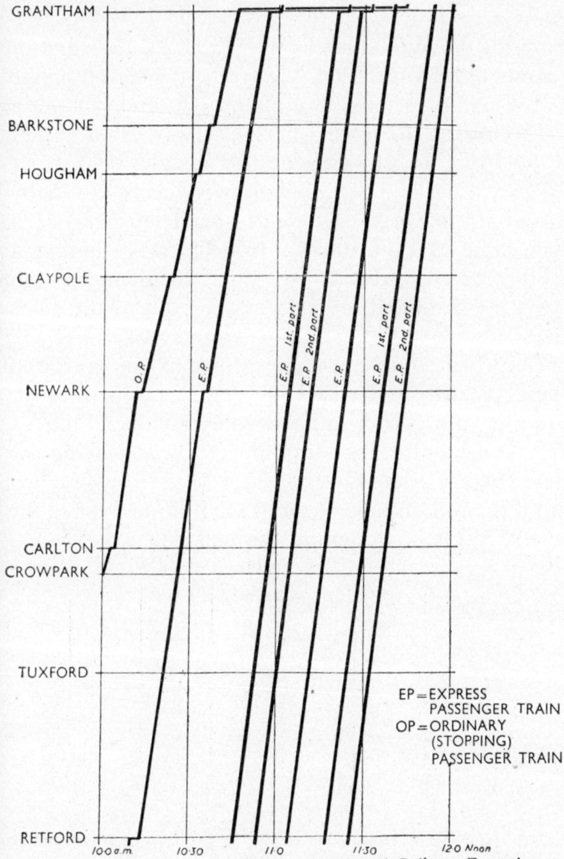

By courtesy of British Railways Executive

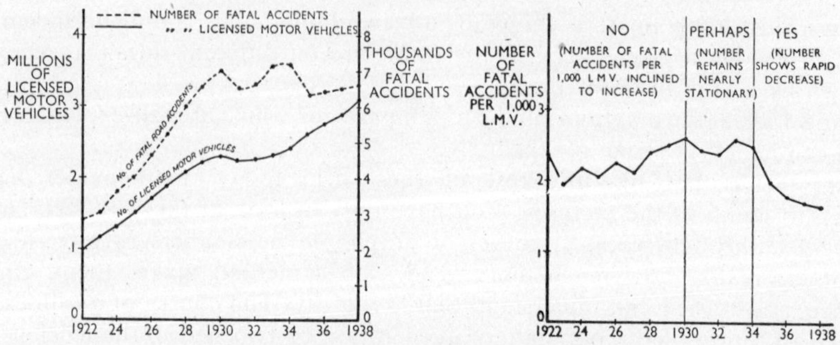

ARE WE LEARNING SAFETY FIRST?

Can the physicist translate the one into the other? Look at the figure below and see it done. Draw a line *AB* 10 cm. long, mark it off in centimetres, and at each division draw two lines, one straight up and the other (distinguished by the minus sign) straight down; their lengths are given in millimetres in the table. Join their ends with two nice even curves, "fair" curves, and you have your wing section at once.

The next illustration brings us down to earth again and is a matter first of everyday practical observation. Watch the track the tyres of a bicycle make when it is wheeled along on a damp surface. Keep it straight and you get a single track, the rear wheel following the front wheel exactly. Turn a corner and the tracks separate, the front wheel being on the outside. It looks as though the machine had grown wider and was now on two wheels set side by side, and not exactly fore and aft, as we know them to be. The tracks of a car taking a curve show the same effect; in fact, a 16-ft. lorry rounding a bend with a radius of 100 ft. seems to grow 16 in. wider. Incidentally, you know now one reason why it is so difficult to get your car out of the gates and round on to the road!

But further: you approach a corner fairly fast, slow down as you go round (or you should—Safety first, please!) and speed up again as you run out. This means that you would like your corner to have some of its bend moved along into the part where you are naturally going more slowly, leaving the road a little straighter where you are going faster.

Look at the illustration on the top of page 263 and see it done. Notice the dotted lines, which show the result of designing the curve in what would

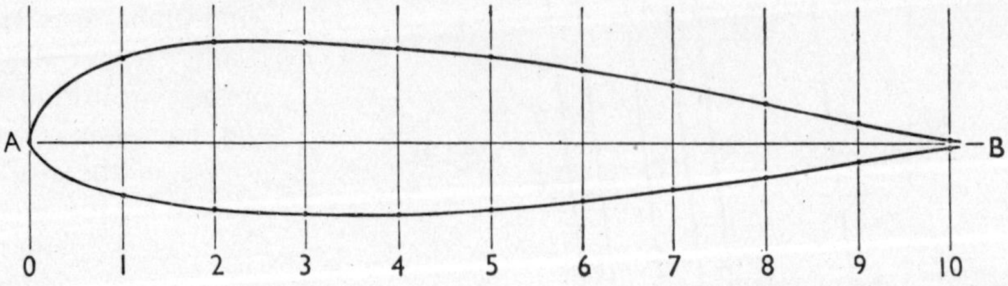

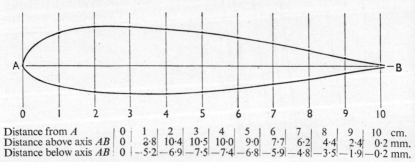

Distance from *A*	0	1	2	3	4	5	6	7	8	9	10 cm.
Distance above axis *AB*	0	3·8	10·4	10·5	10·0	9·0	7·7	6·2	4·4	2·4	0·2 mm.
Distance below axis *AB*	0	−5·2	−6·9	−7·5	−7·4	−6·8	−5·9	−4·8	−3·5	−1·9	−0·2 mm.

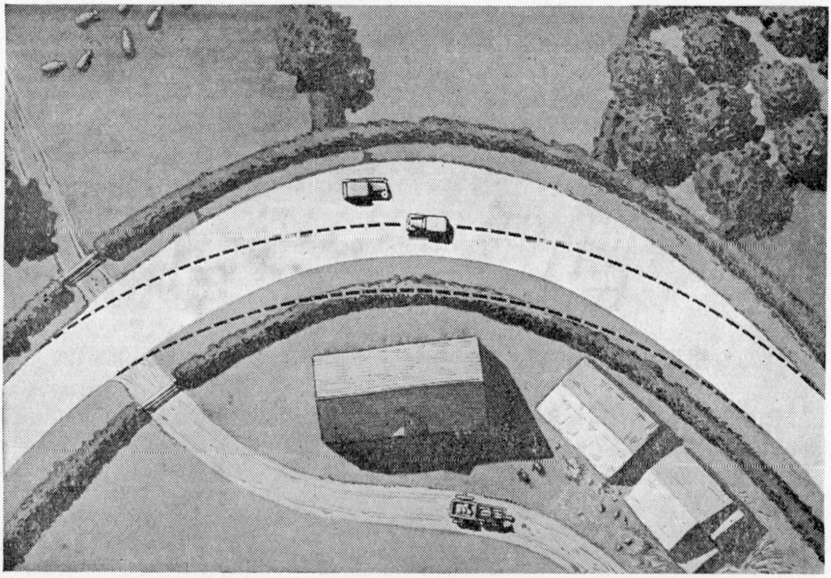

seem to be the obvious and simple way, just swinging around on a circular curve. Notice also the widening at the apex of the corner.

If you would like to set one out for yourself it is quite easily done. Draw two lines at right angles for the inside edge of the road with two more lines outside them as shown below:

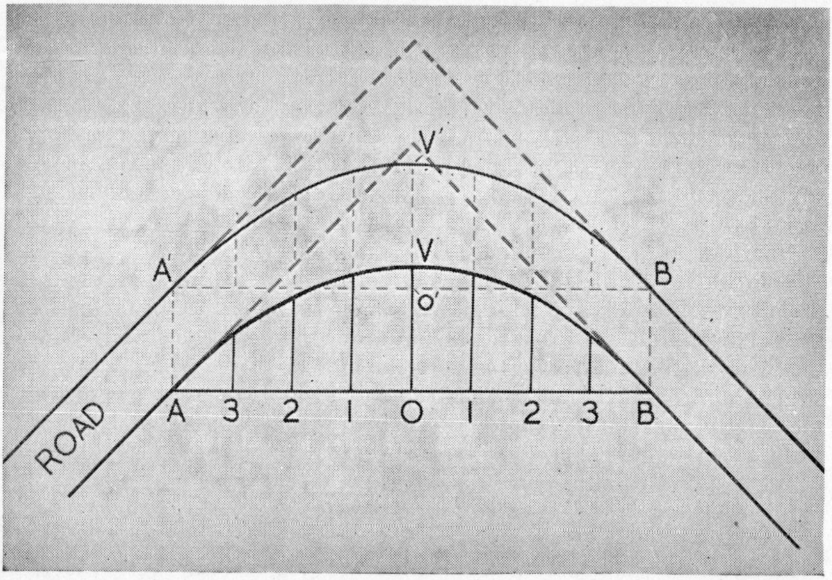

Draw a line *AB* straight across and mark the centre at *O*. Then divide *OA* and *OB* into quarters, and at each division draw lines straight up so that *OV* is half *OB*, the line at 1 is 15/16 of *OV*, at 2 it is $\frac{3}{4}$ and at 3 it is 7/16 of *OV*. Draw a curve through their ends and then, lifting *AOB* up to *A′O′B′*, repeat the same heights, and draw another curve. (If the angle is not a right angle, a little calculation will give the measurements to be used.)

It is interesting to learn that this is a practical design in actual use in more countries than one. Road engineers say it gives a safer road bend, it suits the motion of a loaded car, and is more economical because traffic is more evenly distributed across the road and so wears the surface more evenly, reducing upkeep costs. All this from watching the track of a bicycle and trying to interpret the ready-made graphs it traced out for us!

It is easy enough to make a round pipe from a piece of tin plate by just bending it round a broom handle or something similar. But what is to be done if you want a pipe with a right-angle bend in it as shown by the dotted lines in the figure below? If it were a piece of brass tubing, a perfectly straight cut with a hacksaw at an angle of 45° along the line *AB* would give two pieces

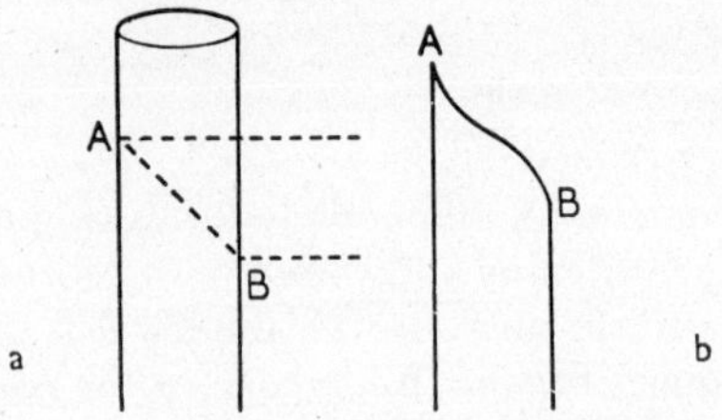

that could be brazed together, and would do the trick. But you cannot do that with tin plate; the pieces will have to be cut separately and then joined together, and *the cut will not be a straight line*. Try it. Roll a piece of fairly stout paper into a cylinder. Mark *A* on the side opposite the join of the two edges and *B* at an angle of 45° from it on the two edges where they meet. Now unroll the paper and cut straight from *A* to *B* on each side. Roll up again, and you will find you have something like this: two cylinders with sharp points at *A*, a curve from *A* to *B*, and no fit at all.

Now look at the figure on page 265.

You can see the height of the cut from the base of the cylinder at any point on the pipe. At the bottom, half of the circumference of the pipe has been shown in plan as a semicircle and divided into six equal parts. Really, there are another six behind these for the far side of the pipe. Lines drawn straight up from them and carried to the join will show the height at which the cut is to come, or, if it is unrolled, the width of tin plate required just there. On the right is the pattern. A sheet of tin plate (or paper), made the right width, and divided into twelve equal parts, is taken, and at each division the right height is carried across from the drawing and marked down. These points are next joined by a curve and a cut then made along it. If you have done this, take your paper and roll it up. The curve disappears, you get a

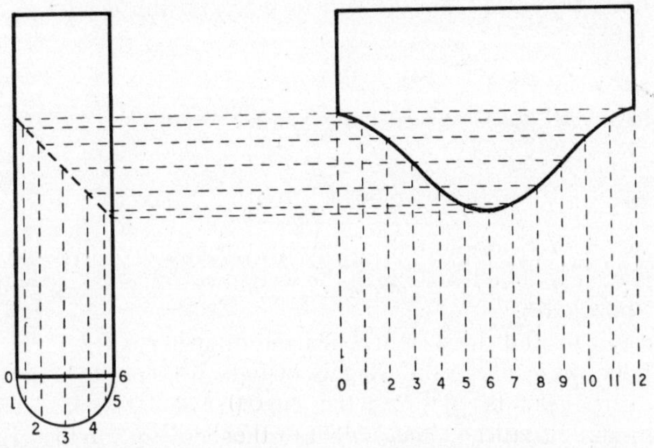

straight-line cut, a fit, and a good join. The problem has been solved by drawing a graph!

These examples make one important point clear. They have all given nice, smooth curves—fair curves. A mathematical curve is almost always like that, and not a jerky series of straight lines joined end to end. (This kind of graph, though, may occasionally have to be used to represent statistical results.)

Have you noticed at the cinema that a rapid sweep of an arm may appear sometimes, not as a smooth sweeping movement, but as a series of jerks; that revolving wheels get up to all sorts of queer tricks, and may even appear to turn backwards though the car is running forwards? Often, in such a case, the movement has been too rapid, or too near the camera, for the photography to do it justice: the in-between positions have not been caught. It is just those in-betweens that mathematics is interested in and that the graph can catch, as we shall see.

But do they really matter? One meets people occasionally who boast that they are the really practical folk, *they* have no use for such refinements. They deal in set sizes, in definite shapes and patterns, because, after all, things are made like that. In these days of repetition work, and mass production especially, that is an appealing argument. Topsy "just growed". So do we all, and are all different. But aeroplane parts, nuts, bolts, screws and so on, must be identical and interchangeable.

Yet you will find that practical experience gives all sorts of curious, unruly measurements, little bits and pieces, and odd lengths that have to be taken into account. (Read the chapter on Geometry and see if you can fit the diameter of a circle round its circumference, or measure exactly the line from corner to corner of a square.)

Here is a case in point. What do steel ball-bearings of different sizes weigh? This is not difficult to work out, but tedious. The volume of a ball, or sphere, is given by the formula $V=\frac{4}{3}\pi r^3$, or $\frac{1}{6}\pi D^3$, where r and D are its radius and diameter respectively. The weight of 1 cu. in. of steel varies slightly, but 4·5 oz. is a very fair value for it. Find the volume of the sphere, then, in cubic inches and multiply it by 4·5 and you have the weight in ounces. This has been done for sizes from 0·1″ up to 0·5″ and the results set out in the following table:

Diameter in inches ..	0	0·1	0·2	0·3	0·4	0·5
Weight in ounces ..	0	0·0024	0·019	0·065	0·15	0·295

These figures have been plotted, a smooth curve drawn through them, and at once you have a table from which the weight of any odd size between those limits can be read.

Let us use it to find the weight when the diameter is 0·15″. If the weight were just half way between the weights of balls 0·1″ and 0·2″ in diameter, it would be very nearly 0·011 oz.; the curve says 0·008 oz.—and so does calculation. Our curve, then, has caught this in-between value correctly.

This seems to be the right stage at which to mention two important practical details. First, the scale of your graphs. Treat each graph on its own merit and make it as large as you reasonably can. This makes for clearness and accuracy. Sometimes a small section of a graph is taken and redrawn on a greatly enlarged scale to obtain a more exact and accurate reading.

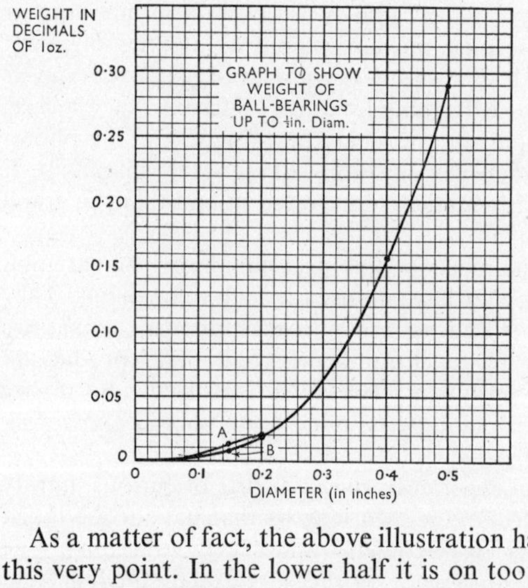

A. Weight of bearing of 0·15 *in. diameter taken from the table as half way between* 0·1 *and* 0·2=0·011 *oz.*

B. Correct value obtained from the curve=0·008*oz.*

As a matter of fact, the above illustration has been drawn so as to illustrate this very point. In the lower half it is on too small a scale to be really satisfactory. We will follow this line of argument by carrying our table on up to weights of spheres 1·0″ in diameter:

Diameter in inches ..	0·5	0·6	0·7	0·8	0·9	1·0
Weight in ounces ..	0·295	0·511	0·81	1·21	1·78	2·38

An attempt to continue the last graph so as to join these to it would result in something quite unmanageable. The weight of the 1″ sphere is eight times that of the $\frac{1}{2}$″ sphere, and 1,000 times that of the $\frac{1}{10}$″ sphere! We must, therefore, draw a second graph and alter the vertical scale of weights to one more suitable. Like this:

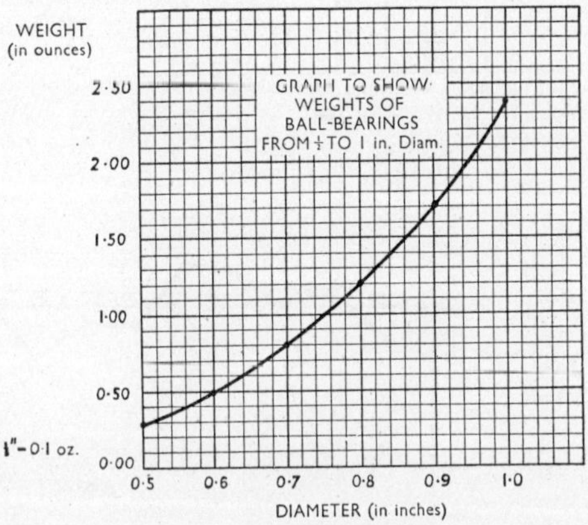

The second point is simple. Don't try to draw a curve from outside. Get your hand inside it, swinging loosely from the wrist, almost like a compass. You soon get the feel of the curve, and will even find your hand pointing out your mistakes by refusing to pass through a wrongly placed point. When that happens, check your point; you will probably find your hand was right and the point was wrong!

Before dealing with the subject from a more theoretical standpoint, a few everyday statistical examples will be interesting, and they will also form a helpful introduction. Their immediate appeal to the eye is often invaluable. They can give you a record and an interpretation, or ask a question demanding an interpretation, at a glance. Instances are so many that it is not finding, but selecting, illustrations that is the difficulty. There are hospital temperature charts, weather records of atmospheric temperature and pressure, factory production charts, costing graphs, and many more—to say nothing of the recording and interpretation of experimental results.

For example, suppose a new section is to start up in a factory. Its output is decided, and then adequate machinery is installed, and the appropriate staff engaged. Records are called for week by week and are shown on page 268 in two forms. Chart I shows how things are going at the end of any particular length of time, and answers the question, "Are we keeping up to our target?" Chart II shows what is being done week by week. What was happening, for instance, in weeks 7, 8, and 9? Was it a 'flu wave, a mechanical breakdown—or only a holiday period?

Notice, too, that we used a series of straight lines to join the successive points because it is not sensible to draw a curve through the points; it would have no meaning. There is a Week 1 total and a Week 2 total, but a Week 1½

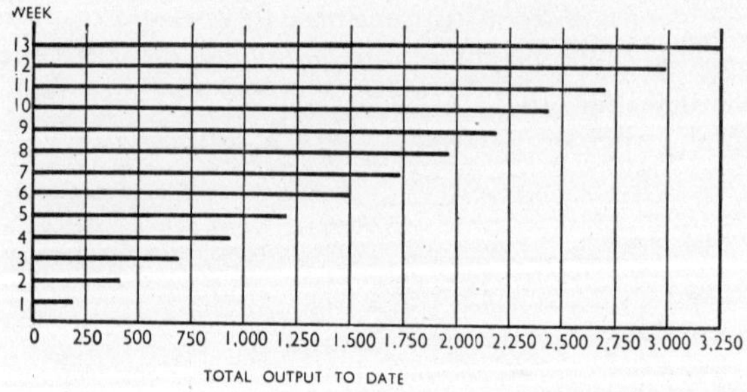

Chart I

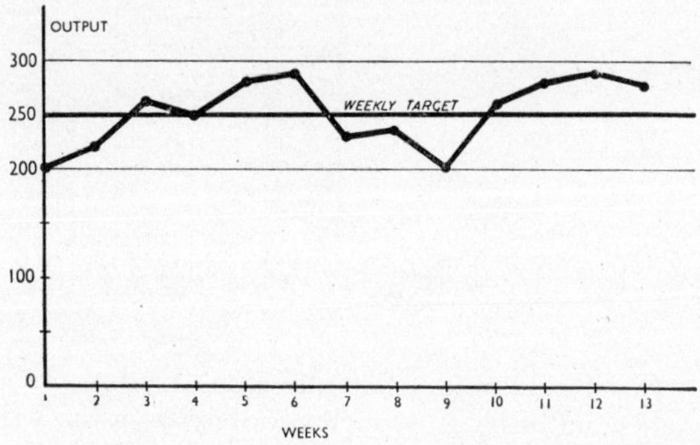

Chart II

total would be meaningless. This is generally the correct way of dealing with statistics.

Now think again. The steel-ball weights were derived from a definite mathematical formula or law: $V=\frac{1}{6}\pi D^3$, and then the weight, $W=4{\cdot}5\times V$. But D would not, or need not, jump suddenly from 1 to 2 and then to 3, like the weeks. But if D can have any value and move by very small changes, then so can V, and so can W. Suppose we had made our curve by weighing a large number of steel balls of different sizes and then plotting weight against diameter? We should have obtained a number of points that would at once, when we joined them, have formed the curve we have already drawn, nice and smooth and regular.

This is a result that needs very careful consideration. A mathematical formula, or law, gives a smooth curve. Then does a purely statistical graph that turns out to be a smooth curve with a proper shape of its own mean that there is a formula or law behind it? Generally it does. One of the thrills of plotting a graph of figures or of experimental results is to find it suddenly almost shouting at us, "There's a law at work here. Come and find it, if you can."

Look at the statistical, "joined by straight lines" population curve on page 269. It shows, what we knew already, that in the last 100 years the population of England has increased very considerably and rapidly. It also shows that the increases have varied considerably; up to about the end of the nineteenth century the increases themselves increased as the population grew.

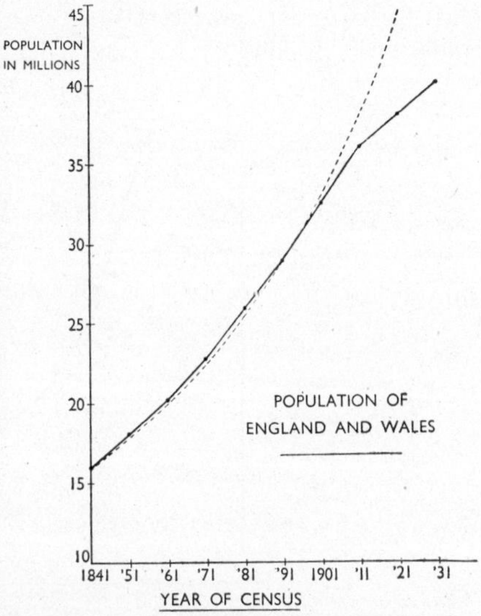

Yet this is what should be expected. Unless new causes begin to operate—lack of living-room, shortage of food, catastrophe—to check the growth, then the more people there are, the larger the increase should be. It is like money increasing at compound interest, when what is earned each year is added to the capital and begins in turn to bear interest itself. £100 at 5% becomes £105 at the end of the first year, earns £5 5s. the next year and becomes £110 5s. at the end of the second year; £115 15s. 3d. at the end of the third year, and so on. It is what is known as the natural law of growth.

Look at the graph once more. Until about the end of the last century those straight lines very nearly fit together into a good fair curve. At once your mathematician scents a formula or law, probably of the type just discussed. By an analysis of the figures, which is beside the point here, he deduces a formula and draws its graph—it is the smooth curve shown with the other. What an excellent fit it is! But what was taking place in the 'nineties and onwards where they part company?

Our conclusions, then, would be as follows. First, a fairly stable and prosperous state of affairs up to some time towards the end of the century, during which time the population increased considerably and in a normal fashion according to the natural law of growth. Second, subsequent to that period, conditions changed in some way and the rate of increase fell off very considerably. Of course, the graph only points these facts out; our mathematics can tell us nothing of the nature of the causes at work.

The closeness of the agreement between the actual and the calculated figures over the period, when they march together, is as striking as their later divergence, and is worth setting out in full in the following table:

Year ..	1841	1851	1861	1871	1881	1891	1901	1911	1921	1931	1941	1951
Actual Pop. (in millions)	15·9	17·9	20·1	22·7	26·0	29·0	32·5	36·1	37·9	40·0	—	?
Cal. Pop. (in millions)	15·9	17·8	20·0	22·5	25·5	29·0	33·1	38·1	44·1	51·3	60·0	70·6

Perhaps it was as well that a new trend appeared when it did!

Just for contrast and interest, a very different picture is given below: the population of Ireland over a similar length of time. Perhaps the reader may like to supply his own comments on this illustration.

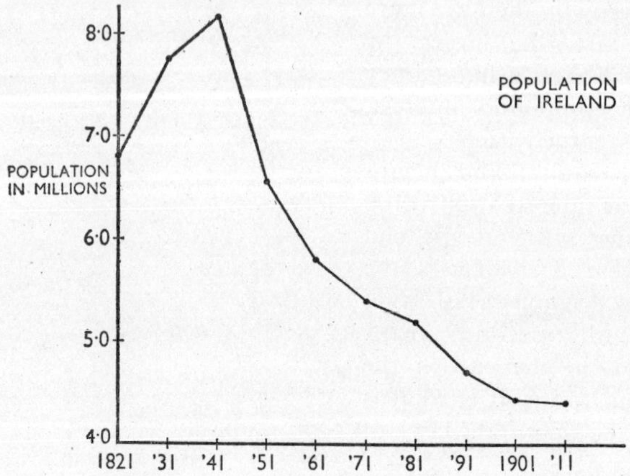

But it is time we became more definitely mathematical over our graphs. Let us see how to use them in a general way, not tied up with weights, measures, sizes, and things, but related only to *numbers*—quite general, or abstract, numbers and quantities.

First of all let us explain some of the names mathematicians use in connection with graphs.

Let us start with a map, and use this to explain the various terms used in connection with graphs.

The figure below shows a journey as it might appear on a map, and the same journey represented on a piece of squared paper.

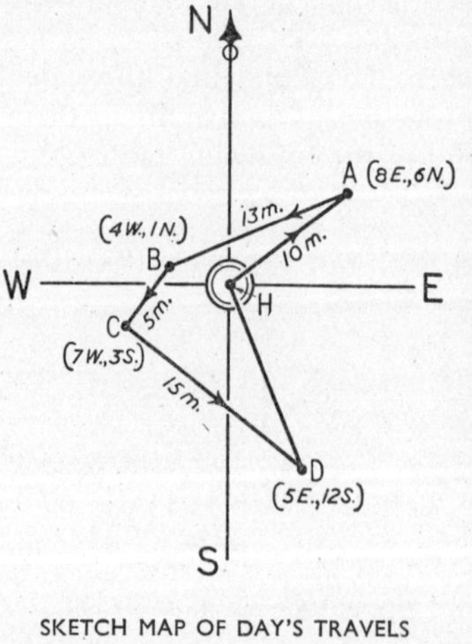

SKETCH MAP OF DAY'S TRAVELS

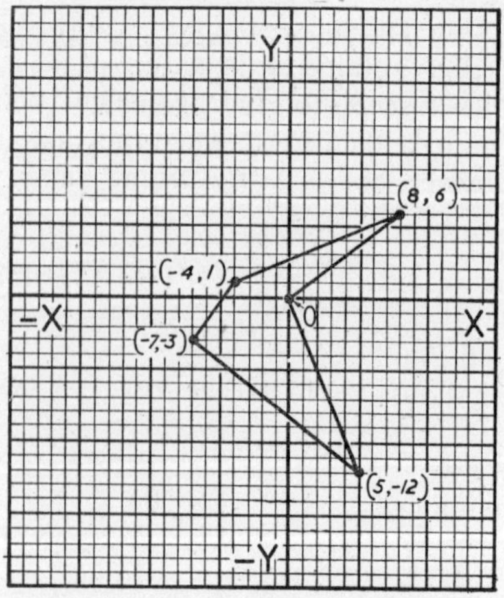

TRAVELLER AS PURE MATHEMATICIAN

We start from home (H), travel to A, B, C and D in turn, and return home to H.

On the map the position of A is fixed by saying that it is 8 miles east and 6 miles north of our home.

On the graph we do not speak of home: we use a more formal term, origin. Everything is measured in terms of its distance east or west, north or south, of the origin, O.

We do not say that A is 8 miles east and 6 miles north of O. We put it in a shorter form. We call A the point (8, 6), which means just the same thing. The first of the numbers is usually called x, the second y. So, for A, $x=8$ and $y=6$.

The two numbers x and y that fix the position of any point are called co-ordinates. Thus, it is said that A has the co-ordinates 8, 6.

How are we to distinguish between a point 4 miles east of O and one 4 miles west of O? Mathematicians have agreed among themselves to represent the first by $x=+4$ (or $x=4$), and the second by $x=-4$.

It is reasonable to use + for east and — for west, if you consider that a journey of 10 miles east followed by a journey of 10 miles west brings you back to your starting point. In a certain sense the two journeys do cancel each other out, like + and —. It is similar to an army advancing 10 miles, and then retreating 10 miles.

So B, which is 4 miles west and 1 mile north is called (—4, 1).

The same idea is applied to distances north and south. $y=+4$ means 4 miles to the north: $y=-4$ means 4 miles to the south.

So D, which is 5 east and 12 south is called (5,—12).

C is 7 miles west and 3 miles south, so *both* its co-ordinates have minus signs. C is (—7,—3).

Instead of the points of the compass being marked N, E, S, W, as on the map, they are marked $Y, X, -Y, -X$ on the graph.

The line through O running east and west, that is, the line $-XOX$, is called the x axis. The line $-YOY$ is called the y axis.

These terms allow us to talk about graphs in quite a general way without bothering whether the points refer to population, or output, or weights. We can study the graph for its own sake, or for the sake of the mathematical law connecting x and y.

The graph on the top of page 272 shows the connection between yards and metres, that 1 metre equals 1·09 yards. Concrete figures again, and the graph runs only from 0 up to 10 metres, or from 0 to nearly 11 yards. But are you quite sure? Isn't it true that *any* point on the line is 1·09 times as far from the x axis as it is from the y axis? That, in other words, expresses the law that $y=1{\cdot}09x$? Continue it to the left, below OX, and you will find that it is still true, that —1 metre=—1.09 yards, which is only another way of saying that, whether you climb a mountain or plunge below the sea, the law will hold true in both directions.

Or you can use it this way. What is the height of Mount Everest in metres if its height is 29,000 feet, say 9,700 yards? Of course the graph does not run up to thousands, but you can find 9·7 on it and then reckon in thousands.

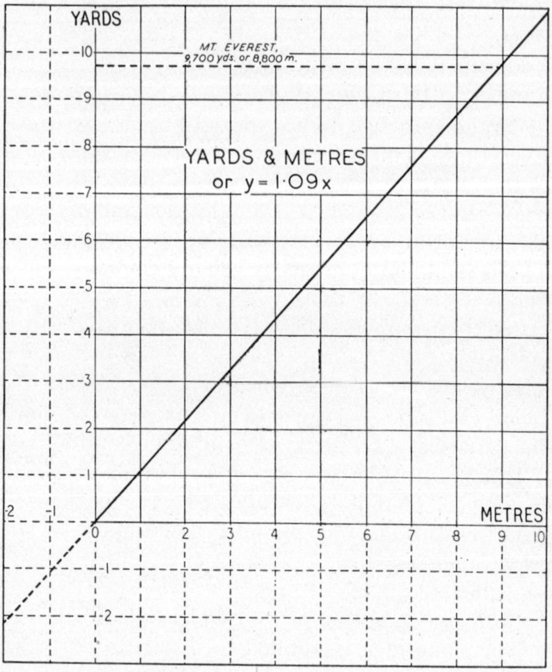

From the graph on the right you will notice that 9·7 yards corresponds to 8·8 metres because where y is 9·7, x is 8·8. So Mount Everest is 8,800 metres high. Any information whatever about yards and metres can be found from it.

Here we make our plunge. Consider the diagram at the bottom of this page. What does $y=x$ mean? That everywhere you are just as far from the x axis as from the y axis. Draw a line to show it; it must bisect the angle YOX and make an angle of 45° with each axis. Anywhere along this line the law $y=x$ is satisfied; carry the line backward and it is still true, say at P, where $-y$ equals $-x$.

Notice the difference between this line and $y=-x$, which is the same as $-y=x$; it is shown on the same diagram.

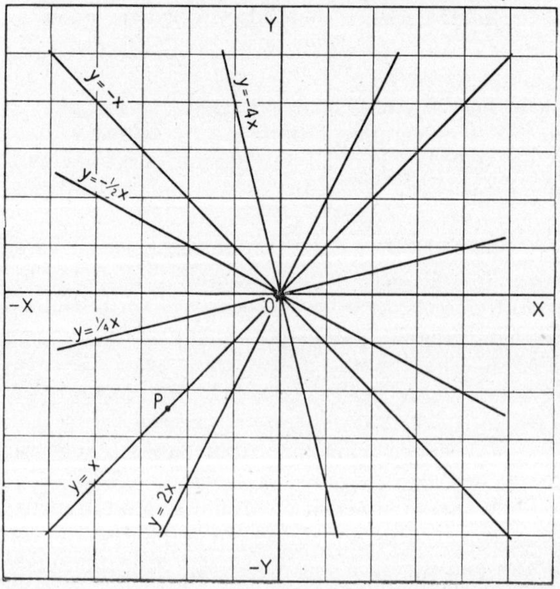

In the diagram on the left a number of these lines have been grouped together and a few moments' consideration will show that they do express the equations, formulae or laws, written against them. They make clear, also, that the effect of changing the number in front of the x, the coefficient of x, is to alter the slope of the graph, and, in addition, that if the signs on both sides of the equation are the same, the graph will slope up to the right; if they are different it slopes up to the left.

Another complication remains to be dealt with. Think of a number, double it; that is, x becomes $2x$, or, as an equation, $y=2x$. We have drawn its graph (see below). Now think of a number, double it and add 1, or $y=2x+1$. Can we graph this? Give x a series of numbers, find what y is for each of them and then put these points on a piece of graph paper in the usual way. Thus, if x is 1, $2x$ is 2, and $y=2+1$, or 3. A table for these is given, and when they are plotted they will be found once more to give a straight line running in the same direction as, and parallel to, $y=2x$, except that it has been lifted up just one unit.

$x=$	0	1	-1	-2	2
$2x=$	0	2	-2	-4	4
$y=2x+1=$	1	3	-1	-3	5

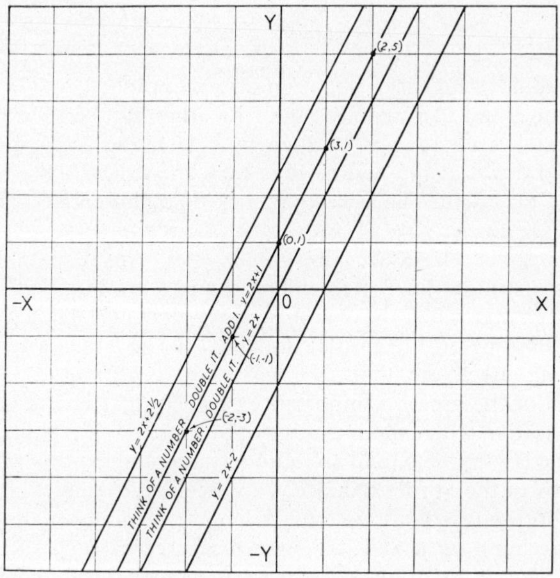

Now, instead of *adding* 1, try taking 1 away, or the equation $y=2x-1$. Instead of being lifted up one unit, the line drops down one; and so on if other numbers are used, as a reference to the graph above shows. It should also be clear from these graphs that the number at the end of the equation $y=ax+b$ (a and b stand for ordinary numbers, either + or −, such as we have been using) tells us where the line cuts the y axis; it is the "intercept on the axis of y."

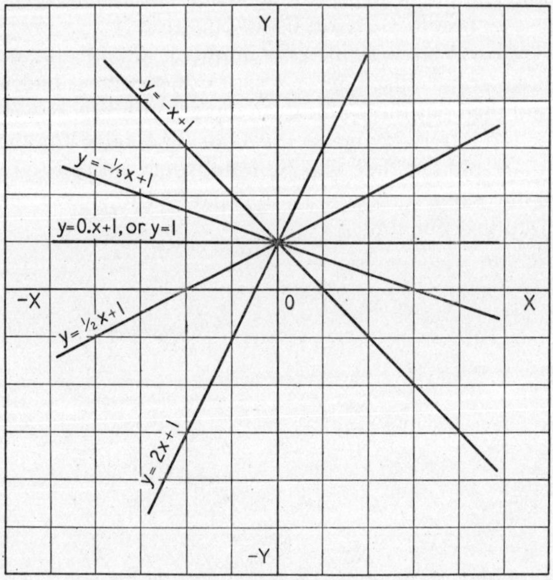

Finally, we have taken an equation already graphed, $y=2x+1$. We have left the 1 alone, and then replaced the 2 by other numbers; by 0, so as to get the equation $y=0x+1$, i.e. $y=1$, then by -1, $\frac{1}{2}$, and a few more. The lines are all nailed down at the point where they cross the y axis, $y=1$, but they swing round that point like a weather cock on a church steeple, as shown in the above diagram.

To sum up. (1) These are all *straight lines*. Any equation of the type $y=ax+b$ is a straight line. (Remember, a and b are numbers, or constants; they do not change when the x and y values alter.) (2) The a, the coefficient of x, fixes the slope or direction of the line. (3) The b tells where to place the line by saying just where it cuts the y axis.

All this is of the greatest importance. The straight line is very frequently used in connection with experimental work to sum up the results in an attempt to obtain the law of them, and so to understand and express what is happening. The Law of the Spring Balance is an excellent example.

A spiral spring was hung up and its length was found to be 25 cm. Then weights were hung on it and its length measured as each successive weight was added. The results were as follows:

Load (W) in grammes ..	0	10	20	30	40	50	60	70	80
Length (L) in centimetres	25	34	42	50	58	65	73	81	88

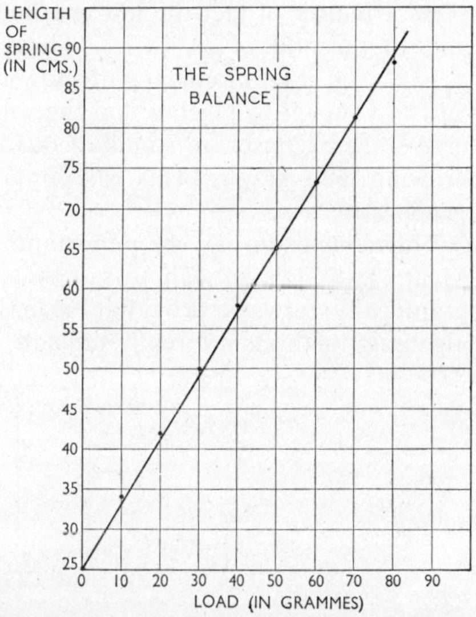

If these figures are plotted on graph paper they will be found to fall almost exactly on a straight line, though not quite exactly because, as they are experimental figures, they are inevitably affected by the usual slight experimental errors.

For this reason the graph was not made to pass through every one of the points in turn, but to lie evenly between them. A length of black cotton was taken and laid over the first point; we can be reasonably sure of the unstretched spring. The cotton was then moved about until what appeared to be the best possible fit was obtained and the line shown was the result.

What do we learn from it? Since it is a straight line its slope is the same all the way along. It isn't simply that W and L, or x and y, increase together, but that the increase in one of them is always exactly proportional to the increase in the other. An extra 10 gm. pulls the spring out by the same amount every time. That is a useful characteristic of the spring balance.

We can even write down one of our equations for it. We know now that b is the intercept on the y axis, then it is the value of L when W is 0, or 25, and the equation becomes $L=aW+25$. Now take another point on the graph, this is better and more accurate than taking one of the actual readings. When W is 80 our graph gives $L=89$, or $89=80a+25$; from this $80a=64$, and $a=0{\cdot}8$. Put these values into our equation so that it reads $L=0{\cdot}8W+25$, and there you are! We have worked back from the graph to its equation, we have found the law of stretch for this particular spring.

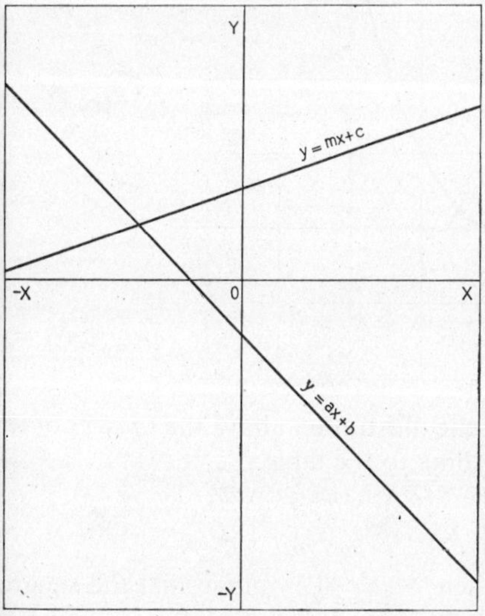

The figure on the left shows two straight lines crossing each other. Is that all? Suppose one of them is the graph of $y=mx+c$, and the other of $y=ax+b$, where a, b, m, and c are just numbers. Then the point where they cross belongs to them both. The value of x and the value of y at that point must satisfy both equations; in other words, we have found a graphical way of solving the pair of simultaneous equations!

As a matter of fact the line marked $y=ax+b$ is the graph of $y=-x-1$, and the second of $y=\frac{1}{3}x+\frac{5}{3}$. These can also be written $y+x=-1$ and $x-3y=-5$. Measurement will show that they intersect at the point (—2, 1). Satisfy yourself by algebra that the solution of the pair is $x=-2$, $y=1$. Then take some exercises on simultaneous equations and solve a few of them by drawing their graphs. This will convince you that equations can be solved graphically.

This conclusion is very important. We shall find further use for it later. Meanwhile, it is enough to say that any equation whatever can be solved graphically (always providing it has a real solution) even when purely algebraic methods are really difficult, or even impossible.

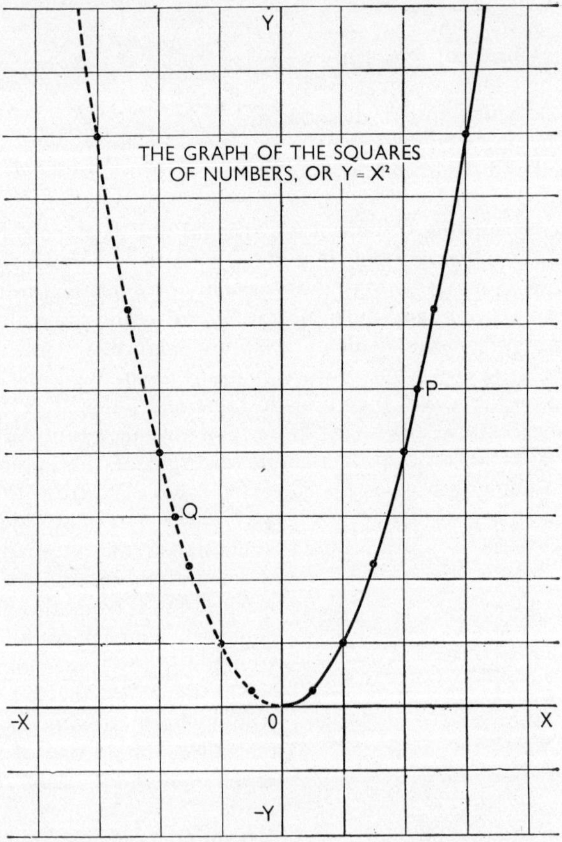

Here is another chance to study. In the illustration above the *squares* of the numbers from 0 to 3 are shown according to the table:

Number	0	$\frac{1}{2}$	1	$1\frac{1}{2}$	2	$2\frac{1}{2}$	3
Square of the number	0	$\frac{1}{4}$	1	$2\frac{1}{4}$	4	$6\frac{1}{4}$	9

It makes a neat, smooth curve. But then $-1\times-1=+1$, so that the squares of the negative numbers, $-\frac{1}{2}$, -1, $-1\frac{1}{2}$, etc., have the same values as those shown in the table for the positive numbers. Our curve has two branches, the second one shown by a broken line. It is beautifully symmetrical, and always above the *x* axis.

Can we give it an equation? Yes, easily. Everywhere along it the ordinate, or *y* value, of a point is the square of the *x* value, or $y=x^2$. What more do you want? Check it. Take any two points on the graph, *P* and *Q*, measure their ordinates and find that these are the squares of the *x* distance. Or you can find the square root of the ordinate and see that it gives you *x*. This, of course, is because if $y=x^2$, $x=\pm\sqrt{y}$. The double sign means that there are always two places on the graph where *y* has the same value—there are two

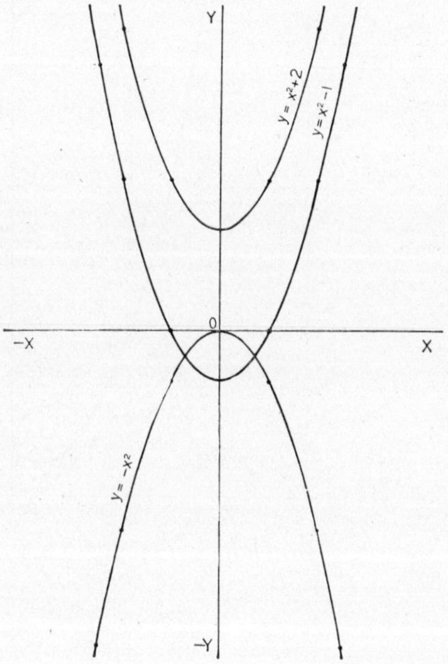

The curve is moved up and down by changing the absolute term (i.e., the b *in* y=ax+b). *It is turned upside down by writing* —x² *instead of* x². *But they are all the same curve, only in different positions.*

THE PARABOLA

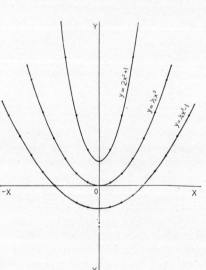

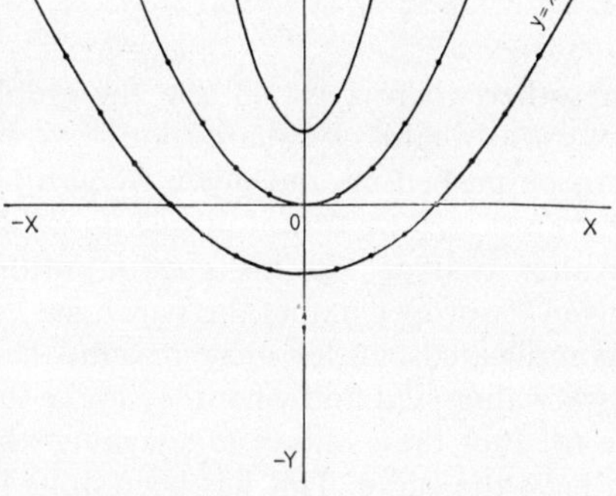

By writing 2x², ½x², ¼x² *the curve is closed up or opened wider. At the same time it is moved up and down as above.*

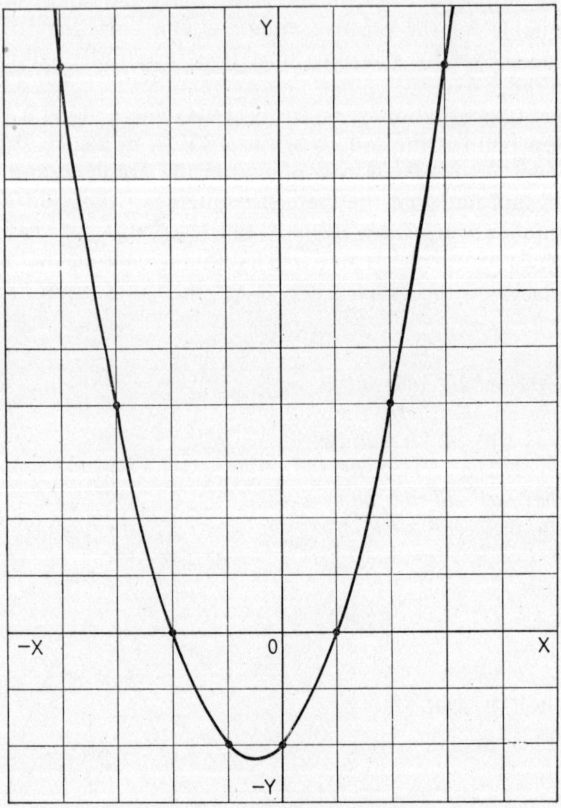

Graph of y=x²+x—2. (*A drawing solves an equation*).

Table of values.

$x=$	—4	—3	—2	—1	0	1	2	3
$x^2=$	16	9	4	1	0	1	4	9
$x^2+x=$	12	6	2	0	0	2	6	12
$y=x^2+x-2=$	10	4	0	—2	—2	0	4	10

places for 9, one where x is 3 and the other where x is —3. So the graph can be used either as a table of squares, or as a table of square roots.

Like the straight lines, the curve can be pushed up and down by writing $y=x^2-1$ or x^2+2, and so on. If we write $y=-x^2$ we turn it upside down. If we put a number in front of the x^2 we alter its slope. All this is set out in the figure on page 277, where it is also given its proper name, the parabola.

A graph like $y=x^2+x-2$ is more complicated, but for more reasons than one must be dealt with. Give x a series of values and find what they make the right-hand side of the equation come to. Plot these values of y against the values of x which gave them and you have the curve. This has been done in the illustration on page 278, where the table of values is also given. The curve is another parabola.

Note that it crosses the x axis at two points, where $x=-2$, and where $x=1$. But at these two points the expression x^2+x-2 is worth exactly nothing, or, in algebraic notation, $x^2+x-2=0$. So once more we have solved an equation, this time a quadratic equation, by means of a graph. Another illustration of what was said previously!

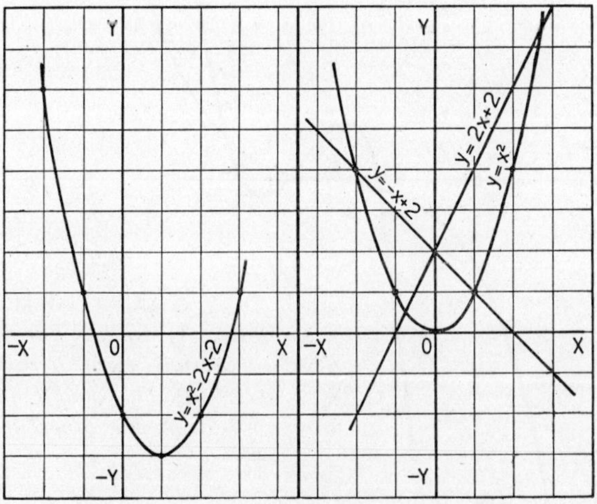

Graphical Solution of Quadric Equations
Table of Values

$x=$	−2	−1	0	1	2	3
$x^2=$	4	1	0	1	4	9
$x^2-2x=$	8	3	0	−1	0	3
$y=x^2-2x-2=$	6	1	−2	−3	−2	1

Now a step further. Here is a rather harder equation, $y=x^2-2x-2$. It is graphed above. This parabola cuts the x axis in two points where x is approximately 2·7 and −0·7. Algebraic solution gives $x=2{\cdot}73$ or $-0{\cdot}73$. It has done the trick again!

Yet one more way of doing this is shown. If the equation to be solved is $x^2-2x-2=0$, it could be written as $x^2=2x+2$. So draw the parabola $y=x^2$ with the straight line $y=2x+2$ across it. As before, where they cut $x^2=2x+2$, you will find that you have the same solution again.

This principle is one of very wide application and is often very important and useful. To illustrate it more fully the graph of $y=-x+2$ has been drawn in the same figure. Where it cuts the curve we obviously have $x^2=-x+2$, or $x^2+x-2=0$. The intersections are at $x=1$ and $x=-2$, again the solution of the quadratic.

The two graphs on page 280 show what a "cubic" curve, one containing x^3,

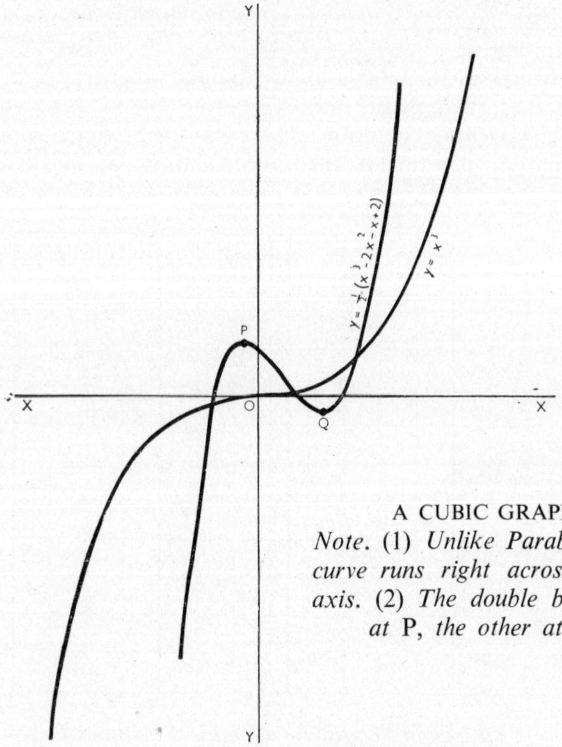

A CUBIC GRAPH

Note. (1) *Unlike Parabola, this curve runs right across the* X *axis.* (2) *The double bend, one at* P, *the other at* Q.

looks like. We have really met an example already when graphing the weights of steel ball-bearings by the aid of the formula $W = \frac{1}{6}\pi D^3 \times 4\frac{1}{2}$. The shape should be remembered, especially the double bend when the equation contains other terms in x besides the simple x^3. Also notice that it always crosses the axis of x somewhere, unlike the parabola, or x^2 curve, which may cross in two places, or may miss it altogether. In other words, a cubic equation always has at least one real solution, a quadratic may have none. This result is most important in the theory of equations, but never mind theory now; learn it from the picture.

Another type of graph must be considered. It will be best to begin by seeing it happen. In all sorts of machines and operations we have to deal with gases under pressure, in pneumatic tyres, internal-combustion engines, gas-storage cylinders. How does a gas behave when it is compressed?

Here are some experimental figures:

Pressure in cm. of mercury ..	111	102	92	81	75	71	63	54	50
Volume in c.c. ..	12·1	12·9	14·4	16·5	17·8	18·7	21·3	24·7	26·3

The graph of these results is shown on page 281. It is a curve, but of a different kind from any we have met with so far. Notice this about it. If we could have

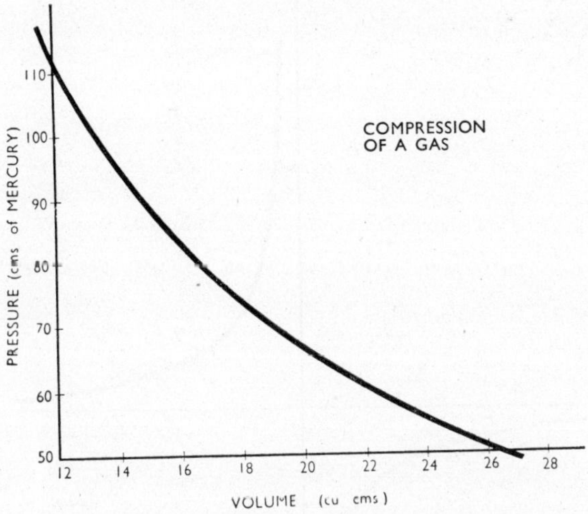

carried it on and tried to find the value of P that makes $V=0$, or the value of V when $P=0$, we should have found ourselves up against the impossible. However great the pressure, there is always some gas, some volume, left. Similarly, you can never have pressure equal to nothing. The curve never reaches the two axes, $V=0$, or $P=0$, though it is always drawing closer and closer to them.

The law it is following is $PV=c$, where c is a number, or constant. In this particular case, as you can easily test for yourself, c is approximately 1,330.

The equation we are really studying, then, is $xy=c$. Let us take it when $c=1$. Here is our table of values:

x	$\frac{1}{4}$	$\frac{1}{3}$	$\frac{1}{2}$	1	2	3	4 . . .	10 . . .	100 . . .
y	4	3	2	1	$\frac{1}{2}$	$\frac{1}{3}$	$\frac{1}{4}$	$\frac{1}{10}$	$\frac{1}{100}$
xy	1	1	1	1	1	1	1	1	1

But there is a second set of values. If all values of x are made negative, and all values of y negative too, their product is still $+1$. So you can see that this curve has two branches, as shown on page 282. It is called the hyperbola. Lines, such as the two axes here, to which a curve draws nearer and nearer, but never quite reaches, are called asymptotes. You will find another illustration later on at the foot of page 284, where the total-cost curve is always trying to reach the y axis on one hand, and the rising straight line on the other. while the current-wasted curve, like our hyperbola here, has the two axes as its asymptotes.

The equation $xy = c$ can also be written $y = \frac{c}{x}$. It is the curve of quantities that vary in inverse proportion. As one grows small the other grows large. An example is the connection between the speed of travel and the time taken. For any particular distance, doubling the speed will halve the time taken (see diagram on top of page 283). It should be contrasted with the straight-line

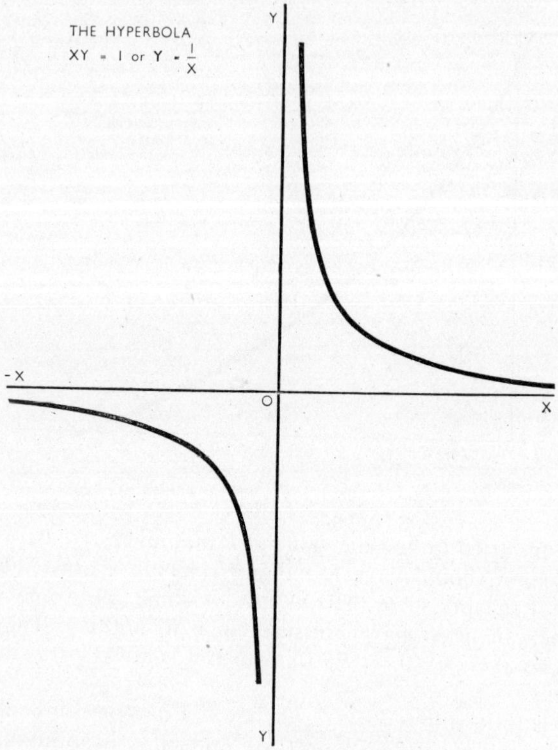

law of direct proportion, where both quantities grow larger or smaller together. See the graph of the stretched spring on the top of page 275.

All this probably seems a close-tangled thicket of theory. We have hacked a way through it, though, and can afford now to emerge into more open country and, we hope, easier going. The question, however, still is, "What can we do with graphs?" The next instances present fresh and quite different answers.

A month-by-month record of the average temperatures at two very different places is shown on the bottom of page 283. We can learn quite a lot by simply looking at it. Do you want a really hot summer holiday? You are more likely to find it in the east at Norwich than in the west at Plymouth. Or do you want to avoid the coldest winters? Go west. Do you like a fairly even temperature throughout the year? You are more likely to find it by the sea at Plymouth than inland at Norwich.

Look again. Both curves have a lowest point at about January and a highest in July or August. Such points are called a minimum and a maximum respectively; only the words are used in a rather different way from the usual popular usage. A maximum is not the highest possible, but a place where a value is higher than it is on either side. It is the top of a hill from which you

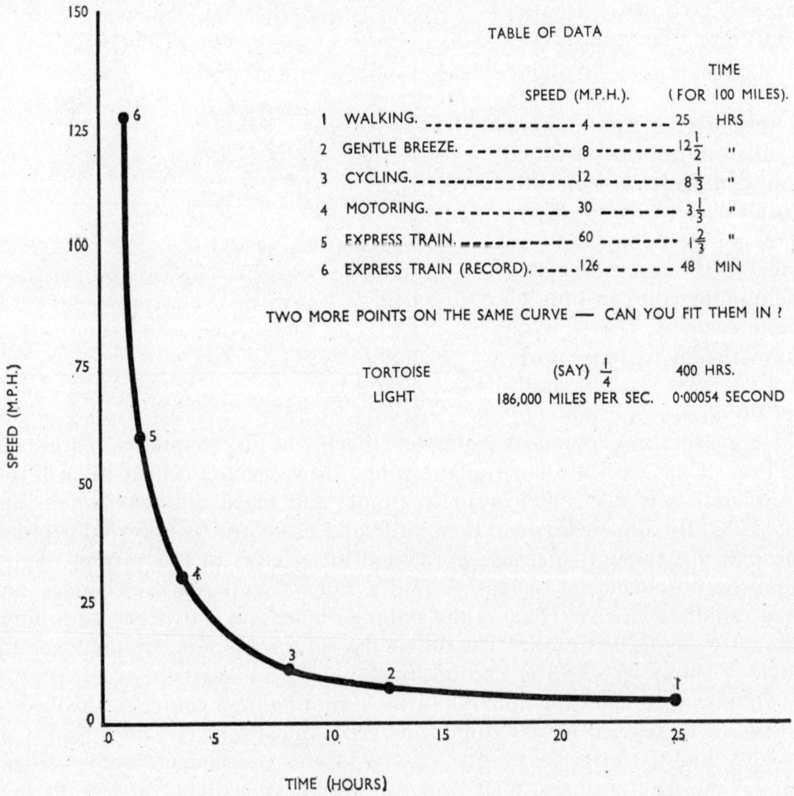
TABLE OF DATA
SPEED (M.P.H.). TIME (FOR 100 MILES).
1 WALKING. 4 25 HRS
2 GENTLE BREEZE. 8 12 1/2 "
3 CYCLING. 12 8 1/3 "
4 MOTORING. 30 3 1/3 "
5 EXPRESS TRAIN. 60 1 2/3 "
6 EXPRESS TRAIN (RECORD). 126 48 MIN
TWO MORE POINTS ON THE SAME CURVE — CAN YOU FIT THEM IN ?
TORTOISE (SAY) 1/4 400 HRS.
LIGHT 186,000 MILES PER SEC. 0·00054 SECOND
SPEED (M.P.H.)
150
125
100
75
50
25
0
0 5 10 15 20 25
TIME (HOURS)

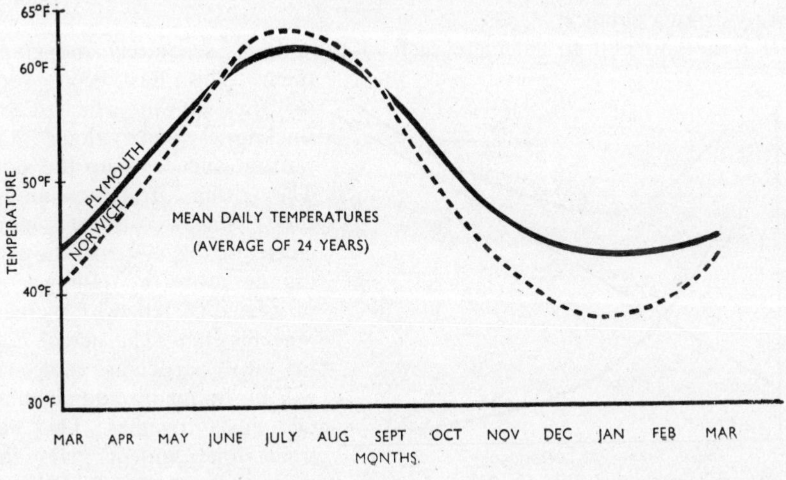
65°F
60°F
50°F
40°F
30°F
TEMPERATURE
PLYMOUTH
NORWICH
MEAN DAILY TEMPERATURES
(AVERAGE OF 24 YEARS)
MAR APR MAY JUNE JULY AUG SEPT OCT NOV DEC JAN FEB MAR
MONTHS.

can only go down, no matter what direction you take—though there may be higher hills near by.

Similarly, a minimum is a valley-bottom from which you can only go up hill. Turn back to the figure showing the cubic graph on page 280 again. *P* is a maximum; you can only go down from it. *Q* is a minimum; begin to move away and you have to start climbing at once.

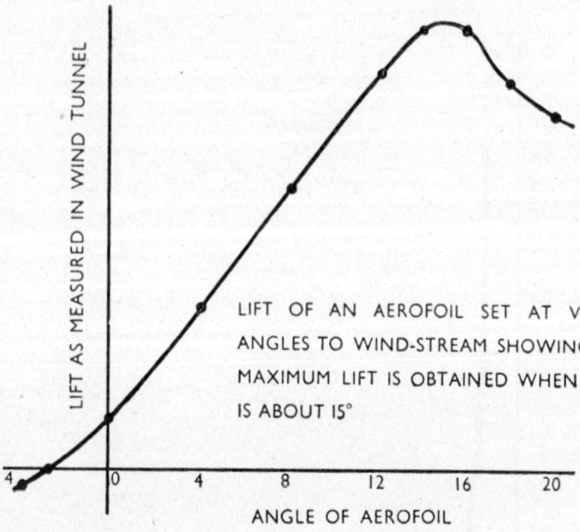

LIFT OF AN AEROFOIL SET AT VARIOUS ANGLES TO WIND-STREAM SHOWING THAT MAXIMUM LIFT IS OBTAINED WHEN ANGLE IS ABOUT 15°

Here are some practical examples. Early in the chapter we drew the section of an aerofoil or aeroplane wing. How effective will it be in lifting the plane? It is suspended in an air-tunnel and set at different angles, first tilted slightly downwards and then more and more up. As the wind is blown through, instruments measure the actual lift it gives at the various angles. First the lift-coefficient increases rapidly, but presently hardly changes, and then rapidly decreases. That is the stalling angle, and if it is passed in flight there is going to be trouble! The lift-coefficient reaches a maximum when the angle is about 15°. This is set out above.

Another problem, this time requiring a minimum. A cable for the electric grid is to be carried across country as economically as possible. Run it up cheaply and so save heavy first cost with the consequent high overhead annual charge for interest! If you do, you have a light cable with high resistance and consequent waste of current and power. Try to save this by erecting a heavier cable and the other expenses increase. What is more, they will increase after a certain point more quickly than your savings do. We have got to strike a balance.

It is not difficult to calculate each of these items separately and graph them. This has been done on the left in which cable thicknesses go along the bottom and costs up the side. The rising straight line is the rising cost of more efficient cable-systems; the falling curve is the falling cost of wasted current with increasing efficiency. The actual cost for any particular cable-size will be found by adding these two costs together. This has been done and it gives the third curve at the top. It has a

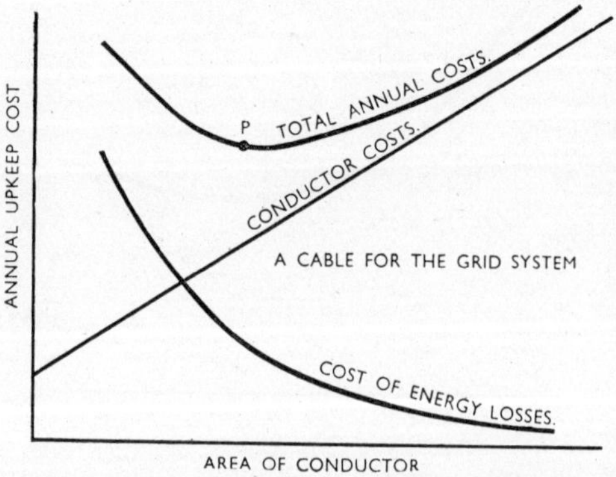

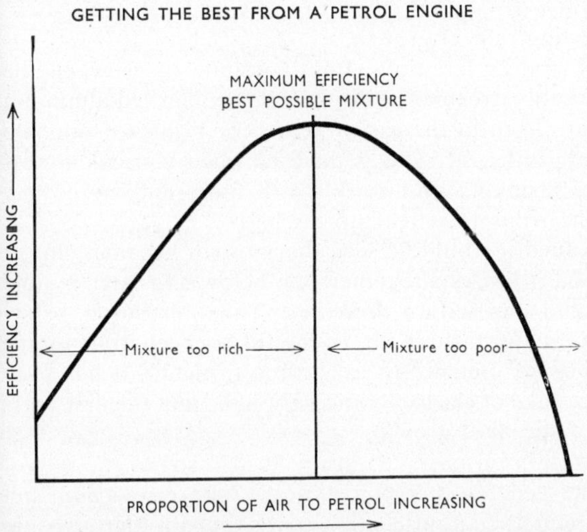

minimum at *P*, indicating the most economical solution of the problem.

What is the most efficient air-petrol mixture in an engine cylinder? All air and no petrol, no explosion and no power: all petrol and no air, again no explosion and no power.

Somewhere between these two extremes must be the best possible. Put the engine on the test-bench and run it with carefully controlled mixtures, and graph the results. The diagram above shows the kind of picture you will get. (In this case the optimum mixture contained about $6\frac{1}{4}\%$ of petrol by weight).

If we make a population graph for Britain as shown on page 269 we should notice that at a certain date a new trend appears; the population no longer goes on increasing at the same rate as it had been, but a new, and slower, rate of growth sets in.

Rates of change are very important, especially when the rate itself is altering. A full treatment belongs to the Calculus and is beyond the scope of this chapter. For all that, there is no harm done in pushing the door ajar and peeping in.

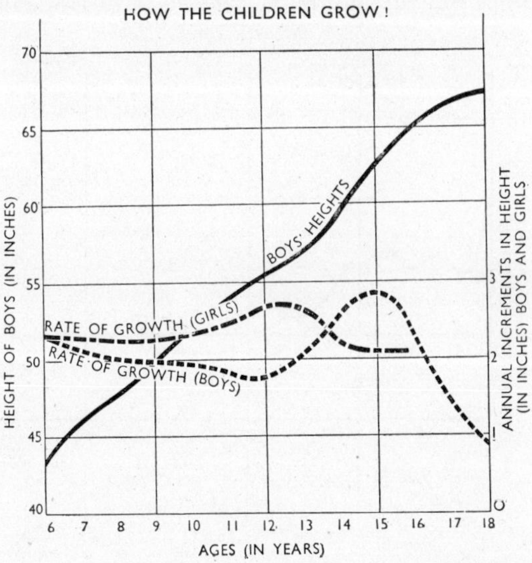

Here is a study of the way children grow. A characteristic measurement, in this case height, has been taken and the average of it at different ages plotted against the ages. The first curve, heights of boys, tells us what we would expect, that the older they are the taller they are. Examining it more closely we see that they do not grow at the same rate all the time.

This must be looked into. How much do they grow each year at different ages? What are the annual increases, or increments, in height? When this has been found we draw the second graph to show how fast they grow; it is a velocity graph showing rate of growth.

The boys' graph shows strange variations. Boys continue to grow all the time, but the rate is remarkably irregular. It displays a very marked minimum at about the eleventh year. Then in the early 'teens they begin to shoot up till about the end of the fifteenth year. This is the time when you can almost watch a boy's coat-sleeves shrinking up his arms with more and more bony wrist at the end, while the trousers retreat up his legs!

If the graph were continued it would be seen that growth becomes slower and slower till in manhood it ceases altogether (see below). In later middle life it goes into reverse and our stature decreases. The illustration below sets this out in a diagrammatic fashion. It is careful to keep true to the facts in general, but makes no pretence to exactitude in detail; it has been slightly exaggerated for the sake of clarity. Notice, though, that the first years of infancy are the time of speediest growth.

Turn back to the illustration on page 285 again. It also shows the rate of growth of girls. The same general characteristics are before us again, but with differences. Until about their fourteenth year it appears that girls are always growing faster than boys—we all know what long-leggety little angels schoolgirls are! Their period of fastest growth comes earlier, in about the thirteenth year. In fact, the whole picture suggests what is common knowledge, that girls are older for their years than are boys.

We will venture one step further. The difference in height between one year and the next is measured by the *slope* of the curve between those two points. It is the slope that tells us how things are changing. If the two points are on the same level there is no change; this first difference, as it is called, is 0. If the line curves slightly, the slope is gentle, and the first difference is small. A big difference means a steep slope and vice versa. The unchanging slope of a straight line means an unvarying rate of change and all the first

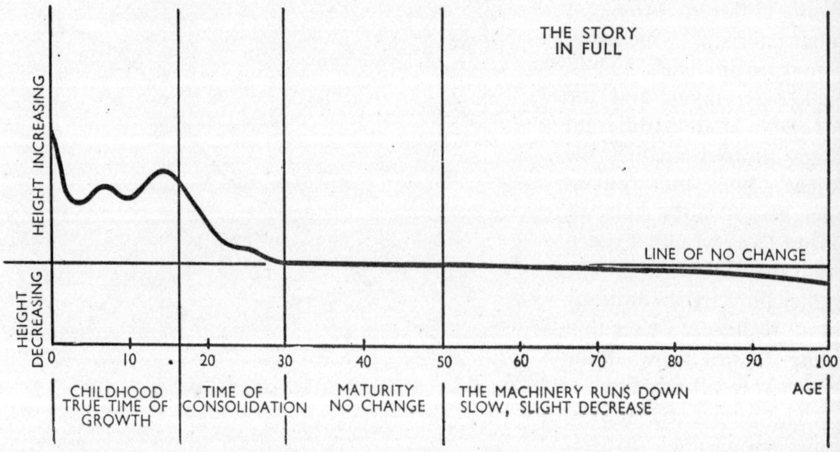

differences taken along it over equal intervals will be the same.

Let us imagine ourselves at the top of a cliff 400 ft. high with the choice of two ways of reaching the bottom. We can jump over and do it suicide-fashion like a falling stone. We shall fall faster and faster, and the crash will come five seconds after the leap. We can take the lift, travel at a steady speed, and reach the foot, say, five minutes after. These two courses are shown here, a broken line for the leap, an unbroken one for the lift.

The first differences are plotted. The lift gives a straight level line, the speed does not vary. Here are the distances a stone falls in each succeeding second calculated from the familiar formula $s = 16t^2$ (s is distance travelled in t seconds):

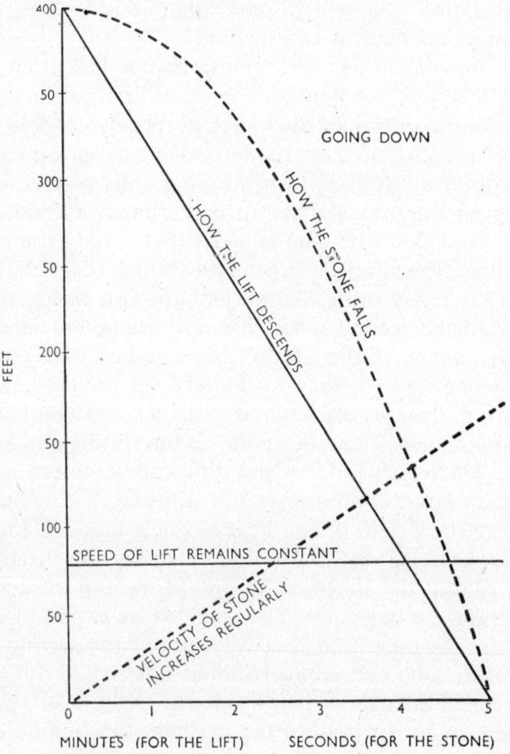

t (seconds)	0	1	2	3	4	5
s (feet)	0	16	64	144	256	400
Differences (feet)	16	48	80	112	144	

These figures do not seem very promising at first, but we will plot them. Since they really fall between the times, we will plot them half-way between the times. And the result is a straight line!

But a straight line means that something is changing at a steady, unchanging rate. Here it is the velocity of the falling stone that changes. The first graph shows that, this second one measures it. It tells us that the velocity is changing in a regular way. Its rate of fall, speed, velocity—what you will—changes, but not the rate of the change.

Which is just what a text-book of dynamics says. It is the pull of the earth that drags the stone down. This does not alter. It pulls all the time, and so has a cumulative effect, making the stone fall ever faster. It is g, the acceleration due to gravity, and its value is approximately 32 feet per second per second. (If you measure up the straight line, velocity-of-stone, graph and find its equation you will discover that it is $y = 32x$. This is the way a falling stone changes its rate of fall.)

A concluding word. This chapter has attempted to do two things. First it has tried to show the manifold applications of graphical methods. That is why the examples used have purposely covered a wide field, from aeroplanes to infants, and from road-accidents to spring-balances. If the subject interests you at all, follow it up. Make graphs of your own; almost anything can be given a graphical illustration. Perhaps you realize that now.

And don't be content with that. Study the graphs when you have drawn them. It is often surprising how much they tell you if you give them a chance. They repay study. Again, perhaps you realize that now!

In the second place, it is an attempt to introduce, as clearly and simply as can be, some of the mathematics that goes with them. Graphs may, at one stage, belong to the ABC of the subject. All our literature is derived from a twenty-six lettered alphabet, but you have to learn to write and spell. If you have found this part less interesting and heavier, don't worry too much.

Try to get hold of the difference between a purely statistical graph, like the output one on page 268 and one that has a mathematical law behind it, like the weight of ball-bearings on pages 266 and 267. But be prepared to find a mathematical law suddenly rearing its head where least expected. Look again at the stretched spring on the top of page 275, and at the population graph on page 269. You might have expected the first of these to provide a law of some kind, but what about the second?

Maxima and minima should not be too difficult to understand. Slope and rate of change may be harder to grasp. Well, even if you don't feel that you can quite get hold of the mathematics behind these ideas you can *see* them and use them. It is the commonsense ability to do this that will help you to find in these curves such serviceable and powerful tools.

And it is the beauty of the graph that it can often make these things so plain that he who runs may read. In fact, if you are ready to listen, they almost shout what they have to say at you.

Exercises

1. Plot the following, joining each point to the next as you proceed, and see what you obtain. (0, 11); (—7, 6); (—3, —2); (—3, —5); (2, —5); (2, —3); (5, —3); (5, —1); (3, —1); (5, 0); (5, 1); (7, 1); (5, 5); (6, 5); (6, 9); (0, 11).

Practise finding equations of the straight lines that you obtain. For example, if $y=mx+c$, the join of (0, 11) and (—7, 6) is

$$5x-7y=-77.$$

2. Tables of times for sunset at fortnightly intervals are given here. With time on the horizontal axis, plot and draw smooth curves. What are the earliest and latest times of sunset and when? Draw tangents at different dates and find rate at which time of sunset is changing, in minutes obtained per day, and compare the results. Time given is G.M.T.

Date Time	Dec. 1 3·54	Dec. 15 3·52	Dec. 29 3·59	Jan. 12 4·14
Date Time	June 1 8·7	June 15 8·18	June 29 8·21	July 13 8·13
Date Time	Jan. 26 4·37	Feb. 9 5·2	Feb. 23 5·28	
Date Time	July 27 7·56	Aug. 10 7·32	Aug. 24 7·5	

CHAPTER IX

ALGEBRAIC OPERATIONS

CHAPTER VI has explained how and why algebraic symbols give us a quick method of writing down a result, and the meaning of such an expression as $3x^2y$ should now be perfectly clear. If you are not quite certain about it, read Chapter VI again, because in this chapter we are going to discuss the various ways in which several such expressions can be combined and manipulated.

We need to carry out such operations for many purposes; for example, from an algebraic statement expressing some general law, we may want to find out the value of some particular quantity (solving an equation), or we may wish to alter the form of such a statement so that it brings out more clearly the manner in which one quantity depends on others (this is called changing the subject of a formula).

Rather more difficult to learn is the art of arguing in algebra; by that we mean the art of combining two or more statements expressing direct observations or already known facts, so as to obtain a new statement which we could not have got by direct observation.

Towards the end of this chapter you will find a few examples illustrating how algebra is used in practical applications. You may not be able to follow all these examples; if this is so, concentrate your attention on the examples that deal with subjects familiar to you. These examples are only included to show you that algebra is useful for practical and scientific purposes. Millions of other examples could be found.

You may like to glance at these examples first, and then come back to the earlier part of the chapter in which (so far as is possible in so small a space) the rules of manipulation with algebraic symbols are explained.

All such manipulations come down, in the last resort, to the use of one or more of the four main rules of arithmetic: addition, subtraction, multiplication, division. So we will begin with an explanation of how these are performed. In this work, as in all algebra, the secret of success is to think back all the time from the names of the symbols to their meaning.

So long as you think of x^2 as "x multiplied by x" you will not go far wrong. When you think of it as a combination of an x and a 2 you are well on the road to making just such a mistake as the schoolboy fallacy:

$$(1 + x)^2 = 1 + x^2$$

He usually says he has only taken the brackets away and what is wrong with that? Check what he is saying: "Add one to a number and multiply the result by itself: you get the same as if you multiplied the number by itself and added one afterwards." Is he right? Well, try it for yourself with some such number as 3 or 5.

In addition, in algebra even more than in arithmetic, it helps enormously to remember that the process of adding is merely a shortened form of counting. If we are taken to a farm and asked to find the total number of horse and carts, we know that we can either count the horses off, one by one, anc then do the same for the carts, or that we can add up the numbers of each a we come to them. If we see two carts each pulled by one horse, a ploug pulled by two horses, a cart with two horses, three carts in the cart shed anc two horses in the stables, we arrive at an answer: "Six carts, eight horses.' Notice that no sane person answers "Fourteen."

Exactly the same problem might appear in algebra as:

"Add together $2c+2h$; $2h$; $c+2h$; $3c$; $2h$." The answer is $6c+8h$. Similarly if we have to add $3x^2+7x+4$, $2x+x^2+5$ and $5+2x^2+x$ we have only tc recognize that x and x^2 are quite different quantities and that neither is of th same kind as a plain number, such as 4.

We total the three varieties of quantities separately and as a result obtair $6x^2+10x+14$.

Minus signs may be met with; they can be thought of as reversing th operation—turning addition into subtraction—or as indicating a measure ment, it may be a length, in the reverse direction. For example: 5—3 can b looked at as meaning:

5, take away 3

or as, five paces to the right; three paces to the left. Now where are you

It is very useful to be able to change quickly from one conception to th other. For instance, subtraction is best done by reversing the operation turning it into addition, and reversing all the signs of the second expression Each pair of similar terms can then be dealt with, by the other approach by thinking of the coefficients, with their signs, as indicating Left and Righ or Up and Down.

For instance: From $5a^3-4a^2b+7ab^2-b^3$
Take $3a^3+2a^2b-3ab^2-2b^3$

Instead of this question we work:

To $5a^3-4a^2b+7ab^2-b^3$
Add $-3a^3-2a^2b+3ab^2+2b^3$

We need then think only:

5 up and 3 down is 2 up.................................. $2a^3$
4 down and 2 down is 6 down.......................... $-6a^2b$
7 up and 3 up is 10 up................................ $+10ab^2$
1 down and 2 up is 1 up................................ $+b^3$

The answer is $2a^3-6a^2b+10ab^2+b^3$.

Notice again that we are only counting things called a^3 and things calle a^2b, etc.

Nothing we do in addition or subtraction can change an ab^2 into an a^2b or any other arrangement of these letters. Addition and subtraction are th operations of the warehouse, where parcels of goods come in and go ou and our job, as storeman, is to keep tally of what is in stock. Some exercise in this kind of storekeeping will be found at the end of the chapter.

In the warehouse the finished articles are only counted; they were made i the factory. The factory processes of algebra are multiplication and divisio Multiplication in algebra is very easy because we never actually do it!

a^2 means a multiplied by a. If it is required to multiply a^2 by b we write a^2b, but all this is saying is, "Take a, multiply by a, now multiply by b" and this is as far as anyone ever goes or can go. The command is sufficient and no executive action is required. When you come to think of it, this is just what we might have expected, because algebra is mainly advance planning of what we shall have to do with certain numbers when we know what they are.

Multiplication by a single term, then, is, so far as the letters are concerned, merely a process of writing the multiplying letters in as additional factors. For example:

$$p^2q^3 \times pqr = p^3q^4r.$$

When numerical coefficients are in front of our terms we have to do a little more. These numbers are not unknown—the multiplication can easily be performed and so we might as well do it.

We could say $3a^2 \times 2b = 3 \times 2a^2b$ but it is quite easy to say $6a^2b$, so we do. Again:

$$18lm^2 \times 15lmn^2 = 270l^2m^3n^2$$

Division is the reverse process; instead of putting factors in we take them out:

$$a^3 \div a = a^2$$

The division is actually carried out where the coefficients are concerned:

$$6x^3y \div 3xy = 2x^2$$

Sometimes we may find ourselves required to remove a factor that isn't there, so to speak, e.g., $a^2 \div x$. We do just the same as before. We issue the instruction and leave it at that:

$$\frac{a^2}{x}$$

This is what we do in some cases in arithmetic, e.g.:

$$2 \div 7 = \frac{2}{7}$$

So far we have considered only multiplication and division of single terms by single terms. Multiplication by two terms, for instance multiplication by $a+b$, is just what we might expect from arithmetic. Read aloud "Multiply by 370" and it tells you what to do—multiply by three hundred, now multiply by seventy and add the two results—so, in order to multiply by $a+b$ we first multiply by a, then by b and add the results.

The work can conveniently be set out like this:

$$(2a-3b)(a+b)$$

$$\begin{array}{lll}
2a-3b & & \\
a+b & & \\
\hline
2a^2-3ab & & \ldots\ldots\ldots(1) \\
\phantom{2a^2-{}}2ab-3b^2 & & \ldots\ldots\ldots(2) \\
\hline
2a^2-ab-3b^2 & & \\
\hline
\end{array}$$

Line (1) is $2a-3b$ multiplied by a

Line (2) is $2a-3b$ multiplied by b

Notice that line (2) is arranged so that each term (factory product) comes into its right compartment for the final counting up which gives the answer in the last line.

It is worth checking this result by using definite numbers for a and b. Suppose a is 7 and b is 2.

Then $2a-3b=14-6=8$

$a+b \quad = \quad 9$

The product should be 72.

$$\begin{aligned} 2a^2-ab-3b^2 &= 2\times7\times7-7\times2-3\times2\times2 \\ &= 98-14-12 \\ &= 98-26 \\ &= 72 \end{aligned}$$

Here is a longer example:

$$(3x^3-4x^2+5x+1)\times(2x+3)$$

$$\begin{array}{r} 3x^3-4x^2+5x+1 \\ 2x+3 \\ \hline 6x^4-8x^3+10x^2+2x \\ 9x^3-12x^2+15x+3 \\ \hline 6x^4+\ x^3-\ 2x^2+17x+3 \end{array}$$

Check with $x=1$: $5\times5=27-2=25$

Multiplication by a negative term is sometimes thought to be difficult, but it need not be so. Let us illustrate the possibilities by an easy example in buying or selling. Suppose we carry out four similar deals on the Stock Exchange, either buying or selling, and let us use signs to indicate which is which. We can take +3 to mean sell three shares and —3 to mean buy three shares. The shares may be either above or below par, their face value. Let us say +5 means £5 above par, —5 means £5 below par. If, as soon as the deal is completed, the shares are redeemed by the company at their face value, we shall experience either a profit or a loss. We will call profits + and losses —.

Case 1. $+3\times+5$.

Sell three shares at £5 above par; we have secured £15 more than if we had waited.

$$+3\times+5=+15.$$

Case 2. $+3\times-5$

Sell three shares at £5 below par; we have lost £15 by selling

$$+3\times-5=-15.$$

Case 3. $-3\times+5$

Buy three shares at £5 above par; we have *lost* £15

$$-3\times+5=-15.$$

Case 4. -3×-5

Buy three shares at £5 below par; we get our shares cheap and we *gain* £15

$$-3\times-5=+15.$$

This is the case that the schoolboy sums up as

"Two minuses make a plus".

This rule is safe enough, like all practical working rules, only so long as we remember what it is for. It is a rule for multiplication and has nothing to do with addition.

One further example:

$$(x-2)(x-1)$$

$$\begin{array}{l} x-2 \\ \underline{x-1} \\ x^2-2x \\ \underline{\quad -x+2} \\ x^2-3x+2 \end{array}$$

Put $x=6$; $(x-2)(x-1)=4\times5=20$

$x^2-3x+2=36-18+2 \qquad =20.$

There are two special cases of multiplication where it is worth while memorizing the results, because of the frequency with which we come across them.

First: an expression multiplied by itself; this is called a perfect square. We usually take $(a+b)^2$. The working is as follows:

$$\begin{array}{l} a+b \\ \underline{a+b} \\ a^2+ab \\ \underline{\quad ab+b^2} \\ a^2+2ab+b^2 \end{array}$$

That is, the first quantity squared, then twice the product of the two quantities, finally the second one squared.

$(a-b)^2$ follows the same rule:

$$\begin{array}{l} a-b \\ \underline{a-b} \\ a^2-ab \\ \underline{\quad -ab+b^2} \\ a^2-2ab+b^2 \end{array}$$

Notice that the minus sign in front of b appears in the ab term but not in the b^2 term. This has plus in accordance with our rule about minus times minus.

We had better test these results to satisfy ourselves of their truth.

$(4+7)^2$ appears to be $4^2+2\times4\times7+7^2$

$= 16+56+49$

$= 121$

But $4+7$ is 11 and 11×11 is 121, so this is a check.

Again $(9-3)^2$ should be $9^2-2\times9\times3+3^2$

$= 81-54+9$

$= 36$

But $9-3=6$ and $6\times6=36$.

There are some numbers whose squares can be worked out very easily indeed by the use of these formulae.

For instance: $(401)^2 = 400^2 + 2 \times 400 \times 1 + 1^2$

$$= 160{,}801$$

and $(3{\cdot}995)^2 = (4 - {\cdot}005)^2 = 4^2 - 2 \times 4 \times \frac{5}{1000} + \left(\frac{5}{1000}\right)^2$

$$= 16 - {\cdot}04 + {\cdot}000025$$

$$= 15{\cdot}960025$$

We shall find another use for these formulae when we come to consider quadratic equations.

Second: two expressions, each of two terms, exactly alike so far as their letters and coefficients are concerned, but having one a plus and the other a minus sign.

$$(a+b) \times (a-b)$$

$$\begin{array}{ll} a+b & \\ a-b & \\ a^2+ab & \\ \quad\; -ab & -b^2 \\ \hline a^2 & -b^2 \end{array}$$

A slightly more complicated example, done in reverse, is: arrange $4x^2-9y^2$ as a product; it will be $(2x+3y)(2x-3y)$.

Verify this, first by multiplying the brackets out, using the letters, and then by putting $x=4$, $y=5$ (or any other numbers you fancy) and making sure that:

$$(2x+3y)(2x-3y) \text{ is the same as } 4x^2-9y^2$$

This device (an example of factorizing) can be put to good use in some kinds of arithmetic. Suppose, for instance, that we require the area of cross-section of an iron pipe 15 in. outside diameter and 13 in. inside diameter.

The formula is $\frac{\pi}{4}\ (D^2-d^2)$

$$\text{i.e. } \frac{\pi}{4}(15^2-13^2) = \frac{\pi}{4}(15+13)(15-13)$$

$$= \frac{\pi}{4}\ 28\ .\ 2 = \frac{22}{7}\ .\ \frac{28}{4}\ .\ 2 = 44 \text{ sq. in.}$$

Division by a compound expression is not often required but at least it gives good practice in multiplication and subtraction.

We follow exactly the method of long division in arithmetic. Divide $4x^3-7x^2+5x-14$ by $x-2$. Since x into $4x^3$ goes $4x^2$ times, multiply $x-2$ by $4x^2$ and subtract

$$\begin{array}{l} x-2)4x^3-7x^2+5x-14(4x^2 \\ \qquad\;\; \underline{4x^3-8x^2} \\ \qquad\qquad\quad\;\; x^2 \end{array}$$

Next we bring down the $5x$ and since x into x^2 goes x times, we multiply $x-2$ by x and subtract.

$$
\begin{array}{l}
x-2)4x^3-7x^2+5x-14(4x^2+x \\
\quad\ \ \underline{4x-8x^2} \\
\qquad\qquad x^2+5x \\
\qquad\qquad \underline{x^2-2x} \\
\qquad\qquad\qquad 7x
\end{array}
$$

Finally, bring down the —14 and $x-2$ goes another 7 times. The whole thing looks like this:

$$
\begin{array}{l}
x-2)4x^3-7x^2+5x-14(4x^2+x+7 \\
\quad\ \ \underline{4x^3-8x^2} \\
\qquad\qquad x^2+5x \\
\qquad\qquad \underline{x^2-2x} \\
\qquad\qquad\qquad 7x-14 \\
\qquad\qquad\qquad \underline{7x-14} \\
\qquad\qquad\qquad\ \ \cdot\quad\ \cdot \\
\qquad\qquad\qquad \underline{\qquad\quad}
\end{array}
$$

EQUATIONS

Now that we have found out how to perform the four basic operations—the four rules of arithmetic—we can begin to use algebra to answer questions. We will begin with the solution of simple equations.

What we do is settled by plain common sense; how we do it we have seen already.

Common sense will tell us that if two quantities are equal and we add the same number to each, the results will be equal.

Now an equation is just that. It is a statement that two quantities are equal.

For instance:

$$2x-4=5-x$$

is read "twice x with four taken away *is equal to* five with x taken away".

To each of these equal quantities add 4.

$$2x-4=5-x$$

becomes $\quad 2x=9-x$

Now add x to each side and we have:

$$3x=9$$

and, dividing by 3, $\quad x=3$

Similarly we may subtract equals from each side, thus:

$$3x+7=x+9$$

becomes $\quad 2x=2 \quad$ ($x+7$ has been subtracted from each side)

from which $\quad x=1$

Multiplication of each side will be required if there are any fractions involved.

For instance, to solve:

$$\frac{1}{3}(x-5)+\frac{1}{4}(2x+1)=5$$

Multiply each side by 12.

$$4(x-5)+3(2x+1)=60$$

$$4x-20+6x+3=60$$

$$10x=77$$

$$x=7\tfrac{7}{10} \text{ or } 7{\cdot}7$$

Very often our equation will be found to have the unknown quantity in the denominator of a fraction. The idea is the same; the only difference is that our multiplication is algebraic instead of plain arithmetic.

$$\frac{2}{5}=\frac{3}{x}$$

Multiplying both sides by 5:

$$2=\frac{15}{x}$$

Multiplying both sides by x:

$$2x=15$$

from which $x=7{\cdot}5$

A more complicated example is:

$$\frac{x-1}{x+1}=\frac{x+3}{x+7}$$

Multiplying both sides by each denominator in turn we get:

$$(x-1)(x+7)=(x+1)(x+3)$$

$$\therefore \quad x^2+6x-7=x^2+4x+3$$

$$\therefore \quad x^2-x^2+6x-4x=3+7$$

$$2x=10$$

$$x=5$$

We will check this equation, just to make sure:

$$\text{Left-hand side} = \frac{5-1}{5+1}=\frac{4}{6}=\frac{2}{3}$$

$$\text{Right-hand side} = \frac{5+3}{5+7}=\frac{8}{12}=\frac{2}{3}$$

Thus the value $x=5$ does make the two sides of the equation equal and the statement is a true one.

We must not allow ourselves to become confused by large, or approximate, numbers occurring in a problem where the algebra is really simple.

Consider the following problem:

A certain sum of money was invested at 3% compound interest, and at the same time twice as much was invested at 5% simple interest. Ten years later the total value of the two investments was £3,000. Find how much was invested at 3%.

Let this amount be £x.

From a table of compound interest we find that £1 at 3% will be worth £1·34392 after 10 years.

$\therefore$ £x will have become £1·34392x. Evidently £2x was invested at 5% simple interest and by common sense it will be worth

$$£(2x+2x\times\frac{5}{100}\times 10)=2x+x$$

$$=£3x.$$

we now have: $1{\cdot}34392x+3x=3{,}000$

$$\therefore \quad 4{\cdot}34392x=3{,}000$$

$$x=\frac{3{,}000}{4{\cdot}34392}$$

The division is rather tiresome, and a slide rule is of no assistance if we want anything like an accurate result (it practically never is) but the answer will be found to be 690·620 correct to three decimal places, i.e., $x=£690$ 12s. 5d. to the nearest penny.

Very often a problem will contain more than one quantity that we have to determine. In such a case we must have more than one equation because we can find endless solutions to a single equation such as $2x+3y=10$

for instance: $x=2 \quad y=2$
$x=\frac{1}{2} \quad y=3$
$x=4 \quad y=\frac{2}{3}$
$x=-1 \quad y=4$
and so on.

In fact, there is a value of y for every imaginable value of x, and vice versa.

Suppose, though, we are also told that:

$$4x-7y=7.$$

This also has an infinite number of solutions, but there will be only one pair of values, one for x and one for y, that will satisfy both equations simultaneously. We proceed as follows:

$$2x+3y=10 \quad \ldots\ldots\ldots(1)$$
$$4x-7y=7 \quad \ldots\ldots\ldots(2)$$

Multiply line (1) by 2

$$4x+6y=20$$

Subtract line (2) $\quad 4x-7y=7$

$$13y=13$$
$$\therefore \quad y=1$$

The principle here has been to get the same coefficient for x in each equation. This can always be done by suitable multiplications. We will return to this point presently; meanwhile we have to find the value of x. The simplest way is to substitute $y=1$ into either equation (1) or (2), it does not matter which; suppose we choose (1):

$$2x+3\times1=10$$
$$\therefore \quad 2x=10-3=7$$
$$\therefore \quad x=3\tfrac{1}{2}.$$

Now let us take another example:

$$5x-7y=17 \quad \ldots\ldots\ldots(1)$$
$$3x+5y=1 \quad \ldots\ldots\ldots(2)$$

Suppose that this time we decide to find x first. This means that we must get rid of y. In line (1) it occurs as $7y$, in line (2) as $5y$. If we take the coefficients of these terms in reverse order, 5 and 7, and multiply line (1) by 5 and line (2) by 7, the y term in each equation will come to $35y$ and we shall have a chance to eliminate y.

Multiply (1) by 5 $\quad 25x-35y=85$
" (2) " 7 $\quad 21x+35y=7$
Adding $\quad 46x \quad =92$
$\therefore \quad x \quad =2$

Substitute $x=2$ in (2)

$$6+5y=\ \ 1$$
$$\therefore\ 5y=-5$$
$$y=-1$$

Ans. $x=2\quad y=-1.$

We added here instead of subtracting as we did before, so that the $-35y$ and the $+35y$ should cancel each other.

Now let us see how, by relying on our ability to solve a pair of simultaneous equations, we can solve a problem in mechanics.

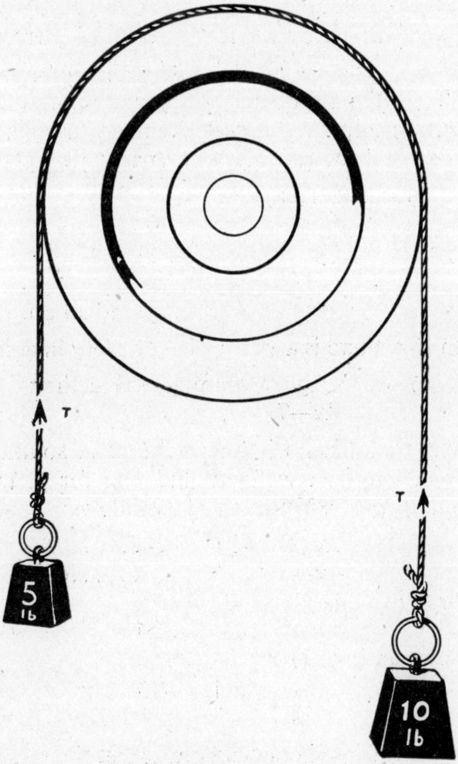

A flexible string carrying a mass of 10 lb. at one end and 5 lb. at the other hangs over a smooth, weightless pulley. Find the tension of the string and the acceleration with which the bodies move.

Clearly the tensions in the two parts of the string will be the same, since it cannot pull harder at one end than at the other. Call the tension T lb.wt.

Assuming that the string does not stretch, the acceleration of the 10-lb. mass downwards is equal to the acceleration of the 5-lb. mass upward. Call this acceleration f ft./sec.^{2}.

The law connecting force with acceleration may be stated: $\frac{\text{Force}}{\text{Mass}}=\frac{f}{g}$ where g is the gravitation constant, approximately 32.

For the 10-lb. mass we have: $\frac{10-T}{10}=\frac{f}{32}$

For the 5-lb. mass, $\frac{T-5}{5}=\frac{f}{32}$

When simplified, these become:

$$32T+10f=320$$
$$32T-\ 5f=160$$

Subtracting: $15f=160$

$$f=\tfrac{32}{3}\ \text{(i.e. the acceleration is } \tfrac{32}{3}\ \text{ft./sec.}^2)$$

whence $32T=320-10\times\frac{32}{3}$

$$T=10-\frac{10}{3}=10-3\tfrac{1}{3}=6\tfrac{2}{3}$$

$\therefore$ The tension is $6\frac{2}{3}$ lb.wt.

Perhaps it would be as well to summarize the steps to be taken in the solution of simultaneous equations:

(1) Simplify the equations as much as possible.

(2) Select multipliers which will give either x or y the same coefficients in the two equations.

(3) Add, or subtract, the transformed equations so as to eliminate one of the letters.

(4) When the value of one letter has been found, substitute this value in any one of the equations to find the value of the other letter.

We will follow these steps through in one more example:

$$\frac{x+4}{3}+\frac{y+5}{4}=\frac{x+2y}{2}$$

$$\frac{x+6}{2}-\frac{y-1}{3}=\frac{9x+4y}{9}$$

To remove fractions multiply the first equation by 12.

$$4(x+4)+3(y+5)=6(x+2y)$$
$$4x+16+3y+15=6x+12y$$
$$2x+9y=31 \quad \ldots\ldots\ldots(1)$$

Multiply the second equation by 18:

$$9(x+6)-6(y-1)=2(9x+4y)$$
$$9x+54-6y+6=18x+8y$$
$$9x+14y=60 \quad \ldots\ldots\ldots(2)$$

Multiply (1) by 9 and (2) by 2:

$$18x+81y=279$$
$$18x+28y=120$$

Subtract $\qquad 53y=159$

$$y=3$$

Substitute in (1):

$$2x+27=31$$
$$2x=4$$
$$x=2.$$

If it is desired to check these answers, always substitute into one of the original equations—otherwise a mistake in step (1) will not be detected.

$$\text{e.g.}\quad \frac{2+4}{3}+\frac{3+5}{4}=\frac{6}{3}+\frac{8}{4}=2+2=4$$

$$\text{and}\quad \frac{2+2\times 3}{2}=\frac{8}{2}=4.$$

EQUATIONS INVOLVING X^2

When we meet an equation such as $x^2-5x+6=0$ we may be able to guess, straight away, that the possible answers are $x=2$ and $x=3$. Substitution will show that our guesses are correct, and so it may be felt that all is well. The thoughtful man, however, will probably not be satisfied by this: he will have an uneasy feeling that next time his guess may not be so lucky, and in point of fact, guesswork will not get us very far with: $x^2-5x+5=0$.

Are there any rules for dealing with such equations? Yes, there is a fairly simple method of solving any quadratic equation (as these are called), though we admit that a lucky guess can be quickest of all.

The method consists of arranging the x terms so that they form part of a perfect square.

Remember that the examples of perfect squares are:

$$(a+b)^2=a^2+2ab+b^2$$
$$(a-b)^2=a^2-2ab+b^2$$

Although we know the answers, let us see how to solve:

$$x^2-5x+6=0.$$

We begin by moving 6, the term that does not contain x, over to the right-hand side.

$$x^2-5x=-6.$$

Now compare the left-hand side with the perfect square models. Because of the minus sign it seems to be closer to the second one:

$$a^2-2ab+b^2$$

Clearly, x has taken the place of a; we still have to find b, which we can do from the fact that $5x$ has taken the place of $2ab$. As x has taken the place of a, we see, therefore, that 5 has replaced $2b$:

i.e. $$2b=5$$
$$b=\frac{5}{2}$$

The last term, b^2, should be: $\left(\frac{5}{2}\right)^2=\frac{25}{4}$

At the moment we have no last term, but we can introduce one by adding $\frac{25}{4}$ *to both sides.*

We now have:

$$x^2-5x+\frac{25}{4}=\frac{25}{4}-6$$
$$=6\frac{1}{4}-6$$
$$=\frac{1}{4}.$$

But $x^2-5x+\frac{25}{4}$ is $\left(x-\frac{5}{2}\right)^2$

So we have $\left(x-\frac{5}{2}\right)^2=\frac{1}{4}$

That is, *a certain number* squared is $\frac{1}{4}$. But $\frac{1}{2}\times\frac{1}{2}=\frac{1}{4}$. If you have any doubts about this, remember that to go half way down a road which is half a mile long, you have to go one quarter of a mile; or half a halfpenny bun is worth $\frac{1}{4}$d.

We must also remember signs; $(-\frac{1}{2})\times(-\frac{1}{2})=\frac{1}{4}$

The possibilities, are then:

$$x-\frac{5}{2}=\frac{1}{2} \quad \text{or} \quad x-\frac{5}{2}=-\frac{1}{2}$$

In the first case $x=\frac{5}{2}+\frac{1}{2}$

$$\therefore \quad x=3$$

In the second case $x=\frac{5}{2}-\frac{1}{2}$

$\therefore \quad x=2$

To solve $x^2-5x+5=0$ we can use nearly all this working until we get to:

$$x^2-5x+\frac{25}{4}=\frac{25}{4}-5$$
$$=6\frac{1}{4}-5$$
$$=1\frac{1}{4}$$
$$\therefore \quad \left(x-\frac{5}{2}\right)^2=\frac{5}{4}$$
$$x-\frac{5}{2}=\pm\frac{\sqrt{5}}{2}$$
$$=\pm\frac{2{\cdot}236}{2} \qquad \text{(from square root tables)}$$
$$=\pm 1{\cdot}118$$
$$\therefore \quad x=2{\cdot}5\pm 1{\cdot}118=3{\cdot}618 \text{ or } 1{\cdot}382.$$

If x^2 has a coefficient, it is best to divide all through by this number, even if it brings in fractions.

For instance: $3x^2+14x-5=0$

$$x^2+\frac{14}{3}x-\frac{5}{3}=0$$
$$x^2+\frac{14}{3}x=\frac{5}{3}$$
$$\left[\text{Think: } \left(x+\frac{7}{3}\right)^2=x^2+\frac{14}{3}x+\frac{49}{9}\right]$$
$$x^2+\frac{14}{3}x+\frac{49}{9}=\frac{49}{9}+\frac{5}{3}$$
$$\therefore \quad \left(x+\frac{7}{3}\right)^2=\frac{49}{9}+\frac{5}{3}$$
$$=\frac{49+15}{9}$$
$$=\frac{64}{9}$$
$$\therefore \quad x+\frac{7}{3}=\pm\frac{8}{3}$$
$$x=-\frac{7}{3}+\frac{8}{3}=\frac{1}{3}$$
$$\text{or} \quad x=-\frac{7}{3}-\frac{8}{3}=-\frac{15}{3}=-5$$

MANIPULATION

Now let us consider some cases in which our results can be simplified by manipulations in algebra.

(*a*) From a straight portion of railway track a right-hand turn-out is being made with an average radius of R feet. The gauge is g feet. What is the dis-

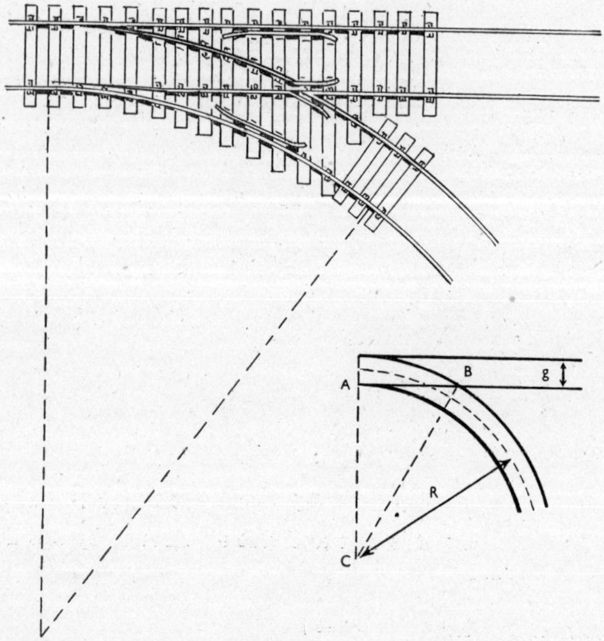

tance from the point to the spot where the left-hand curved rail crosses the right-hand straight rail?

In the diagram *AB* is the distance we wish to find; call it l feet.
AC is the mean radius minus half the gauge: $=R-\frac{1}{2}g$.
BC is the mean radius plus half the gauge: $=R+\frac{1}{2}g$.
By Pythagoras' Theorem:

$$l^2+(R-\tfrac{1}{2}g)^2=(R+\tfrac{1}{2}g)^2$$
$$\therefore\quad l^2=(R+\tfrac{1}{2}g)^2-(R-\tfrac{1}{2}g)^2$$

This will give an answer, but not in a very simple form.
Let us remember that:

$$a^2-b^2=(a+b)(a-b)$$

We use that formula here, and get:

$$l^2=(R+\tfrac{1}{2}g+R-\tfrac{1}{2}g)(R+\tfrac{1}{2}g-R+\tfrac{1}{2}g)$$
$$=2R.g$$

giving the simple result: $l=\sqrt{2Rg}$.

(*b*) In a hot-wire ammeter, a wire *AB*, originally straight, has its middle point linked to the pointer mechanism and is pulled by a light spring.

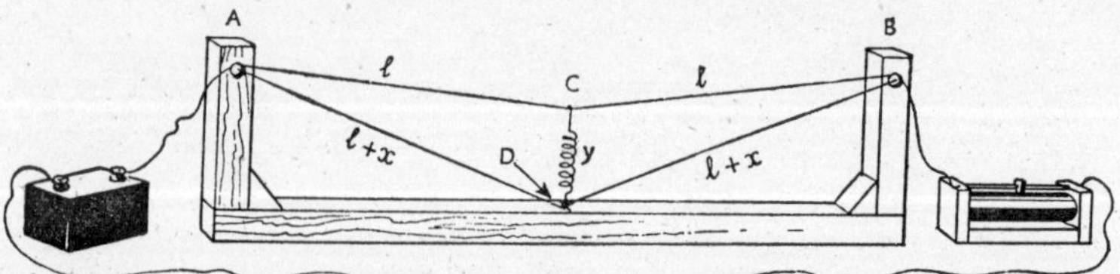

When a current, either D.C. or A.C., passes, the wire is heated and expands. The mid-point is now able to move from C to D, and the pointer rotates. It is required to find the distance CD.

Suppose it to be y. Let the length of the wire be $2l$ when cold and $2l+2x$ when hot, so that:

$$AC=l,\ CD=y,\ AD=l+x.$$

By Pythagoras' Theorem:

$$\begin{aligned}(l+x)^2&=l^2+y^2\\ \therefore\quad y^2&=(l+x)^2-l^2\\ &=(l+x+l)(l+x-l)\\ &=(2l+x)(x)\\ &=2lx+x^2\end{aligned}$$

In practice, x is very small, and so x^2 can be neglected and we have an approximate answer:

$$y=\sqrt{2lx}$$

(*c*) The pressure p at which a cylindrical pipe will burst is given by the formula:

$$p=\frac{d'^2-d^2}{d'^2+d^2}f$$

where d' is the outer diameter, d is the inner diameter and f is the ultimate tensile strength of the material.

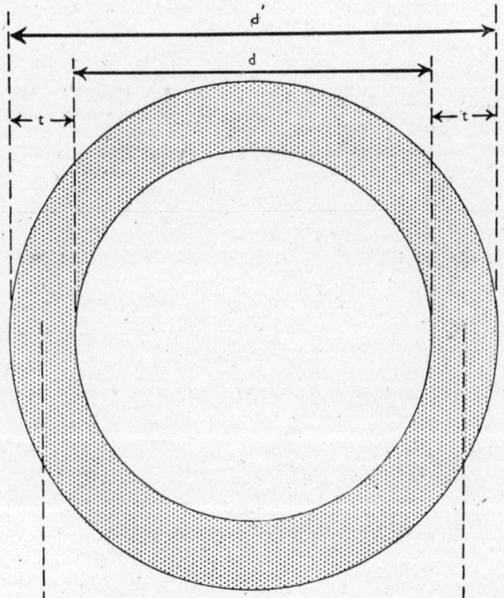

Let D be the mean diameter of the pipe and t the thickness of the walls: we have $d'=D+t$, $d=D-t$.

The formula becomes:

$$\begin{aligned}p&=\frac{(D+t)^2-(D-t)^2}{(D+t)^2+(D-t)^2}f\\ &=\frac{4Dt}{2D^2+2t^2}f\\ &=\frac{2Dt}{D^2+t^2}f\end{aligned}$$

If the walls of the pipe are thin, t will be small compared with D, and t^2 can be neglected in comparison with D^2, so that we have the simple form:

$$p=\frac{2Dt}{D^2}f$$

and finally: $$p=\frac{2t}{D}f$$

CHANGING THE SUBJECT OF A FORMULA

Very often it is necessary to change the subject of a formula; that is to twist a formula into a new shape so that it will give us information about one of the quantities that we were previously regarding as known to us. As a very simple example: Ohm's Law is usually quoted as:

$$I=\frac{E}{R}$$ giving current in terms of volt drop and resistance.

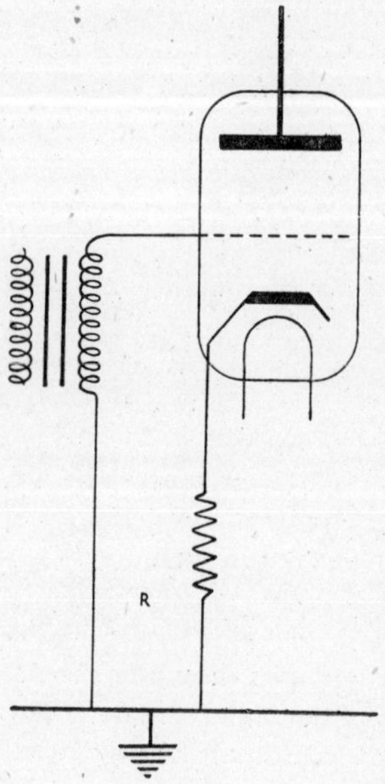

But suppose we wish to calculate the size of bias resistor required in a certain circuit such as that on the right. It would be more convenient to have a formula:

$$R=?$$

We can make the transformation easily by regarding:

$$I=\frac{E}{R}$$

as an equation in which R is our x and I and E are just numbers. Think back to:

$$2=\frac{3}{x}$$

We should multiply both sides by x.

$$2x=3$$

whence $$x=\frac{3}{2}$$

So here: $$I=\frac{E}{R}$$

gives $$IR=E$$

and $$R=\frac{E}{I}$$

Now if we require a bias of —4 volts, and the valve is passing 50 milli-amps, we have:

$$R=\frac{4}{50\div 1{,}000}=\frac{4{,}000}{50}=80 \text{ ohms.}$$

Or again, from the formula $s=ut+\frac{1}{2}ft^2$, which gives the distance covered in t sec. by an object starting with velocity u and moving with constant acceleration f, find a formula for acceleration in terms of initial velocity, distance covered and time taken.

f is here the unknown quantity; i.e., we have to find its value.

$$s=ut+\tfrac{1}{2}ft^2$$

$$\therefore \quad s-ut=\tfrac{1}{2}ft^2$$

$$\therefore \quad 2s-2ut=ft^2$$

$$\therefore \quad f=\frac{2s-2ut}{t^2}$$

Here is another example.

The voltage built up across a tuned circuit is given by:

$$V=\sqrt{\left\{RI\right\}^2+\left\{L\omega I-\frac{I}{C\omega}\right\}^2}$$

where R is resistance, L inductance, C capacity.

$\omega=2\pi f$, f=frequency, I=current.

What current will flow in the circuit if a voltage V is applied?

Squaring both sides:

$$V^2=\left\{RI\right\}^2+\left\{L\omega I-\frac{I}{C\omega}\right\}^2$$

taking out I^2

$$V^2=\left[R^2+\left\{L\omega-\frac{1}{C\omega}\right\}^2\right]I^2$$

$$I^2=\frac{V^2}{\left[R^2+\left\{L\omega-\frac{1}{C\omega}\right\}^2\right]}$$

$$I=\frac{V}{\sqrt{R^2+\left\{L\omega-\frac{1}{C\omega}\right\}^2}}$$

This process of changing a formula is essential when we wish to derive a new formula from two that we have already. For instance in dynamics we quickly establish:

$$v=u+ft \qquad \ldots\ldots\ldots(1)$$

and $$s=\tfrac{1}{2}(u+v)t \qquad \ldots\ldots\ldots(2)$$

for uniformly accelerated motion.

Substitute for v from (1) into (2)

$$s=\tfrac{1}{2}(u+u+ft)t$$

$$s=ut+\tfrac{1}{2}ft^2 \qquad \ldots\ldots\ldots(3)$$ a standard formula.

Again, to obtain a formula which does not involve t take (1) and change it to give t:

$$ft=v-u$$

$$t=\frac{v-u}{f}$$

Now substitute this in (2):

$$s=\tfrac{1}{2}(u+v)\frac{(v-u)}{f}$$

$$2fs=(v+u)(v-u)$$

$$=v^2-u^2$$

or, putting it in its more usual form:

$$v^2=u^2+2fs \qquad \ldots\ldots\ldots(4)$$

If we now bring in force by the formula expressing Newton's second law of motion:

$$P=mf \qquad \ldots\ldots\ldots(5)$$

we can obtain the usual equations concerning momentum and energy.

For the first, multiply (5) by t:

$$Pt=mft$$

but from (1) $ft=v-u$

Substituting this we have

$$Pt=mv-mu$$

(Impulse = change in momentum.)

For the second, multiply (5) by s

$$Ps=mfs$$

from (4) $2fs=v^2-u^2$

$$\therefore \quad Ps=\tfrac{1}{2}mv^2-\tfrac{1}{2}mu^2$$

(Work done = change in kinetic energy.)

In electricity we have two simple formulae:

$$I=\frac{E}{R} \qquad W\text{ (power)}=EI$$

We can combine these to get:

$$W=\frac{E^2}{R} \qquad \left(\text{by putting } I=\frac{E}{R}\right)$$

giving the power dissipated when a given resistance is placed across a source of potential, as in a voltmeter;

or $W=I^2R$ (by putting $E=IR$)

giving the power absorbed when a given resistance is made to convey a given current, as in an ammeter shunt.

In optics, the standard formulae are:

$$\frac{1}{f}=\frac{1}{v}+\frac{1}{u}$$

connecting focal length, f, of a lens with v, distance of the image from the lens, and u, distance of the object,

and:

$$m=\frac{v}{u}$$

giving the magnification; that is the ratio between the size of the image and the size of the object.

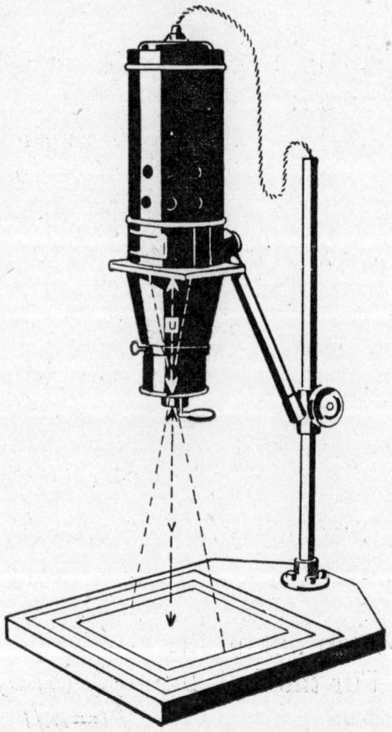

In designing an enlarger, we should be more concerned with the total distance of the enlarger body carrying the negative, which is the object, from the screen which receives the image. Call this distance d.

We now have:

$$\frac{1}{f}=\frac{1}{v}+\frac{1}{u} \qquad \ldots\ldots\ldots(1)$$

$$m=\frac{v}{u} \qquad \ldots\ldots\ldots(2)$$

$$d=v+u \qquad \ldots\ldots\ldots(3)$$

To get rid of v and u proceed thus:

Multiply (1) by v

$$\frac{v}{f}=1+\frac{v}{u}$$

$$\therefore \quad \frac{v}{f}=1+m \qquad \text{using (2)}$$

$$v=f+fm$$

From (2) $\quad u=\frac{v}{m}=\frac{f}{m}+f$

From (3) $\quad d=\left(f+fm\right)+\left(\frac{f}{m}+f\right)$

$$\therefore \quad d=f\left(m+\frac{1}{m}+2\right)$$

$$=\frac{f}{m}(m^2+1+2m)$$

$$d=\frac{f}{m}(m+1)^2$$

If, therefore, we wish our enlarger to range from the same size, $m=1$ to $m=3$ ($2\frac{1}{4}'' \times 3\frac{1}{4}''$ into whole plate) using a lens of 3 in. focal length, we can see that the height of the negative carrier must be adjustable between:

$$\frac{3}{1}(1+1)^2=12 \text{ in.}$$

and $\quad \frac{3}{3}(3+1)^2=16$ in.

Actually, this range would not be enough, and a worker with 35 mm. film would require a magnification of at least 8 diameters.

This would require $\quad d=\frac{3}{8}(8+1)^2=\frac{3\times 81}{8}$

$$=30\tfrac{3}{8} \text{ in.}$$

and he would probably decide to use a lens of shorter focal length.

Examples of manipulation of formulae could be multiplied almost indefinitely, but if the reader has understood that all such manipulations resolve themselves into applications of the four simple rules—addition, subtraction, multiplication, division—he should have no great difficulty in following the transformations he may meet in technical handbooks. If any such difficulty is met, it will probably be due to the fact that the author of the handbook has performed one or more steps in his head without setting them out in the text. In such a case let the reader seize pencil and paper and it will be surprising if he cannot fill in the gaps for himself.

Exercises

Add Together:

1. $3x+2y-z$; $4z-3y-x$; $5x+6y-2z$.
2. $11p-8q-5r$; $9q+10r-3p$; $6r-5q-2p$.
3. $3m^3+2m^2n-mn^2+n^3$; m^3-n^3; m^2n-mn^2.

Subtract:

4. $18pq+3qr$ from $26pq+10qr$.
5. $2a-3b+c$ from $3a-b-c$.
6. x^2-7x-5 from $2x^2+8x-3$.

Multiply:

7. $x+3$ by $x-2$.
8. $2a+3b$ by $3a+2b$.
9. x^2-x+1 by $x+1$.
10. $a^2+3ab-b^2$ by $a-2b$.

Divide:

11. x^2+3x-4 by $x-1$.
12. $2a^2-5ab+3b^2$ by $a-b$.
13. $3a^3+4a^2b+ab^2+10b^3$ by $a+2b$.

What is the square of:

14. $x+3y$.
15. $4p-7q$.
16. $x-\frac{1}{2}$.
17. $4m^2+3mn$.
18. 499.
19. 100·5.

Write in factor form:

20. x^2-y^2.
21. $4a^2-b^2$.
22. p^2-25q^2.
23. $(x+y)^2-(x-y)^2$.
24. 19^2-18^2.
25. $18{\cdot}6^2-17{\cdot}4^2$.

Solve the equations:

26. $3x-1=2x+1$.
27. $3(3x-1)-2(2x+1)=15$.
28. $\frac{x-1}{4}+\frac{2x+1}{3}=1$
29. $1{\cdot}2(x+1)-{\cdot}7(x-3)=4{\cdot}8$.
30. $\frac{x-2}{2x+1}=\frac{x+3}{2x-5}$
31. $\begin{cases} 3x-2y=8. \\ x+y=6. \end{cases}$
32. $\begin{cases} 7x+3y=4. \\ 2x-\ y=3. \end{cases}$
33. $\begin{cases} \frac{2x-1}{9}+\frac{2y+1}{4}=\frac{x+y}{3} \\ \frac{2x+1}{5}-\frac{4y-1}{2}=\frac{x-2y}{2} \end{cases}$
34. $x^2-4x+3=0$.
35. $x^2-2x-3=0$.
36. $2x^2-x-2=0$.

37. Simplify the formula:
$$F=\frac{m}{(d-l)^2}-\frac{m}{(d+l)^2}$$
What does this become if l is very small?

38. As quoted in the text:
$$I=\frac{V}{\sqrt{R^2+\left\{L\omega-\frac{1}{C\omega}\right\}^2}}$$
What does this become at the resonant frequency, when
$$\omega=\frac{1}{\sqrt{LC}}\ ?$$

39. One formula for the inductance of a single layer solenoid is:
$$L=\frac{0{\cdot}2\,A^2N^2}{3A+9B}$$
Turn this into a formula for N. (N=number of turns; A=diameter of coil in inches; B=length of winding in inches.)

40. The time of oscillation of a simple pendulum is given by $t=2\pi\sqrt{\frac{l}{g}}$ where l is the length. Express this as a formula for l in terms of t, g and π.

41. From the formulae:
$$F=\frac{2\,m\,k}{d^2+l^2}$$
$$k=\frac{l}{\sqrt{d^2+l^2}}$$
$$M=2ml$$
obtain a formula for F in terms of M, d, l only. What does this become if l is very small?

42. The horse-power developed by one double-acting cylinder is given by:
$$H=\frac{2PAnl}{550}$$
P=steam pressure, A=piston area, n=number of strokes per sec., l=length of stroke, H=horse-power.
The number of strokes per sec. is given by:
$$n=\frac{88V}{60\pi D}$$
where V=speed in m.p.h., D=diameter of driving wheels. Obtain a formula for V in terms of horse-power developed and the engine dimensions (two cylinders).

CHAPTER X

LABOUR-SAVING OPERATIONS

YOU may have wondered why this chapter has been given such a late place in the book, especially as frequent references have been made to the devices which will now be given special consideration. It is disturbing to notice that there is an extravagant waste of time in places of learning due to an insistence on hard work for its own sake. Boys and girls are still expected to spend hours and hours of their lives carrying out laborious calculations for results that no one is really interested in, and which, in any case, could be found in a moment or two if reference were made to the appropriate tables or charts.

Square roots for example; why should everybody be condemned to learn how to work out the square root of 103·87 when it can be found in a table without any trouble save a correct use of the eye and where there is no risk of a slip in the working? Again, why should one be tortured with long compound interest calculations with a hundred good chances of making a mistake, when the answer has already been worked out for every one who is interested? Bankers and building societies do not expect their employees to work them out: they are more studious of economy and efficiency in their respective businesses, and so they provide the employees with reference tables containing all the answers.

Any device that reduces the possibility of personal error, saves time, and lightens the load on human memory, is not to be regarded with suspicion as an evasion of man's doom to toil and sweat for his bread, but as an all-round boon. The decision to put this matter near the end of the book, is, in itself, a labour-saving device. You ought to be able if necessary to make your own aids to speed and efficiency, and with the mathematical background you have now acquired, it will be possible for you to learn how to do so. The tables will be together for quick reference—and you will have used some of them many times.

Here is a list of devices that should be available to every student of mathematics. Some of them he may rarely wish to use, but they should be there if he wants them. The list is by no means exhaustive: there is scarcely a place of business in existence that does not include in its equipment tables, charts, and instruments peculiar to the kind of work that goes on there.

Tables of measure	Squares, square roots
Multiplication tables	Reciprocals
Adding machines (which also subtract)	Sines, cosines, tangents, and logs of each
Conversion tables; metric to English, etc.	Logarithms and anti-logarithms
Vulgar fraction to decimals	Slide-rules
Percentage tables	Graphs of various kinds
Ready reckoners of costing	Nomograms
Interest tables	

Some of these devices have already been dealt with in earlier parts of th
book, and some repetition may, therefore, occur.

CONVERSION OF VULGAR FRACTIONS TO DECIMALS

In the engineering trades most instruments for measuring use a decima
system of calibration. Vulgar fractions, however, are still used to represen
the dimensions in jobs under construction. It is common, therefore, fo

Fraction	Decimal	Fraction	Decima
$\frac{1}{64}$	·0156	$\frac{33}{64}$	·5156
$\frac{1}{32}$	·0313	$\frac{17}{32}$	·5313
$\frac{3}{64}$	·0469	$\frac{35}{64}$	·5469
$\frac{1}{16}$	·0625	$\frac{9}{16}$	·5625
$\frac{5}{64}$	·0781	$\frac{37}{64}$	·5781
$\frac{3}{32}$	·0938	$\frac{19}{32}$	·5938
$\frac{7}{64}$	·1094	$\frac{39}{64}$	·6094
$\frac{1}{8}$	·125	$\frac{5}{8}$	·625
$\frac{9}{64}$	·1406	$\frac{41}{64}$	·6406
$\frac{5}{32}$	·1563	$\frac{21}{32}$	·6563
$\frac{11}{64}$	·1719	$\frac{43}{64}$	·6719
$\frac{3}{16}$	·1875	$\frac{11}{16}$	·6875
$\frac{13}{64}$	·2031	$\frac{45}{64}$	·7031
$\frac{7}{32}$	·2188	$\frac{23}{32}$	·7188
$\frac{15}{64}$	·2344	$\frac{47}{64}$	·7344
$\frac{1}{4}$	·25	$\frac{3}{4}$	·75
$\frac{17}{64}$	·2656	$\frac{49}{64}$	·7656
$\frac{9}{32}$	·2813	$\frac{25}{32}$	·7813
$\frac{19}{64}$	·2969	$\frac{51}{64}$	·7969
$\frac{5}{16}$	·3125	$\frac{13}{16}$	·8125
$\frac{21}{64}$	·3281	$\frac{53}{64}$	·8281
$\frac{11}{32}$	·3438	$\frac{27}{32}$	·8438
$\frac{23}{64}$	·3594	$\frac{55}{64}$	·8594
$\frac{3}{8}$	·375	$\frac{7}{8}$	·875
$\frac{25}{64}$	·3906	$\frac{57}{64}$	·8906
$\frac{13}{32}$	·4063	$\frac{29}{32}$	·9063
$\frac{27}{64}$	·4219	$\frac{59}{64}$	·9219
$\frac{7}{16}$	·4375	$\frac{15}{16}$	·9375
$\frac{29}{64}$	·4531	$\frac{61}{64}$	·9531
$\frac{15}{32}$	·4688	$\frac{31}{32}$	·9688
$\frac{31}{64}$	·4844	$\frac{63}{64}$	·9844
$\frac{1}{2}$	·5	1.	1.

micrometers to carry an engraved list of equivalents between fraction and decimal that is handy (literally) for reference whenever the instrument is in use.

If you are making frequent conversions from halves, quarters, eighths, sixteenths, thirty-seconds and sixty-fourths to decimals, you can easily prepare your own table like this:

	1	·015625	(D)	½ of (C)
	2	·03125	(C)	This is ½ of (B)
	3			
	4	·0625	(B)	Then this is ½ of (A), i.e., $\frac{\cdot 125}{2} = \cdot 0625$
Sixty-	5			
fourths	6			
	7			
	8	·125	(A)	Start here: $\frac{8}{64} = \frac{1}{8} = \cdot 125$ (by division)
	9			
	10			
	—			
	—			
	—			
	—			
	—			

You would proceed by addition of results, e.g. the first gap is filled by the sum of the top two readings, the next by the first and fourth readings.

This would yield a table containing sixty-four pairs. As we prefer to reduce fractions in our minds, a reference table would be happier if it spoke of 1/16 rather than 4/64 and ¾ rather than 48/64. For this reason the figures in the left-hand column have been staggered. The final result is shown on page 310.

A more versatile table can be made like this:

		Numerator			
		1	2	3	
	2	·5			
	3	·3333	·6667		
	4	·25	·5	·75	
	5	·2	·4	·6	
	6	·1667	·3333	·5	
Denominator	7	·1429	·2857	·4286	
	8	·125	·25	·375	
	9	·1111	·2222		
	11	·0909	·1818		and so on
	12	·0833	·1667		
	13	·0769	·1538		

In this form, the table would be useful to people whose arithmetical jobs include dealing with unusual denominators like 7, 11, 13, and higher primes.

The whole thing can be made more compact if you know what denominators you are *not* likely to need—these can then be left out.

Tables of this kind can be constructed to give any degree of accuracy that you may choose: we have worked to four significant figures, but very little extra space would have been taken up by readings of seven figures.

You will not obtain a reliable table by multiplying the readings in the first column by the appropriate numerator to fix the column of readings for that numerator. For instance, 6/7 is not ·8574 (·1429 × 6) but ·8571 (by direct division).

The work put into the making of the table is certainly monotonous, but once carried out it need never be repeated.

CONVERSION OF MILLIMETRES TO INCHES

The basic relationship is 1 in. = 25·400 mm.
or 1 mm. = ·03937 in.

Before constructing any table which is to be really useful, one must decide the range over which the conversions should extend. For example, the engineer working in thou's (thousandths of an inch) might need a table converting millimetre readings between ·01 mm. and 1 mm. to inches. For another purpose, this range might be insufficient or of too low an order. Here is a sample:

		1	2	3	4	—	—
·0	0	·0004	·0008	·0012	·0016		
·1	·0039	·0043	·0047				
·2	·0079	·0083					
·3	·0118	·0122					
·4	·0157						
—				etc.			
—							
—							

PERCENTAGE TABLES

These are really a particular kind of multiplication table. Percentage of a pure number, for example, 68% of 12, is straightforward multiplication and does not call for special tables. On the other hand percentage of compound quantities (for example, tons, cwt., lb., oz.), is difficult of calculation, and special tables are invaluable: an entire ready-reckoner could well be devoted to this subject alone. We do not go further because we only desire to point the way, and many people should know this.

TABLES OF SQUARE ROOTS

These need not deal with the whole range of numbers because if the root of 49 is known to be 7, then the square root of ·49 will be ·7 because

$$\cdot 49 = \frac{49}{100}$$

$$\therefore \quad \sqrt{\cdot 49} = \sqrt{\frac{49}{100}} = \frac{7}{10}$$

Any number can be regarded as the product of a number between 1 and 100 and a power of 100:

e.g.

$$169 = 1{\cdot}69 \times 100$$

$$\cdot375 = \frac{37{\cdot}5}{100}$$

$$\cdot081 = \frac{8{\cdot}1}{100}$$

$$50{,}000 = 5 \times 100^2$$

It is accordingly sufficient to have tables giving the square roots of numbers from 1 to 100. Usually these are split up into two parts, one giving the roots of numbers from 1 to 10, the other dealing with numbers between 10 and 100.

It is important to be in the correct part. For instance, in a book of tables, $\sqrt{1{\cdot}236}$ is 1·112. On the next page of the tables we find $\sqrt{12{\cdot}36}$ is 3·515. 1·236 and 12·36 contain the same set of numbers, but their square roots, 1·112 and 3·515, are completely unlike each other. Accordingly if, when we are intending to look up $\sqrt{12{\cdot}36}$, we accidentally look at the wrong page and find $\sqrt{1{\cdot}236}$, a serious error will result.

The tables dealing with numbers between 1 and 10 have to cover all the numbers from 1·000 to 9·999, if we are working to four figures. There are 9,000 different numbers in this range. To show each result separately would require enormous space. In order to avoid this, the main part of the table deals only with the first three figures, and the last figure is found from a special set of columns at the side, known as difference columns. The procedure is best explained by an example.

Suppose we want to find the square root of 13·75. The first two numbers are found at the left-hand side of the top table shown on page 314.

These are shown by the arrow *A*. We look along the top of the main table for the third number, 7, marked by the arrow *B*. We select the number in

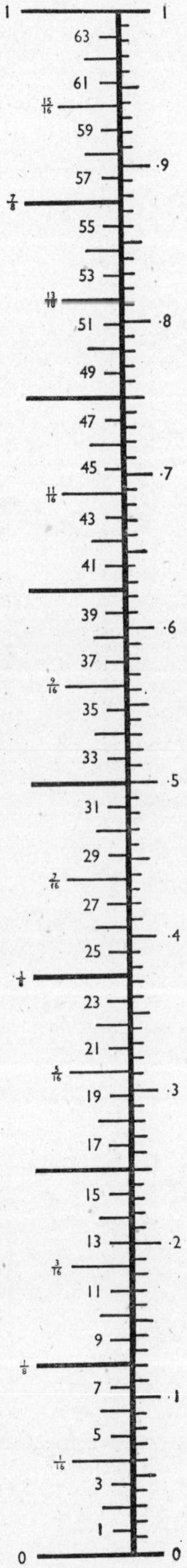

CONVERSION SCALE: 64THS TO DECIMALS.

A few minutes' work making a scale of this type saves a good deal of calculation.

Its advantage over the table is that it can be read in either direction.

Its disadvantage is that the accuracy obtained with it depends on the quality of its construction and the efficiency of the operator in reading it.

For this reason the engineer would prefer a conversion table.

A similar scale could be made for metric - English conversion.

the row, *A*, which is also in the column *B*. This number is 3·701. 3·701 is th square root of 13·7.

The fourth number, 5, is then found in the difference columns, as show by the arrow *C*. Underneath this 5, still in the row *A*, we find the singl number 7. This 7 has to be added on to the last number in 3·701 to give th square root required.

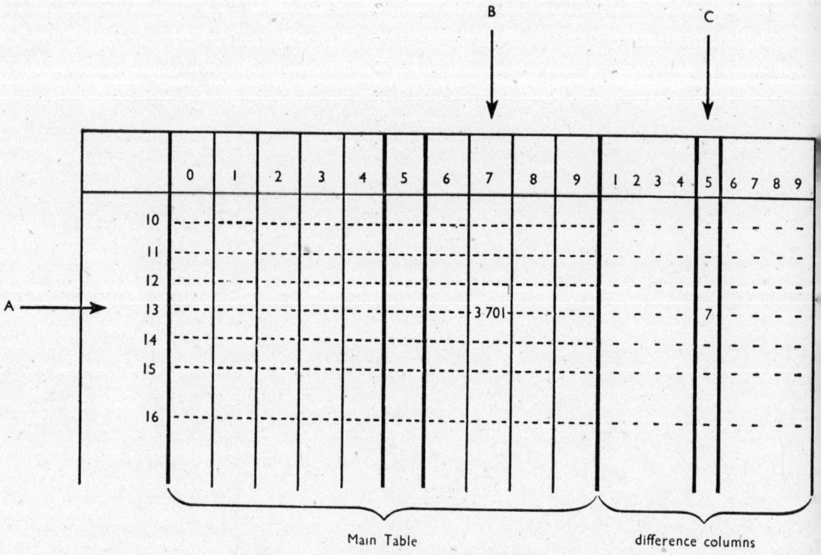

	3·701	the square root of 13·7.
	7	correction for the fourth figure 5.
Adding,	3·708	is the square root of 13·75.

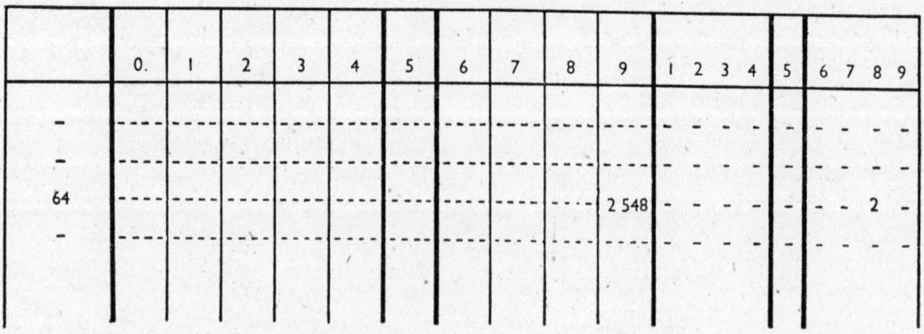

As another example, we may find $\sqrt{6{\cdot}498}$.

The square root of 6·49 is	2·548
Correction for last figure, 8	2
The square root of 6·498 is	2·550

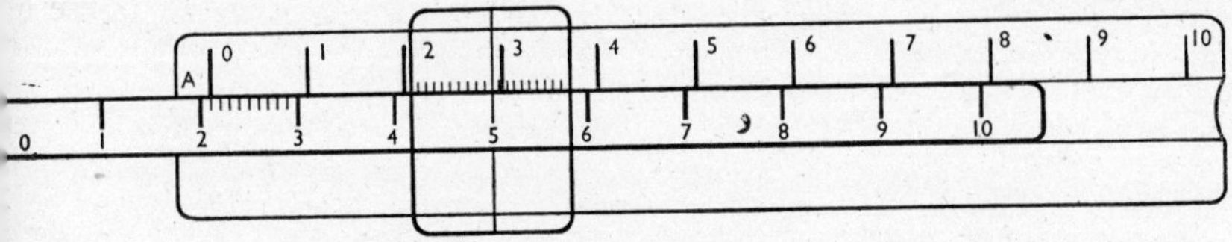

SLIDE-RULES

FOR ADDITION AND SUBTRACTION

A slide-rule is a pair of rules, each with its own scale, fitted together so that the scale of one slides along the scale of the other. The simplest form of slide-rule is for adding and subtracting as shown above.

Two ordinary rulers can be worked together for this purpose. The sketch shows how to add 2·1 to any other number. Scale *B* is moved until the zero on scale *A* is opposite 2·1. If we want to add 2·9 to 2·1 we find 2·9 on scale *A* and see what reading lies opposite on scale *B*. This is the answer: 5.

A cursor is useful: it is a thin straight line marked on a window that can travel along the scales. You set the cursor over 2·9 on scale *A* and then you need not remember 2·9 any longer—just think about reading scale *B* under the cursor line.

Subtraction is the same operation in reverse.

Example:

Subtract 5·7 from 7·5.
Set the cursor over 7·5 on scale *A*.
Move slide *B* until 5·7 is also under the cursor line.
Now we see what the zero of scale *B* indicates on scale *A*.
Note.—If you start with a number on scale *A* your answer will be on scale *A*, both for subtraction and addition.

FOR MULTIPLYING AND DIVIDING

Normally, when we speak of a slide-rule, we mean one for multiplying and dividing. Addition and subtraction are so simple that it does not pay to have a special instrument for these operations—except perhaps as an aid to school teaching.

The adding slide-rule is quite an obvious device. It is more surprising that multiplication can be done by means of a slide-rule. Yet it is possible. You can see the principle involved by making a simplified slide-rule, like this:

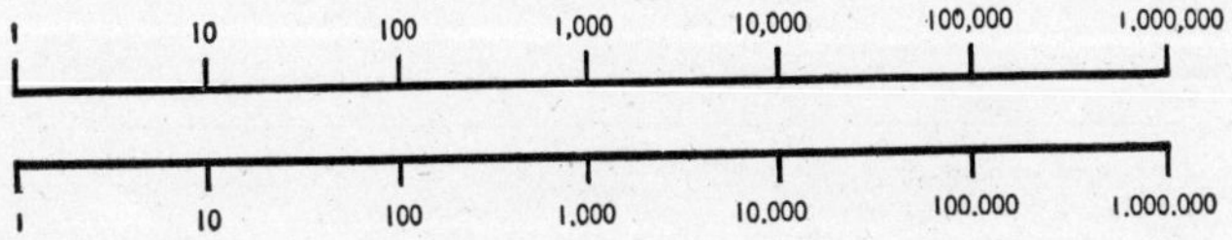

The marks on the two rulers are evenly spaced, as on an ordinary ruler.

But instead of writing 1, 2, 3, etc., against these marks, we write 1, 10, 100, etc.

Now push the bottom ruler along until the 1 on it is underneath 10 on the top ruler, thus:

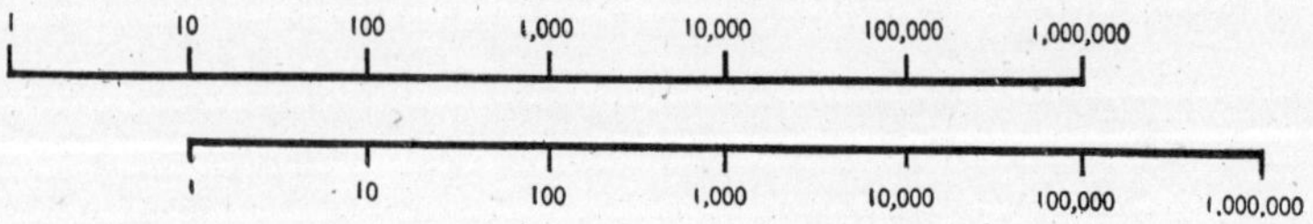

Above any number on the bottom ruler, we find a number ten times as large.

In the same way, if we set the slide-rule like this:

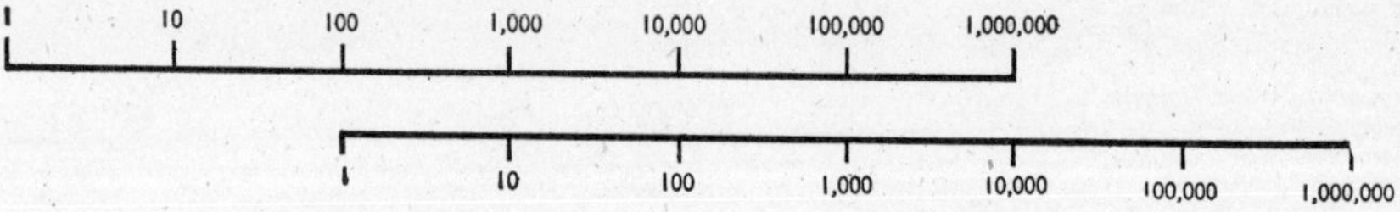

above each number on the lower scale we shall find that number multiplied by 100.

That is to say, in the first example, we have set the slide-rule for multiplication by 10: in the second example we have set it for multiplication by 100.

Needless to say, such a slide-rule is of no practical use as it stands. Before it can become of any use, we must find some way of putting in the numbers between 1 and 10, and between 10 and 100, and so on.

If it is possible to do this—and it should be possible, as there is no essential difference between multiplying by 10 and multiplying by 3, or by 4·7, or by 5·62—if it is possible to put these other numbers in, we shall have a very useful instrument, an instrument that will multiply any two numbers together almost in a flash. This, in fact, is what the slide-rule does.

Here is a slide-rule with the numbers from 1 to 100 marked in:

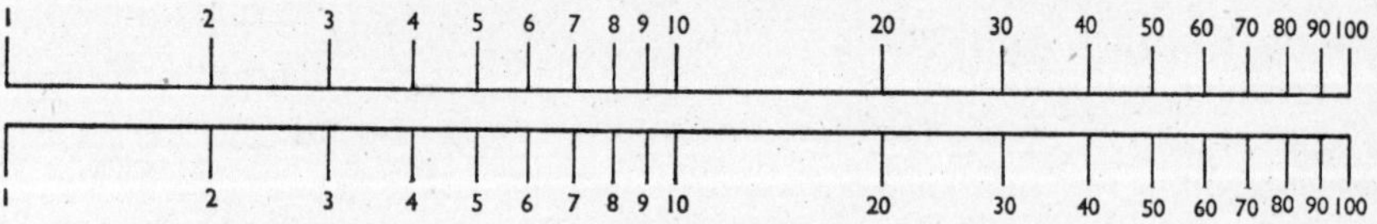

This is how it would be set to multiply by 6:

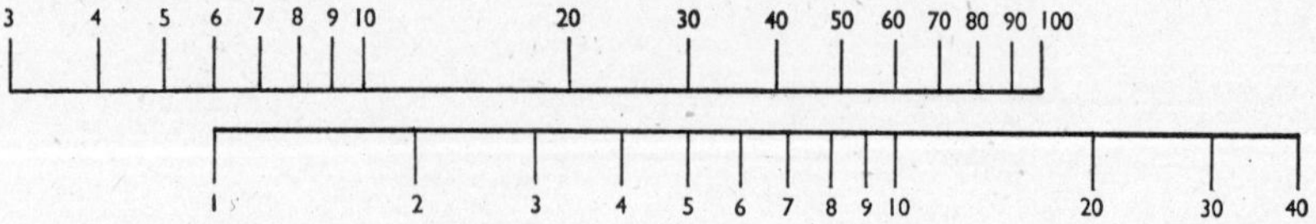

To work out 6 × 7, you simply look at 7 on the bottom scale, and above it you find the correct answer, 42.

If you look at a slide-rule, you will see two scales on it, marked from 1 to 100, very much like the scales above. You should buy or borrow a slide-rule, and practise setting these scales for simple multiplications such as 4 × 5, 8 × 8, 9 × 11, and so on. You know the answers beforehand, so you will immediately detect it if you set the rule incorrectly. You will find that when you have set a slide-rule a few times you will begin to feel how to do it. People who use a slide-rule become like knitters—they can do it while thinking or talking about something else.

When you begin to get the feel of multiplying, you can learn how to divide. Division is just multiplication done backwards. For instance, to divide 42 by 7, we should push the bottom 7 under the top 42 (this is the same setting of the ruler as in our last illustration). The 1 of the bottom scale then comes below 6, and 6 is the answer.

To work out x divided by y (x and y being short for any two numbers), you push y under x, and read off the number that comes over 1.

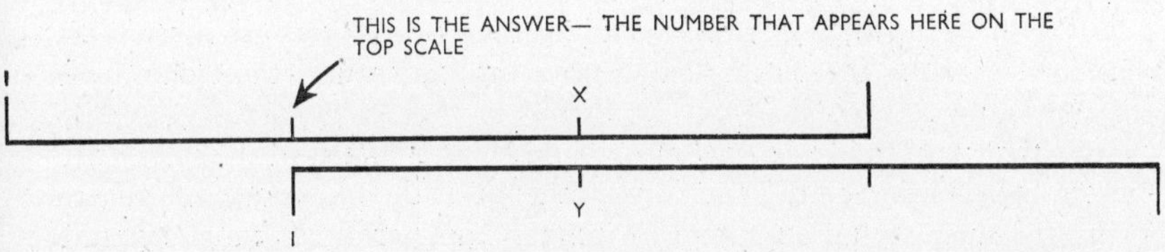

Try a few simple division processes, such as the following, which lead to whole number answers: 72÷12, 56÷7, 65÷13 and 72÷24.

Example. We carry on as we did for subtraction on the old twin-rulers.

72 ÷ 12

Bring 12 on the slide scale opposite 72 on the fixed scale.

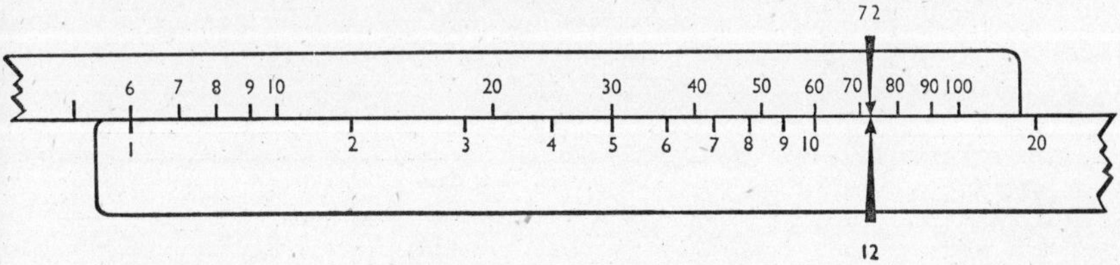

The 1 on the slide scale indicates the answer, 6, on the fixed scale.

Note: The scale showing the number to be divided also shows the answer—a rough mental check is *always* advisable.

After a little practice with whole numbers, you will be able to afford to be more expansive by operating with numbers of three figures—using the decimal markings on the scales. The scales carry numbers that include decimal points; for instance, there is a 1·8. This reading may be regarded as 18 or ·018 or 18,000 or any other product of 1·8 and a power of 10, that is any number containing the pair one and eight preceded or followed by noughts. The decimal point is only included to serve as a guide to the neighbouring unlabelled calibrations on the scale.

Here is a picture of a small portion of the scale.

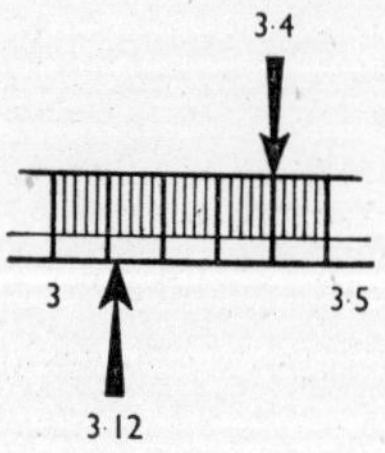

Between 3 and 3·5 on the scale are other lines which are not labelled, and again, there are a great many imaginary lines to be read too.

If 34 is required, look for it between 3 and 3·5.

If 312 is required, find it between 3·1 and 3·2.

There is no marked line for 3·23 so a line between 3·22 and 3·24 must be imagined.

You will have no difficulty with reading the scale if you are already experienced in reading the tenths scale on an ordinary ruler; the technique is exactly the same.

Of the two pairs of scales on most slide-rules, the ten-inch scales (with about ten inches between the markings 1 and 10) is the one to use for general working, because its graduations are longer and permit of more accurate readings.

Example. Multiply 5·8 by 34 (on the ten-inch scales).

Bring 1 on the slide opposite 5·8 on the fixed scale: now look for the answer indicated by 3·4 on the slide and there is an empty space!

In this event, bring 10 instead of 1 opposite 5·8, and again look for the number indicated by 3·4 on the slide. You will find the answer between 197 and 198.

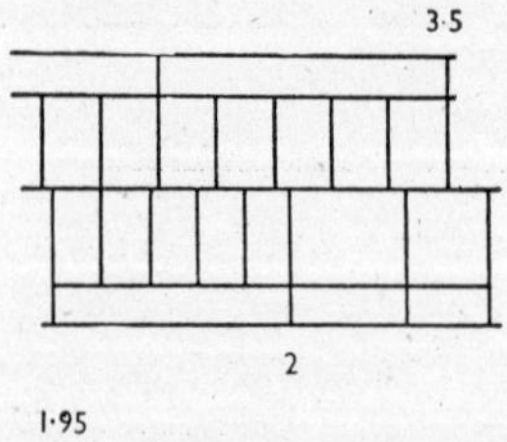

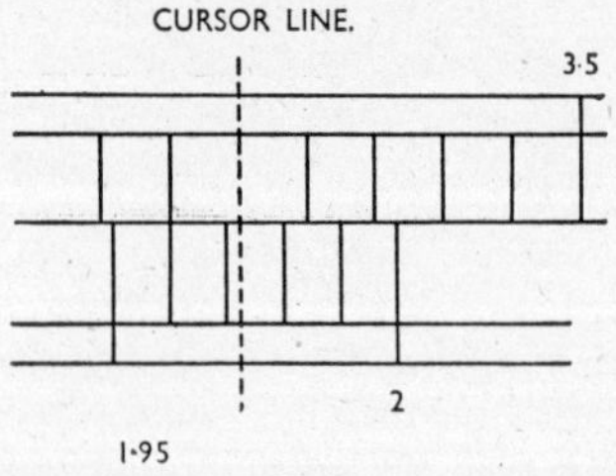

The reading is 1972. (It is obvious that the fourth figure must be two by reason of the fact that ———8 × ———4 = ——————2.)

There are two things to notice before we proceed.

First, if the "1" end of the scale does not oblige by leading us to a reading, the "10" end will. This is always true.

Second, the position of the decimal point is not given by the slide-rule. It must be put in by the operator.

5·8 is nearly 6, and 34 is rather more than 30, so the answer to the product will be within a short range of 180.

This establishes the answer as 197·2.

The lower end of the scale is graduated to three significant figures; it can be read to *four* (as in the example above).

The higher end of the scale (towards which the calibrations are crowded) is graduated to two figures; it can be read to *three* significant figures.

Give yourself plenty of practice in using the slide-rule for multiplication, using the ten-inch and the five-inch scales until you are quite happy about procedure and proficiency.

Then practise division more thoroughly too, making good use of the cursor line when you have to deal with numbers of several figures.

Example. Divide 4·26 by 5·98.

The answer is indicated on the scale you use for the 4·26.

The "1" end of the other scale gives no reading, so you use the 10 line as the indicator instead. The reading is 712, and you place the decimal point yourself; ·712.

When you are satisfied with your skill on straightforward jobs of multiplication and division you can try some more ambitious calculations of the types given below:

$$(a)\quad \frac{3{\cdot}85 \times 10{\cdot}25}{27} \qquad\qquad (b)\quad \frac{8{\cdot}53}{{\cdot}64 \times 3{\cdot}75}$$

Type (*a*) is of very common occurrence in arithmetic: we frequently find ourselves multiplying a number by a fraction. All proportion sums lead to calculations of this form. One of the delights of the slide-rule is that at a single setting it can give us the answers to any number of sums where the operating fraction is the same.

We will do example (*a*) and you will appreciate this fact more readily.

Set the slide-rule for $\frac{3{\cdot}85}{27}$

1 on the 27 scale indicates the result of the division (which we are not particularly interested in), but we have yet to multiply by another number. The rule is already set for reading the answer. 10·25 indicates the answer on the original scale used for 3·85, and the cursor can be moved into position to give us the accurate reading 1462. Putting in the decimal point we have 1·462.

The same setting gives us the answer to any other product of the fraction $\frac{3{\cdot}85}{27}$ and another number. The cursor is the only part that need be moved.

We are provided with a powerful means of reducing a large set of numbers as one might need to do in reducing the scale of a model. If we prefer to build the model on a scale of $\frac{5}{8}$ of that indicated in the specification, we set the slide-rule at $\frac{5}{8}$ and simply read off our answers on the 5-scale one after another.

The same is true of enlarging, of course. If you want to increase a scale in the ratio 12 to 5, you may set the slide-rule at 12/5 and proceed as before.

We mentioned earlier on that percentage tables, though useful, are unnecessary if you have a slide-rule. You will now understand why: percentage is a ratio. Reducing by 15% means multiplying by $\frac{85}{100}$ or ·85.

(Note 1 and 10 on the scale mean *any* integral power (10, ·001, 100, ·1, etc.). Increasing by 12½% means multiplying by $\frac{125}{100}$.

We cannot give a complete guide to the slide-rule—the limitations of space forbid, but we must mention another of its uses.

The 5-in. scale readings are squares of their opposite numbers on the 10-in. scale. For example, 2 is opposite 4, and 5 opposite 25.

To find the square of any number then, we have only to read across from one scale to the other by means of the cursor.

Similarly, we may read square-roots in the opposite direction. Why learn complicated mechanical drills for calculating square roots!

Most slide-rules carry log-log scales. The chief use of these is to raise any number to any power (fractional indices are no impediment). If you purchase a slide-rule it will be accompanied by instructions for making full use of its many devices.

HOW IS A SLIDE-RULE MADE?

It was said earlier that the numbers between 1 and 10, and between 10 and 100, *could* be marked in on a slide-rule, but no indication of how this is to be done was given.

At first this seems a very hard problem. We know that 2 comes between 1 and 10—somewhere between: we have very little idea where.

This problem must have puzzled the inventor of the slide-rule. Eventually he discovered a way out of the difficulty, on the following lines.

We saw that it was easy to mark in 1, 10, 100, 1,000 and so on, and make a slide-rule like this.

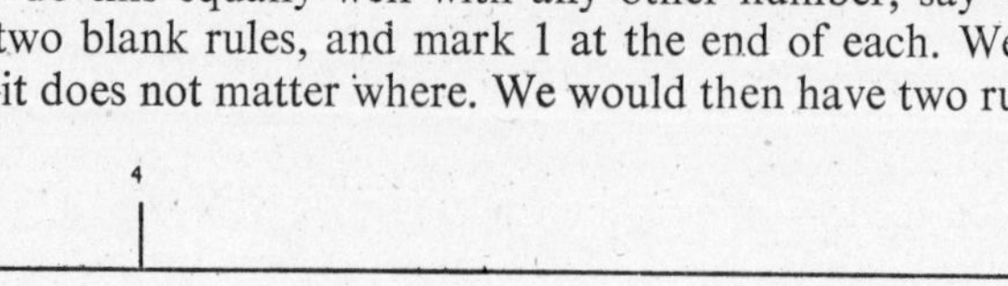

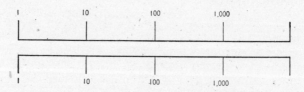

We could do this equally well with any other number, say 4. We would begin with two blank rules, and mark 1 at the end of each. We would also mark 4 in—it does not matter where. We would then have two rules like this:

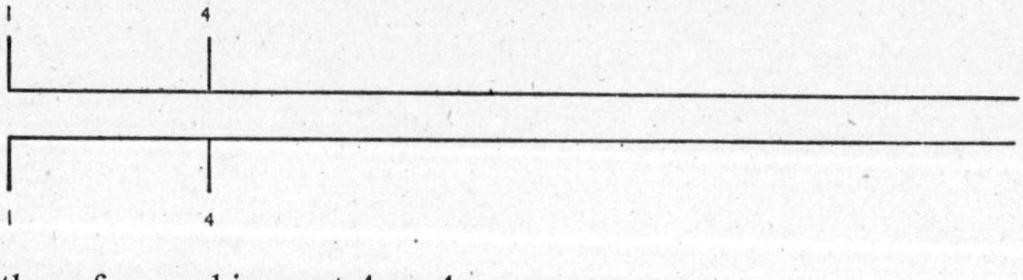

Set these for working out 4 × 4.

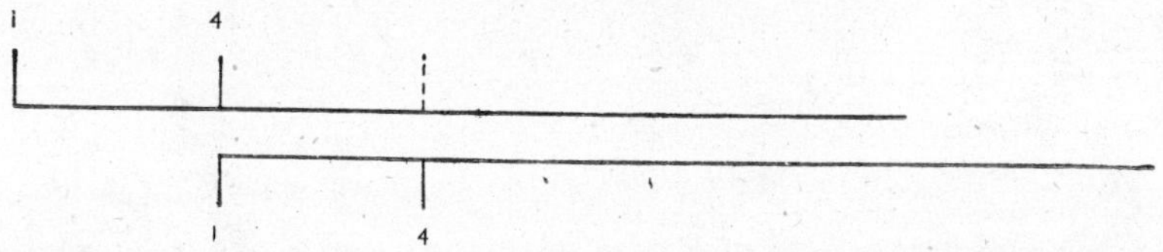

We know 4 × 4 is 16, so 16 must be marked in where the dotted line stands. 16 must also be marked in the corresponding position on the lower scale.

Now setting the rules for multiplying by 16, we can mark in 64 (which is 4 × 16) and 256 (which is 16 × 16):

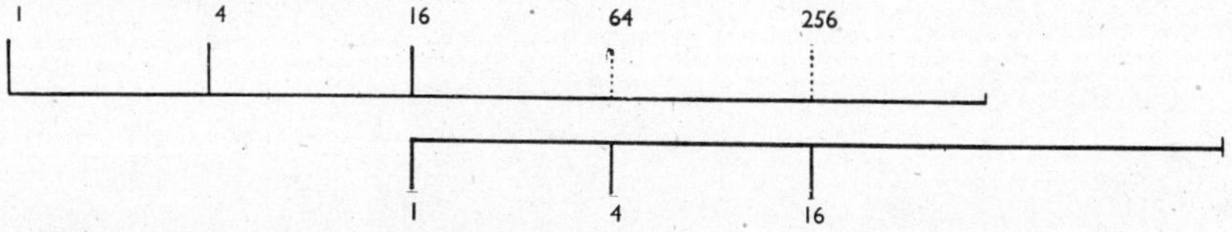

We could go on like this indefinitely. All the numbers we obtained would be powers of 4, i.e., we should obtain the numbers 4, 4 × 4, 4 × 4 × 4, and so on. (These may also be written more shortly as 4, 4^2, 4^3. See Chapter V.) We should not have the numbers 10, 100, 1,000 that we had before, so we seem to have lost as much as we have gained.

Actually, this is not quite so bad as it looks.

On our first rule we had 1, 10, 100 and 1,000—to confine ourselves to numbers between 1 and 1,000.

On the second rule, based on 4 instead of 10, we have the numbers 1, 4, 16, 64, 256 and then 4 × 256 is 1,024 which is just over 1,000.

Instead of a rule with four numbers on it, we have one with five, and the sixth number (1,024) is only just outside the range.

The gaps on our second rule, then, are not quite as big as on the first.

We could improve things still more by taking 3 instead of 4. By exactly the same method as before we should be able to mark in the seven numbers 1, 3, 9, 27, 81, 243, 729, each of which is a power of 3.

Better still, we could use 2 and obtain the nine numbers, 1, 2, 4, 8, 16, 32, 64, 128, 256, 512. The tenth number 1024 would be just outside the range 1 to 1,000. (Note that we have all the numbers on the "4" rule, and others as well.)

We cannot get any further than this if we stick to whole numbers, since 2 is the number next to 1. But we can reduce the gaps if we allow fractions or decimals.

For instance, we might start off our slide-rule by marking in 1 and 1·5. Each number we then marked on the scale would be 1·5 times the previous one. Thus we should get:

$$(1{\cdot}5)^2 = 1{\cdot}5 \times 1{\cdot}5 = 2{\cdot}25$$
$$(1{\cdot}5)^3 = 2{\cdot}25 \times 1{\cdot}5 = 3{\cdot}375$$
$$(1{\cdot}5)^4 = 3{\cdot}375 \times 1{\cdot}5 = 5{\cdot}0625$$

and so on, until we reach

$$(1{\cdot}5)^{17} = 985{\cdot}22.$$

This rule has seventeen numbers in the range 1 to 1,000. Most of them are rather awkward fractions, not very convenient for marking on a scale. But a few of these numbers are very nearly whole numbers—for instance $(1{\cdot}5)^4$ is 5·0625, which is not so very far from 5.

By taking numbers still closer to 1, such as 1·1, or 1·01 or 1·001, we can make the gaps between the powers as small as we like.

For instance, if we start with a rule marked only for 1 and 1·001, and keep multiplying by 1·001, we obtain (to 6 places of decimals):

$$(1{\cdot}001)^2=1{\cdot}002001$$
$$(1{\cdot}001)^3=1{\cdot}003003$$
$$(1{\cdot}001)^4=1{\cdot}004006$$
$$(1{\cdot}001)^5=1{\cdot}005010 \text{ and so on.}$$

Calculating these numbers is slow, but not difficult. For instance, to obtain the next number after those shown above, $(1{\cdot}001)^6$, we should have to multiply 1·005010 by 1·001—that is to say, we have to increase 1·005010 by one-thousandth part of itself. Dividing 1·005010 by 1,000 we obtain ·001005, which has to be added on. So $(1{\cdot}001)^6=1{\cdot}006015$.

The work may be set out like this:

$$\begin{aligned}(1{\cdot}001)^5&=1{\cdot}005010\\ &\;\underline{{\cdot}001005}\\ (1{\cdot}001)^6&=1{\cdot}006015\\ &\;\underline{\phantom{1{\cdot}00}1006}\\ (1{\cdot}001)^7&=1{\cdot}007021 \text{ and so on.}\end{aligned}$$

Each time we add on one thousandth part of the previous number.

Continuing in this way we should eventually arrive at something like this:

$$\begin{aligned}(1{\cdot}001)^{693}&=1{\cdot}999908\\ &\;\underline{\phantom{1{\cdot}99}1999}\\ (1{\cdot}001)^{694}&=2{\cdot}001907\end{aligned}$$

Both the numbers 1·999908 and 2·001907 are very close to the whole number 2. Accordingly, 2 would have to be marked between 693 and 694 times as far down the scale as 1·001.

To make the slide-rule of reasonable size, we should have to put 1·001 very close to the end of the scale.

In the same way, we should find that:

$(1{\cdot}001)^{1097}$ is very nearly 3.
$(1{\cdot}001)^{1386}$ is very nearly 4.
$(1{\cdot}001)^{1609}$ is very nearly 5.
$(1{\cdot}001)^{1792}$ is very nearly 6.
$(1{\cdot}001)^{1946}$ is very nearly 7.
$(1{\cdot}001)^{2079}$ is very nearly 8.
$(1{\cdot}001)^{2197}$ is very nearly 9.
$(1{\cdot}001)^{2302}$ is very nearly 10.

Accordingly, whatever distance 1·001 is marked from 1 on the slide-rule, 3 must be 1,097 times as far down the rule: 4 must be 1,386 times as far: 5 must be 1,069 times as far, and so on, until we reach 10, and that must be 2,302 times as far.

Now we can see how to put the numbers 2, 3, 4, 5, 6, 7, 8 and 9 in a slide-rule which already has 1 and 10 marked.

We know that 10 is marked 2,302 times as far down as 1·001.

So 1·001 must be marked $\frac{1}{2{,}302}$ of the way from 1 to 10.

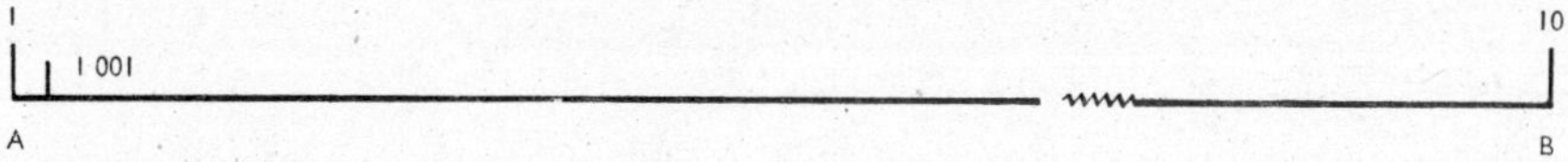

This is $\frac{1}{2{,}302}$ of the length *AB*.

And we know that 2 must be marked 693 times as far along as 1·001.

So 2 must be marked at $\frac{693}{2{,}302}$ of the distance from 1 to 10.

Similarly, 3 must be marked $\frac{1{,}097}{2{,}302}$ of the way from 1 to 10.

The positions of the other numbers may be found by the same method.

INTRODUCING LOGARITHMS

If we work out those fractions as decimals, we find:

2 must be marked at 0·3010 of the distance from 1 to 10.

3 must be marked at 0·4771 of the distance from 1 to 10.

4 must be marked at 0·6020 of the distance from 1 to 10.

And so on for 5, 6, 7, 8 and 9.

The number 0·3010 is called the *logarithm* of 2, or log 2 for short.

The number 0·4771 is called the *logarithm* of 3, or log 3.

For any number, the logarithm tells you what proportion of the distance from 1 to 10 on the slide-rule that number must be marked,

For instance, the logarithm of 3·1623 is 0·5, that is, $\frac{1}{2}$. So 3·1623 would be marked on the slide-rule exactly half way between 1 and 10.

The logarithm of 17·783 is 1·25, or $1\frac{1}{4}$. This means that 17·783 should be marked $1\frac{1}{4}$ times as far down the rule as 10.

The logarithm of 100 is obviously 2, because 100 is marked twice as far down as 10.

The logarithm of 1 is 0, because 1 is at the end of the slide-rule, that is distance nought along the scale.

Let us sum up what we have said so far.

(1) A slide-rule may be made by taking any number (say x) and marking the powers of x at equal intervals along a line like this:

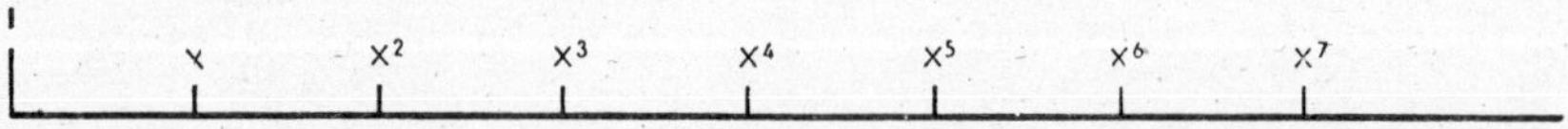

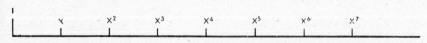

(2) If x is a whole number, such as 10 or 3 or 2, there will be many numbers that are not powers of x, and we do not know where they are to be marked.

(3) If x is taken nearly equal to 1 (say $x=1{\cdot}001$), the powers of x differ from each other by very small amounts. We can find an exact power of x

that is *nearly* equal to any number we like. So every number has its place on the slide-rule.

(4) The fraction of the distance from 1 to 10 at which any number is marked is called the logarithm of that number. The simplest way of stating this is to say, "If a slide-rule is made so that 10 is unit distance from 1, the distance of any number from 1 is called the logarithm of that number."

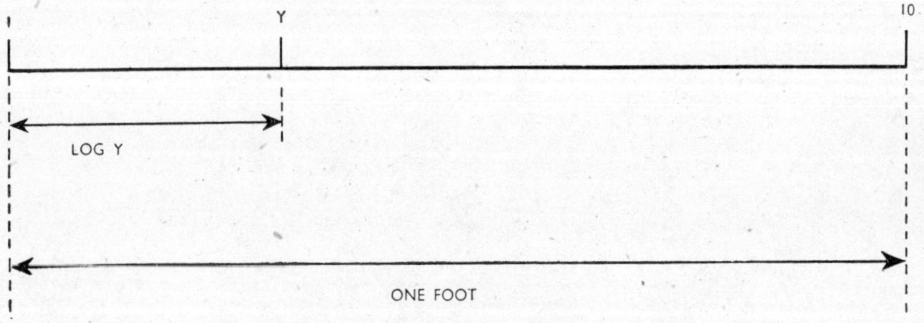

FRACTIONAL AND NEGATIVE INDICES

In most books on mathematics, logarithms are explained by means of *fractional indices*, signs such as $10^{\frac{1}{2}}$ or $10^{0 \cdot 301}$. It will be as well to explain what these signs mean, as it is often convenient to use them when speaking of logarithms.

We have seen that a slide-rule could be made to show numbers as large as we liked (actual slide-rules usually stop at 10 or 100). Suppose we have a slide-rule that goes on for ever. We have seen that 10, 10^2, 10^3, 10^4, etc., are marked at equal intervals.

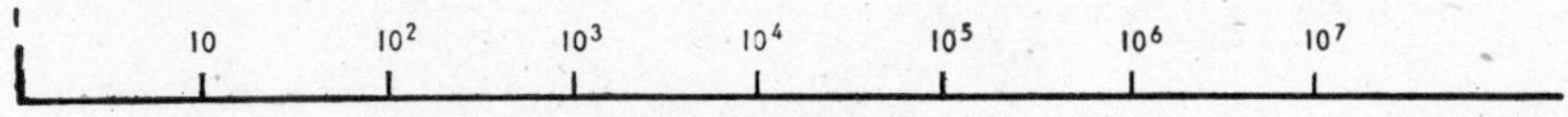

So 10^2 is marked *twice* as far along as 10
10^3 is marked three times as far along as 10
10^4 is marked four times as far along as 10
10^5 is marked five times as far along as 10.

We may sum this up by saying:

10^n is marked n times as far along as 10.

So far n has been a whole number: we have not yet attached any meaning to the sign $10^{\frac{1}{2}}$.

$10^{\frac{1}{2}}$ has not *in itself* any meaning. It is just a label which we can fix to anything we like—in the same way that we can call a new street anything we like.

Mathematicians have agreed among themselves that 10^n is to be used as an abbreviation for "the number that is marked on the slide-rule n times as far along as 10", even when n is not a whole number.

So $10^{\frac{1}{2}}$ is short for the number that is marked half way from 1 to 10.

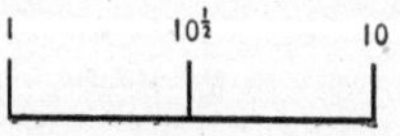

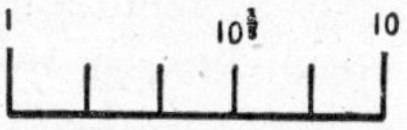

In the same way $10^{\frac{3}{5}}$ will be the number on the slide-rule $\frac{3}{5}$ of the way from 1 to 10.

By measuring on a slide-rule you could find roughly the value of $10^{\frac{1}{2}}$.

If you were asked to work out $10^{\frac{1}{2}} \times 10^{\frac{1}{2}}$ on a slide-rule, you would set the rule like this:

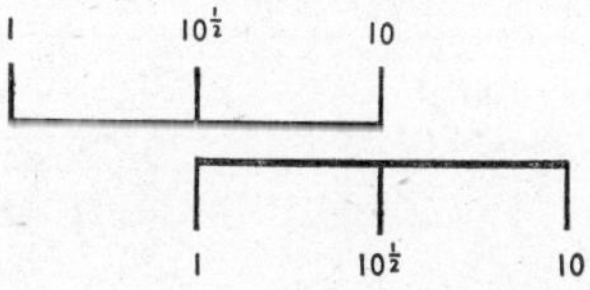

This shows you that $10^{\frac{1}{2}} \times 10^{\frac{1}{2}}$ is 10. So $10^{\frac{1}{2}}$ multiplied by itself is equal to 10. As $\sqrt{10} \times \sqrt{10} = 10$, $\sqrt{10}$ and $10^{\frac{1}{2}}$ must mean the same thing.

$$10^{\frac{1}{2}} = \sqrt{10}.$$

In the same way, you can find out for yourself facts about $10^{\frac{1}{3}}$ or $10^{\frac{2}{3}}$ or $10^{\frac{3}{5}}$. Take any of these numbers and keep multiplying it by itself, using a sketch of a slide-rule (as in the diagram just used). In time you will come to a number such as 10 or 100 or 1,000.

The same idea of fractional index may be applied to any number, not only to 10. For instance, $9^{\frac{1}{2}}$ means the number half way from 1 to 9 on the slide-rule.

Negative indices arise if we try to give a meaning to 10^n when n is a minus number. For example, in 10^{-1}, 10^{-3}, $10^{-2\frac{1}{2}}$ the index (the power of 10 considered) is a minus number.

To arrive at these negative indices we must extend the slide-rule to the left as well as to the right, like this:

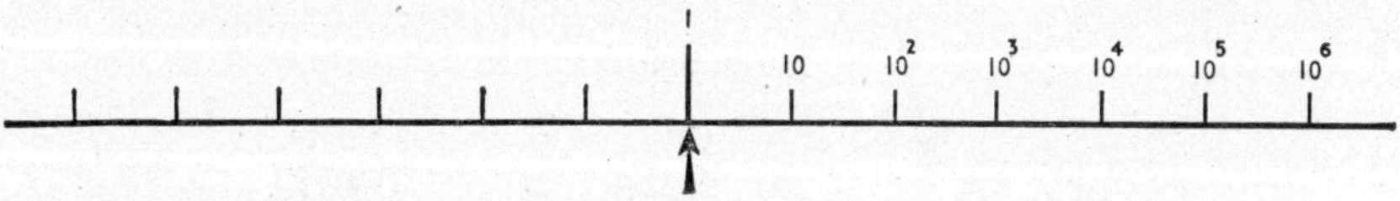

The arrow is opposite 1, which is normally the end of the slide-rule.

We saw that 10^n was marked n times as far along as 10. What does it mean to say that something must be marked —3 times as far along as 10?

We could say—it means nothing. But mathematicians have found that very simple and helpful results arise if we agree that "—3 times as far" is to mean "3 times as far, but in the opposite direction." If we accept this, it means 10^{-3} must be put at the third mark to the left of the arrow.

Using this explanation, we can mark in 10^{-1}, 10^{-2}, and other negative powers, like this:

Now we can find out the meaning of these numbers. Set the slide-rule to multiply 10^{-1} by 10. It will be like this (for simplicity only the right half of the lower scale has been shown).

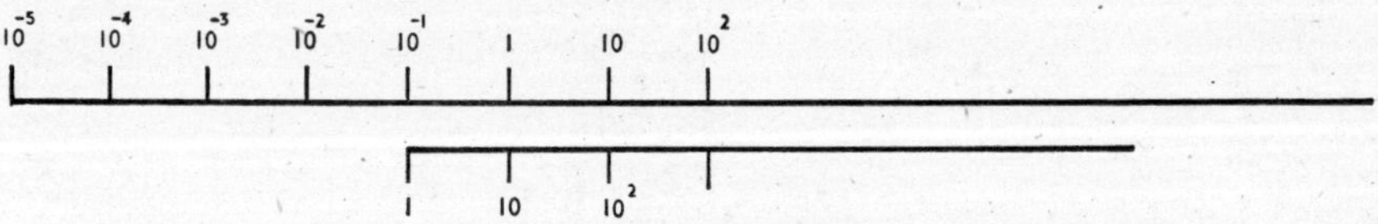

This shows that $10^{-1} \times 10 = 1$. So 10^{-1} must be 0·1, one-tenth.

In the same way, you can show that 10^{-2} must be $1 \div 100$ or 0·01, and that 10^{-3} is $1 \div 1{,}000$ or 0·001. In short, 10^{-n} is $1 \div 10^{n}$.

CONNECTION BETWEEN LOGARITHMS AND INDICES

The connection between indices and logarithms can be seen by comparing two statements that have been made. These statements are:

(I) 10^{n} is marked n times as far along as 10.

(II) y is marked $\log y$ times as far along as 10.

Both statements tell us where some number has to be marked on the slide-rule. The two rules must give the same answer. What does this imply?

Let us consider a particular number, say 100,000. As 100,000 is 10^{5}, rule (I) tells us that 100,000 must be marked 5 times as far along as 10.

But rule (II) says that 100,000 must be marked log 100,000 times as far as 10.

These two conclusions only agree if log 100,000 is 5.

In the same way, you can show for any number n that $\log 10^{n}$ must be the same as n.

$$\log 10^{n} = n.$$

We can obtain this result another way by comparing the numbers in rules (I) and (II). This leads us to the conclusion:

$$\left.\begin{array}{l}\text{If } y = 10^{n} \\ \log y = n\end{array}\right\}$$

This works equally well the other way round.

$$\left.\begin{array}{l}\text{If } n = \log y \\ y = 10^{n}\end{array}\right\}$$

For instance:

$$0{\cdot}301 = \log 2$$
$$\therefore \quad 2 = 10^{0\cdot301}$$

AN IMPORTANT RESULT

This result helps us to see about how big the logarithm of any number is. Take 137 for example. *Roughly* how big should log 137 be?

137 lies between 100 and 1,000. That is, between 10^{2} and 10^{3}. Log 10^{2} is 2, log 10^{3} is 3. As 137 is between 100 and 1,000, log 137 must be between log 100 and log 1,000—that is, between 2 and 3. This tells us that log 137 must be 2·****, where the stars stand for numbers that we do not yet know. In words, log 137 is "2 point something."

People often have trouble in finding, say, log 0·00024 from the tables. The same method will work. 0·00024 lies between 0·0001 and 0·0010; that is, between 10^{-4} and 10^{-3}. So its logarithm must be between -4 and -3.

We shall find this useful when we come to use tables of logarithms. The tables give us the fraction part of the logarithm, but we have to decide the whole number part for ourselves.

THE OBJECT OF LOGARITHMS

Generally speaking, a slide-rule is the best and quickest instrument to use when a fairly rough answer is sufficient. A slide-rule will tell you in a few seconds that $1{\cdot}73 \times 2{\cdot}42 \times 7{\cdot}35$ is just about 30·8, and often it is very useful to know such results.

But sometimes it is necessary to have answers correct to 4, or 5, or 6 figures. Obviously with a slide-rule one cannot read off an answer to so many figures.

We cannot even make a slide-rule to a great degree of accuracy. For instance, on a slide-rule ten inches long, the number 3 ought to be marked 4·771213 in. from the end. But we cannot make marks to an accuracy of one-millionth of an inch. The line that we draw to mark the position will itself be many times thicker than one-millionth of an inch.

Logarithm tables are, therefore, made to tell us where each number *ought* to be marked, if such precision were possible.

It is supposed that 10 is marked at *unit* distance, as in the figure on page 326.

Log tables, then, tell us that 3 should be marked at a distance 0·4771213. (In the last paragraph, 10 was supposed to be marked at a distance of *ten* inches, so 3 had to be at $0{\cdot}4771213 \times 10$ in., that is, 4·771213 in.)

They also tell us that 2 should be at a distance 0·3010300, and 6 at 0·7781513.

Now imagine a slide-rule set for multiplying 2 by 3. It would be like this:

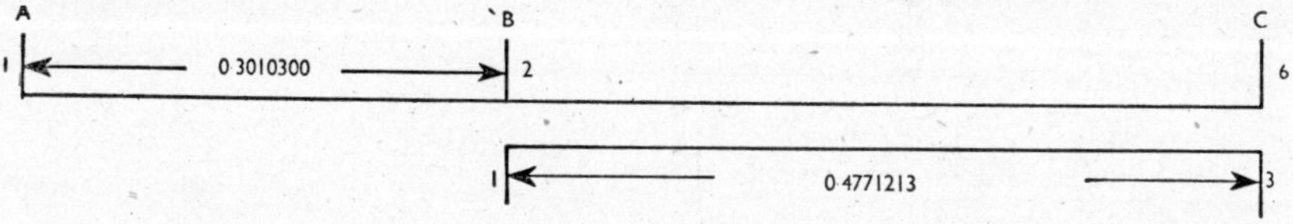

The distance AC is clearly $AB + BC$, that is, $0{\cdot}3010300 + 0{\cdot}4771213$.

So the distance at which 6 is marked is obtained by adding together the distances at which 2 and 3 are marked.

That is, $\log 6 = \log 2 + \log 3$.

or $\log (2 \times 3) = \log 2 + \log 3$.

This argument could be applied to any two numbers. It shows that log tables allow us to change an example in multiplication, finding 2×3, into an example in addition, adding log 2 and log 3. Of course this is not advantageous for such simple numbers as 2 and 3; but it is very useful for more complicated numbers.

Example. Find $2{\cdot}1627 \times 3{\cdot}1354$.

$$\begin{aligned}\log (2{\cdot}1627\times 3{\cdot}1354) &= \log 2{\cdot}1627+\log 3{\cdot}1354\\ &= 0{\cdot}3349963+0{\cdot}4962930 \text{ (from the tables)}\\ &= 0{\cdot}8312893.\end{aligned}$$

From the tables, 0·8312893 is the logarithm of 6·78093.

So 6·78093 is $2{\cdot}1627 \times 3{\cdot}1354$.

It is interesting to compare this with the exact value of the answer.

By logarithms, $2{\cdot}1627 \times 3{\cdot}1354 = 6{\cdot}78093$.

By full multiplication, $2{\cdot}1627 \times 3{\cdot}1354 = 6{\cdot}78092958$.

You will see how closely the answers agree.

Here we have been using logarithms to 7 places of decimals. The tables giving these logarithms are rather bulky—they fill 200 pages of a book about the same size as this one! Usually, students use log tables going to 4 or 5 places only. These are small enough to be carried about comfortably, and are quite cheap to buy.

USING TABLES OF LOGARITHMS

It has already been mentioned (see the section, *An Important Result* on page 326) that log tables only give us the fraction part of the logarithm.

When you see in the log table, for instance:

20	3010	—
21	3222	—
22	3424	—
—	—	—

this really means

$$\begin{aligned}\log 2{\cdot}0 &= 0{\cdot}3010\\ \log 2{\cdot}1 &= 0{\cdot}3222\\ \log 2{\cdot}2 &= 0{\cdot}3424.\end{aligned}$$

In fact, the log tables give the logarithms of numbers between 1 and 10.

On the slide-rule, 1 is marked at the end of the rule—at distance 0. 10 is marked at unit distance. So all the numbers between 1 and 10 are marked at distances between 0 and 1. That is, their logarithms are between 0 and 1, so they all are of the form 0·****, "nought point something".

What are we to do if we want to know the logarithm of some number outside 1 to 10, say 21 or 210 or 0·021?

We simply write down the same fraction as for log 2·1, with a different whole number in front.

For instance,

$$\begin{aligned}\log 2{\cdot}1 &= 0{\cdot}3222\\ \log 21 &= 1{\cdot}3222\\ \log 210 &= 2{\cdot}3222.\end{aligned}$$

There are various ways of seeing why this is done. One way is to say that $21 = 10 \times 2{\cdot}1$, so $\log 21 = \log 10 + \log 2{\cdot}1$ (since multiplying means addition of logs). But log 10 is 1. So $\log 21 = 1 + \log 2{\cdot}1 = 1 + 0{\cdot}3222 = 1{\cdot}3222$. Similarly $210 = 100 \times 2{\cdot}1$. Log 100 is 2. So $\log 210 = \log 100 \times \log 2{\cdot}1 = 2 + 0{\cdot}3222 = 2{\cdot}3222$.

This can also be explained by indices.

Once you understand it, the quickest thing to do is probably to argue as suggested earlier. 21 is between 10 and 100, that is between 10 and 10^2. So its logarithm must be between 1 and 2. That is, log 21 is "one point something." The something is given by the tables as ·3222. So log 21 = 1·3222.

	0	1	2	3	4	5	6	7	8	9	Mean Differences								
											1	2	3	4	5	6	7	8	9
20	----	----	----	----	----	----	----	----	----	----	--	--	--	--	--	--	--	--	--
21	3222	----	----	----	----	----	----	----	----	----	--	--	--	--	--	--	--	--	--
22	----	----	----	----	----	----	----	----	----	----	--	--	--	--	--	--	--	--	--

We have still to deal with 0·021. 0·021 is 2·1 ÷ 100. Just as *multiplying* by 100 *adds* 2 to the logarithm, *dividing* by 100 *subtracts* 2. So log 0·021 = log 2·1 —2 = 0·3222—2.

At this stage we do a curious thing. Instead of working out 0·3222— 2 (and getting — 1·6778), we just leave the subtraction sum as it is. (The reason for this is that it is more convenient, if later we want to ask, what number is this the logarithm of?

We do, however, bring in a certain special sign. We write the minus sign over the 2, like this, $\bar{2}$. This is called bar 2 but it still just means minus 2. We write this number $\bar{2}$ at the front, like this, $\bar{2}$·3222.

This still means exactly the same as before, — 2 + 0·3222, or 0·3222— 2.

In the same way, log 0·21 is $\bar{1}$·3222, and log 0·0021 is $\bar{3}$·3222. All these are strange mongrels of plus and minus.

Certain special names are used in talking about logarithms. The fraction part, ·3222 in the examples just considered, is called the mantissa. The whole number part, whether positive or negative, is called the characteristic.

So in log 210, which is 2·3222, the characteristic is 2. In log 21, which is 1·3222, the characteristic is 1. In log 2·1, or 0·3222, the characteristic is 0. In log 0·21, which is $\bar{1}$·3222, the characteristic is $\bar{1}$, or — 1, whichever you like to call it. In log 0·021, or $\bar{2}$·3222, the characteristic is $\bar{2}$.

Another example is for 139·7.

	0	1	2	3	4	5	6	7	8	9	Mean Differences								
											1	2	3	4	5	6	7	8	9
12	----	----	----	----	----	----	----	----	----	----	--	--	--	--	--	--	--	--	--
13	----	----	----	----	----	----	----	----	----	1430	--	--	--	--	--	--	23	--	--
14	----	----	----	----	----	----	----	----	----	----	--	--	--	--	--	--	--	--	--

The logarithm is 2·1453.

Here is another set of examples of numbers with their logarithms.

log 1·778 = ·25	log 17780 =4·25
log 17·78 =1·25	log ·1778 =$\bar{1}$·25
log 177·8 =2·25	log ·01778 =$\bar{2}$·25
log 1778 =3·25	log ·001778=$\bar{3}$·25

The only help we shall need from the tables of logarithms will be in finding the mantissa of the logarithm, and this depends on the sequence of figures which comprises the number *and nothing else.*

We will now examine some log tables and find out how to use them.

The main body of the table is the ten columns of four-figure numbers, these are the mantissae readings for numbers of three figures. It will be easier to understand if we take an example: suppose you want the logarithm of 28·3.

You know the characteristic will be 1.

Now look down the left-hand index column for 28 and move *along* the row of readings until you come to the column headed 3. The reading you have found is the mantissa of the log of 283: it is 4518.

The logarithm of 28·3 is, therefore, 1·4518.

Suppose we want log 139·7.

The characteristic will be 2.

Proceeding for the mantissa we find the reading in the tables for 139 and keep a finger under it: 1430.

The minor section of the table (on the right), called "the mean difference columns" enables us to correct this reading by an addition which will be found under column 7 of the same row: 23.

∴ The mantissa of log 139·7 is ·1453 and log 139·7=2·1453.

You now know what a logarithm is and how to use your brain and a log table in concert to find the logarithm of *any* number in about six seconds. We will return to the *use* of logarithms.

Example. Calculate 61·5 × 3 × ·85.

Write down their logs and add them together	1·7889
	·4771
	$\bar{1}$·9294
	2·1954

then find the number that has this log.

The answer is 156·8 (Check: 60 × 3 × 1 = 180)

To save routing out the answer in the log tables mathematicians have provided themselves with tables of antilogarithms. These tables are handled in exactly the same way as log tables but they only deal with mantissae. In the example, we look up antilog ·1954 and nurse the characteristic 2 in our minds for the placing of the decimal point in the reading the tables off. They give:

antilog ·1954=1568

∴ antilog 2·1954=156·8.

As a constant reminder that they do not deal with characteristics, antilog tables always precede their figures in the left-hand index column with a decimal point.

Example.	·307 × 120·4 × ·68	$\bar{1}$·4871
		2·0806
		$\bar{1}$·8325
	Answer = 25·13	1·4002
	(Check: 120 × ·2 = 24)	

We have said nothing yet about division.

$$\frac{100{,}000}{1{,}000}=\frac{10^5}{10^3}=10^{5-3}=10^2$$

which may be translated $\log\left(\frac{100{,}000}{1{,}000}\right)=\log 100{,}000-\log 1{,}000$

$$=5-3$$
$$=2$$

and antilog 2 = 100 (the mantissa is ·0000).

Division, therefore, requires subtraction of logarithms.

Example.

75 ÷ 39	1·8751
	1·5911
Answer = 1·923	·2840

[Rough check: 80 ÷ 40 = 2]

Try each of these for yourself *before* you refer to the sample workings.

Example.

12·5 ÷ ·8375	1·0969
	$\bar{1}$·9230
Answer = 14·92	1·1739

[Check: 12 ÷ 1 = 12]

Example.

$\frac{\cdot 0567}{23\cdot 25}$	$\bar{2}$·7536
	1·3664
	$\bar{3}$·3872

Answer = ·002439

[Check: ·05 ÷ 20 = ·0025]

Example.

$\frac{\cdot 008}{\cdot 3125}$	$\bar{3}$·9031
	$\bar{1}$·4949
	$\bar{2}$·4082

Answer = ·0256

[Check: ·009 ÷ ·3 = ·03]

These examples introduce most of the variations in the nature of addition and subtraction that may occur in work using logarithms. They will serve as references.

INDICES

Logarithms are very useful for finding the powers of numbers.

Example.

$$(8\cdot 3)^3 = 8\cdot 3 \times 8\cdot 3 \times 8\cdot 3$$
$$\therefore \log (8\cdot 3)^3 = \log 8\cdot 3 + \log 8\cdot 3 + \log 8\cdot 3$$
$$= 3 \log 8\cdot 3$$
$$= 2\cdot 7573$$
$$\therefore (8\cdot 3)^3 = 571\cdot 9$$

Example.

$$\sqrt[3]{216} = (216)^{\frac{1}{3}}$$
$$\log (216)^{\frac{1}{3}} = \tfrac{1}{3} \log 216$$
$$= \cdot 7782$$
$$\therefore \sqrt[3]{216} = 6$$

Before closing this section on logarithms, it should be pointed out that four-figure tables do not always lead to accuracy to four significant figures. The fourth figure shown in the table is an approximation, and when these are combined in subtractions and additions (and in the case of powers in multiplication) their approximation becomes less reliable.

Where more accuracy is required 5-, 6- or 7-figure tables may be consulted.

TRIGONOMETRICAL TABLES

Little need be said about these tables. Their use will be appreciated when you read Chapter XI. The tables give reliable values of the sine, cosine, and tangent for angles given to one minute of accuracy.

Degrees are indicated in the left-hand column and minutes are given in the body of the tables with the help of mean difference columns. Readings are found in the same way as for logarithms and antilogarithms.

Trigonometrical calculations are usually done either by logs or by the slide-rule. In the former case one may require the logarithm of the sine of an angle (log-sine) more frequently than the sine itself. Hence the log-sine, and similarly log-cosine and log-tangent tables.

RULERS FOR SCALE DRAWING

Draughtsmen, architects, model-makers and others who make or read reduced scale drawings, avoid a lot of calculation by using specially prepared rules calibrated in units representing those that will obtain in actuality.

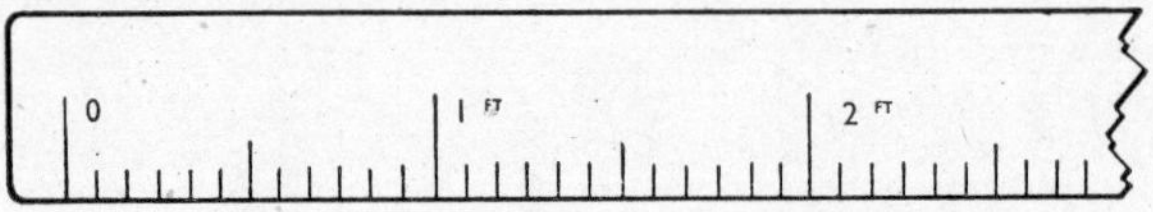

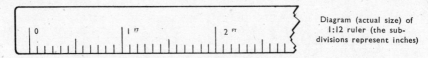

Diagram (actual size) of 1:12 ruler (the sub-divisions represent inches)

Pattern-makers use special rulers calibrated ostensibly in feet and inches. In fact the units have been enlarged to represent lengths of hot molten metal, which, when cold, will have contracted to the dimensions intended. They require a different rule for each different metal.

NOMOGRAMS, OR ABACS

Nomograms are one of the easiest calculating devices to use. You do not need to know the formula on which the nomogram is based: you do not need to know anything about the problem. You simply place a ruler on to a diagram, and read off the answer.

A typical nomogram is shown in the figure on page 334. It enables us to find the horse-power needed to drive a model aeroplane. The horse-power is that of the petrol engine or rubber motor that must be fitted to the plane.

This horse-power depends on two things; the speed (velocity) at which the plane is to fly, and the air resistance (drag) that has to be overcome. One finds a point on the right-hand scale corresponding to the speed of the plane, and a point on the left-hand scale corresponding to the drag. The straight line joining these two points will cut the middle line at a certain point. The number corresponding to this point is the answer, the horse-power required.

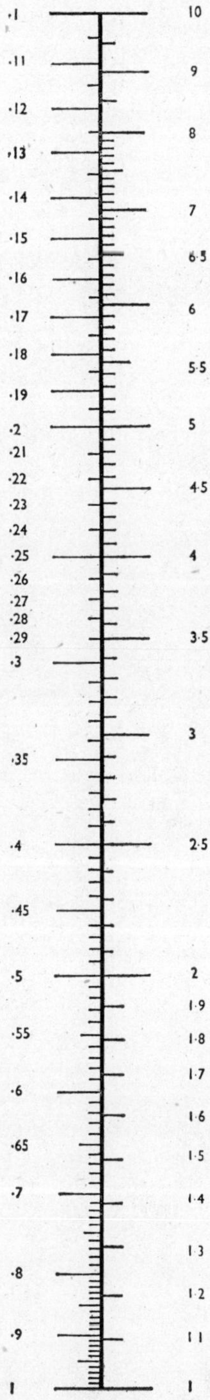

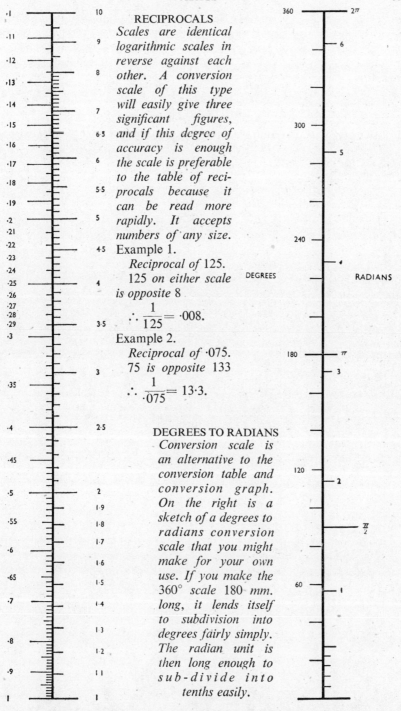

RECIPROCALS

Scales are identical logarithmic scales in reverse against each other. A conversion scale of this type will easily give three significant figures, and if this degree of accuracy is enough the scale is preferable to the table of reciprocals because it can be read more rapidly. It accepts numbers of any size.

Example 1.

Reciprocal of 125.

125 *on either scale is opposite* 8

$$\therefore \frac{1}{125} = \cdot 008.$$

Example 2.

Reciprocal of ·075.

75 *is opposite* 133

$$\therefore \frac{1}{\cdot 075} = 13\cdot 3.$$

DEGREES TO RADIANS

Conversion scale is an alternative to the conversion table and conversion graph. On the right is a sketch of a degrees to radians conversion scale that you might make for your own use. If you make the 360° *scale* 180 *mm. long, it lends itself to subdivision into degrees fairly simply. The radian unit is then long enough to sub-divide into tenths easily.*

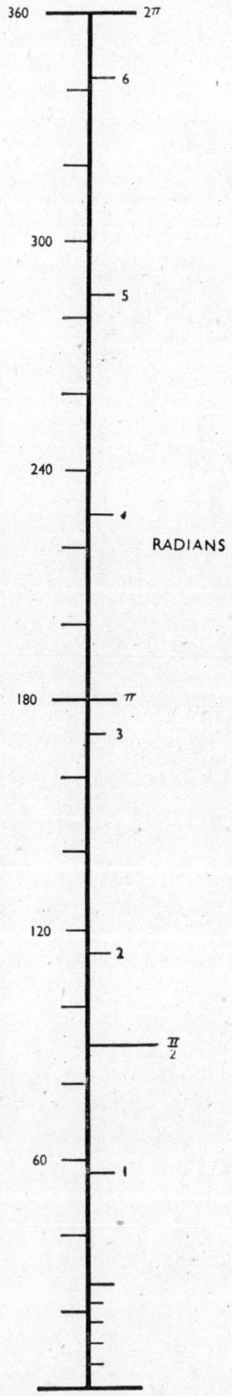

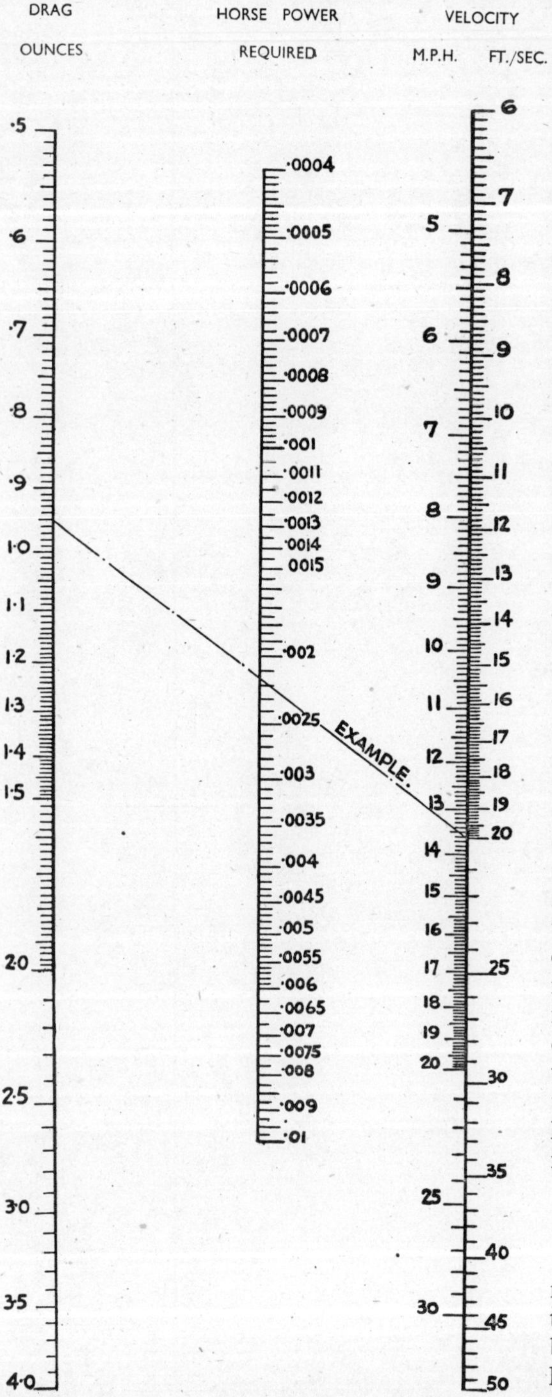

The method of using should be quite clear from the illustrations on the left and on page 335, and no further explanation seems to be called for.

It is quite another matter if you wish to design and make nomograms for yourself. This is a most interesting and instructive thing to do, and is a great time-saver for people who have to carry out the same type of calculation again and again.

The theory is not difficult, *provided you are so familiar with the use and theory of logarithms that you can follow arguments about logarithms without any effort.*

Until you have reached this stage, it is not wise to delve into the theory of nomograms, and it is suggested that the next few pages are, for the time being, only given a cursory glance as you may find some of the nomograms useful without understanding how they are made, but return to these pages when you have mastered the arguments on logarithms.

THEORY OF NOMOGRAMS

The way in which nomograms are constructed may be understood by considering a particular example. Suppose we

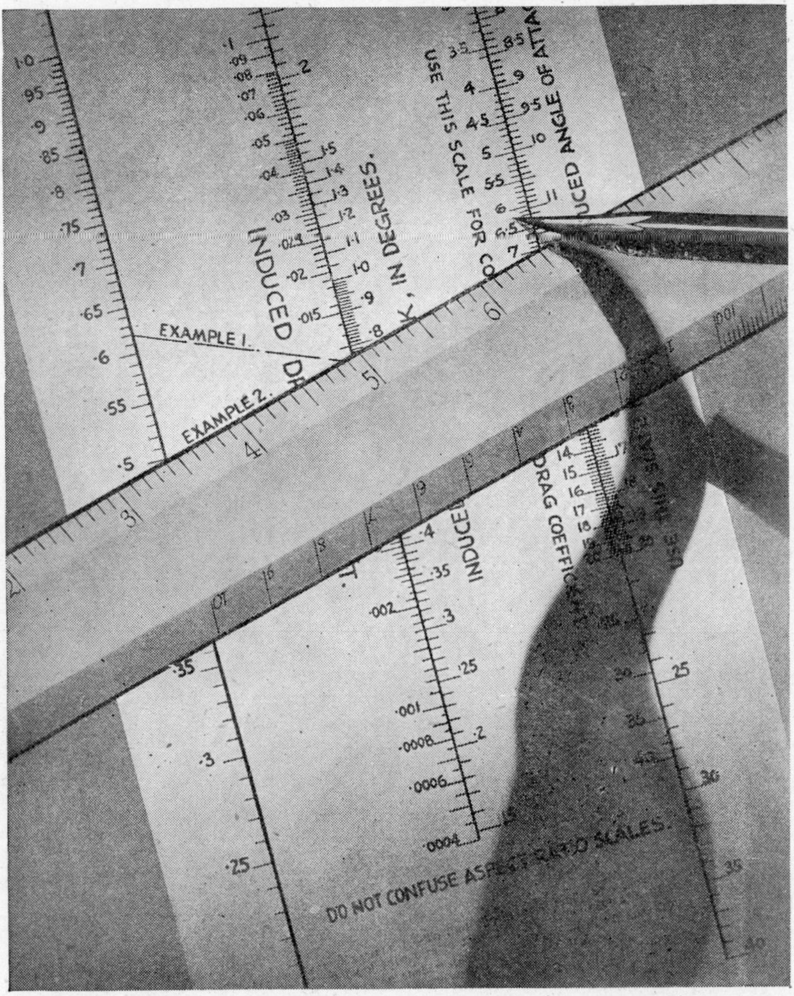

have two quantities B and C (like the velocity and drag in a previous example), and there is some quantity A (like the horse-power) that we wish to find. Suppose that A is proportional to B multiplied by C, that is:

$$A=kBC$$

where k is some fixed number.

By taking logarithms we can turn this multiplication into an addition question.

$$\log A=\log k+\log B+\log C.$$

It is not convenient to add three different things, so we group together $\log k$ and $\log B$.

$$\log A=(\log k+\log B)+\log C=\log kB+\log C.$$

Now we want to find some simple geometrical construction for carrying out an addition.

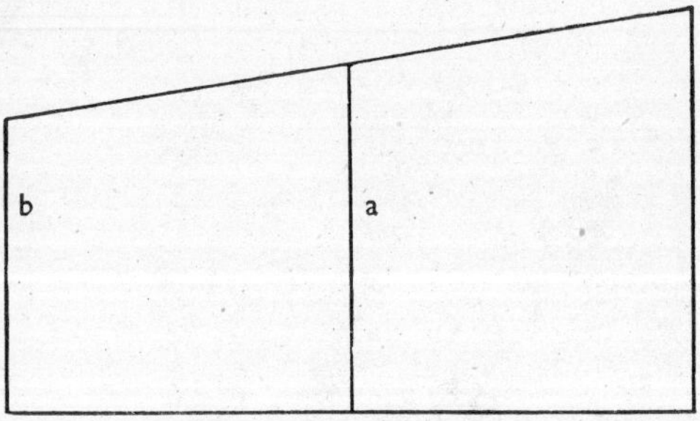

The nomogram uses a simple geometrical relationship for this purpose.

The three vertical lines are parallel and the middle one is equidistant from the other two.

Then, $2a=b+c$,

and given any two of these lengths the third can be measured.

Place three rulers with their decimal-scaled edges parallel in the manner indicated in the diagram, and lay any straight-edge across them and test the truth of $b=2a-c$, $c=2a-b$, and $a=\dfrac{b+c}{2}$

Now if we wish we may calibrate the three scales in logarithms similar to the slide-rule scale.

We may make $b=\log kB$, $2a=\log A$, and $c=\log C$, i.e. $a=\frac{1}{2}\log A$.

The diagram is then the picture of the formula, and will consist of two outer logarithmic scales of equal intervals and a central one of half the intervals of the other two. The B scale will have a shift in its calibrations resulting from $\log k$ (constant, because k is a constant).

We will take a particular formula that is constantly used by electricians:

$$\text{Amps}=\frac{\text{Volts}}{\text{Ohms}}$$

$$\therefore \quad \log(\text{Amps})=\log(\text{Volts})-\log(\text{Ohms}).$$

The central scale (on facing page) then will be the volts scale.

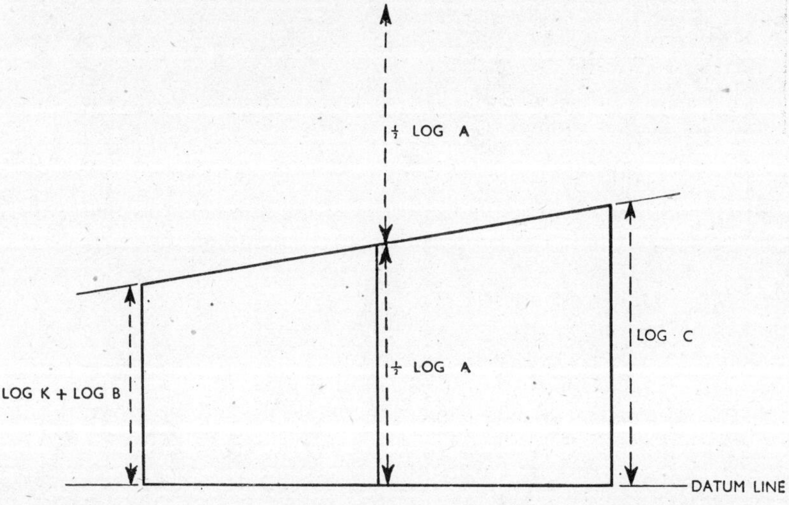

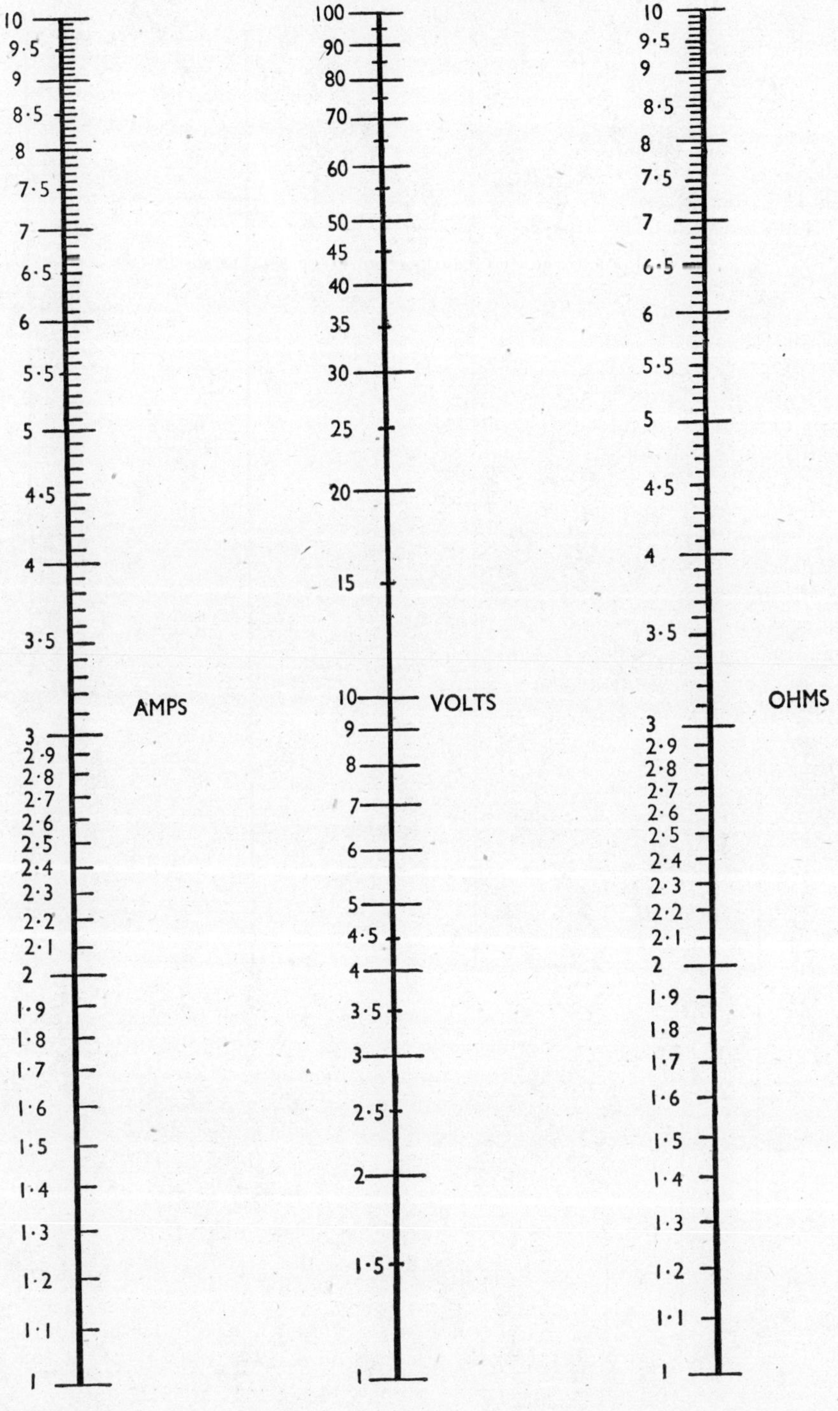
AMPS
VOLTS
OHMS
10
9·5
9
8·5
8
7·5
7
6·5
6
5·5
5
4·5
4
3·5
3
2·9
2·8
2·7
2·6
2·5
2·4
2·3
2·2
2·1
2
1·9
1·8
1·7
1·6
1·5
1·4
1·3
1·2
1·1
1
100
90
80
70
60
50
45
40
35
30
25
20
15
10
9
8
7
6
5
4·5
4
3·5
3
2·5
2
1·5
1

The radio technician often works with small currents, fairly high voltages and large resistances.

The scales can be marked with those powers of 10 that are most convenient.

On the right is a variation on the same nomogram. The scales are exactly as before but the markings are differently numbered so that we may deal with small currents (·001 amp to ·01 amp) and larger voltages.

If the range of voltages ran higher still and the resistances also, a further improvement of the scales could be carried out by squeezing the volts and ohms scales thus:

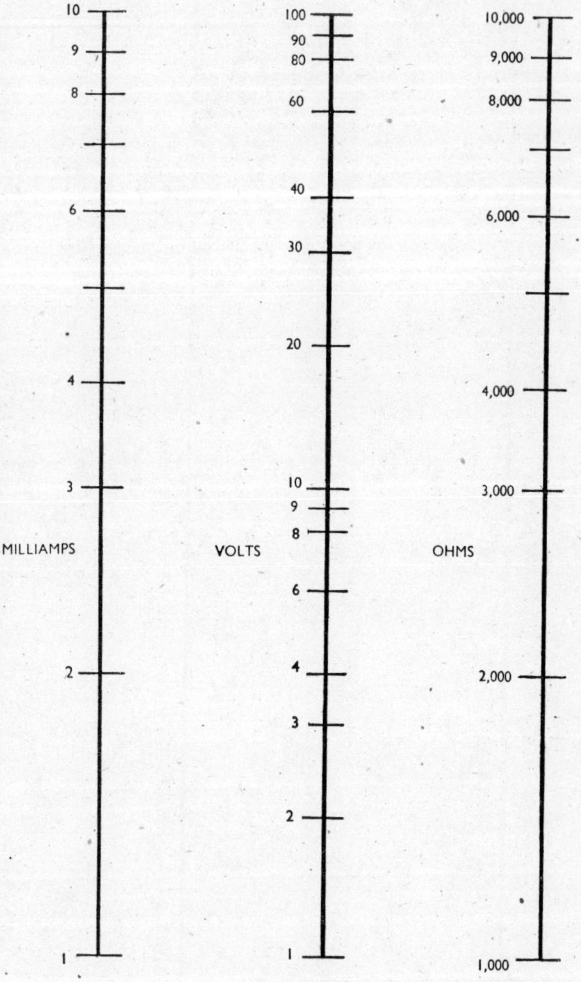

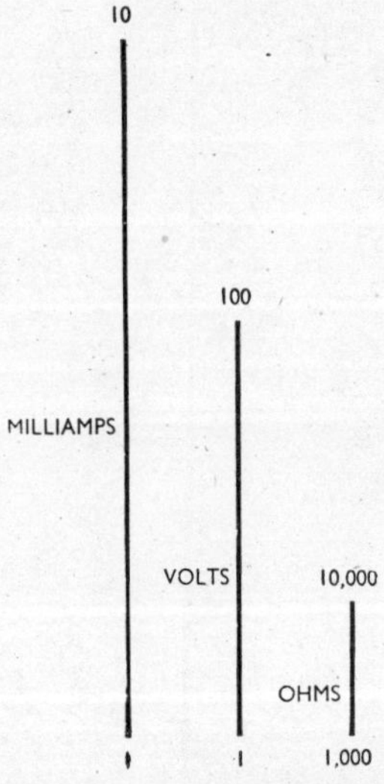

Extra calibrations could then be added, increasing the volts range nearly tenfold calibrating and the ohms range in megohms.

Nomogram for formula:

$$A=\frac{4}{3}\,B.C.$$

Scale B, shown on page 339, has an upward displacement of $\log\frac{4}{3}$ because

$$\log\frac{4}{3}B=\log\frac{4}{3}+\log B.$$

Otherwise, scales B and C have intervals double the corresponding ones on A.

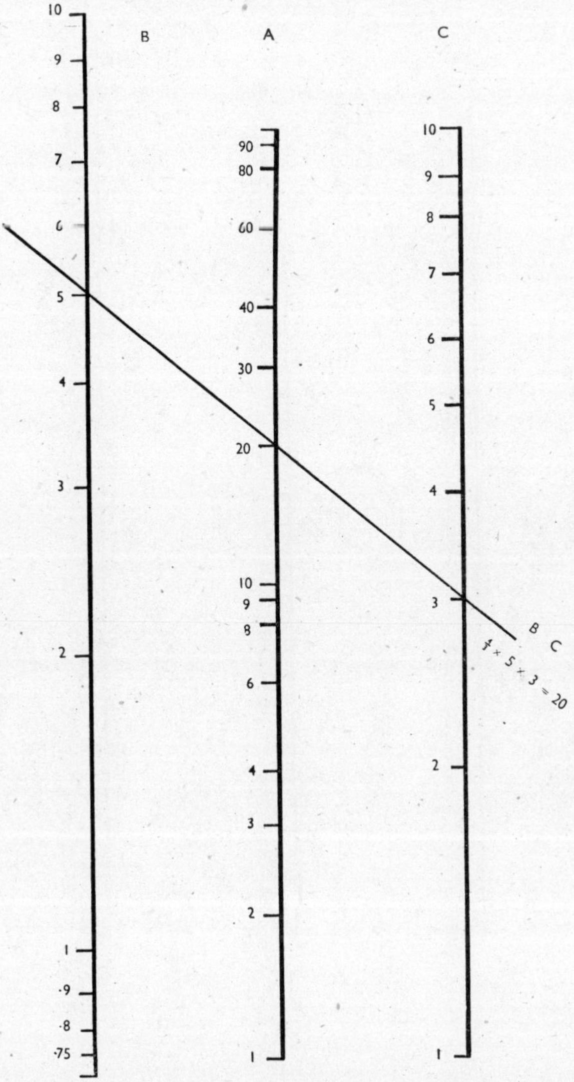

Test the scale as we do in the following example to satisfy yourself of its reliability.

[It has not been calibrated fully because it has only been used as an illustration.]

Find value of C when A is 8 and B is ·75.

We will show another variation of the basic idea by the use of the well-known electrical formula:

$$\text{Amps} \times \text{Volts} = \text{Watts}$$

$$\log (\text{amps}) + \log (\text{volts}) = \log (\text{watts}).$$

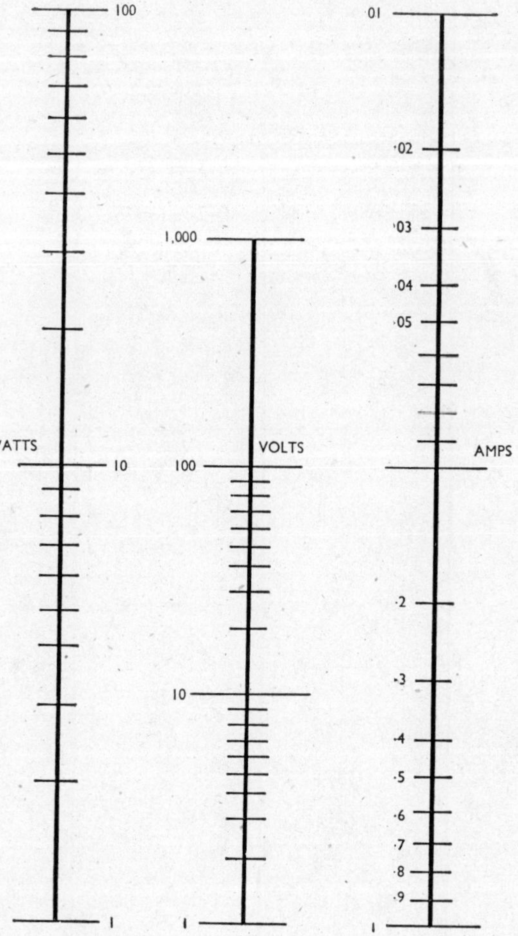

This can be re-arranged:

$$\log(\text{volts}) = \log(\text{watts}) - \log(\text{amps})$$

which we shall tie with $2a=b+(10-c)$ in the manner shown below:

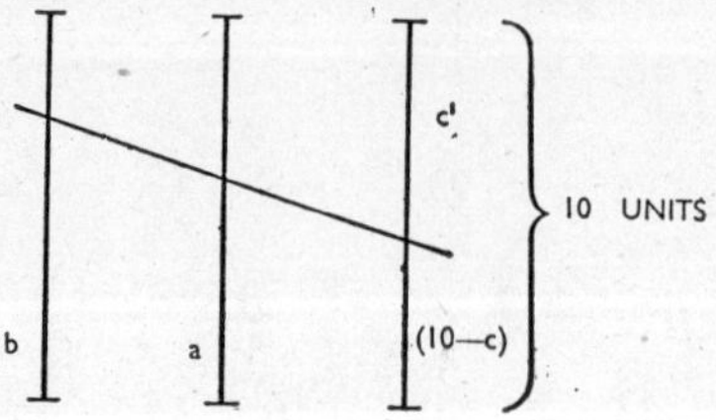

then b measures logs of watts
a measures $\frac{1}{2}$ logs of volts
and c' measures logs of $\dfrac{\text{amps}}{10}$

The effect of using this idea is to obtain greater spacing for a smaller range of watts and at the same time a greater range of volts.

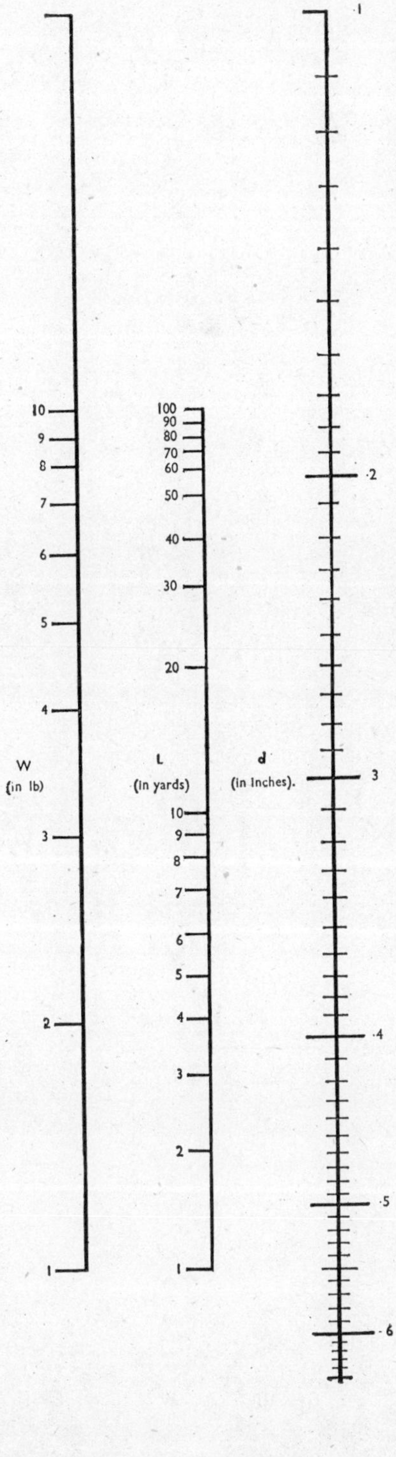

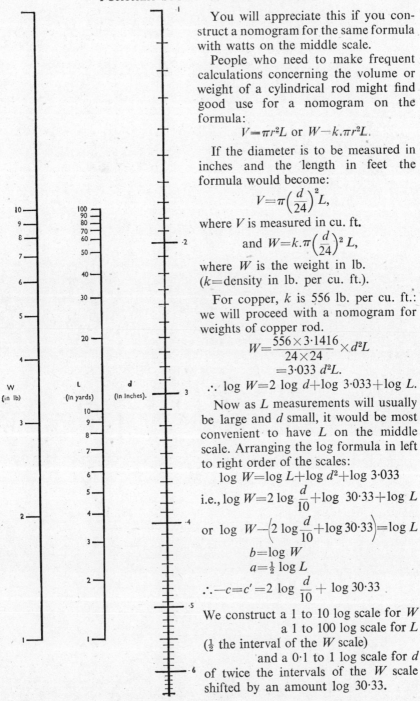

You will appreciate this if you construct a nomogram for the same formula with watts on the middle scale.

People who need to make frequent calculations concerning the volume or weight of a cylindrical rod might find good use for a nomogram on the formula:

$$V=\pi r^2L \text{ or } W=k.\pi r^2L.$$

If the diameter is to be measured in inches and the length in feet the formula would become:

$$V=\pi\left(\frac{d}{24}\right)^2L,$$

where V is measured in cu. ft.

$$\text{and } W=k.\pi\left(\frac{d}{24}\right)^2 L,$$

where W is the weight in lb. (k=density in lb. per cu. ft.).

For copper, k is 556 lb. per cu. ft.: we will proceed with a nomogram for weights of copper rod.

$$W=\frac{556\times 3{\cdot}1416}{24\times 24}\times d^2L$$
$$=3{\cdot}033\ d^2L.$$

$$\therefore \log W=2\log d+\log 3{\cdot}033+\log L.$$

Now as L measurements will usually be large and d small, it would be most convenient to have L on the middle scale. Arranging the log formula in left to right order of the scales:

$$\log W=\log L+\log d^2+\log 3{\cdot}033$$

$$\text{i.e., } \log W=2\log\frac{d}{10}+\log 30{\cdot}33+\log L$$

$$\text{or } \log W-\left(2\log\frac{d}{10}+\log 30{\cdot}33\right)=\log L$$

$$b=\log W$$
$$a=\tfrac{1}{2}\log L$$

$$\therefore -c=c'=2\log\frac{d}{10}+\log 30{\cdot}33$$

We construct a 1 to 10 log scale for W a 1 to 100 log scale for L ($\frac{1}{2}$ the interval of the W scale) and a 0·1 to 1 log scale for d of twice the intervals of the W scale shifted by an amount log 30·33.

If you have difficulty in preparing the third scale you can always fix it by taking known values of the other two variables, and fixing a few points (preferably 1, 10, 100 or ·1) and you will soon see how to strike off the rest of the scale.

E.g., from the formula when $W=1$ and $L=1$, $d=\cdot57$,
and when $d=\cdot1$, and $L=100$, $W=3\cdot03$.

Exercises

1. Find the square roots of the following numbers:

2·439   5·008   8·999
10·89   31·06   89·99
37   2·51   26·1

2. Measure on your slide-rule and see what $9^{\frac{1}{2}}$ is. What numbers are the following?—$16^{\frac{1}{2}}$, $25^{\frac{1}{2}}$, $49^{\frac{1}{2}}$, $100^{\frac{1}{2}}$, $8^{\frac{1}{3}}$, $8^{\frac{2}{3}}$, $16^{\frac{3}{4}}$.

3. What are the characteristics of the logarithms of the following numbers?

28·35   93·4   3,500   52,080
7·225   3·08   ·0803   20·63
139·7   150   100·4   40
·08725   ·007   77·2   ·462

4. What are the mantissae of the same 16 numbers in exercise 3? Write down the complete logarithm of each of them.

5. Find the antilogarithms of 0·3010, 0·9031, 0·6021, 0·4771, 0·8451.

6. What are the antilogarithms of
2, 5, 0, 3, 1, $\bar{2}$, $\bar{1}$, $\bar{6}$?

7. What are the antilogarithms of 2·3010, 5·3010, 3·3010, 1·3010, $\bar{2}\cdot3010$, $\bar{1}\cdot3010$, 2·9031, 5·9031, 3·9031, 1·9031, $\bar{2}\cdot9031$, $\bar{1}\cdot9031$, 2·6021, 5·6021, 3·6021, 1·6021, $\bar{2}\cdot6021$, $\bar{1}\cdot6021$, 2·4771, 5·4771, 3·4771, 1·4771, $\bar{2}\cdot4771$, $\bar{1}\cdot4771$.

8. Find the antilogarithms of 0·1234, 1·1234, $\bar{1}\cdot1234$, 0·2553, 1·2553, $\bar{1}\cdot2553$, 0·8751, 1·8751, $\bar{1}\cdot8751$, 0·9876, 1·9876, $\bar{1}\cdot9876$, 0·5185, 1·5185, $\bar{1}\cdot5185$, 0·7384, 1·7384, $\bar{1}\cdot7384$.

Typical calculations to be worked by the use of logarithms.

9. 37×145.
10. $12\cdot75\times31\cdot25$.
11. $\cdot6542\times22\cdot5$.
12. $397\cdot2\times\cdot0018$.
13. $2\cdot63\times\cdot078\times65\cdot3$.
14. $204\cdot7\div32\cdot04$.
15. $17\cdot9\div25\cdot6$.
16. $3\cdot5\div112\cdot5$.
17. $53\div\cdot981$.
18. $\cdot087\div29\cdot5$.
19. $1\div\cdot0067$.

20. Find the following powers by logarithms:
$(2\cdot646)^2$, $(1\cdot587)^3$, $(8\cdot434)^3$, $(4\cdot472)^2$, $(5\cdot477)^4$, $(1\cdot817)^6$.

21. Find the following roots:
$\sqrt[5]{2}$, $\sqrt[5]{10}$, $\sqrt[5]{32}$, $\sqrt[7]{13}$, $\sqrt[6]{125}$, $\sqrt[4]{2401}$, $\sqrt[5]{7\cdot595}$.

22. If you were making a table of logarithms and you had worked out log 2 ($=a$, say) and log 3 ($=b$, say), you could immediately write down log 6, because $6=2\times3$, so log $6=$ log 2 plus log $3=a+b$. How would you find the logarithms of the numbers below, and why would your rules work?

4, 8, 16, 32, 64.
9, 27, 81.
12, 24, 48, 96.
36, 72.
5, 25, 75.
1·5, 7·5.

CHAPTER XI
TRIGONOMETRY

WE have seen how geometry is designed to help us to understand the laws governing figures such as triangles, polygons and circles. This understanding has enabled man to grapple with the problems of building and engineering construction.

The theorems on similar triangles, for example, form the basis of scale drawing, used so extensively in design and draughtmanship.

However, there is a serious limitation involved in drawing to scale. For example, precision instruments often depend upon a high degree of accuracy in their manufacture; their components may need to be made to measurements involving thousandths of an inch. The engineering trade talks commonly in terms of thou's. If this work is carried out from scale drawings, all manner of errors may reduce their reliability to worthlessness. The thickness of a line, the small error in a measurement of a line or angle, the shrinkage of paper due to weather conditions, are a few contributions to the weakness of the scale drawing.

Trigonometry is an attempt to by-pass the scale drawing and its attendant troubles by putting the laws of geometry on the footing of arithmetic; that is, to devise methods of calculation rather than measurement.

An angle seldom occurs in isolation: its boundary lines usually link up with other lines. The triangle is the commonest home of the angle.

The angle at *A* can be found as one of a trinity in an infinite number of triangles of various sizes and shapes.

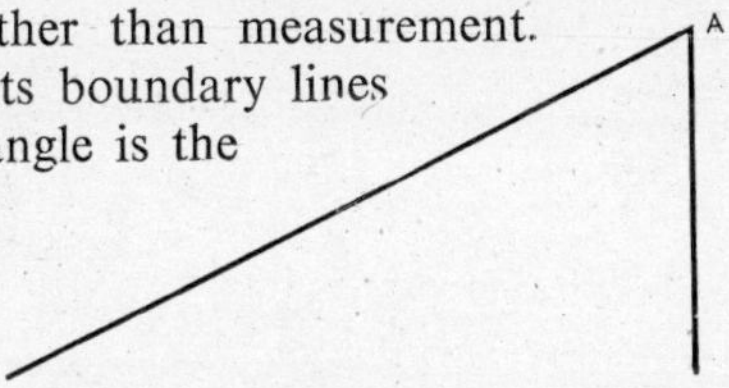

It will be of the greatest help if we restrict the number of companion angles so that we are able to confine our attention to *A* itself. This can be done by thinking of the right-angled triangles in which *A* is to be found.

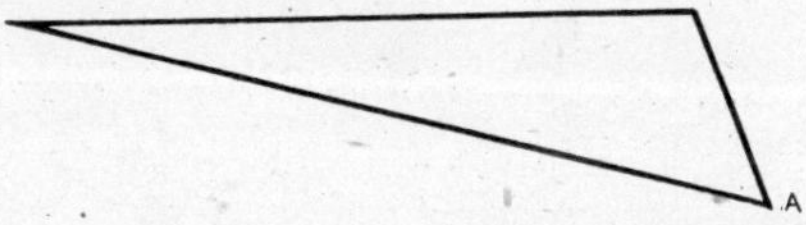

Draw angle *A* as shown on the top of page 344 and then draw a few transversals each at right-angles to one or other of the arms.

The triangles so formed are equiangular because they all contain *A* and a right-angle; the remaining angles must, therefore, be equal.

Therefore, the length of the sides of these triangles must always bear the same relationship to each other.

i.e., $PQ : QA : AP :: RS : SA : AR$

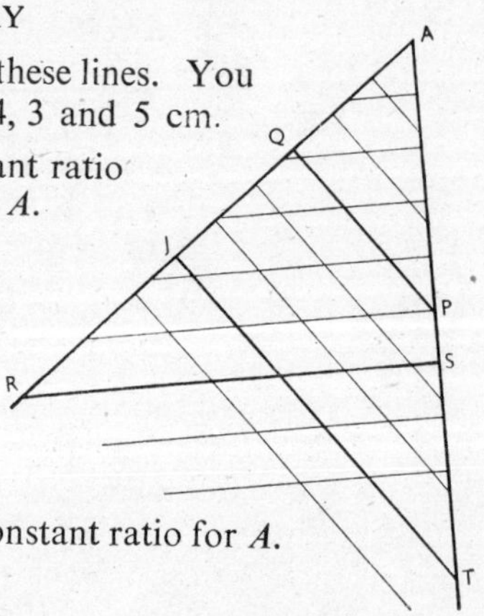

Test the truth of this by actually measuring these lines. You will find their respective lengths are 2, $1\frac{1}{2}$, $2\frac{1}{2}$, 4, 3 and 5 cm.

Thus $\frac{PQ}{QA} = \frac{RS}{SA} = \frac{TJ}{JA}$ etc., = a constant ratio for A.

In our example:

$$\left.\begin{aligned}\frac{PQ}{QA} &= \frac{2}{1\frac{1}{2}} \\ \frac{RS}{SA} &= \frac{4}{3}\end{aligned}\right\} = 1\tfrac{1}{3} \text{ or } 1{\cdot}33$$

And, again, $\frac{QA}{AP} = \frac{SA}{AR}$, etc., = another constant ratio for A.

In our example:

$$\left.\begin{aligned}\frac{QA}{AP} &= \frac{1\frac{1}{2}}{2\frac{1}{2}} \\ \frac{SA}{AR} &= \frac{3}{5}\end{aligned}\right\} = \frac{3}{5} \text{ or } 0{\cdot}6$$

Draw A again.

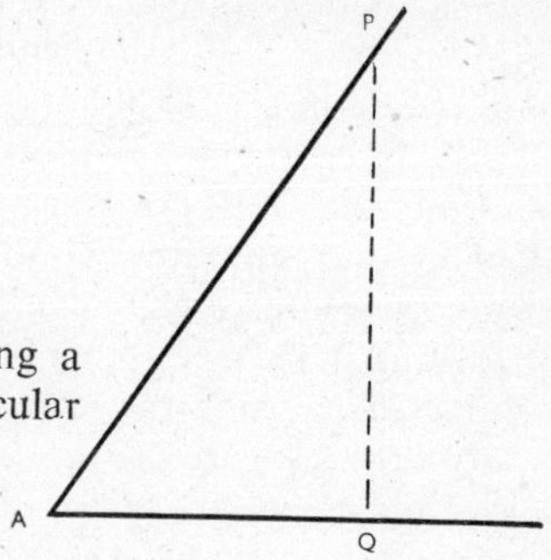

Make any right-angled triangle by choosing a point P in one arm and drawing PQ perpendicular to the other arm.

We have found that:

$\frac{PQ}{QA}$ is a constant ratio for the angle A.

Test this deduction for yourself by choosing half-a-dozen different positions for P, measuring PQ, QA and working out the ratio. If you wish to satisfy yourself, make $A = 63\frac{1}{2}°$; you should then find that the ratio $\frac{PQ}{QA}$ is always 2.

Because the ratio $\frac{PQ}{QA}$ is a constant depending only on A, we may call it a function of A, and give it a name. It is known as the tangent of A, and is usually written tan A.

$$\tan A = \frac{PQ}{QA} = \frac{\text{side opposite } A}{\text{distance of opposite side from } A.}$$

Notice that we have arrived at this decision without the need for accurate drawings, except for the purpose of testing our conclusions. We may next compile a table showing the values of the tangents of all angles. It would be a lengthy task for one person to do this from thousands of scale drawings: there are more reliable methods for doing the job, so we will content ourselves for the moment by relying on the labour of others. A table of tangents can be found in most books of Mathematical Tables.

There are already many uses to which we can put this first step in trigonometry.

Example.

From the top of a 50-ft. tower on the coast, the water-line of a distant ship is observed to be depressed at an angle of 15° to the horizon. How far away is the ship?

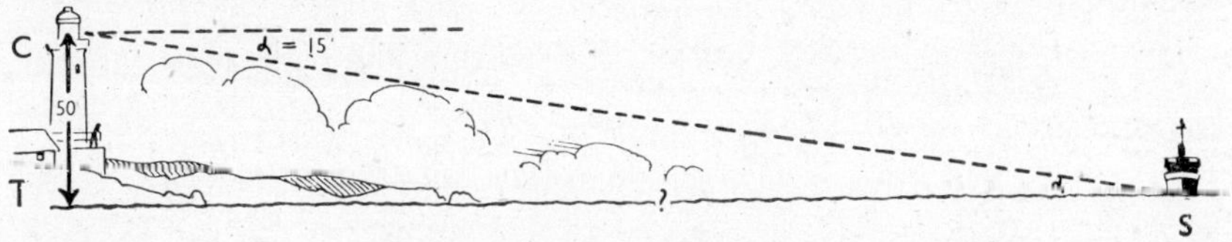

Using the fact that $\frac{TC}{TS}=\tan \alpha$

we write $\frac{50}{TS}=\tan 15°$

$$\therefore \quad TS=\frac{50}{\tan 15°}$$

$$=\frac{50}{\cdot 2679} \qquad (\tan 15=\cdot 2679)$$

$$=186\cdot 6 \text{ ft.}$$

An approximate sketch will furnish a rough check on the result.

Example.

Driving along a straight road, a distant church is observed to have a bearing of 78°. The speedometer reads 05347·4. The bearing is found to be 90° when the reading has moved to 05348·2. How near is the church to the road?

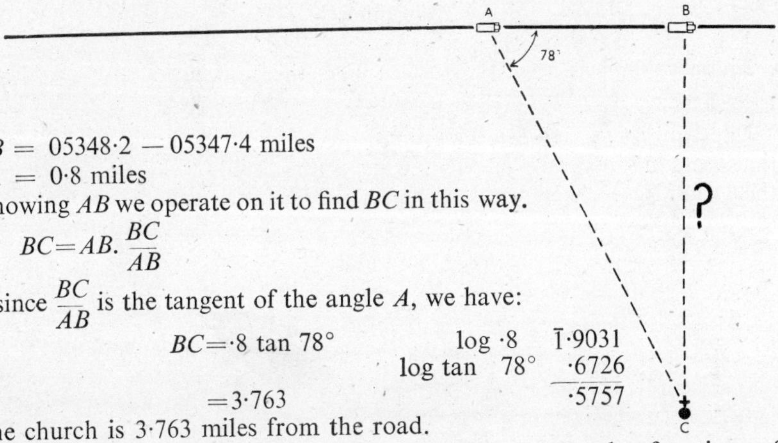

$AB = 05348\cdot 2 - 05347\cdot 4$ miles

$= 0\cdot 8$ miles

Knowing AB we operate on it to find BC in this way.

$$BC=AB.\ \frac{BC}{AB}$$

and since $\frac{BC}{AB}$ is the tangent of the angle A, we have:

$$BC=\cdot 8 \tan 78°$$

log ·8	$\bar{1}\cdot 9031$
log tan 78°	·6726
	·5757

$$=3\cdot 763$$

The church is 3·763 miles from the road.

Refer once more to the figure on page 344. There were other functions of A showing constancy beside the tangent.

$\frac{PQ}{PA}$ is a constant ratio, known as the sine of the angle A and written sin A.

$$\sin A=\frac{PQ}{PA}=\frac{\text{side opposite } A}{\text{hypotenuse}}$$

Test this statement by your own construction and measurement of an angle of say, 44½°, for which the value of the sine will be found always to be

0·7. Repeat the exercise for an angle of your own choice and verify your result by reference to a table of sines.

Example.

An aeroplane navigator observes a distant landmark with a bearing at right-angles to his straight-line track. After flying a further 6 miles he finds the new bearing is 106° from his track. How far is he now from the landmark?

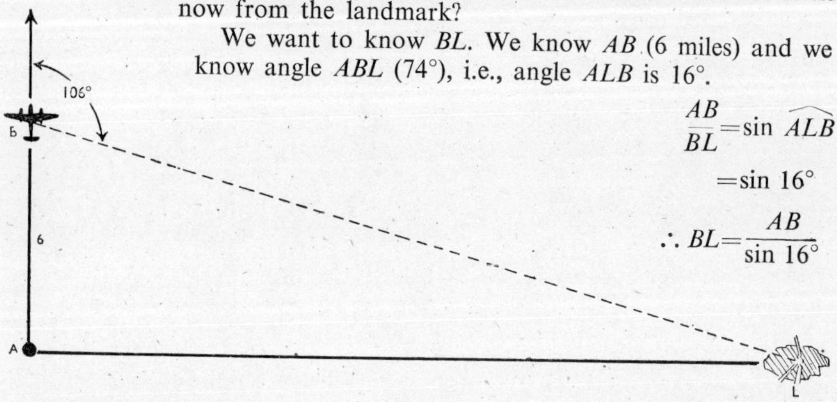

We want to know BL. We know AB (6 miles) and we know angle ABL (74°), i.e., angle ALB is 16°.

$$\frac{AB}{BL}=\sin \widehat{ALB}$$

$$=\sin 16°$$

$$\therefore BL=\frac{AB}{\sin 16°}$$

By calculation then:

Distance of landmark now $=\dfrac{6}{\sin\ 16°}$ miles

$=21·78$ miles

log 6	=	·7782
log sin 16°	=	$\bar{1}$·4402
		1·3380

The aeroplane is now 21·78 miles from the landmark.

Example.

The sun's rays strike level ground at 20° with the horizontal. Assuming that the sun's rays are parallel, what is the intensity of the radiation on the ground compared with that on a surface at right angles to the ray?

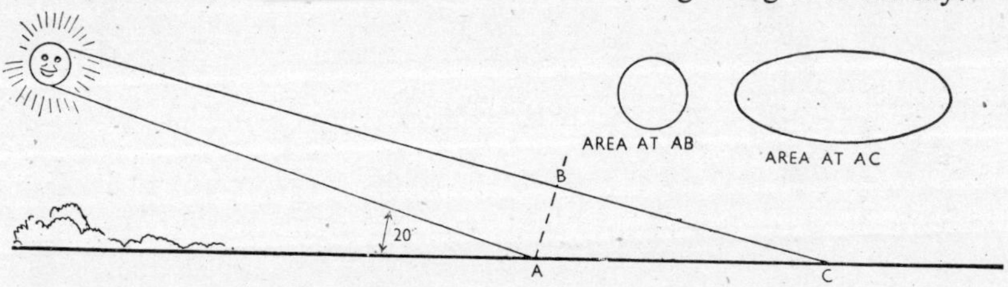

The diagram shows that the intensity on the ground (AC) will be less than on AB, because the radiation is spread over a larger area.

$$\text{The ratio of the areas}=\frac{AC}{AB}=\frac{1}{\sin C}$$

$$\text{Ratio of intensities of radiation}=\frac{AB}{AC}=\sin C:1$$

$$=\sin 20°$$

$$=·3420:1.$$

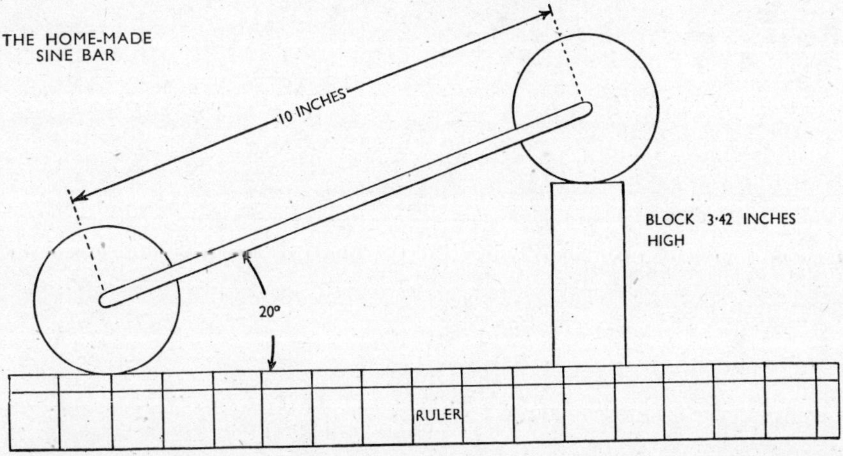

In industry, angles are frequently checked by means of a sine bar. The principle of the sine bar is shown above. Two equal discs are fastened to a straight bar, so that their centres are 10 in. apart.

Suppose it is desired to construct an angle of 20°. We proceed as follows. The sine of 20° is 0·3420. We multiply this by 10 (since the discs are 10 in. apart). This gives 3·42 in. A block 3·42 in. high is made, and put against a straight ruler, as shown above. The sine bar is then placed in position, so that one disc touches the ruler and the other rests on top of the block. The bar will then be inclined at 20° to the ruler.

Of course, by choosing a block of some other height, any desired angle can be obtained. To make an angle of $x°$, the height of the block must be $(10 \sin x°)$ in.

In factories, the blocks are built up from Johannsen gauges (see Chapter III), or Joeys. The actual construction of the sine bar used in industry is not quite the same as that shown here, but no new principle is used.

By using blocks graded to a thousandth of an inch, angles can be constructed with far greater accuracy than would be possible by using a protractor.

Try for yourself making angles of 30°, 40°, 50° and other sizes, by this method.

A final reference to the figures on page 344 will suggest that we give heed to the function of A involving AQ and AP.

The ratio $\frac{AQ}{AP}$ is known as the cosine of A, and usually written $\cos A$.

$$\cos A = \frac{AQ}{AP} = \frac{\text{adjacent side}}{\text{hypotenuse}}$$

Test the constancy of this ratio, the cosine, for any angle of your choice, by construction and measurement.

Example.

What is the vertical height of a right cone with a semi-vertical angle of 12° and a slant height of 25 in.?

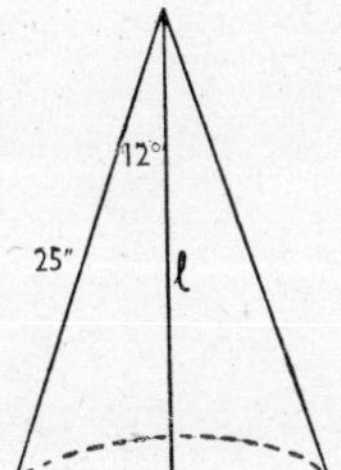

$$\frac{l}{25} = \cos 12°$$
$$l = (25 \cos 12°) \text{ in.}$$
$$= 24{\cdot}45 \text{ in.}$$

$$\log 25 = 1{\cdot}3979$$
$$\log \cos 12° = \bar{1}{\cdot}9904$$
$$1{\cdot}3883$$

The vertical height of the cone is 24·45 in.

You will probably have noticed that cos 12° has the same value as sin 78°. For this reason, it is not necessary to have tables of sines and of cosines: tables of sines can be used for finding cosines. Remember that the cosine of an angle is the sine of its complement.

VECTORS

It is not always possible to express mathematical quantities completely in terms of simple numbers. For example, the coastguard reporting his observation of a ship at sea would be telling only half the story if he reported its speed alone. Complete information about its movement would include a statement on its course. Similarly, the ground control of an aeroplane must take note of speed and direction of flight. Quantities involving magnitude (size) *and* direction (angular measurement) are called vectors.

The study of vectors is of immense technical importance in the modern world, and it entails extensive use of geometry and trigonometry.

Suppose a blind man is told to push a wagon along. The wagon is round and runs on a rail-track, so it can only move along the track no matter where the unfortunate man directs his effort.

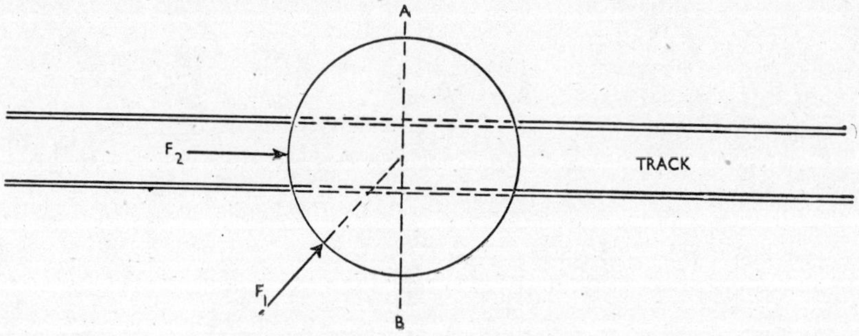

If F_1 represents his push (in magnitude and direction), it is clear that the truck will tend to move along the track to the right. As soon as the wagon begins to move the man will sense that there is a better pushing position and he will move into the new position represented by the vector F_2 where his force will have the maximum effect. There are two positions, *A* and *B*, and only two, where a direct push would have no effect because the rails would take the entire thrust. At all other positions his direct push would tend to move the wagon, those near *A* and *B* very slightly, and those near the track with greater effect. Therefore, we may think of the man's pushing force as having two distinct parts, one along the track and the other across the track, i.e. at right-angles to each other.

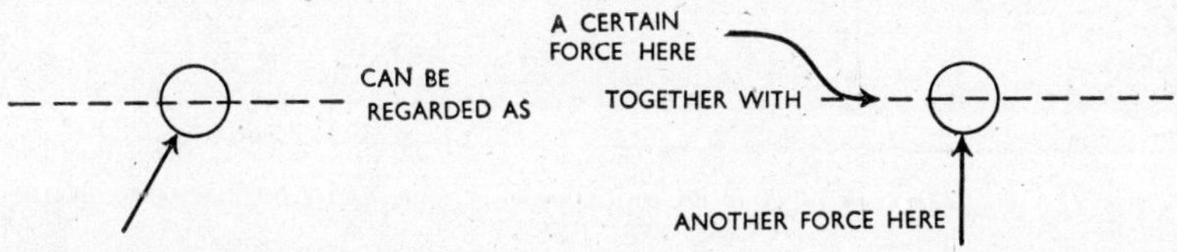

Each of these parts or components will be less in magnitude than the magnitude of the man's force. We cannot yet represent them in the diagram because we do not know their magnitudes.

The extreme cases give us a clue to the mathematics of the problem.

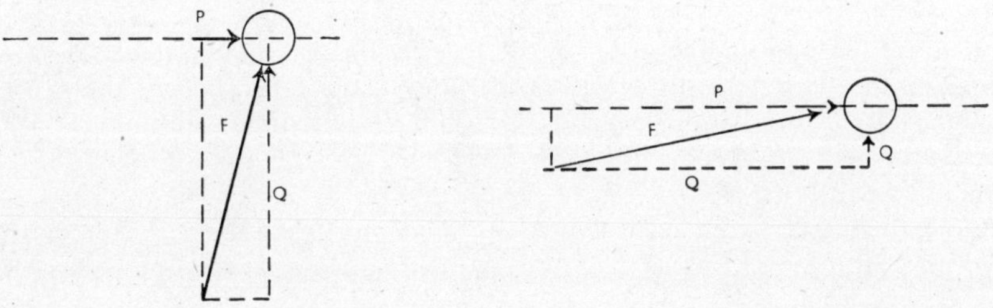

These diagrams suggest that the vector of the man's force can be represented as the diagonal of a rectangle in which the two sides are the vectors of the two components P and Q. The track component (P) is the only one that can be effective in causing motion because the other will be wasted in tending to displace the rails.

If this theory is sound—and an experimental test will be suggested in the paragraphs below—any force F can be resolved into an equivalent pair of forces at right-angles to one another.

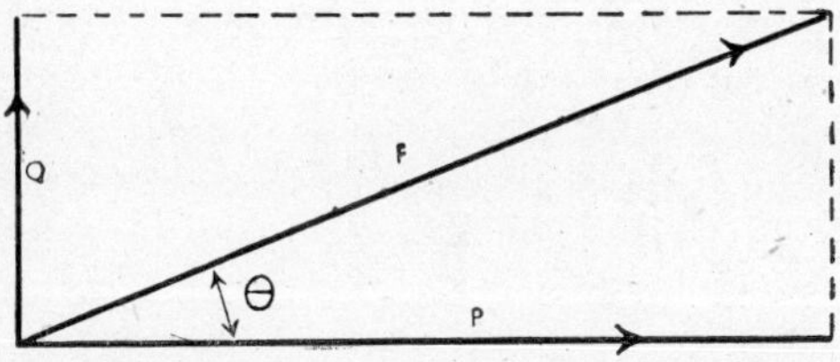

As the lengths in the figure represent the magnitudes of the forces, we may say that the magnitudes of these two components are:

$$F \cos \theta \ (= P) \text{ and } F \sin \theta \ (= Q)$$

where θ is the angle between F and its component P.

You should now improvise an experiment to test this mathematical theory. It can be done with a model railway truck on a piece of model railway track, thus:

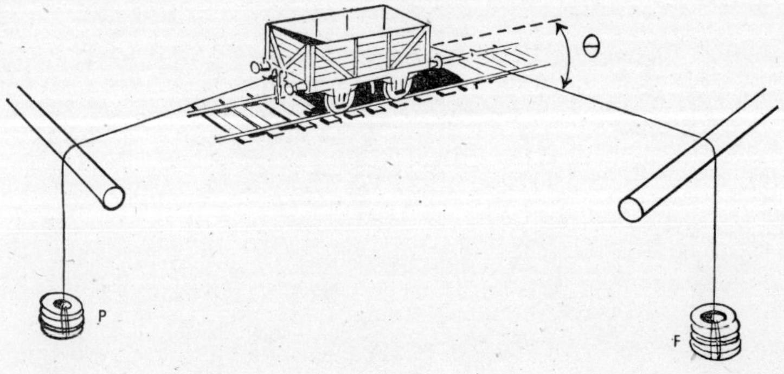

The force F is created by attaching weights to a piece of thread passing over a smooth rod or roller or pulley. To measure the component P which is effective in pulling the truck along the rails, you may attach another thread to the truck, this thread to be parallel to the rails and passing over a similar guide to carry another load of weights. Adjust the weighting until the truck is just on the point of moving. Then measure the angle θ between the F thread and the track.

Work out $F \cos \theta$ and see if it is equal (but opposite) to the force down the track preventing movement. The more refined your apparatus the closer will be the agreement.

There is excellent practice in basic trigonometry to be obtained by a succession of experiments of this type; such practice will be worth more than a whole bookful of artificial theoretical exercises. By way of variation you may measure the angle ϕ between the F thread and the sleepers: in this case, the effective component of F causing motion will be $F \sin \phi$.

THE THREE-MAN TUG-OF-WAR

Any three people pulling against each other, the Three Bears for instance, can be arranged to produce equilibrium (deadlock). The Baby Bear can be positioned to defy all the might and main of the Father Bear on one hand and the Mother Bear on the other hand. Do you think he would hold his ground in either of these vector diagrams?

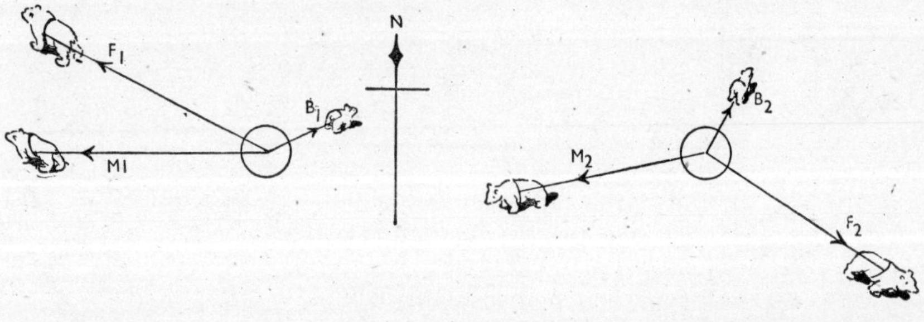

If you think the ring would move, try to predict the direction of its movement in each case.

You will probably agree that the next diagram is more likely to represent

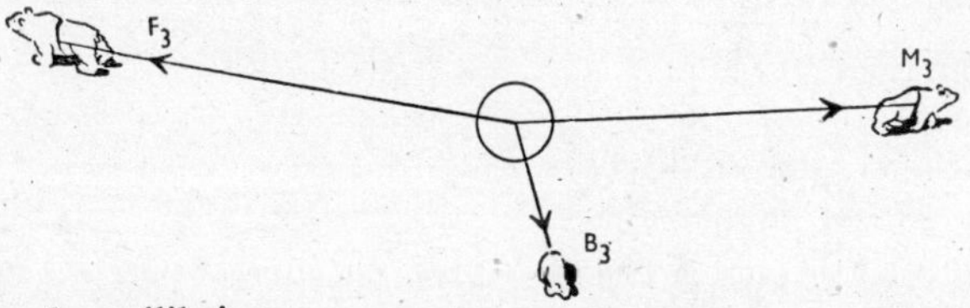

a condition of equilibrium.

See if you can sketch some alternative solutions: a little later on you will be able to judge the accuracy of your own attempts. There are a great many solutions, all different, and we will now see if we can bring our mathematical skill to bear on the general problem in order to calculate the conditions of equilibrium instead of guessing them.

Look again at the solution offered above. M_3 and B_3 must both be contributing components to build up opposition to F_3 (in the next view of the situation we will leave out the suffix $_3$).

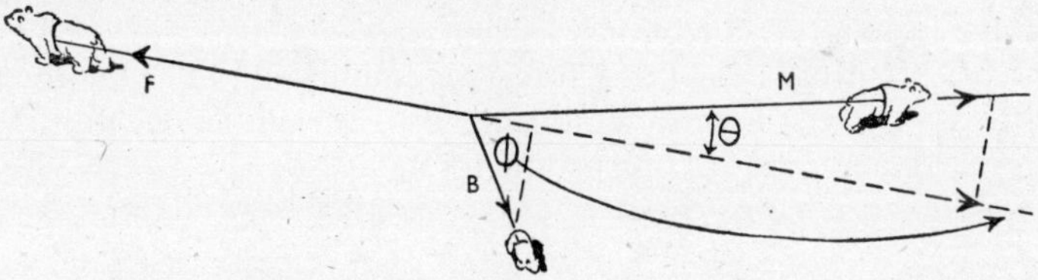

The component of M opposing F is $M \cos \theta$, and the component of B aiding and abetting it is $B \cos \phi$. We may add these two together algebraically because they have the same direction. Thus, we have:

$$M \cos \theta + B \cos \phi = F \quad . \; . \; . \; . \; . \; . \; . \; . \quad \text{(i)}$$

By a similar argument, the remaining components of M and B will be in direct opposition to each other, while F will have no influence on their private tug-of-war because F is at right angles to them.

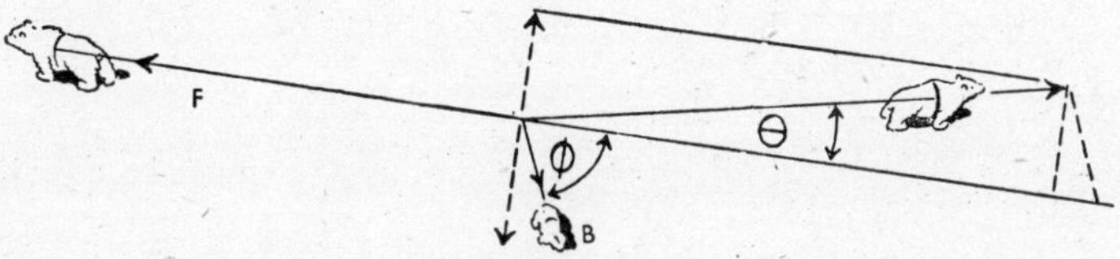

As there is equilibrium we may state:

$$M \sin \theta = B \sin \phi \quad . \; . \; . \; . \; . \; . \; . \; . \quad \text{(ii)}$$

The statements (i) and (ii) together tell us all that we want to know about the angles between *any* three forces F, M and B in equilibrium. Again, we should not be satisfied without an experimental test of the mathematics. Some such arrangement as is sketched at the top of page 352 may be used.

Friction at the turn of the threads as in this illustration will reduce the accuracy of the results, but you may at least try the approximate truth of the laws, and if you are keen you will think out refinements for reducing friction. To measure the angles put a sheet of paper on the tray and trace the positions of the threads on it, marking the magnitude of the force in each case *before* removing the sheet. You will then be able to use a protractor with comfort.

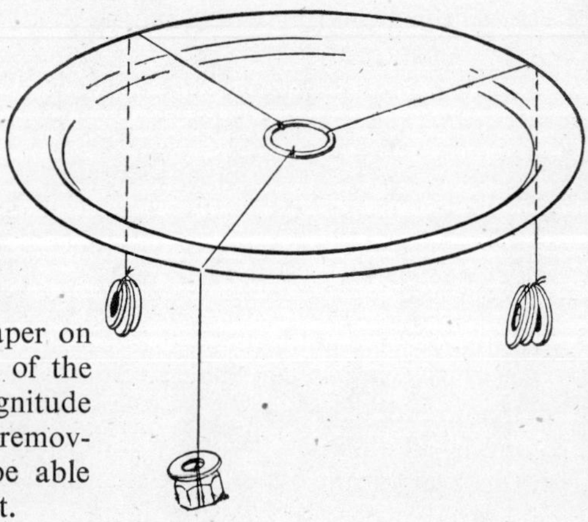

Not only will you be able to test the truth of the statements (i) and (ii) but you may find further trigonometrical entertainment. Instead of resolving each of the forces along a particular pair of lines at right angles to one another (one of these lines being the direction of one of the forces), see if you may resolve in *any* two directions at right angles. That is to say, trace the positions of the threads for three forces in equilibrium (P, Q, and R) then through O draw any straight line XX' and YY' at right angles to it. Measure the angles α, β and γ with your protractor.

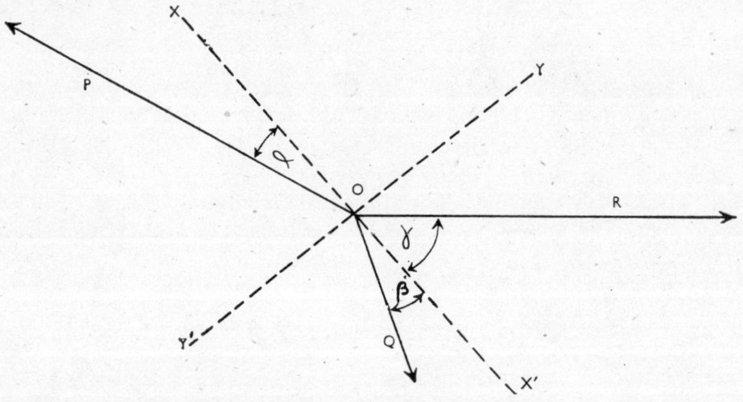

Because O is stationary, all forces acting along OX' must be equal in size to those acting along OX.

$$P \cos \alpha = Q \cos \beta + R \cos \gamma \text{ (test the truth of this).}$$

Again, because O is stationary, all forces acting along OY are together equal to those acting along OY'.

$$R \sin \gamma = P \sin \alpha + Q \sin \beta \text{ (test the truth of this).}$$

These mathematical laws are fundamental to the design of machines and machinery, and of the structures of bridges and buildings in which enormous stresses and strains might play havoc if not given due consideration.

Any three forces in equilibrium may be represented like this:

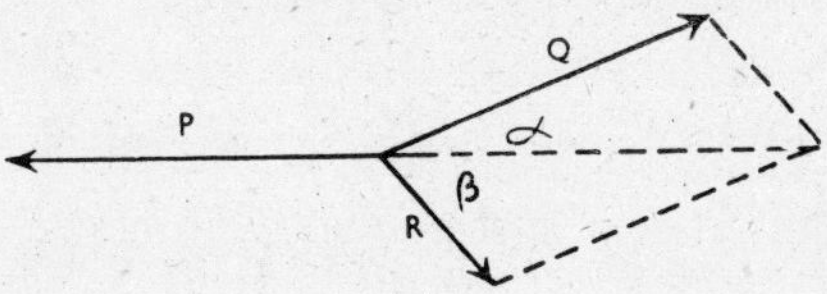

OR LIKE THIS :

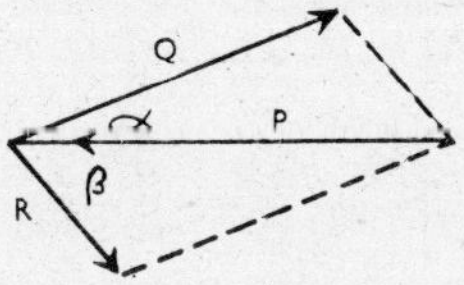

OR LIKE THIS :

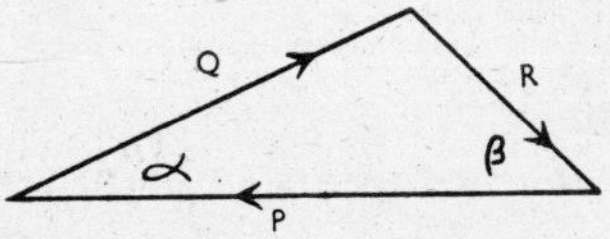

The vectors have the same magnitude and direction in each case:

(a) is usually called the parallelogram of vectors,

(b) is usually known as the triangle of vectors.

You should make yourself quite familiar with the main trigonometrical ratios, the sine, cosine, and tangent, before attempting to proceed further with the study of the subject. Another practical way of doing this is to make a simple clinometer (angle measurer) and use it in elementary surveying experiments. In the next drawing, a suggestion is made for the design of a home-made clinometer using a piece of straight narrow tubing mounted on a horizontal pivot carried on a swivel post.

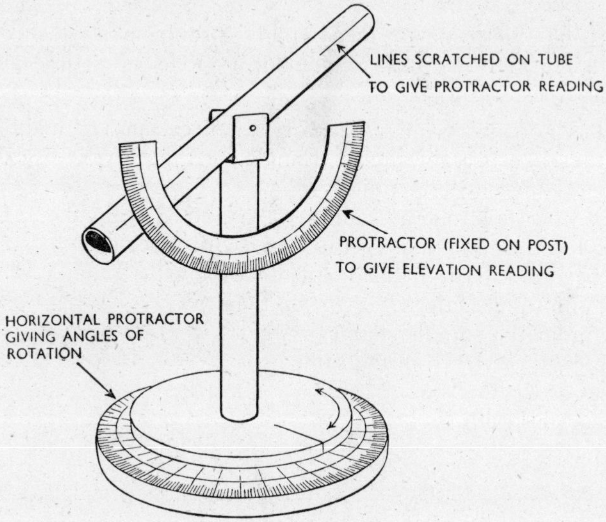

There are many simple refinements that you may introduce if you wish (for example levelling-screws and a plumb-line).

(i) You may use this for measuring the heights of posts, points on buildings, etc., by the following method.

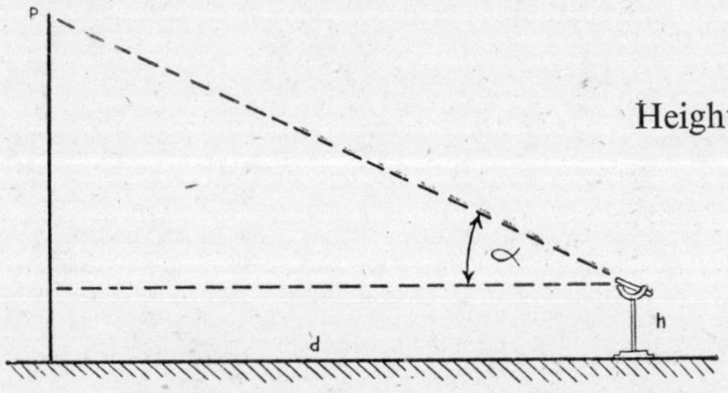

Height of $P = d \tan \alpha + h$.

(ii) Here is a method for measuring the distance of a distant object.

(a) Observe object, then turn through 90°.

(b) Set up a post B on this line of vision at a measured distance from A

(c) Finally, measure angle B.

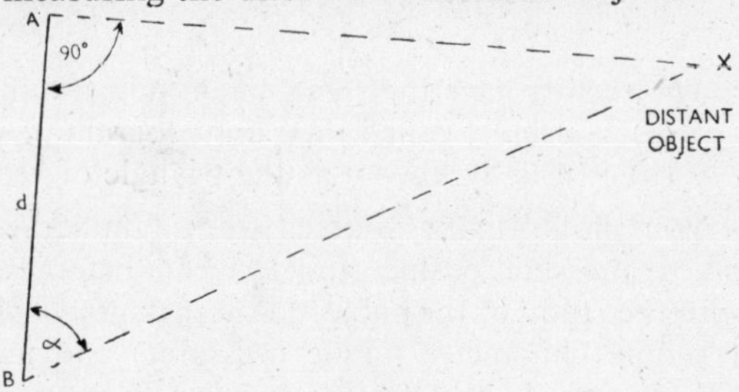

Then distance of A from object $= d \tan \alpha$

or distance of B from object $= \dfrac{d}{\cos \alpha}$

You will be able to devise many similar problems in which one measurement of length and one measurement of angle (besides the right angle) are used as the basis of calculation.

(iii) It is not always possible, nor is it necessary, to manoeuvre into a position that gives a right-angled triangle for the purpose of calculating the distance of an inaccessible point.

Suppose you have taken readings d, α and β from the positions A and B, and you wish to find the distance of P. It would be quite easy to make a scale drawing with this data, and to measure AP or BP on the drawing. Trigonometry should enable us to calculate BP or AP from the same data—and give us a far more accurate result.

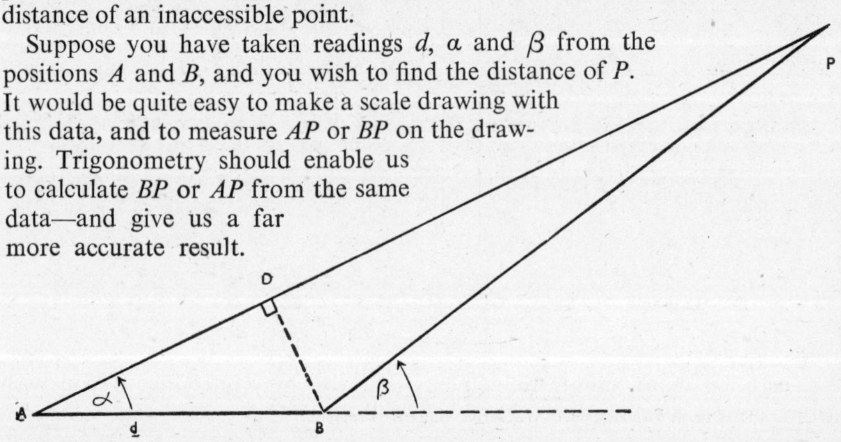

The perpendicular BD is common to two right-angled triangles. One gives its length as $d \sin \alpha$ and the other as $BP \sin P$.

$$\therefore \quad d. \sin \alpha = BP. \sin P$$

But β is the exterior angle of the triangle ABP.

$$\therefore \quad \text{angle } P = \beta - \alpha$$
$$\therefore \quad d. \sin \alpha = BP. \sin (\beta - \alpha)$$
$$\text{and we have } BP = \frac{d. \sin \alpha}{\sin (\beta - \alpha)}$$

Try this formula on small-scale observations that you can verify by measurement before you try anything more ambitious. It constitutes an important step forward—*knowing two angles and one side of any triangle* (no longer the special case of the right-angled triangle)—and we find ourselves in a position to solve the triangle completely.

Draw any triangle ABC; drop a perpendicular from C on to AB and see if you can show the truth of the formula

$$\frac{a}{\sin A} = \frac{b}{\sin B} \text{ (which can be extended to) } = \frac{c}{\sin C}$$

This general formula is used in surveying, in mechanics and in astronomy (to find the distance of stars from the earth, using a diameter of the earth's orbit as a base-line).

It would be equally useful to have a formula for finding the third side of a triangle when we know the lengths of two of the sides and the angle contained by them. There is such a formula and we will find it.

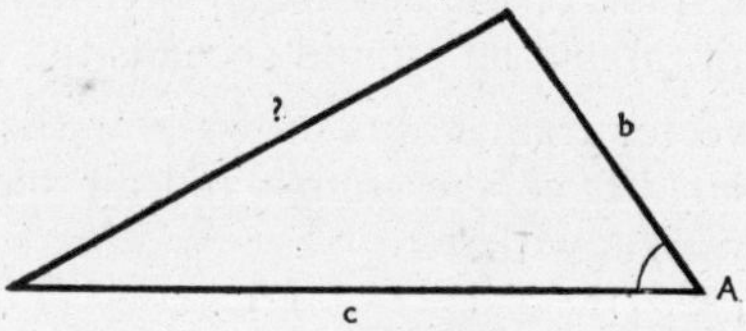

We wish to relate a, b and c and the angle A. We shall try to confine all trigonometrical ratios to the angle A.

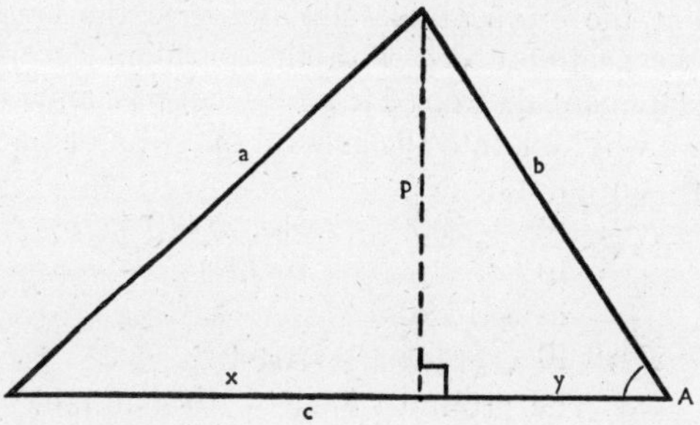

The perpendicular p, dividing the side c into two parts, x and y, gives two right-angled triangles.

$a^2 = p^2 + x^2$ (Pythagoras)

We are not interested in p and x except as steps in the direction of b, c and A.

$p^2 = b^2 - y^2$ (Pythagoras)

$$\therefore a^2 = b^2 - y^2 + x^2$$

Of x and y we prefer y because $y = b \cos A$.

We may also substitute $(c - y)$ for x, or, better still:

$$c - b \cos A \text{ for } x$$

$$\text{Thus,} \quad a^2 = b^2 - b^2 \cos^2 A + (c - b \cos A)^2$$
$$= b^2 - b^2 \cos^2 A + c^2 + b^2 \cos^2 A - 2bc \cos A$$
$$\therefore a^2 = b^2 + c^2 - 2bc \cos A$$

The same formula tells us how to find an angle (each angle, in fact) of a triangle when the three sides are known.

$$\cos A = \frac{b^2+c^2-a^2}{2bc}$$

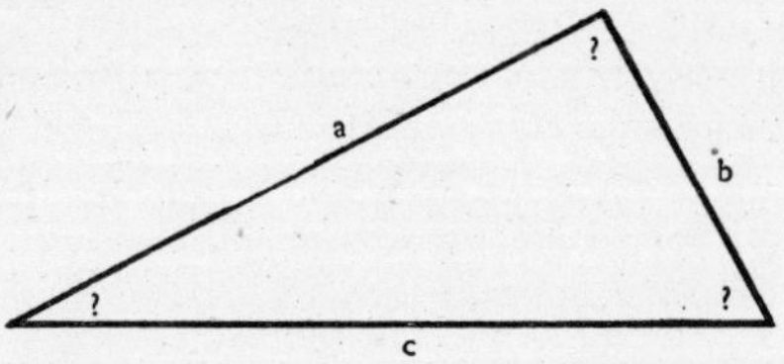

Example.

An aeroplane is flying on a course of 15° at an air speed of 200 m.p.h. The wind is blowing eastward at 10 m.p.h. Find its ground speed, track and drift.

If we imagine the air to be still, the situation appears as in the vector diagram (*a*).

As the entire mass of air is on the move relative to the ground, by the time the aircraft has reached *B* in the mass of air, both *A* and *B* will have been shifted eastward to the positions *A′* and *B′* over the ground.

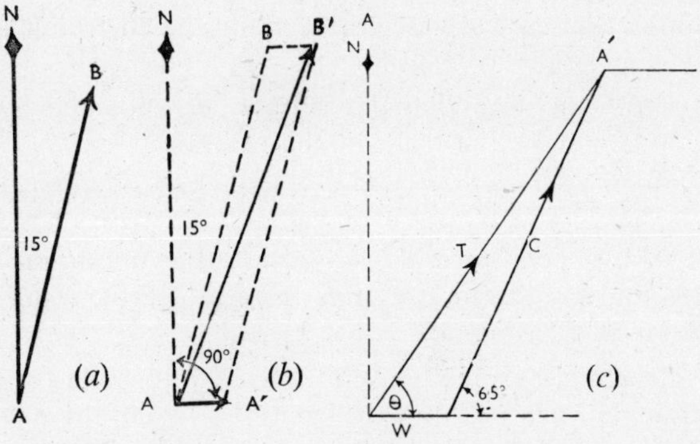

The track of the aeroplane over the ground is, therefore, the line joining *A* to *B′* (*b*) and its ground speed is the magnitude of the same vector *AB′*.

A vector triangle (*c*) shows how the true movement of the plane can be calculated from the course and air speed (*C*) and the wind (*W*).

We know that:

$$T^2 = W^2 + C^2 - 2W.C. \cos 115°,$$

but the cosine tables do not give the cosines of angles greater than 90°. We shall proceed with the problem accepting for the moment the bald statement that cos 115° = — cos 65°, and at the conclusion of the calculation we will look into the general question of sines, cosines and tangents of angles that are not acute.

$$T^2 = 10^2 + 200^2 + 2.\ 10.\ 200(0{\cdot}4226)$$
$$= 10^2\,(1 + 400 + 16{\cdot}904)$$
$$= 10^2\,(417{\cdot}904)$$
$$T = 10\sqrt{417{\cdot}904} = 204{\cdot}4$$

The ground speed is 204.4 m.p.h.

Using the formula $\dfrac{a}{\sin A} = \dfrac{b}{\sin B}$, we have $\dfrac{T}{\sin 115°} = \dfrac{C}{\sin \theta}$

Again you must accept that sin 115° = sin 65° and verify it later.

$$\sin \theta = \frac{C}{T} \sin 65° \quad = \frac{200}{204{\cdot}4} \sin 65°$$
$$\theta = 62°\ 28'.$$

and the angle called track is the complement of this angle; 27° 32′.

Drift is the angle measured clockwise between the course and the track. In our example the drift is 2° 32′.

Air navigators usually obtain their results by scale drawing rather than calculation; the results are then less accurate, but to compensate for this they use frequent observations to check and re-check their working.

SINE, COSINE AND TANGENT FOR ANGLES GREATER THAN 90°

We will now consider the trigonometrical functions for angles of *any* size. A home-made gadget will be very useful. The essential parts are a rotor arm pivoted against a vertical card or wall, and a vertical strip suspended at the free end of the arm and bearing a scale (two-directional) from the suspension pin as zero. The units on the scale are equal in length to the radius of the circle traced by the pin when the arm rotates. A similar scale is marked out against a horizontal line drawn through the centre of the circle.

The sketch will give you the idea. If you can use celluloid or Perspex for the suspended strip you will be able to mark a reference line for the vertical scale running through the pin.

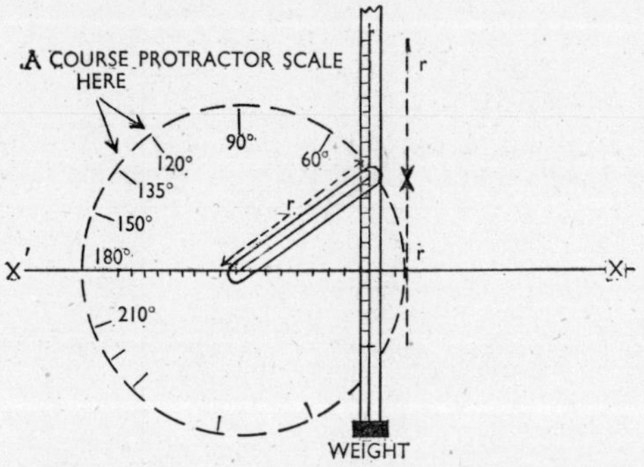

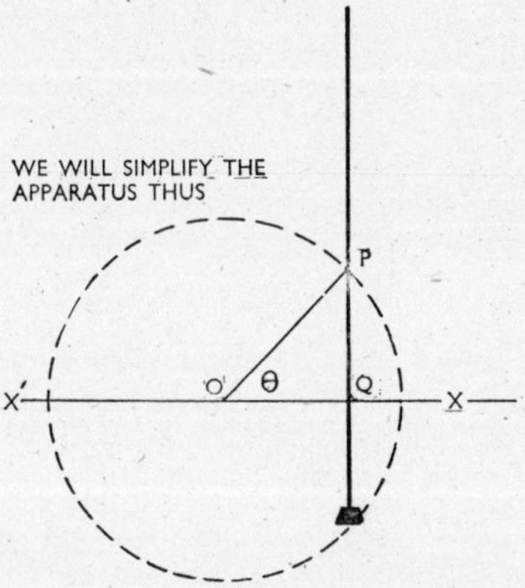

Wherever the rotor arm is held at rest a right-angled triangle will be formed; its hypotenuse, the arm, will be one unit in length, and the lengths of the other two sides can be read on the two scales.

Starting as (*a*), we have an angle of 0° between the rotor arm and OX. This angle between the rotor arm and OX will always be referred to as θ.

$$\text{When } \theta=0^\circ,\ \sin\theta=0\ \left(\frac{0}{1}=0\right)$$

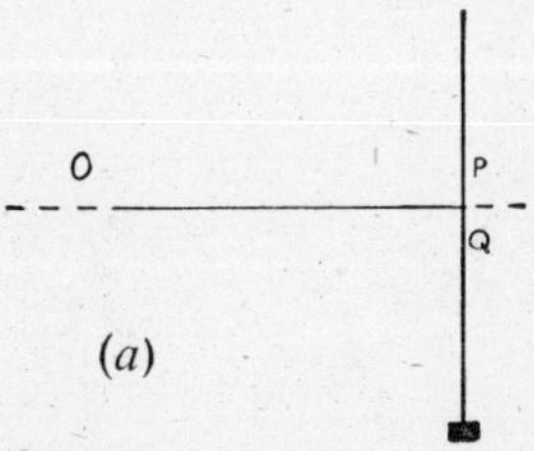

(*a*)

As the arm is raised (*b*), θ increases and its sine can be measured directly on the vertical scale because the hypotenuse is 1 unit. We now have an acute angle.

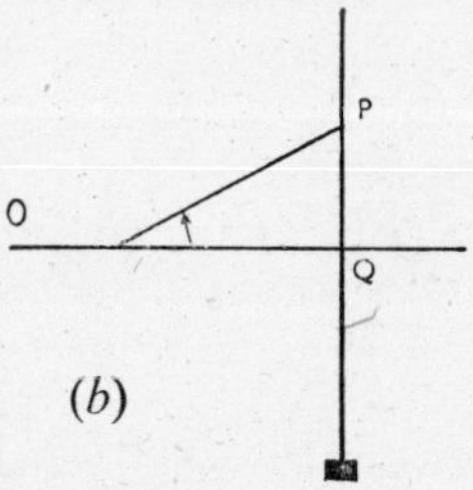

(*b*)

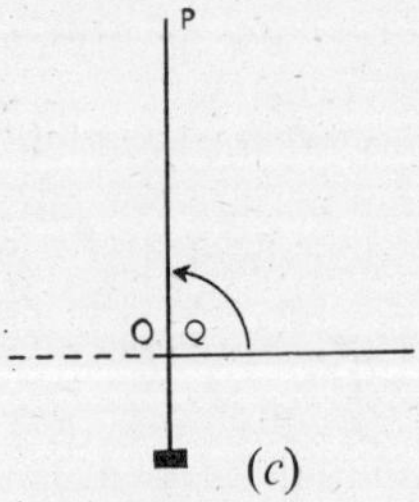

(c)

When $0^\circ < \theta < 90^\circ$,
$O < \sin\theta < 1$

In the third position $\theta = 90^\circ$, and we have the diagram (*c*):

$\sin\theta = 1$

As the angle is further increased its sine decreases, so we have, as at (*d*), passed 1 as a maximum value.

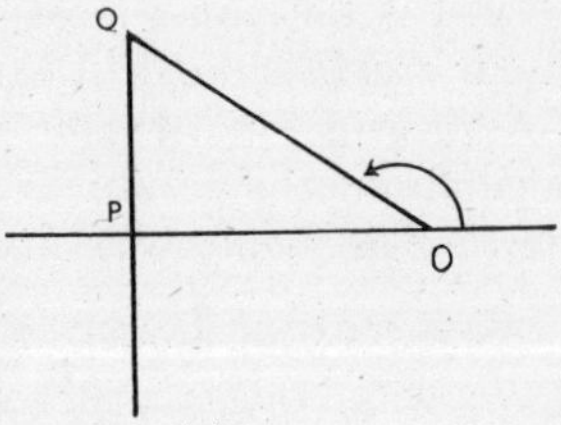

(*d*)

When $90^\circ < \theta < 180^\circ$,
$1 > \sin\theta > 0$.

Dwelling on this situation for a moment, with the aid of a drawing (*e*), we may find out the value of sin 115°.

$\sin POX = \sin P'OX$

because PQ and $P'Q'$ are equal

$\therefore \sin\theta = \sin(180^\circ - \theta)$

and for our particular case:

$\sin 115^\circ = \sin 65^\circ$.

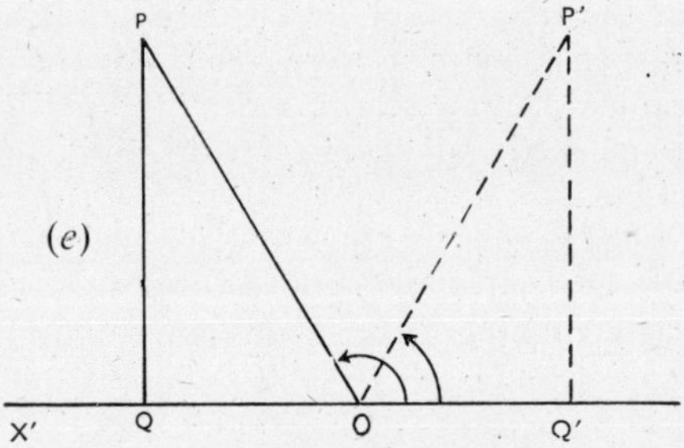

(*e*)

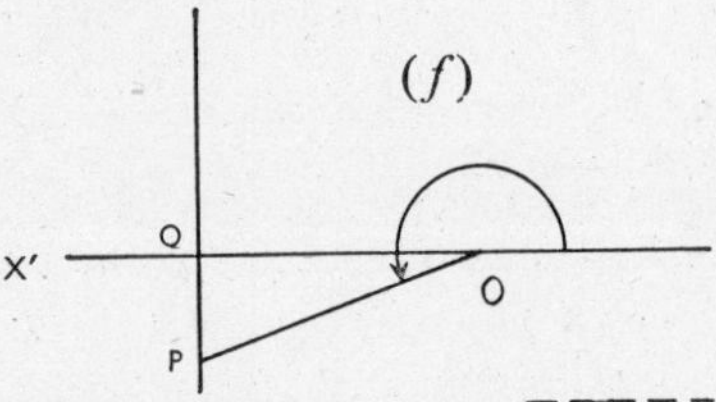

(*f*)

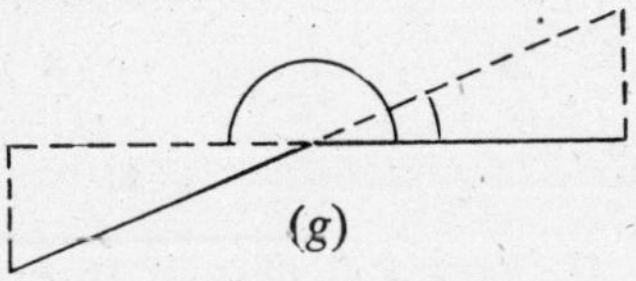
(*g*)

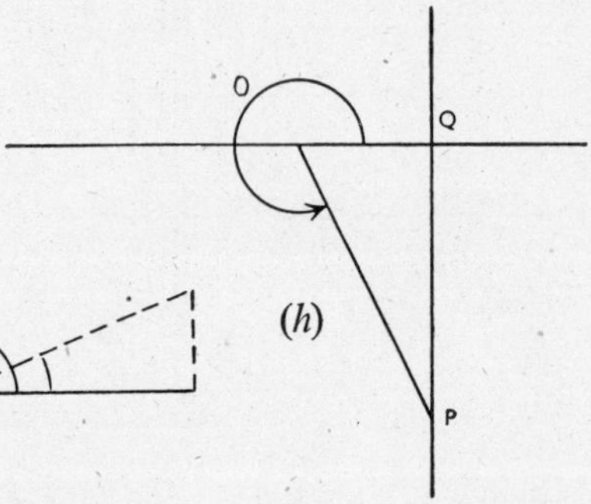

(*h*)

When the arm passes below OX' (*f*), we have a reflex angle, and PQ is negative. For $180^\circ < \theta < 270^\circ$ (*g*), $\sin\theta > -1$. To be more explicit, we now have $\sin\theta = -\sin(\theta - 180^\circ)$.

You will see in (*h*) that for $270^\circ < \theta < 360^\circ$, $-1 < \sin\theta < 0$, and $\sin\theta = -\sin(360^\circ - \theta)$.

It should be pointed out, before leaving this, that 360° is not the greatest possible angle; the same cycle may be repeated indefinitely.

A graph summarizes the whole matter. Plot a graph of $\sin\theta$ against θ and use the fewest possible calculations.

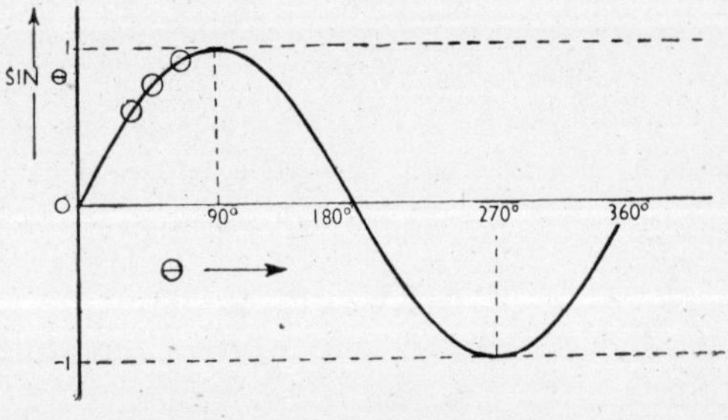

Now check some sample readings from the sine curve with results for the same values of θ read from the home-made instrument.

Every angle greater than 360° or less than 0° could be given a position on this curve. The curve serves many useful purposes (it occurs frequently in the mathematics of the electrical engineer). Our purpose in introducing it is to give you a comprehensive view of this function called the sine.

Without reference to the tables find the value of the sine for angles of 30°, 45°, and 60° respectively.

These three angles are more familiar than most others—except the right angle—because they occur in those time-honoured figures the square and the equilateral triangle.

If the side of the square is a units, the diagonal is $a\sqrt{2}$ (Pythagoras).

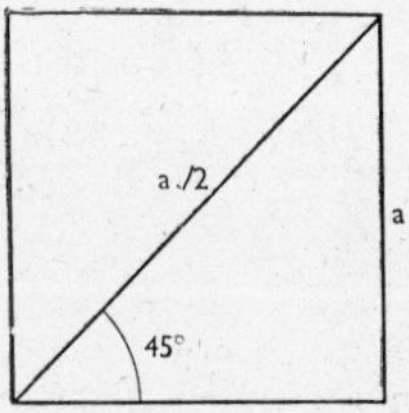

This gives us:

$$\sin 45° = \frac{1}{\sqrt{2}} \text{ or } \frac{\sqrt{2}}{2}$$

The equilateral triangle of side $2a$ units gives us:

$$\sin 30° = \tfrac{1}{2}$$

And since the perpendicular is $a\sqrt{3}$ (Pythagoras), we have:

$$\sin 60° = \frac{\sqrt{3}}{2}$$

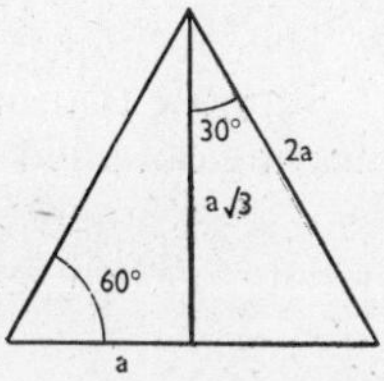

These three results are worth memorizing. Do they tally with the readings given by your home-made instrument?

Tangents of angles greater than one right angle can be determined in the same way (that is, by the use of the instrument you have been using).

Draw a tangent curve for angles ranging from 0° to 90°, obtaining the necessary information from your instrument. You will have to set the vertical strip (after removing its weight) at right angles to the rotor arm—it is best to work in a horizontal plane instead of a vertical plane.

Produce the line $X'OX$ to the right.

$$\text{Now } \tan \theta = \frac{PR}{OP}$$

But OP is one unit of length; therefore, PR will give a direct reading of tan. θ

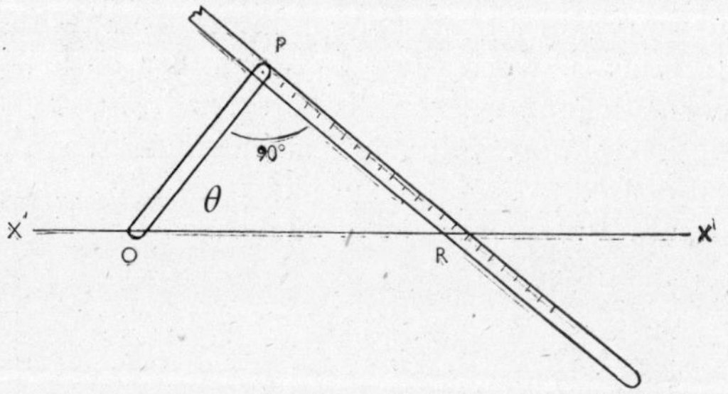

Navigation by sea and air is helped greatly by the directional use of radio transmission. The operator uses a receiver that tells him the direction of the transmitter. Two receiving stations, a known distance apart and in telephone communication with each other, can make simultaneous estimates of the bearing of a distant craft and combine their observations to pin-point its position.

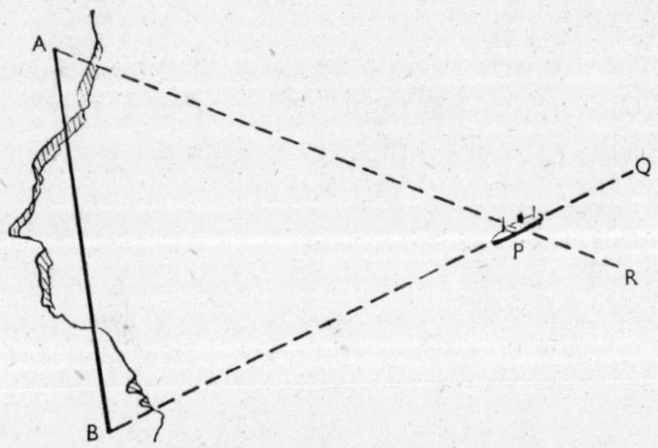

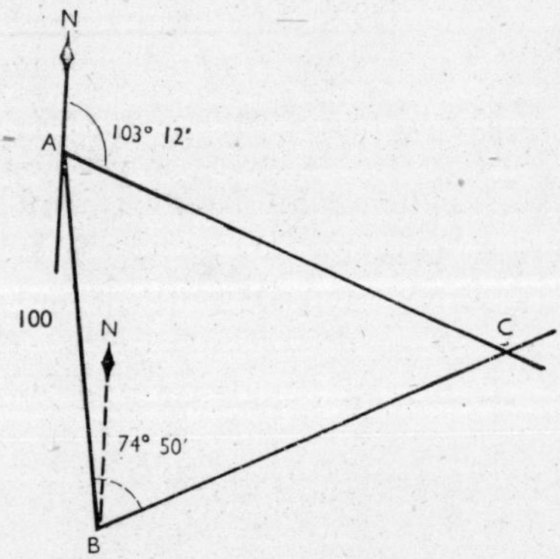

A finds that the craft lies on the line *AR*.
B finds that the craft lies on the line *BQ*.

The craft must, therefore, be at the point of intersection, *P*, of *AR* and *BQ*.

Suppose that in a particular case *A* and *B* are 100 miles apart, and that the bearing obtained by *A* is 103° 12′ while the bearing obtained by *B* is 74° 50′.

Suppose that the bearing of *B* from *A* is 166° 36′.

$$\begin{aligned} \text{Then}\quad A &= 166^\circ\,36' - 103^\circ\,12' \\ &= 63^\circ\,24'. \\ \text{and}\quad B &= 180^\circ - 166^\circ\,36' + 74^\circ\,50'. \\ &= 88^\circ\,14'. \\ \therefore\quad C &= 180^\circ - (63^\circ\,24' + 88^\circ\,14') \\ &= 28^\circ\,22' \end{aligned}$$

Using the formula $\dfrac{a}{\sin A} = \dfrac{b}{\sin B}$

$$AC = \frac{100 \times \sin 88^\circ\,14'}{\sin 28^\circ\,22'}$$

You can complete this yourself and find *BC* in the same way.

In large-scale constructions such as bridge building it is often necessary to start work from two or more distant sites and build the two or more sections of work towards each other until they meet. If they are to meet correctly, the work must be carried out to fine tolerances: calculation will be a far more valuable instrument than scale drawing. Steel work is pre-fabricated to accurate specifications and it must then be erected with equally accurate measurement of angle.

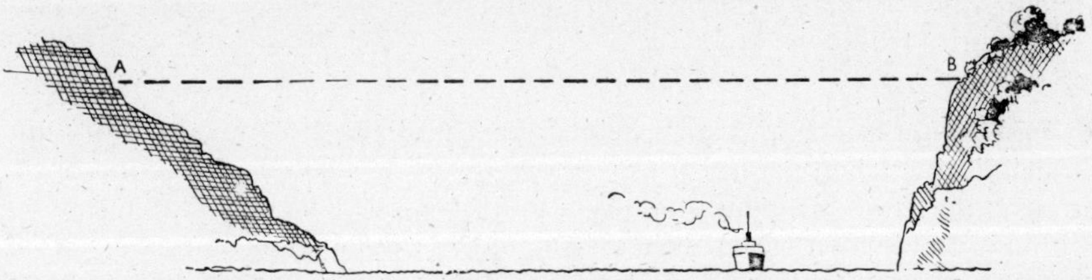

VERTICAL SECTION OF VALLEY

This sort of thing happens.

The distance between A and B is calculated by careful surveying (the base line for railway surveys is so accurate that it may take a day to measure *one* 300 ft. long).

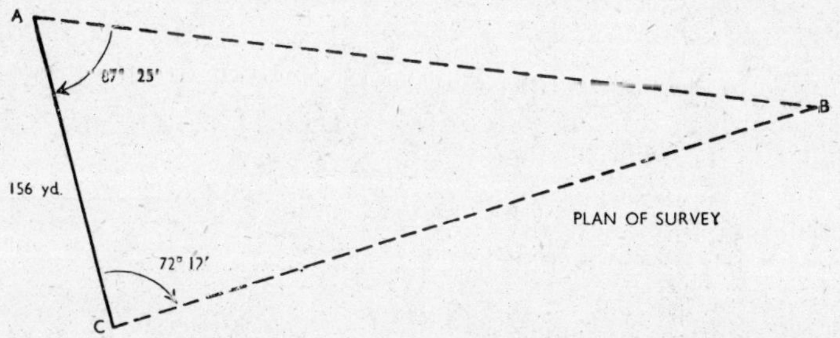

The bridge with its intricate net-work of steel is then designed. It will contain many triangles formed by steel members such as this (which has been simplified) which call for calculation.

CIRCULAR MEASUREMENT OF ANGLES

We have used the degree and its sub-units, the minute and the second, as the unit of angular measurement. There is, however, a more natural unit than the degree. You will recall that the ratio of circumference to diameter for a circle is constant for all circles and is denoted by π. The exact value of π is of no concern to us at the moment; this is fortunate, for it is not possible to state its numerical value with any finality.

The angle covered in one complete rotation of an arm (we have called this angle 360°) can be stated in terms of the length of the arc traced by the tip of the arm.

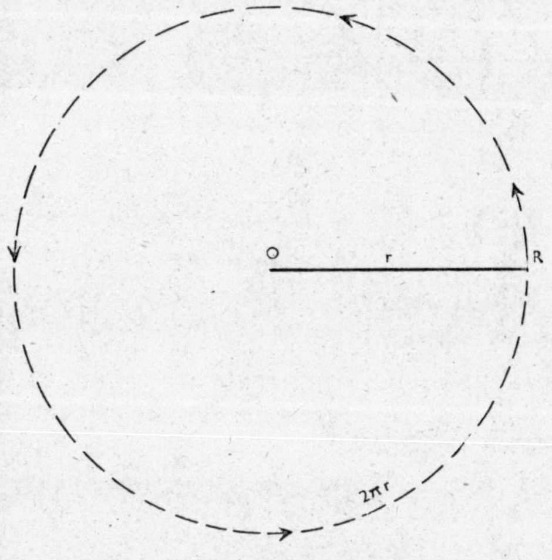

This length of arc is $2\pi r$, that is 2π times the radius.

The full turn then may be regarded as 2π units of angle, because no matter how long the rotor arm may be the full turn will use up an arc 2π times as long.

The full turn is an angle of 2π units, and these units are named *radians*.

Having stumbled on to radians we shall now want to see what one radian looks like. This presents us with a simple proportion sum.

$$2\pi \text{ radians} = \text{one revolution}$$
$$1 \text{ radian} = \frac{1}{2\pi} \text{ revolutions}$$

and we can arrive at this from our knowledge of the circle.

The distance all the way round the circle is $2\pi r$, so $\frac{1}{2\pi}$ of this will be an arc of length r.

Therefore one radian is the angle subtended by an arc of length equal to its radius at the centre of the circle of origin.

The definition is of necessity rather prosy, but the drawings make its meaning clear.

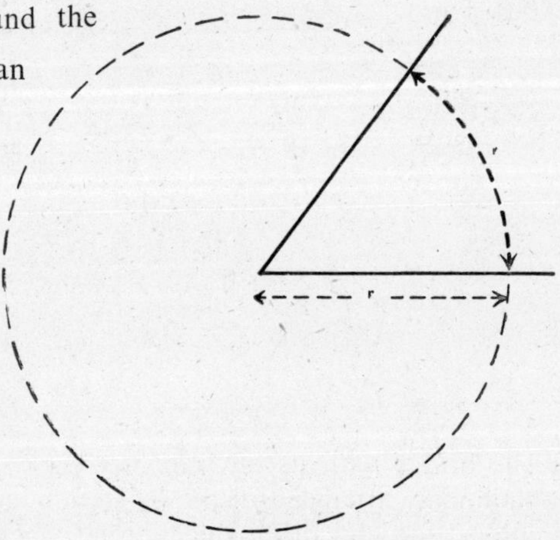

1 RADIAN $\left(\frac{\text{arc}}{\text{radius}} = 1\right)$

It is important to remember that *angle* is "amount of turning". The circle is one obvious peg on which to hang this illusive thing, and radian measure does so. The right-angled triangle is another peg that we have been learning to use and appreciate.

The use of the radian as a measure of angle requires the measurement of arc, and this is not easy except on a sphere or cylinder. The difficulty is not

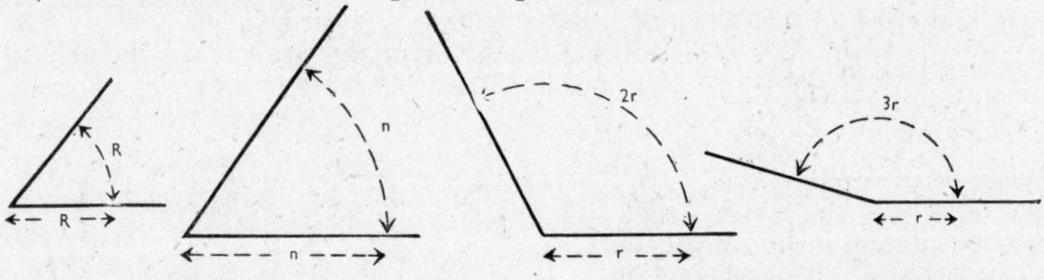

1 RADIAN 2 RADIANS 3 RADIANS

really a new one. The degree also demands the measurement of arc but we become so accustomed to using the ready-made protractor with all the tiresome work done for us that we tend to forget that arcs have had anything to do with it.

Degrees, minutes and seconds, are more popular among the practical men, and the reason is probably that numbers like 360 and 60 are robust and substantial compared with a number which is given its own symbol, π. Mathematically, there is a lot to be said for the radian, and it is a highly convenient measure of angle in more advanced work with implications for the electrical and mechanical engineer.

A rough-and-ready way of remembering the radian is:

$$\text{Angle in radians} = \frac{\text{arc}}{\text{radius}}$$

Remember also π radians $= 180°$.

Exercises

1. In a similar case to the example on page 345, the speedometer readings were 02379·6, 02383·3 and the bearing angle 64°. Calculate the distance of the church.

2. The semi-vertical angle of the cone of effective light from a street lamp is 50°. What is the radius of the

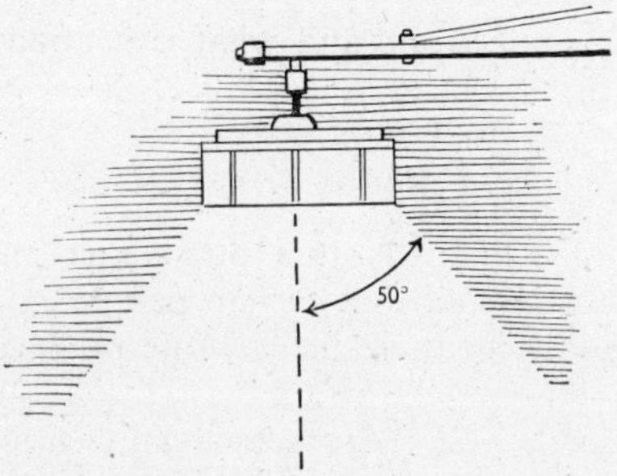

area it illuminates from a height of 25 ft. above the street level?

3. How many times as powerful is the sun's radiation on level ground for an elevation of 50° compared with one of 25°?

4. A 60° set-square has a hypotenuse of 23·7 cm.: what should be the lengths of the other two sides?

5. The two parts of a clothes-horse are to be hinged with two-inch webbing. What length of webbing is needed for each complete figure-eight?

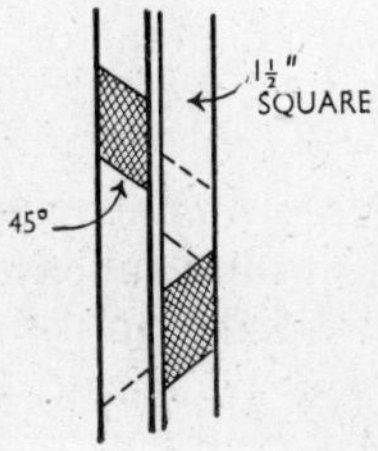

6. One side of a rectangular field measures 181 yards and the angle between this side and a diagonal is found to be 72°. What is the area of the field?

7. The vertical height of a piece of sheet metal (triangular) is 2 ft. 6 in. The angles at the base are 42° 44′ and 37° 16′. What is its area?

8. What is the angle between the face of a pyramid generated from a cube and its base, and what is the angle between a sloping edge and the diagonal of the base beneath it.

Use the instrument described on page 357 to complete the statements made in questions 9–12, noting first that distance measured from O towards X are positive, while distances from O towards X' are negative.

9. When $0<\theta<90°$ $\cos\theta$ lies between ? and ?.

10. When $90°<\theta<180°$, $\cos\theta$ lies between ? and ?.

11. When $180°<\theta<270°$, $\cos\theta$ lies between ? and ?.

12. When $270°<\theta<360°$, $\cos\theta$ lies between ? and ?.

13. Use the home-made instrument described on page 357 to find formulae relating the functions of negative angles to those of positive angles of the same magnitude.

$\sin(-\theta)=?$
$\cos(-\theta)=?$
$\tan(-\theta)=?$

14. Find the position of the ship observed from stations A and B, 100 miles apart, A due North of B, to have a bearing from A of 54° 30′ and from B, 18° 42′.

15. How many radians (in terms of π) are there in a right angle?

16. Convert π radians to degrees.

17. Convert 60° to radians.

18. Convert one radian to degrees, and minutes.

GUIDE TO FURTHER STUDY

In the eleven chapters of this book some account of arithmetic, algebra, geometry and trigonometry has been given. You may very well wonder whether anything remains to be learnt. Have we done the whole of algebra and trigonometry and geometry? Are there still other parts of mathematics, completely different subjects, and if so, what are they about?

The answer to these questions is that there is still plenty to be learnt. Whether you will desire or need to learn it depends on who you are and what you intend to do with your life.

Where does all this extra mathematics come from, and what is it about? Why was it discovered or invented?

HOW MATHEMATICS GROWS

Mathematical discoveries and inventions, like all other discoveries and inventions, are due to two causes: first, to the fact that certain people exist who delight to discover and invent; secondly, to there being some practical problem that needs solving.

The desire to discover has been put first, and the practical application second, because in many cases the practical application is only found after the discovery has been made. When Röntgen discovered X-rays, he was not looking for a way of treating cancer or taking photographs of people's insides. First X-rays had to be discovered, through scientific curiosity: then practical applications of X-rays followed. To produce the X-rays themselves one needs electrical apparatus, which again was not invented in order to produce X-rays. A discoverer rarely knows what use will be made of his discovery.

The men who first played around with magnets, and thereby laid the foundations of the science of electricity and magnetism, surely never dreamt that their activity would lead to the saving of lives at sea by wireless telegraphy, or to electric light and heat in houses. They may perhaps have had some interest in the mariner's compass, but even for this to be invented someone must first have been fascinated by the fact that a magnet would pick up pieces of iron.

What is true of science is equally true of mathematics. Mathematicians, once they have acquired a certain skill in their subject, delight to use that skill, just as a man who is physically fit delights to use his muscles. So you must think of mathematicians, when they have learnt to solve all the problems in the text-book, as looking round to find new problems to solve, and not merely new problems but new types of problem.

They find their new problems in two ways. Sometimes a mathematician becomes interested in the work of a scientist, or an engineer, or some other practical man, and their work suggests mathematical problems to him. In this way, Maxwell, for instance, took the electrical discoveries of Faraday, and built out of them a mathematical theory, or Newton gave a mathematical explanation of the facts that Kepler had noticed about the movements of the planets. This is one way of finding problems to solve.

Another way is from mathematics itself. Suppose you have been taught to solve the equation $2x+3=7$, and also how to solve $x^2+x=20$, you may say to yourself, "Why stop there? Why only have x and x^2 in the equation? Why not have x^3, or x^4 or x^5?"

So you would start trying to find some way of solving equations like $x^3-x^2+3x=10$ or $x^5+x=35$.

You may think this is a waste of time; that it is bad enough having to solve the equations in the book without looking for still harder ones. Many practical men do feel like that: they want to do as little mathematics as possible. The result is that one day a practical problem comes along, in which a harder equation than usual arises, and the practical man has no idea what to do with it. The mathematician, on the other hand—that is to say, the man who enjoys experimenting with mathematics—says, "Now I remember, a few weeks ago I was playing about with a problem rather like this, and I found a way of dealing with it."

The mathematician in fact is not content to do only the problems that have been set to him: he wants to feel sure that he will be able to solve any problem that anybody ever may bring to him. So he is continually trying to extend what he can do. He knows how to solve one problem by a certain trick: he asks himself if there might not be other problems that could be solved by the same trick. He tries to find out just why that trick works. He tries to group problems into families, to work out a way of classifying problems, so that as soon as you put a problem to him, he knows to which group it belongs, and what type of method is likely to solve it.

You will see that this is an active state of mind, and it is doubtful if anyone will do much good with mathematics who has not come to feel this mental adventurousness. Many people certainly could feel it, who do not feel it at present because they have been badly taught. Teachers are in far too much of a hurry to stuff information into a child's mind, when they should be encouraging it to experiment and make discoveries for itself. There is a satisfaction in discovering something for yourself, even if the discovery is not new to the rest of the world. Most children enjoy finding things out for themselves, but this enjoyment—at any rate in connection with arithmetic—is usually crushed out of them by the schools: only a feeble flicker of it survives—that some interest does survive is shown by the fact that newspapers publish arithmetical puzzles.

Now of the two kinds of mathematics that have been mentioned—applied mathematics and pure mathematics, as they are called—it is much easier to describe the applied mathematics. It might be that a certain type of mathematics was developed in order to explain how the planets move in the sky, or to give the best way of designing a dynamo, or to show what happens inside an atom. You have seen the stars in the sky, you know what a dynamo is, you have heard about the atom. It seems reasonable enough that calculations should in some way be connected with these things.

You will see, too, that there must be very many different kinds of applied mathematics, because there are so many different types of object that can be studied. The mathematics used to design a telescope will not help you to build a skyscraper: the mathematics of radio engineering will not help you in manufacturing a typewriter.

Mathematical symbols have to be found to describe how water flows and how rubber stretches, how a hot body cools and how plants grow. There is no limit to the tasks that mathematics may be required to perform. Mathematics is continually growing. New methods are continually being invented to solve new problems, and in these new methods you can see the imprint of the problem they were made to fit.

Fortunately, a completely new type of mathematics is not needed for every new problem. It often happens that the same mathematics—or at any rate the same type of mathematics—will do for many different problems. If this were not so, there would be no point in learning mathematics.

There is a famous example of one equation applying to two quite different subjects. In 1864, Maxwell published some of his work on electricity and magnetism, in which he put the discoveries of Faraday into mathematical form. He obtained two sets of equations, and from these he was led to the equation:

$$\frac{\partial^2 V}{\partial x^2} + \frac{\partial^2 V}{\partial y^2} + \frac{\partial^2 V}{\partial z^2} = \frac{1}{c^2}\frac{\partial^2 V}{\partial t^2}$$

You will not be able to understand the meaning of this equation, because it contains signs the meaning of which has not been explained to you, but Maxwell knew this equation. He had met it before. This equation occurs in the theory of sound. It describes the way in which waves of sound spread out from a bell, or any other body that is making a noise.

The fact that the same equation now turned up in connection with electricity had a very important meaning: it meant that there must be electric waves that would spread out in just the same way that sound waves did. Maxwell in fact had discovered, by mathematics, that such a thing as wireless waves ought to exist. Naturally, the experimental scientists tried to produce these electric waves, but it was not until 1887 that Hertz succeeded in doing this, by means of electric sparks. It took the experimenters twenty-three years to find a way of doing what Maxwell had shown ought to be possible.

This is a very good example of how mathematicians work. You will see that Maxwell was not content just to find an equation. He wanted to know what the equation *meant*, and he was able to express the meaning in terms that anybody can understand, "This equation indicates that waves spread out."

You will notice that mathematics enabled him to do a rather remarkable thing: to turn knowledge about sound into knowledge about electricity.

Some students, who are learning mathematics for a trade, want to learn only the mathematics of that particular trade and feel it a waste of time to learn anything about other trades, or about science in general. This is a great mistake. If Maxwell had decided to study electricity alone, if he had never bothered to learn how a sound wave passes through the air, he would never have discovered wireless. The whole point of mathematics is that it enables you to take a pattern, an idea, from one subject and apply it to some quite different subject. A mathematician must be interested in everything.

It is for this reason that the second type of mathematics—pure mathematics—is so important. By means of pure mathematics we can knit together all the different kinds of applied mathematics, and see that the same underlying ideas, the same methods, are being used again and again. This makes mathematics very much easier to learn.

When a mathematician is given a practical problem to solve, he does not concern himself in the least with what industry or what science produced the problem : he is only concerned with the shape of the problem itself. Is it a problem of algebra alone? Is it a problem of trigonometry? Is it a problem of more advanced mathematics? Or is it a problem of a completely new type, that will have to be investigated purely on its own merits, and from which a whole new branch of mathematics may possibly come?

Accordingly, if you wish to go further in your study of mathematics there are two main parts of the subject to bear in mind (though each of these parts helps and supports the other).

On the one hand are all the various applications of mathematics to science or to industry, such subjects as dynamics, which deals with the motion of heavy bodies; statics, which deals with the stresses and strains in bodies that stay still, such as bridges or buildings; optics, dealing with telescopes and cameras, and everything concerned with lenses; electricity and magnetism, both in its general theory and in its practical uses; hydrostatics and hydrodynamics, dealing with the behaviour of liquids; aerodynamics, dealing with the flow of air and the design of aircraft: all these and a host of others are branches with obvious practical uses and applications.

On the other hand, there are branches of pure mathematics. Even in books on the most practical themes, you will find yourself held up by ignorance of the mathematical processes used, and be forced to make yourself acquainted with the study of mathematical methods.

Some parts of mathematics may be regarded as belonging to pure or applied mathematics, according to taste. This is true, for instance, of solid geometry, which deals with the shapes of actual objects. (Ordinary geometry deals only with the shapes of flat surfaces; that is, it deals only with shapes that can be drawn on a piece of paper. It does not consider solid objects, such as a brick or a ball.)

Solid geometry is a very practical subject, of growing importance in workshops. On the other hand, it has a very old history, and can be regarded and treated as part of pure mathematics.

The nature of applied mathematics will be clear to you from the very names of the subjects with which it deals. It is not possible to say anything more about applied mathematics here. A whole book would be needed to describe the mathematics of electricity, or of statics, or of any of the other subjects mentioned earlier. If you are interested in any of these, you will find books in libraries to satisfy your curiosity.

The pure mathematics that you will meet if you continue to study consists

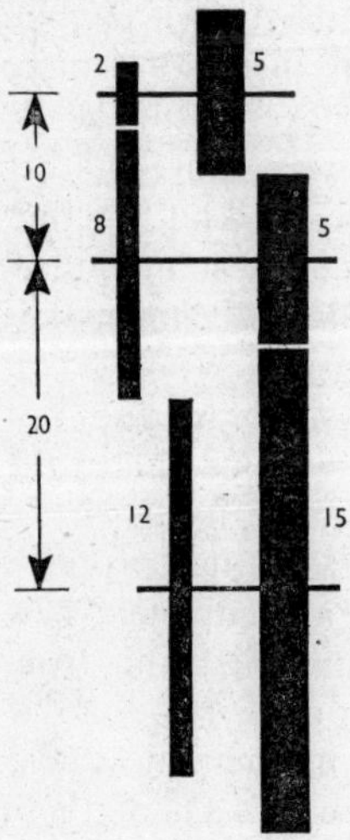

(*a*) Bottom Gear Gearing, $\frac{2}{8}\times\frac{5}{15}=\frac{1}{12}$

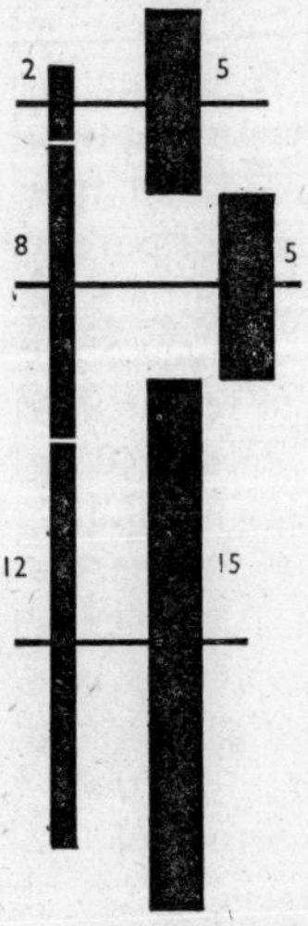

(*b*) Second Gear Gearing, $\frac{2}{8}\times\frac{8}{12}=\frac{1}{6}$

(*c*) Third Gear Gearing, $\frac{5}{5}\times\frac{5}{15}=\frac{1}{3}$

(*d*) Top Gear Gearing, $\frac{5}{5}\times\frac{8}{12}=\frac{2}{3}$

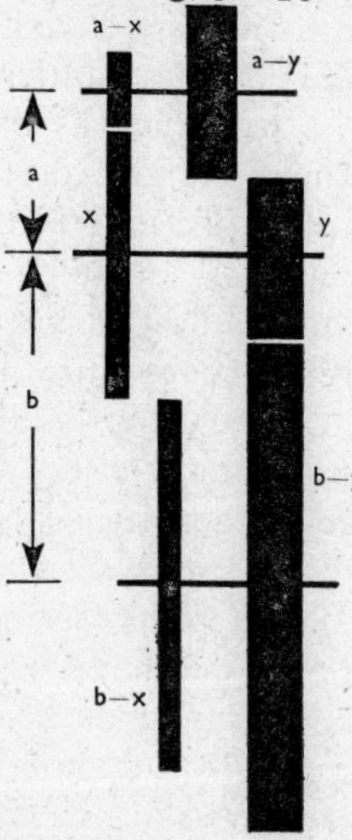

(*e*) Gearbox with generalized measurements Gearing in bottom gear, $\left(\frac{a-x}{x}\right)\left(\frac{y}{b-y}\right)$

ALGEBRA OF GEARBOX DESIGN

(*a*), (*b*), (*c*), (*d*) *represent a particular gearbox in the various gears, going from bottom to top. The gear ratios are* $\frac{1}{12}$, $\frac{1}{6}$, $\frac{1}{3}$, $\frac{2}{3}$. *You may notice that each ratio is twice as large as the one before. The problem is to design the gearbox so that each ratio will be* three times *the previous ratio. In the diagrams* ((*a*), (*b*), (*c*), (*d*)) *the numbers by the gears represent the radius of each gear. We have to replace these numbers by other numbers. It may also be necessary to change the distances between the axles. In the diagram* (*e*), *the particular numbers have been replaced by general symbols x, y, a, b. Designing consists in finding the values for x, y, a, b that will satisfy the conditions of the problem. It will be noticed that only elementary algebra is necessary for the solution of this problem, but considerable deftness in handling algebraic expressions is called for.*

partly of new subjects, such as calculus, partly of extensions of subjects already known to you, such as algebra and trigonometry.

After reading this book, you will probably find that you can follow the algebra in, say, a simple book on engineering, but you may not be able to solve problems for yourself. If you want to make discoveries, or to design apparatus yourself, you will need to practise working with algebra until you are able to solve problems of many different kinds, and are thoroughly familiar with algebraic processes. You will not only have to be interested in the applications of algebra, but in the algebra itself, so that when any new problem is brought to you, you will be able to go systematically about solving it.

Once you have reached the stage where you know what algebra is about and you want to master it, you will find the old-fashioned school algebra book very useful. In fact, it is essential that you should read such books. The only criticism of the old books is that they have no appeal to beginners. Once you have ceased to be a beginner, once you have acquired the taste for mathematics, you will find the orthodox text-books invaluable.

In your further work on algebra you will not meet very many new ideas. It is rather a question of knowing how to apply basic principles, which you have already met, to all kinds of problems, and of being so practised in the use of algebra that you can carry out the operations almost without thinking.

You will find an example of an algebraic problem on page 368, the problem of the gearbox. To solve this problem you do not need to use any algebra more advanced than that already outlined in Chapter IX. But—and this is a big BUT—you must know just how to go about it. You need to be quite expert in knowing what to do, and when to do it. The gearbox question is included here as an example of a problem that can be done by someone with a good knowledge of algebra, but not by a novice. It is not expected that someone who has only read this book will be able to solve it unaided.

Just as algebra can be carried further than has been done in this book, so can trigonometry. There are many questions we have not discussed at all. For instance, how are trigonometrical tables to be calculated? We do not need to calculate trigonometrical tables today, but the problem had to be solved when trigonometry began, and in the course of solving it many interesting and useful things were discovered about the properties of sin x and cos x. In studying this question, algebra is used more and more, and in time a stage is reached where algebra and trigonometry are so much mixed up that you cannot say which is which. In fact, it becomes possible to explain everything about trigonometry by means of algebra, so that trigonometry ceases to be a separate subject and becomes simply a part of algebra.

In bringing about this marriage (or annexation) of trigonometry to algebra, a large part is played by calculus. You have probably heard of calculus and wondered what it was.

It is usual to refer to calculus as being part of "the higher mathematics". Why should this be so? Calculus is no harder than algebra: much of it is simpler, and it has been taught without difficulty to boys of fourteen years of age. Calculus is an interesting subject, and often it shows us ways of solving a problem by very quick and easy methods, where without calculus long and troublesome calculations would be required.

In text-books and encyclopaedias it is usual to say that calculus deals with continuously varying quantities, or some such phrase. This is true enough in its way, but it does not convey any very definite picture to one's mind.

It would be better to say that calculus deals in the first place with questions of *speed*, though later on it is used for all kinds of applications that seem, at first glance, to have no connection with speeds.

You know what speed means, and you will see that there is nothing mysterious about a subject dealing with the calculation of speeds.

Let us consider a particular example for the sake of definiteness. In many machines, from the domestic sewing machine to the most complicated mechanisms, it is necessary that at certain times a particular object shall be lifted through a certain distance. One way of achieving this is by means of a cam.

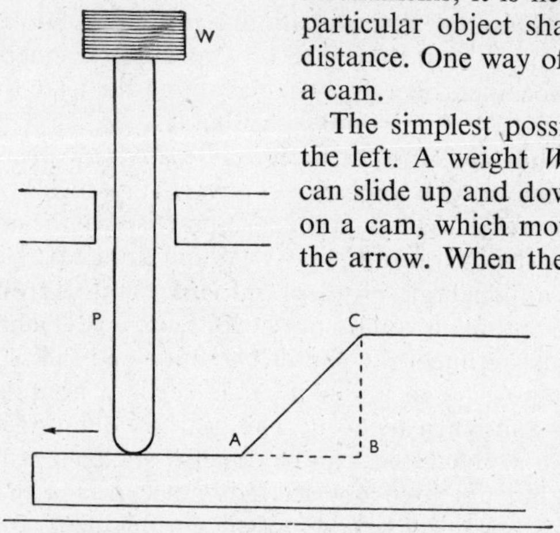

The simplest possible type of cam is shown on the left. A weight W rests on a plunger P, which can slide up and down in a slot. The plunger rests on a cam, which moves steadily in the direction of the arrow. When the point A reaches the plunger, the weight will begin to rise. The upward movement will cease after the point C has passed the plunger.

It is quite easy in this case to find the speed with which the weight rises. Let us suppose that the cam is moving at the rate of one inch a second, that AB is 3 in., and that BC is 2 in.

It will then take 3 sec. for the weight W to make its upward journey, and in this time W will rise through a height equal to BC, that is, 2 in.

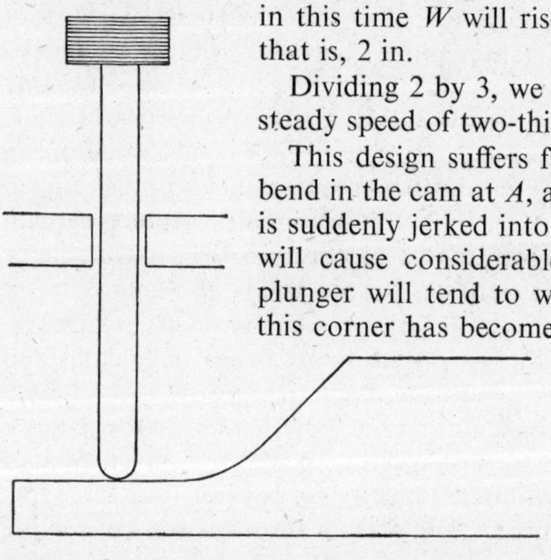

Dividing 2 by 3, we find that W moves upwards at a steady speed of two-thirds of an inch a second.

This design suffers from a defect. There is a sudden bend in the cam at A, and this means that the weight W is suddenly jerked into motion. If W is at all large, this will cause considerable wear of the mechanism. The plunger will tend to wear away the corner at A, until this corner has become quite rounded. The appearance of the mechanism will then be as shown on the left.

By the time the cam has been worn to this shape the jerk will have disappeared. The plunger will gradually gather speed as the curve of the cam becomes steeper and steeper. The design would, therefore, be improved by rounding this corner from the first, instead of leaving it to chance to wear it to this shape.

We are, therefore, led to consider curved cams. A convenient way of describing the shape of a curve is provided by the methods already explained in the chapter on graphs.

Let us suppose that we choose for the shape of our cam the curve whose equation is $y = x^2$.

It will no longer be possible to find the speed of the weight at any time by the method used before. That method applies only to objects moving at a steady speed. Here we are dealing with a weight that rises slowly at first, while the curve is still fairly level, but faster and faster as the steeper portions are reached. We shall have different speeds for different times.

This problem can be worked out by arithmetic if we bear in mind that *small parts* of a curve are very hard to distinguish from straight lines. If we consider what happens in a very short part of the time, in which the plunger moves up a very short part of the curve, we ought to be able, *by the same method as before*, to discover *something like* the truth. There may be some small error due to the fact that even a small part of a curve is not exactly straight, but this should not be enough to cause serious trouble. The smaller time we consider, the better our result will be.

The figure on page 373 shows the graph of the curve $y = x^2$. The cam is to be made to the shape of this curve. In order to draw the curve accurately, points have been plotted at intervals of one-tenth of an inch, from the figures in the table below.

Table for $y = x^2$

x	0	0·1	0·2	0·3	0·4	0·5	0·6	0·7	0·8	0·9	1·0	1·1
y	0	0·01	0·04	0·09	0·16	0·25	0·36	0·49	0·64	0·81	1·00	1·21

x	1·2	1·3	1·4	1·5	1·6	1·7	1·8	1·9	2·0	2·1
y	1·44	1·69	1·96	2·25	2·56	2·89	3·24	3·61	4·00	4·41

The figure on page 372 shows different stages in the rise of the plunger as the cam passes through. We are assuming, as before, that the cam advances at the rate of one inch a second.

The question we now have to answer is the following: how fast is the plunger rising at the different stages of the motion? What is the speed of the plunger when it is in contact with C as in diagram (*b*) of the figure on page 372? When it is in contact with F, as in diagram (*c*)? And when it is in positions (*d*) and (*e*)?

Let us consider these questions one at a time. How fast is the plunger rising at the moment illustrated in (*a*)?

We are trying to find the speed of the plunger. Speed is equal to distance travelled divided by the time taken.

We must, therefore, consider what happens in a small interval of time,

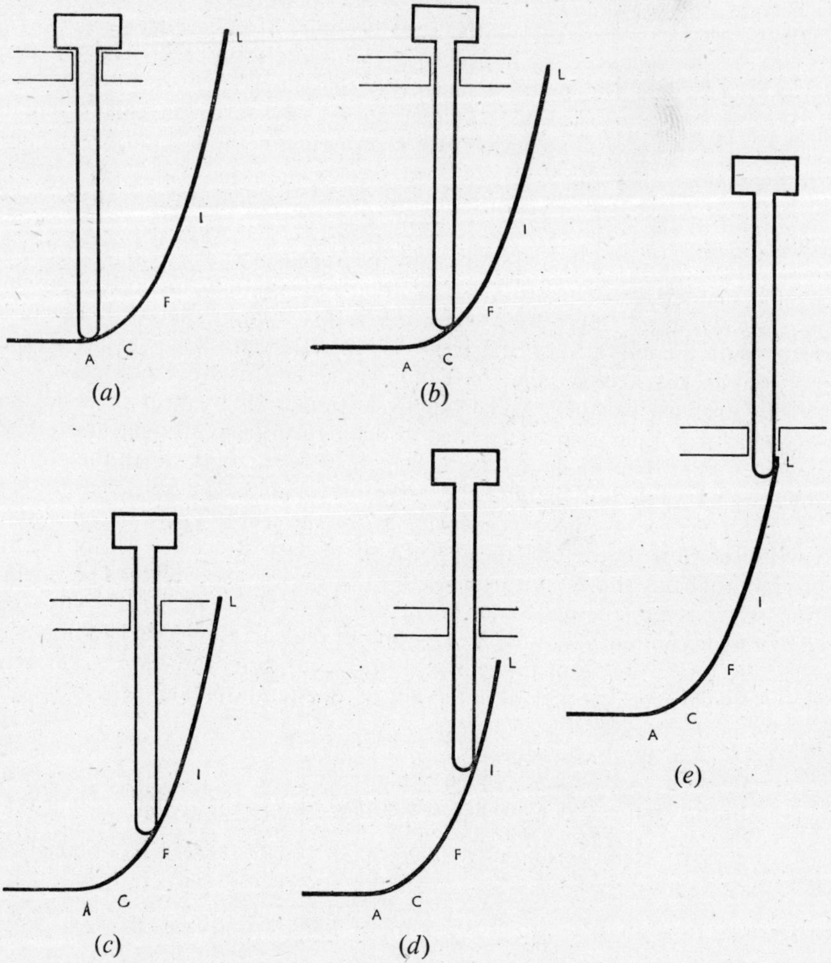

STAGES IN MOTION OF CAM AND PLUNGER

(*a*) *Plunger at foot of curved part of cam.* (*b*) *Half a second later than* (*a*). (*c*) *One second later than* (*a*). (*d*) *One-and-a-half seconds later than* (*a*). (*e*) *Two seconds later than* (*a*).

for example when the plunger is passing over the point *C*. Let us take the interval in which the plunger climbs from the point *B* to the point *D*. (*B* is the point where the plunger touches the cam, one-tenth of a second before it reaches *C*. *D* is the point of contact one-tenth of a second after the plunger has reached *C*.)

By choosing a small interval in this way, *C* corresponds to the middle of the time considered, and this is usually the best arrangement.

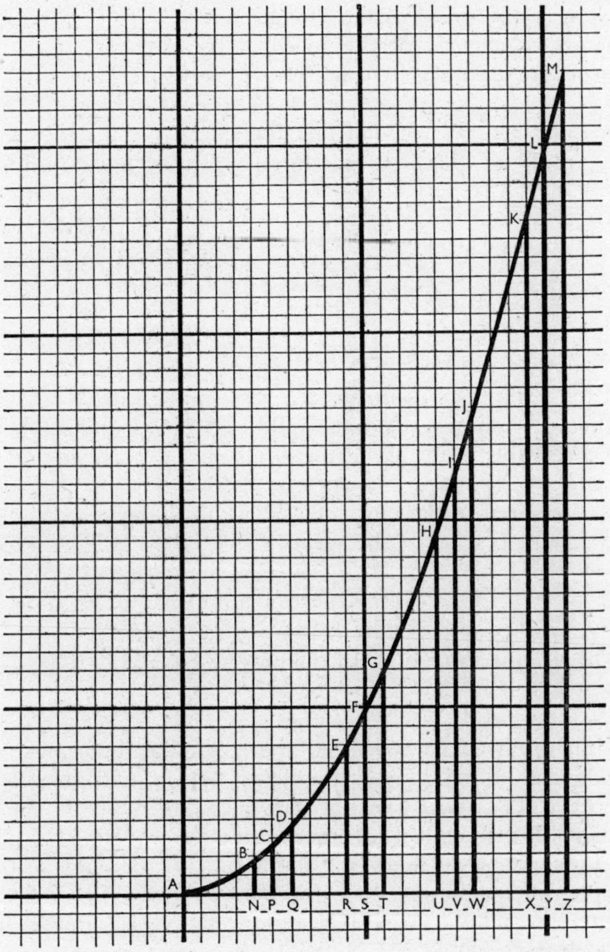

Graph of The Cam, $y=x^2$

The exact position of the points B, C, and D, on the graph paper above can be seen from the table we used when plotting the graph. B is the point $x = 0{\cdot}4$, $y = 0{\cdot}16$; C is $x = 0{\cdot}5$, $y = 0{\cdot}25$: D is $x = 0{\cdot}6$, $y = 0{\cdot}36$.

The time taken for the plunger to rise from B to D is 0·2 sec. Through what height does the plunger rise in this time? B is at a height 0·16 in. above A (since B was plotted at the height $y = 0{\cdot}16$). D is 0·36 in. above A (for a similar reason).

The height of D above B is, therefore, $0{\cdot}36 - 0{\cdot}16 = 0{\cdot}20$ in.

Accordingly, the plunger has risen 0·2 in. in this interval.

But the time taken was 0·2 sec.

$$\text{Hence, the speed is:} \quad \frac{0{\cdot}2}{0{\cdot}2} = 1$$

Hence, in the interval B to D, the plunger is rising at a speed of 1 in. per sec.

This we take as giving us the speed as the plunger passes over C. (Strictly, this method gives us a *rough idea* of the speed as the plunger passes C. Actually, in this particular example, it so happens that this result is exactly equal to the speed).

By using just the same method, we can find the speeds for the intervals E to G, H to J, and K to M. These give estimates for the upward speed of the plunger at F, I, and L respectively.

If you work these speeds out for yourself, you will find the results shown below:

At C, speed = 1
At F, speed = 2
At I, speed = 3
At M, speed = 4

You will see that these numbers conform to a very simple rule. It is clear that if we went on the next numbers to come would be 5, 6, 7, 8 and so on.

It is possible to express this result by means of algebra. C corresponds to $x = \frac{1}{2}$; F to $x = 1$; I to $x = 1\frac{1}{2}$; M to $x = 2$.

If we use the sign v for speed (v for velocity), we have this table:

When $x = \frac{1}{2}$, the speed $v = 1$
$x = 1$, the speed $v = 2$
$x = 1\frac{1}{2}$, the speed $v = 3$
$x = 2$, the speed $v = 4$

The speed v is just twice the value of x. In symbols we have the result:

$$\text{if } y = x^2$$
$$v = 2x$$

Here is a very simple result, giving the speed at any point on the cam. It is much easier to use the rule found above—double x—than to find the speed by arithmetic, as we have done above.

The business of calculus is to collect together all the rules of the kind just obtained. It is found that whenever there is a simple rule for the shape of the curve, there is a simple rule for the speed v.

For instance, if the cam has the curve $y = x^2 + x$, the speed is given by the rule $v = 2x + 1$. If the curve is $y = x^3$, the speed is given by $v = 3x^2$.

These results could be obtained by arithmetic alone, but the work would be rather long.

Calculus gives results quickly, but they could be obtained with much more labour by using arithmetic alone.

There is nothing mysterious then about calculus. Calculus was discovered in very much the way explained above (though not in the designing of cams!). People were doing calculations using arithmetic and algebra, and they noticed certain simple rules about the results. By using these simple rules they saved themselves work.

Calculus grew gradually, and quite naturally, out of arithmetic and algebra. No one can really say where algebra ends and calculus begins.

There are other subjects more advanced than calculus, but the great majority of people who use mathematics find that a knowledge of arithmetic, algebra, geometry (including solid geometry), trigonometry and calculus is sufficient to solve the problems they meet. These are the main parts of pure mathematics that are necessary for the man who wants to be a competent mathematician, but does not wish to make mathematics his profession.

CHOICE OF STUDY

If you desire to study further, you can do it on your own by reading books, or in company by attending a class.

In most cases, Evening Institutes and Technical Colleges provide classes for part-time students. Evening Institutes deal with the junior work, and cater for students up to the age of sixteen. In a good Technical College, courses are available, covering everything from the most elementary work (i.e. from where the Evening Institutes leave off) up to and beyond Honours Degree standard.

Usually by enquiring among your friends and fellow workers, you can get a good idea of how things are done.

Books on mathematics fall into several types.

First of all, there are the books that any student can pick up and read with pleasure and understanding. Very few books indeed belong to this category.

Secondly, there are school books. Some of these consist only of examples. Others provide some explanation that may be intelligible to a really good pupil who has followed all the earlier work. Generally, school books are grim and forbidding, at any rate to the beginner.

Thirdly, there are books on workshop calculations and technical mathematics. These make some effort to cater for the needs of apprentices and similar students, though they are often tinged with the academic approach more than is necessary. The possible fault is that a man who has devoted enough of his time to mastering the intricacies of a trade, has not had enough time to delve deeply into mathematics. As a result, he does not realize how much rubbish there is in the older text-books, and he does not break away sufficiently from the traditional explanations.

On the other hand, the writer with a deep knowledge of mathematics rarely understands apprentices.

Part of the difficulty lies in the fact that an expert tradesman really needs to know quite a lot of the text-book mathematics. The difficulty is so to arrange the presentation that the work begins with things which the practical man knows, understands and likes, and from this beginning develops gradually and naturally to the more abstract topics.

A fourth type of mathematics book deals with puzzles, games and so forth. These books have their value, since they accustom readers to the use of figures and symbols.

A fifth, and very useful, type of book is one that skirts around the edges of mathematics, and deals with the history of mathematics, the lives of mathematicians, and mathematical gossip of all kinds. One can read such books when one is tired. There is only a small proportion of mathematics in them but they help to stir up what one already knows about mathematics, and sometimes they give new ways of looking at some mathematical truth. If you perpetually read *around* mathematics in such books, you will keep meeting references to subjects and ideas you have not yet studied, such as calculus, vectors, determinants and so forth. You will wonder, "What is calculus? What are vectors? What are determinants?" If one day a teacher says, "Now I am going to deal with calculus (or vectors, or determinants)", you will feel, "Now I am going to find out,"—which you would not have felt if you had never heard the word before.

It is rarely wise to buy a book on someone else's recommendation. What one person finds easy another finds incomprehensible. The books mentioned below are, therefore, suggestions for you to consider. You may be able to look at them in libraries or in bookshops, and decide if you want to buy a copy. Even if you do buy a book, do not read that one book alone. Make the fullest possible use of libraries. No book is, or can be, perfect. The writer has to leave something out, from lack of space. Different writers have different ideas on what is important and what can be sacrificed. By reading many books you can fill in the gaps in each. Each book will revive your memory of the others.

The difficulties that people find with mathematics often go back to the fact that they never learnt arithmetic properly at school. It may interest some readers to know the kind of book that is replacing the old arithmetic text-book in schools today.

Very young children may begin with a book such as *Arithmetic in Action* by Brideoake and Groves. A very attractive book for young children is Mary Robinson's *With Ruler and Compasses.* Also, there are C. E. Gurr's *Work and Play Arithmetic* and H. C. Godfrey's *My Family Budget.* O. Morgan's *Arithmetic for Girls* should be mentioned.

Books specially designed for revision include *A Revision Arithmetic* by E. H. Lockwood; arithmetic and other subjects are dealt with in Hooper's *A Mathematical Refresher*. Fawdry's *Polish up your Mathematics* and H. McKay's *Mathematics for All.* H. McKay is a lively writer, and his *The World of Numbers*, which is not a text-book but a sort of arithmetical gossip, is well worth reading.

Another book with a very individual approach is H. Levy's *Elementary Mathematics*. The way this book begins is particularly worthy of notice.

Books of mathematics written in the first place for technical students are *National Certificate Mathematics* (in three volumes; Volume I by Abbott and Kerridge; Volume II by Abbott; Volume III by Abbott and Marshall), and *Mathematics for Technical Students* by Geary, Lowry and Hayden. These books have been found useful by university students as well as by apprentices. Also technical in bias are Chapman's *Workshop Calculations* and L. Turner's *General Mathematics*.

Technical works generally drive a very long, narrow path into the jungle of mathematics. The student gets a long way, but he is rather unsure about things that lie even a little to one side of the path he has been brought along.

It is, therefore, wise for anyone who has had a technical upbringing to broaden his ideas by looking at the books used in grammar schools and universities.

If you have reached the stage where you understand what mathematics is about, you should find even the older text-books enjoyable. For instance, Hall and Knight's *Elementary Algebra for Schools* (first published about fifty years ago) and *Higher Algebra* are very interesting for anyone who wants to be able to solve any (or almost any) problem of algebra that may arise.

Durell has written a number of books, which are intended for students to read and understand with little or no help from a master. The best of these is *Elementary Algebra* by Durell, Palmer and Wright. There are some good points in *Elementary Algebra* by Godfrey and Siddons.

A good book on more advanced algebra is Lockwood's *Algebra for Science and Engineering Students.*

Two excellent little booklets are E. T. Chiswell's *Find the Formula* and *From Formula to Calculus.* These are ideal for students working on their own.

Milne and Westcott's *A First Course in the Calculus* deals with the beginnings of calculus at a leisurely pace, well suited to beginners.

Teach Yourself Calculus by Abbott must be counted with the academic books. It has been found useful by students reading for degrees. It plunges straight into the mathematics of the subject, without any introduction to explain what calculus is or why we should want to study it. Beginners will find the same author's *National Certificate Mathematics* (mentioned earlier) much more helpful.

A. W. Bain's *Elements of Trigonometry Simplified* uses throughout an academic presentation (the author quotes chapter and verse from the books of Euclid), but the work is made as simple as possible. It is designed mainly for School Certificate, Matriculation and similar examinations.

The classical trigonometries, such as Loney's, are excellent for anyone desiring a systematic academic treatment. The remarks made earlier about Hall and Knight's algebra books apply equally to Loney's *Trigonometry.*

Histories of mathematics and general works on mathematics include such books as T. Danzig's *Number, The Language of Science* (particularly the earlier chapters), E. T. Bell's *Men of Mathematics*, H. W. Turnbull's *Great Mathematicians*, D. Larrett's *The Story of Mathematics*, F. W. Westaway's *The Endless Quest* (science, including mathematics), Hogben's *Mathematics for the Million* and *Science for the Citizen.* The more formal histories of mathematics, such as Cajori's and D. E. Smith's, contain much valuable material. The best method of reading these is to dip into them until you find something understandable: or to seek in them for the answer to some definite question such as, "When did algebra begin, and why?" or "Who invented quadratic equations, and why?" These two histories are in most libraries.

Books of puzzles such as Dudeney's *Amusements in Mathematics* and *Canterbury Puzzles*, Caliban's *Brush up Your Wits,* and many others like these—best found by looking on the "Indoor Amusements" shelf at a public library—can be most fully appreciated by someone familiar with the elements of algebra and geometry. They afford one of the more interesting ways of keeping in practice with the use of elementary mathematics.

Answers to Exercises

CHAPTER I

1. 15·36 cm., 24·4 mm. approximately. **2.** 3, 6 or 9. **3.** Yes; 0, 1 or 4; 0, 1, 3 or 4; 0, 1, 2 or 4. **4.** (a) 4; (b) 8; (c) 16. Yes, 2^n. **5.** 64. **6.** 28; 55.

CHAPTER II

1. 49. **2.** B is 10; C is 20; D is 29; E is 39. **3.** B is 55; D is 67. **4.** 63. **5.** 16; 11; 8; 9; 5; 16. **9.** Very small. Between ·578% and ·585%.

CHAPTER III

1. $8\frac{3}{4}$ in. × $5\frac{7}{8}$ in. **2.** $4\frac{1}{2}$ in. **3.** $51\frac{1}{2}$ sq. in. approximately. **4.** $\frac{3}{4}$ ft. is longer by 1 in. **5.** $2\frac{1}{2}$ in., $2\frac{2}{4}$ in., $2\frac{4}{8}$ in., $2\frac{8}{16}$ in., $2\frac{16}{32}$ in., $2\frac{32}{64}$ in. **6.** Drills: $\frac{3}{8}$ in., $\frac{3}{16}$ in., $\frac{3}{32}$ in. Spanner: $\frac{1}{4}$ in., $\frac{3}{16}$ in. Gauge: A, $\frac{1}{16}$ in.; B, $\frac{9}{32}$ in.; C, $\frac{1}{4}$ in.; D, $\frac{7}{32}$ in.; E, $\frac{3}{16}$ in.; F, $\frac{9}{64}$ in.; G, $\frac{7}{64}$ in. **7.** 2·54 cm. **8.** 4; 6. **9.** ·3 in. is larger by $\frac{1}{10}$ in. **10.** 8 and ·1 in. or $\frac{1}{10}$ in. over. **11.** $\frac{6}{100}$ in.; ·06 in. **12.** Three feet square is the larger. **13.** $\frac{1}{8}$ in., $\frac{3}{16}$ in., $\frac{7}{16}$ in., $\frac{1}{4}$ in.

CHAPTER IV

1. 15 lamps rated at 16 volts each, or 20 lamps rated at 12 volts each. There are, of course, other possible combinations. (i) 40 lamps rated at 6 volts each; (ii) 53 lamps. **2.** 1 lb., 2 lb., 4 lb., 7 lb., 14 lb. **3.** 1 gm., two of 2 gm., 5 gm.; Three; No. **4.** Divide length of chain by length of one link. **5.** 16. **6.** Divide 12 by voltage of one dry cell. **7.** Add the lengths of the three sides together (the perimeter). **8.** Measure two adjacent sides in yards; multiply these two measurements together and the answer is the number of ounces of seed required. **9.** (a) 20·25 ft. (b) 12·15 ft. **10.** $1\frac{1}{5}$ ohm. **11.** $1\frac{13}{47}$ ohm. **12.** $2\frac{4}{7}$ ohm. **13.** $1\frac{1}{11}$ ohm. **14.** (a) 24; (b) 12; (c) 36; (d) 6. **15.** (a) 7·1; (b) ·3; (c) ·25. **16.** (a) $\frac{2}{3}$; (b) 1; (c) $\frac{1}{3}$; (d) $\frac{1}{2}$. **17.** (a) 12; (b) $7\frac{1}{5}$; (c) 6. **18.** (a) $3\frac{3}{4}$ in.; (b) 5 in. **19.** 4 miles. **20.** (a) 48; (b) 96; (c) 80; (d) 64. **21.** (a) 20 teeth; (b) 100 teeth. **22.** (a) $4\frac{12}{25}$ lb.; (b) $2\frac{2}{7}$ lb. **23.** (a) 30 sq. in.; (b) $56\frac{1}{4}$ sq. in. **24.** Fast. **25.** 180 triangles. **27.** $174\frac{2}{9}$ lb., $49\frac{7}{9}$ lb. **28.** $2\frac{2}{5}$, $\frac{3}{5}$. **29.** $\frac{9}{11}$, $\frac{9}{22}$, $\frac{3}{11}$. **30.** $87\frac{1}{2}$ r.p.m. **31.** 15 gm., 21 gm. **32.** 0·8. **33.** 33·8 m.p.h.

CHAPTER V

1. 352 mgm., 815 mgm., 545 mgm., 148 mgm. **2.** (a) 374 mgm.; (b) 648 mgm. **3.** (a) 5·0773; (b) 2·8352; (c) 7·4918. **4.** (a) 4 in., ·55 in., ·114 in., ·1005 in.; (b) 1 in., ·3 in., ·112 in., ·1005 in.; (c) 4 in., 1 in., ·15 in., ·137 in., ·1005 in.; (d) 4 in., 3 in., 1 in., ·75 in., ·149 in., ·110 in., ·1003 in.; (e) ·85 in., ·132 in., ·1005 in. **5.** ·149 minus ·104; (·05 plus ·1005) minus ·128; (·05 plus ·1003) minus ·137; (·1 plus ·1005) minus ·138; (·15 plus ·1004) minus ·127. **6.** (a) ·02 in.; (b) ·02 in.; (c) 20; (d) ·05 cm., ·05 cm., 25; (e) ·871, 1·126, 1·078, ·300. **7.** (a) 164; (b) 100; (c) ·1; (d) 50; (e) 300; (f) 10,300.

8. (a) 2,000; (b) 71,900; (c) 650; (d) 8,400; (e) 37,000; (f) 1,020; (g) 680; (h) 7; (i) 9; (j) ·54. **9.** (a) 81·6; (b) 163·2; (c) 652·8; (d) 66·05. **10.** 144. **11.** 10%, $1\frac{7}{13}$%, 1·63%, 0·4%. **12.** $\frac{2}{5}$, $\frac{3}{20}$, $\frac{1}{8}$, $\frac{5}{8}$, $\frac{2}{3}$, $\frac{1}{200}$, $\frac{1}{1000}$. **13.** (a) 1·21; (b) ·49; (c) $\frac{4}{9}$; (d) $\frac{1}{25}$; (e) $\frac{9}{4}$; (f) ·0009; (g) ·000144; (h) $6\frac{1}{4}$. **14.** 9, 1, 1, ·4, 1·2, ·2, ·05, $1\frac{1}{2}$, $2\frac{1}{2}$. **15.** 2, ·5, 12, 4, ·09. **16.** (a) 4; (b) 10; (c) 9; (d) 5; (e) ·2; (f) 1; (g) ·5; (h) ·01; (i) 100.

CHAPTER VI

1. (i) lb; (ii) lbh; (iii) $l+b$; (iv) $l-b$; (v) $\frac{h}{l}$; (vi) $2l+2b$, (vii) bhh or bh^2; (viii) $\frac{bh^2}{l}$; (ix) $(2l+2b)h$. **2.** (i) 40; (ii) 120; (iii) 14; (iv) 6; (v) 3/10; (vi) 28; (vii) 36; (viii) 3·6; (ix) 84. **3.** (i) 60; (ii) 420; (iii) 17; (iv) 7; (v) 7/12; (vi) 34; (vii) 245; (viii) $20\frac{5}{12}$; (ix) 238 **4.** 94. Total surface area. **5.** (i) $2n$; (ii) $\frac{1}{2}n$ or $n/2$; (iii) $n+1$; (iv) $4n+3$; (v) nn or n^2; (vi) $n\ (n-1)$; (vii) $\sqrt{n}$; (viii) $100/n$. **6.** (i) 4, 2; (ii) 9, 5; (iii) 16, 10; No. **7.** (i) 4, 4; (ii) 9, 9; (iii) 16, 16; Yes. **8.** $\frac{3}{4}$, 2, $3\frac{3}{4}$, 6, $8\frac{3}{4}$, 12; $x=6\frac{1}{2}$. **9.** $2x+2y+2z$; 15 in. **10.** (i) a^2; (ii) b^2; (iii) a^2-b^2. **11.** 7. **12.** 5, 15. **13.** A little larger than 8. **14.** About $5\frac{1}{2}$. **15.** $x+y+2z$. **16.** (i) $a-b$; (ii) a+b; (iii) (a−b) (a+b). **17.** $5^2-2^2=21=7\times3$. Always the same. **18.** (i) $x=5y$; (ii) $x+y=12$. **19.** $x=10$, $y=2$. **20.** Always true. $x-z=(x-y)+(y-z)$. **21.** Always true. **22.** Yes.

CHAPTER VII

1. Triangle. **2.** Two sides of same length. **3.** A chord. **4.** The diagonals should be equal. **5.** Reflex angle. **6.** 90 deg. **7.** 45 deg. **8.** Isosceles right-angled triangle. **9.** (a) $x=v$; (b) $u=t$; (c) $y=180°-x-v=140°$; (d) $z=180°-y=40°$; (e) $t=70°$ and $u=70°$ because $t=u$ and $t+u+z=180°$; (f) $v=x=20°$; (g) Angle$=v+u=70°+20°=90°$; a right angle; (h) Unaltered; (i) Theorem 20. As OA=OC=OB. A, B and C lie on a circle, centre O. AB is diameter. C is on semicircle.

CHAPTER VIII

2. *From the graph.* Earliest sunset, about December 15 at 3-52 p.m.; latest sunset, about June 25 at 8-22 p.m. *Rates of change.* Tangent, for examples: on December 29, approximately 1 minute per day later; on August 15, approximately $1\frac{1}{2}$ minutes per day earlier. *Note.*—Results may be checked from a table of lighting-up times.

CHAPTER IX

1. $7x+5y+z$. **2.** $6p-4q+11r$. **3.** $4m^3+3m^2n-2mn^2$. **4.** $8pq+7qr$. **5.** $a+2b-2c$. **6.** $x^2+15x+2$. **7.** x^2+x-6. **8.** $6a^2+13ab+6b^2$. **9.** x^3+1. **10.** $a^3+a^2b-7ab^2+2b^3$. **11.** $x+4$. **12.** $2a-3b$. **13.** $3a^2-2ab+5b^2$. **14.** $x^2+6xy+9y^2$. **15.** $16p^2-56pq+49q^2$. **16.** $x^2-x+\frac{1}{4}$. **17.** $16m^4+24m^3n+9m^2n^2$. **18.** 249,001. **19.** 10,100·25. **20.** $(x+y)(x-y)$. **21.** $(2a+b)(2a-b)$. **22.** $(p+5q)(p-5q)$. **23.** $4xy$. **24.** 37×1. **25.** $36\times1{\cdot}2$. **26.** $x=2$.

27. $x=4$. **28.** $x=1$. **29.** $x=3$. **30.** $x=\frac{7}{16}$ **31.** $x=4$ $y=2$. **32.** $x=1$ $y=-1$. **33.** $x=2$ $y=\frac{1}{2}$. **34.** $x=3$ or 1. **35.** $x=3$ or -1. **36.** $x=1{\cdot}28$ or $-{\cdot}78$. **37.** $F=\frac{4mdl}{(d^2-l^2)^2}$; $F=\frac{4ml}{d^3}$. **38.** $I=\frac{V}{R}$. **39.** $N=\frac{1}{A}\sqrt{5L(3A+9B)}$. **40.** $l=\frac{gt^2}{4\pi^2}$. **41.** $F=\frac{M}{(d^2+l^2)^{3/2}}$; $F=\frac{M}{d^3}$. **42.** $V=\frac{375\pi DH.}{4PAl}$

CHAPTER X

Note.—An error of 1 or 2 in the final figure need not indicate faulty working.

1. 1·562, 2·238, 3·000, 3·3, 5·573, 9·487, 6·083, 1·584, 5·109. **2.** $9^{\frac{1}{2}}=3$; 4, 5, 7, 10, 2, 4, 8. **3.** 1, 1, 3, 4; 0, 0, $\bar{2}$, 1; 2, 2, 2, 1; $\bar{2}$, $\bar{3}$, 1, $\bar{1}$. **4.** Mantissae: ·4526, ·9703, ·5441, ·7167, ·8588, ·4886, ·9047, ·3145, ·1452, ·1761, ·0017, ·6021, ·9407, ·8451, ·8876, ·6646. Complete logarithms: 1·4526, 1·9703, 3·5441, 4·7167, 0·8588, 0·4886, $\bar{2}$·9047, 1·3145, 2·1452, 2·1761, 2·0017, 1·6021, $\bar{2}$·9407, $\bar{3}$·8451, 1·8876, $\bar{1}$·6646. **5.** 2, 8, 4, 3, 7. **6.** 100, 100,000, 1, 1,000, 10, 0·01, 0·1, 0·000001. **7.** 200, 200,000, 2,000, 20, 0·02, 0·2, 800, 800,000, 8,000, 80, 0·08, 0·8, 400, 400,000, 4,000, 40, 0·04, 0·4, 300, 300,000, 3,000, 30, 0·03, 0·3. **8.** 1·328, 13·28, 0·1328; 1·8, 18, 0·18; 7·5, 75, 0·75; 9·718, 97·18, 0·9718; 3·3, 33, 0·33; 5·475, 54·75, 0·5475. **9.** 5,365. **10.** 398·5. **11.** 14·72. **12.** 0·7150. **13.** 13·40. **14.** 6·390. **15.** 0·6993. **16.** 0·03111. **17.** 54·03. **18.** 0·00295. **19.** 149·2. **20.** 7, 4, 600, 20, 900, 36. **21.** 1·149, 1·585, 2, 1·442, 2·237, 7, 1·5. **22.** $2a$, $3a$, $4a$, $5a$, $6a$ (powers of 2); $2b$, $3b$, $4b$ (powers of 3); $2a+b$ (since $12=2\times2\times3$), $3a+b$ (since $24=2\times2\times2\times3$), $4a+b$ (since $48=2\times2\times2\times2\times3$), $5a+b$ (since $96=2\times2\times2\times2\times2\times3$); $2a+2b$, $3a+2b$; log $5=1-a$ (since $5=10\div2$), log $25=2-2a$ (since $25=5\times5$), log $75=2-2a+b$ ($75=25\times3$), log $1{\cdot}5=b-a$ ($1{\cdot}5=3\div2$), log $7{\cdot}5=1-2a+b$ ($7{\cdot}5=75\div10$).

CHAPTER XI

1. 7·586 miles. **2.** 29·8 ft. **3.** 1·837. **4.** 11·85, 20·52. **5.** 19 in. **6.** 100,800 sq. yds. **7.** 7·49 sq. ft. **8.** 63° 26′; 54° 44′. **9.** 1, 0. **10.** 0, —1. **11.** —1, 0. **12.** 0, 1. **13.** $-\sin\theta$; $\cos\theta$; $-\tan\theta$. **14.** $AC=54{\cdot}81$ miles, $BC=139{\cdot}2$ miles. **15.** $\frac{\pi}{2}$. **16.** 180°. **17.** $\frac{\pi}{3}$. **18.** 57° 18′ 45″

INDEX

MADE AND PRINTED IN GREAT BRITAIN BY
JOHN GARDNER (PRINTERS) LTD.
LITHERLAND . LIVERPOOL, 20